ENVIRONETICS

Design and Operation
of
Clean Rooms

DESIGN AND OPERATION OF CLEAN ROOMS

by

PHILIP R. AUSTIN
Senior Aeronautical Engineer
Chief of the United States Air Force Clean Room Project
Olmsted Air Force Base, Pennsylvania

and

STEWART W. TIMMERMAN
Senior Industrial Engineer
Chief Special Projects Branch
Olmsted Air Force Base, Pennsylvania

BUSINESS NEWS PUBLISHING COMPANY · DETROIT, MICHIGAN

1965

Library of Congress Catalog Card No. 64–22703

DESIGNED BY WILLIAM A. BOSTICK

PRINTED IN THE UNITED STATES OF AMERICA BY KINGSPORT PRESS, INC.

"In this age of rapidly moving technology, we move beyond the limits of our own work only by studying the experience of others. The source cannot surmise where the river will eventually flow."

ANONYMOUS

Preface

This book has been written to fill what appears to us to be a gap in the literature of clean room design and operation. We have divided the book into two major parts, although some overlapping does occur. The first part is concerned with the design of clean rooms, and the second involves the operation of clean rooms.

The book has been written to meet the needs of the practicing contamination control engineers, as well as the requirements of class instruction. The text is based, in part, on material developed by us while working together in the Special Projects Branch, Directorate of Maintenance, Middletown Air Materiel Area (MAMES), Olmsted Air Force Base, Pennsylvania. Much of the material contained in this text is an abstraction of published data in this field, but hitherto never collected under one cover.

In the first section of the book, we have presented theoretical relationships governing airborne particulate matter, substantiated by experimental size-distribution data. In this part of the book, analysis of filtration, product requirements, and design of conventional and second-generation clean rooms are discussed.

In the second section of the book, the operation of clean rooms and clean work stations, along with the particular subjects of monitoring, garmenting, cleaning of parts, and clean room specifications, is discussed.

We wish to express our appreciation to the United States Air Force, Air Force Logistic Command, Middletown Air Materiel Area, for initially defining clean room problems and for their enthusiastic support in the pursuit of completely objective solutions to these problems. Special acknowledgment is given to Colonel I. R. Perkin, Director of Maintenance (1960–63), Middletown Air Materiel Area, who gave the revision of the U.S. Air Force Technical Order 00–25–203 on clean rooms the much-needed encouragement which led to the development of an informed and knowledgeable group of clean room practitioners. We are proud to be a part of this group and are equally thankful for the continued support of the Industrial Engineering Division, Directorate of Maintenance, Olmsted Air Force Base.

We are grateful to those members of the American Association for Contamination Control whose technical advice, papers, and presentations have helped to make our text a more complete work. To the associations, institutes, companies, and corporations, and their representatives, who with their time and energy have assisted in the quest of clean room knowledge, we are especially indebted. The cooperation of industry, government, and research personnel engaged in clean room work is exceptional and should be commended.

We have drawn freely from the unclassified literature on contamination control. Because of the amount of literature in this field, undoubtedly some worth-while contributions have been overlooked. A real effort has been made to assure that the acknowledgments to the literature are complete. If any errors of commission or omission have inadvertently been made, we express our sincere regrets and hope that they will be called to our attention.

We wish to point out that the views expressed herein are those of the authors and do not necessarily represent official policy or reflect the views of the U.S. Air Force or Department of Defense.

Stewart W. Timmerman
Philip R. Austin

Contents

Chapter 1.	*Introduction to Clean Rooms*	PAGE 1
Chapter 2.	*Particulate Matter*	8
Chapter 3.	*Filtration*	79
Chapter 4.	*Product Requirements*	96
Chapter 5.	*Conventional Clean Room Design*	136
Chapter 6.	*Conventional Clean Room Operation*	175
Chapter 7.	*Laminar-Flow Clean Room Design*	194
Chapter 8.	*Laminar-Flow Clean Room Operation*	232
Chapter 9.	*Clean Room Monitoring*	252
Chapter 10.	*Garments*	316
Chapter 11.	*Parts Cleaning*	357
Chapter 12.	*Clean Work Station Design*	384
Chapter 13.	*Clean Work Station Operation*	400
Chapter 14.	*Clean Room Standards*	409
	Index	423

Chapter 1. *Introduction to Clean Rooms*

Why a Clean Room?

As precision instrument manufacturers advanced the state of their art, they came face to face with a problem about which they knew very little. The problem was how to control "contamination." When failures were attributed to contamination, or when contamination was a suspected cause of failures, a general cleanup of working areas and working procedures was initiated. In an effort to control the dirt falling out of the air, filtration and air-conditioning systems were installed in factory areas. Thus the first clean rooms were born.

What Is a Clean Room?

A clean room is any room or area in which *an attempt* is made to limit and control the amount of airborne dust (particulate matter). This is a very limited definition, certainly not complete, but for the purpose of an introduction to the problem it will suffice. The key words in this definition are "an attempt." The great majority of clean room designers had little knowledge of what cleanliness level they were achieving with their design. They also had little knowledge of what cleanliness level they wanted. With limited knowledge available concerning airborne particulate matter, the clean room designer and operator groped for a solution to their contamination problems. Improvements were made, and a gradual tendency developed toward overdesign.

During the period from shortly before World War II until recent years, the clean room practitioner was in the unenviable position of not knowing his enemy, *airborne particulate matter*. Developments in particle counting and research on airborne particulate matter, coupled with several major breakthroughs, have given us new tools with which to fight the contamination problem. The first major breakthrough came in 1950, when a new high-efficiency particulate air filter (HEPA) was marketed. Another was in 1962, when an entirely new concept in clean room air handling was developed. This new concept will enable clean room operators to take a "giant step," circumventing a number of major problems.

Consider yourself in this situation, which is often the plight of the clean room practitioner. Your company is manufacturing a certain device which everyone knows must be made in a clean room. In order to protect the device properly, you should know at least three things:

1. What size particle will render the device inoperative?
2. What is the make-up of the air in the clean room? (How many particles of critical or other size are there?)
3. What is the probability of a critical-size particle's landing in a critical area?

In addition, there are other problems such as transfer contaminants and migration and agglomeration of particles to be considered. Answers to the above three questions are paramount. To provide adequate clean room control, these answers must be known.

In general, the answers to these questions have been known to few practitioners. They have resorted to obtaining the best atmosphere possible with the hope that an unknown critical-size particle would not fall in a critical area. In many cases the best was not good enough. Comprehensive investigations into the problem of determining the critical-size particle for various types of devices are still to be undertaken. Preliminary studies have indicated that a complete study of this problem would be of gigantic proportions. The number of independent variables associated with the study would make research difficult*(1)*.

With the 1962 breakthrough in air-handling technique, however, the answers to these questions are no longer necessary in relation to achieving adequate airborne contamination control. This new concept in air handling isolates dust particles within essentially parallel streamlines of air, so that their path in the clean room can best be predicted. By using super-interception (HEPA) filters, clean air is produced which is two orders of magnitude better than that normally found in conventional clean rooms. The contamination level of these rooms is independent of the number of people or the work performed in them. This is not possible in a conventional clean room. A clean room so designed will be able to eliminate airborne particulate matter to the point where it can no longer be considered a source of contamination. This statement applies to any device now manufactured or contemplated in the near future, with the exception of new processes or products which might be developed, that must consider minute quantities of airborne dust or particles approaching molecular size. One fact must be remembered: Airborne contamination plays a minor role when compared to the other types of contamination which can occur during manufacture. When it is eliminated as a source of contamination, however—and it must be—the clean room operator can concentrate on the prevention of process, transfer, and associated sources of contamination.

What Is Contamination?

For now, contamination will be considered to be any foreign substance that will have a detrimental effect on the mechanism or process in question. Later presentations will elaborate on these points. As was stated previously, contamination can come from many sources. The discussions contained herein, however, will be concerned primarily with control of airborne contamination. The primary purpose of a clean room is to limit or eliminate airborne contaminants. Airborne contamination consists of anything that can be distributed in the air in the form of fine particles or fibers. These particles are acted upon by gravity and fall out in relation to their density and weight. Their "life" in air varies considerably, with some particles remaining suspended almost indefinitely. Some of the particulate matter found in the air of clean rooms includes sand, dirt, human skin, hair, carbon, and lint.

How the Clean Room Achieves Control

The control of airborne particulate matter is accomplished by five means (the five P's):

1. *Preventing* entry of particulate matter. This is accomplished by filtration of the air entering the clean room.

2. *Purging* of particulate matter. The air-handling system changes the air in the room and thus removes particulate matter generated within the room.

3. *Prohibiting* the generation of particulate matter. Clean room clothing is made of "limited-linting" fabric which will not produce excessive quantities of lint as it is flexed. Similarly, room appointments, floors, etc., are chosen for this resistance to particle generation.

4. *Protecting* the product from impact and settling of particulate matter. The low level of particulate matter in clean rooms contains a majority of the smaller-size particles which settle out very slowly. These smaller particles have a very long "life."

5. *Providing* an area for the cleaning of parts and personnel. Everything entering the clean room is cleaned so that as little contamination as possible is added to the room atmosphere by transfer from dirty objects.

History of Clean Rooms

The clean rooms of today are the result of advancing technology in the field of mechanical science. They produce the environment necessary to manufacture the many modern-day products of sophisticated design. Control of the factors in and about a product is a function of technological advancement in science. This can be shown to be the case in many sciences. The first science to recognize this need was medicine. Medical science controlled the environment with a device called an "operating room." In the crudest sense, this was the place where work was performed on a product. Here, "work" is that operation which the surgeon performs, and the product is the human being. It is interesting to note that a simile relative to the nature of work performed can be drawn between operating rooms and clean rooms. Both types of facilities are used for the birth of new products and for the continual repair and overhaul of older products. Other similes may be drawn between the "human being" and the "machine" to show the likeness between operating rooms and clean rooms. These will become evident as the discussion progresses.

An insight into operating rooms and the reasons why they were constructed will assist in an understanding of clean rooms. The primary reason for the construction of operating rooms was to provide an area that would lessen the chances of infection to the patient. Control of both airborne and transfer contamination becomes a paramount function of any operating room. This is quite evident in the meticulous care a surgeon and his assistants take during "scrub-up" procedures and during the actual operation. It emphasizes the very definite need for environmental control of the room. Without this control, the probability of a successful operation is severely diminished. This same statement holds true for clean rooms.

It has been pointed out that room environmental control is required for the patient within the room, but it is equally important that the operating room provide an effective isolation from other patients. This isolation prevents the transfer of infections to other patients in the hospital and is a major consideration in the design of operating rooms. In many hospitals this isolation is partially achieved by having an entire floor devoted to surgery, along with stringent room cleanup and sterilization procedures. For certain "dirty"[1] types of operations, complete closing of the room for 24 or 48 hours after cleanup is required. Many current conventional clean rooms require the same type of control. Room decontamination functions are both necessary and vital to continued, successful clean room operation.

The operating room provides other functions besides contamination control. Such a room provides an area in which all the surgical and support equipment necessary for an operation can be concentrated. This concentration of equipment is not a by-product of the room operation but a very definite function of the room, since an operation's success is based on equipment available as well as on the surgeon's skill. No amount of surgeon's skill can substitute for the surgical knives, operating tools, and operating-room equipment. A true operating room (and this holds true for a clean room) exists only when the necessary support equipment is present to perform the work.

In conjunction with the above statement, operating rooms are also designed as cleaning facilities, for which they have a threefold assignment. The first cleaning assignment is imposed on the tools and equipment to be used in the room. Sterility of these items is all-important to the success of the operation. Meticulous care is taken to see that every unit has been thoroughly prepared prior to the operation. The second cleaning assignment is to prepare the surgeon. An area must be provided for "scrub-up" and gowning of the surgeon. This area must also be sterile to prevent contamination of the surgeon during and after "scrub-up" and gowning. The third cleaning function is provided for the patient; he also must be cleaned and prepared for the operation. Yet, had but a few words been changed in this paragraph, a description of a clean room would have been presented.

The old axiom "History repeats itself" is well applicable to this subject. The events leading to the development of operating rooms were initially paralleled by the events leading to the development of clean rooms. With greater and greater emphasis being placed on miniaturization of products by the Space Age, however, cleanliness requirements for some clean rooms exceed those for operating rooms.

Modern-day operating rooms can be considered as having their beginning in the late 1800's. In the United States, the Civil War played a very important role in developing these rooms. About that time, the prime pieces of operating-room equipment were the surgeon's knives and the strap-down table for the patient. The development of anesthesia added more sophistication to the operating room. This single development did more to assist surgeons in the operating room than any other technological breakthrough, since it allowed the surgeon to concentrate on his work. It also allowed him to concentrate on how to improve the oper-

[1] Any operation that exposes a large number of bacteria.

ating-room environment. As a result, the cleanliness problem was attacked with vigor. The turn of the century saw new hospitals being built which stressed cleanliness of both room and surgeon. World War I brought further advances in operating-room support equipment, and with World War II came electronic equipment and air conditioning. Today, modern science continues to explore ways of providing the cleanest operating rooms possible.

At this point it might be well to discuss those areas that are common ground to both operating rooms and clean rooms. Qualitatively, it can be said that both types of facilities require a high degree of environmental cleanliness. Quantitatively speaking, there is difficulty in stating the exact number, size, and type of airborne particulate matter allowable per volume of air in a given facility. To date, empirical data have been used to establish acceptable contamination levels. This topic will be discussed later in detail. What is important is the fact that both types of facilities—the operating room, which is concerned with human beings, and the clean room, which is concerned with sophisticated machines—require a high degree of environmental cleanliness. This cleanliness level should be better than that normally found outdoors.

In conjunction with cleanliness, both operating rooms and clean rooms normally require stringent room cleanup procedures. Such procedures can call for complete wall, floor, and ceiling cleanup as well as all room equipment cleanup. This requirement can be costly and should be minimized by the design of the room. Proper room air-flow patterns and adequate filtration will greatly decrease this operational expense.

Cleaning areas for support equipment, personnel, and the product must be provided in both operating rooms and clean rooms. The product in either type of facility must undergo cleaning of one type or another prior to the initiation of work. It is generally accepted that a surgeon must undergo extensive cleaning preparatory to work, but this same requirement exists to a lesser degree for the employee of the clean room. The same is true for the support equipment; whether it be operating-room equipment or clean room equipment, it must receive adequate cleaning.

The clothing worn by personnel in both types of rooms is similar in nature. Both types of clothing require special cleaning processes and packaging. The clothing performs the function of a personnel contaminant filter for both surgeon and clean room employee. Although the individual costume may vary, the essence of the garment is the same. It prevents gross contamination from the clothing of the individual from being deposited into the air and onto the work. The exterior surface of the garment should be designed so that it will do little if any harm to the work, if it comes in contact with the work.

Techniques of workers in operating rooms and clean rooms are similar in that they are controlled. Various objects, tools, and areas are considered to be either contaminated or uncontaminated. The worker's actions are governed by these considerations.

The major difference between operating rooms and clean rooms is that in operating rooms sterility of objects is of paramount importance. In clean rooms, the quantity of particulate matter is of paramount importance. Particulate matter is of little importance in an operating room as long as it is sterile. Clean rooms have experienced little difficulty with bacterial growths on items. This can be attributed to several reasons: the lack of bacteriological food, the lack of bacterial colonies, and the low humidity, which is not ideal for their growth.

Industry Clean Rooms

Just as the development of operating rooms can be linked to wars, so can the birth and development of clean rooms be tied to wars. Clean rooms or rooms that were the predecessors of the modern-day clean room can trace their beginning back to World War I days. They did not have the generic name "clean room" attached to them at that time, but they did perform a similar function. For all intents and purposes, they were controlled areas within factories or laboratories in which an attempt was made to eliminate the gross contamination associated with manufacturing areas. This contamination, consisting of heavy dust-laden air, had caused seizure of small bearings and gears used in the first aircraft instruments. As a result, controlled assembly areas were built. This technique of assembly—and it was considered only a technique of assembly at first—allowed the products to be manufactured with a respectable useful life. Today's clean rooms require contamination levels to be many orders of magnitude better than originally was thought to be acceptable.

Today's clean rooms, as did their predecessors, provide an area where parts may be cleaned and then kept clean. This is one function of a clean room that cannot be neglected. Parts thoroughly cleaned and then kept clean will ensure a clean assembly.

The "assembly operation" of a critical product can be considered the prime function of a clean room. This is one of the main reasons why clean rooms are built. The phrase "assembly operation" is taken in the broadest sense of the meaning; an assembly operation is that action which makes a unit from its parts. It could be the piecing together of a mechanism as well as the coating of film or other work action.

Justification for the use of clean rooms is not limited to the reasons mentioned above. Clean rooms provide better inspection areas. A good quality-control check on clean room products is necessary if the need and expense of a clean room are to be justified. Test and calibration areas for clean room products are also needed so that the product will not be contaminated during these phases.

Generally speaking, the clean room tries to control three major types of contamination. The first of these is airborne contaminants. This type of contamination can be of any shape, size, or nature and is transferred by either air convection currents or trajectory of the particle. In either case, the medium of transfer is air. The next type of contamination that is controlled is particulate matter transferred from one object to another by direct contact. This is a prevalent way of contaminating a product and should receive as much attention as airborne contamination. The third type of contamination is the transfer of particulates by means of fluids. This occurs with cleaning solutions as well as with lubricants and propellants. Contaminants in petroleum products include bacterial matter, which has not been a significant contaminant elsewhere.

In this brief introduction to clean rooms, it is important to realize that the science is in the developmental stage. The discussions in this book refer to the state of the art of clean rooms; as such, it might be interesting to note how contamination control was effected without knowledge of airborne contaminants. Knowledge in this field has only recently been available, owing to new monitoring devices and techniques being developed.

Contamination control was first effected by good housekeeping practices, by segregating the work area from other manufacturing operations, and by providing a filtered air supply. With the advent of World War II, better filtration systems were developed; air conditioning and room pressurization were considered essential. Personnel protective clothing was added later, as were air showers and personnel cleaning equipment. Further improvements were gained by better parts cleaning equipment and improved personnel work techniques.

Military Clean Rooms

Clean rooms are not particular to the industrial establishment. Military clean rooms represent the second largest group of clean rooms in the United States, and some of the credit for the development of clean rooms belongs to the military. The Army Air Force developed some of the first items requiring controlled areas at Wright Field, Ohio,[2] prior to World War II.

Today the military services use clean rooms primarily to overhaul and maintain items that have entered their inventory from industry. Many of these products require periodic overhaul after a set number of hours' use. Others are sent through maintenance shops or clean rooms when they fail to perform properly. In either case, a large workload exists of products requiring controlled-environment facilities during their tear-down, repair, and build-up. The military also uses clean rooms for photographic reproduction work. This type of activity requires a high degree of control of airborne particulate matter. In many cases, this control is required to be better than that achieved by most clean rooms.

Past experience in World War II and the Korean War demonstrated the high cost of unreliability.

[2] Now Wright-Patterson Air Force Base.

During the Korean War, over one million replacement electronic parts were needed for only 160,000 units of equipment. During the same period, radar equipment was inoperative 84% of the time; sonar equipment, 48% of the time. The Army found that at a given time approximately 65% to 75% of its electronic equipment was inoperative and that the annual maintenance bill exceeded twice the original procurement cost. The Air Force and the Navy reported similar experiences. Air Force equipment maintenance over a five-year period amounted to more than ten times the initial cost of the equipment. Today, as a result of clean room utilization, 92% and 95% reliability factors are quite common. The results can be quite startling; for example, in one guidance manufacturing plant where gyroscopes were first built without dust control, every 10 units required 120 reworks on the average. With control of airborne contaminants, the number of reworks dropped to 2*(2)*.

Clean rooms can be found in several areas of the military organizations. The majority of Air Force clean rooms are operated by the Air Force Logistic Command. The clean room facilities are established at the Air Force Bases housing the Air Materiel Areas.[3] The Air Force activity having the largest square footage of clean rooms is Middletown Air Materiel Area, Olmsted Air Force Base, Pennsylvania. These bases perform the function of maintenance and overhaul of items. Also within the Air Force are other special groups requiring clean rooms. Photoreconnaissance groups of the Strategic Air Command and some groups assigned to research projects require controlled-environment facilities. Those involved in maintaining precision measurement laboratories or standards laboratories require similar facilities.

The first document accepted as a workable clean room document was Air Force Technical Order 00-25-203, entitled "Standard Functional Criteria for the Design and Operation of Clean Rooms," and renamed, as of July 1, 1963. "Standards and Guidelines for the Design and Operation of Clean Rooms and Clean Work Stations." It was prepared because of the confusion existing within the Air Force relative to the various contamination, temperature, humidity, and pressure requirements for clean rooms. Each manufacturer had his own clean room specifications and required that his product be overhauled under his environmental control conditions. Since the Air Force is the recipient of many products, it was burdened with providing many different types of rooms. In time, it was noticed that similar products had similar clean room requirements, although in some cases the variance was great. As a result, in late 1958, a project was initiated to develop a technical order for clean rooms.

The group charged with the responsibility for writing this technical order made several extended tours of industry and military facilities to gather data. Some of the confusion on clean rooms began to fade as four general groupings of products with their respective clean room requirements began to develop. Since more definitive knowledge on airborne contaminants and product requirements was lacking, four classes of clean rooms were established. This document was finished in early 1960. It then underwent severe scrutiny by Wright-Patterson Air Force Base, Ohio, since it would affect many millions of dollars already spent, and to be spent, on clean room facilities.

In 1961 Technical Order 00-25-203 was published. In 1962 a table classifying the various items into clean room groupings was added to the basic technical order. During this time, advancement in the state of the art necessitated a closer look at the documents. The assignment to revise the technical order was given to a group of engineers of the Special Projects Branch, Industrial Engineering, Directorate of Maintenance, Olmsted Air Force Base, Pennsylvania. After intensive research and study on this subject, the Air Force standard clean room and the clean work station principles were developed and incorporated into the revised technical order in 1963.

The Navy office primarily concerned with clean rooms is the Bureau of Naval Weapons. The first Navy clean rooms were used for bearing repair. The Navy's use and need for clean rooms paralleled Air Force developments, however. One of the better-known Navy installations is at North Island, San Diego, California.

Other governmental agencies besides the military

[3] Air Materiel Areas represent geographic sections of the United States. Each section contains an Air Force Base operated by the Air Force Logistic Command.

require the use of clean rooms. These agencies include the U. S. Atomic Energy Commission (in which Sandia Corporation, Albuquerque, New Mexico, has played a major role), the National Aeronautics and Space Administration (NASA), the National Bureau of Standards, and the U. S. Public Health Service. Each of these agencies has made contributions to the clean room field particular to its operations.

REFERENCES

1. Lieberman, Alvin. *Contamination Effects Study*. ARF 3216-5. Chicago, Ill.: Armour Research Foundation, November 1962. Prepared for Sandia Corp., Albuquerque, N. Mex.
2. Waite, Robert. *The Clean Room*. Valley Forge, Pa.: General Electric Space Technology Center, September 1961.

Chapter 2. *Particulate Matter*

Introduction

Particulate matter takes all forms and shapes. It can be any material, organic or inorganic, of miniature dimensions. Normally, particulate matter is considered that size of material which can present a problem as potential contamination to an item. Particulate matter is relevant to the space or environment it occupies. It may be found in gases, liquids, and solids as either suspended or settled material.

Particulate matter may also be categorized by physical characteristics such as size, shape, and hardness. The amount of control of this material within a clean room depends primarily on the product being processed within the room. Because of the immense number of different types of material found in everyday living and the large number of ways in which particulates are formed, an infinite number of shapes and sizes are possible. To those concerned with clean rooms, these shapes and sizes of particulate material are important. Normally, microcopic techniques are needed to determine the shape and size of particulate matter. As such, microscopic scales must be used to measure each particle. Since the particle usually has three major dimensions, some method of size description is necessary. There are pros and cons for the several methods now used to describe the size of particles.

Since particles are three-dimensional objects, they can be described by their volume, by their cross-sectional area perpendicular to line of sight, by their longest dimension, or by a dimension taken on all particles in the same direction. The choice of the method is a function of the product the particle will contaminate. In the case of LOX (liquid oxygen), fuel, deionized solution, and other fluids, volume measurement of particles is the method needed. Cross-sectional area techniques are used as a substitute for volume measurements. For items with clearance problems, the longest dimension of the particle becomes critical. Where speed in sizing of particles is important, the length of the particle is taken in the same direction for all particles. This method results in the average length of particles being stated as much smaller than they actually are.

Various methods are used to measure quantity of matter. These methods can be divided into two categories, analog and digital. Analog methods measure many particles as a group, whereas digital methods measure each particle as a unit. Digital methods of determining quantity are refinements on analog techniques in many cases.

Sometimes it becomes necessary to identify single, very small airborne particles. Conventional and electron microscopes are most useful tools when the sample is extremely small or is composed of a mixture of very miniature particles. To identify single small particles, the microscopist utilizes the same mental processes he uses in identifying large objects such as people, automobiles, and food. In this identification process, which is termed morphological analysis, the microscopist uses the shape characteristics either of the object as a whole or of the significant component parts. In situations where the particle is not readily identifiable, additional pertinent physical properties must be noted. These properties are considered the morphological characteristics(*1*) of the particle and are listed as follows: (1) Size. (2) Shape. (3) Surface markings. (4) Transparency, translucency, or opacity. (5) Occlusions or other discontinuities, including coatings. (6) Color, by transmission and/or reflection. (7) Anisotropy and birefringence. (8) Refractive indices and dispersion. (9) Conoscopic observation.

Usually it is unnecessary to measure the more complicated optical properties (items 7 through 9), although such properties of very small particles are often useful.

In clean rooms and earth atmosphere, the particulate matter suspended in a gas is called airborne particulate matter, or an aerosol. Settled airborne particulate matter on tools, parts, and work surfaces is considered a potential contaminant. This particulate matter is in an ideal position to be transferred into the product and thus could better be labeled transfer particulate matter. Particulate matter suspended in liquid is often referred to as fluid contaminant, whereas particulate matter settled in liquid is often referred to as silt. Particulate matter suspended in a solid is normally called an "included contaminant."

Comparisons often assist in picturing relative size dimensions. One question that can be posed is, "How big is a millionth of an inch?" If you take a normal human hair and split it longitudinally into 1000 equal parts, one of these parts is equal to a millionth of an inch. Through the use of interferometry, gauge blocks can be calibrated to a millionth of an inch. Because of adjustments that have to be made for temperature, barometric pressure, humidity, etc., the National Bureau of Standards will certify the accuracy of the standards to only 2.5 millionths.

The conventional unit of measurement for fine particles is the micron (μ). A micron[1] is a millionth of a meter, or approximately 0.000040 of an inch. A human hair varies from 30 to 200 microns in diameter, with the average human hair being approximately 100 microns(2) (see Figure 2-1).

Airborne particles range in size from 0.001 micron to 1000 microns, the latter having a very short "life." Rain would be a good example of a 1000-micron particle. Particles of 0.001 micron are bordering on molecular size, and as yet it has not been necessary to control particles of this size in clean rooms. In general, clean rooms will control particles in the 0.5-micron size range and up.

Contaminant Properties[2]

It is important in any battle to know your enemy to the best of your ability. Failure in this respect will often produce dire consequences. The clean room is a battlefield. The enemy is contamination. The battle to be waged is an everyday affair, that of preventing contamination from entering the product. The victory is not always immediately discernible. It may be days, months, or years before the product will be utilized or the results of contamination seen. It is at this time that victory is important. As such, it is imperative to know as much as possible about contaminants.

[1] One micron equals 0.00003937 inch. There are 25,400 microns per inch.

[2] For a more detailed discussion on this subject, see Lieberman, cited in references to Chapter 1.

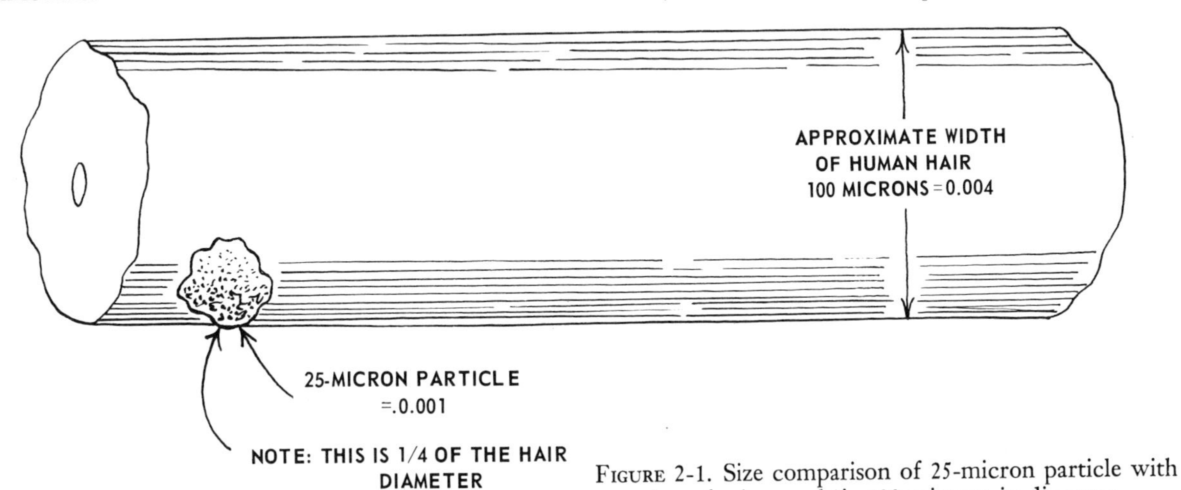

FIGURE 2-1. Size comparison of 25-micron particle with that of a human hair 100 microns in diameter.

A material must have certain properties before it can be considered a contaminant. (The universal movie axiom that all persons wearing black are villains does not hold true here.) The criterion that governs whether a specific material or particulate matter is a contaminant in the case of precise devices is its ability to cause damage. Two conditions must be met. First, the particulate matter must have the physical properties that will produce damage to the component. Second, the particulate matter must be able to migrate to or be in place at the vulnerable location. Particulate matter that meets the first condition can be classed a potential contaminant. The difference between a potential contaminant and an actual contaminant, however, is only location. Since to change location requires time, it might better be expressed that the difference between a potential contaminant and an actual contaminant is time and place. Since today's potential contaminant is tomorrow's actual contaminant, both are one and the same enemy. It must also be pointed out that there are many more potential contaminants than actual contaminants. Only one potential contaminant in a device need graduate to the status of an actual contaminant to produce trouble. It is obvious that a device with a specified design life can stand a given number of potential contaminants, one of which after a period of time will graduate to an actual contaminant and cause failure of the device. Therefore, it appears that, if the life of a given device depends on the length of time it takes for a potential contaminant to become an actual contaminant, then reduction of potential contaminants will increase product life.

Lieberman states(*3*):

The dandruff on our coat collars is not a contaminant until it gets into the components which can be harmed. Even gaseous materials cause problems. In the case of metals, acid vapors produce metal salts which can cause damage in other locations and, in addition, by virtue of their formation, can cause local weaknesses. The organic vapor in noble metal reaction products of course covers the brown polymer situation. Particles which are present in sizes too small to cause any physical damage cannot be considered as contamination until or unless they diffuse or otherwise travel to a location where their size is critical or if they agglomerate into a larger particle. Potential contaminants may be present in systems whose materials are hard and/or tough enough to destroy the particle without damage to the system. In this case, although the particle is present in quantities that would normally be harmful in other systems, it is not a contaminant but is just a particle that is about to be rejected by a tough system.

[Figure 2-2] shows the type of material which can be a problem. This is an electron micrograph of material which was collected in a laboratory atmosphere. This material was deposited by a low efficiency electrostatic precipitator so that the agglomerates would not be harmed. The material was then shadow-casted with germanium and the electron microscope was used to obtain a photograph. As you notice, we shadow-casted in two directions. The agglomerate in the upper center is a little better than a micron in length. It is composed of particles which are themselves only a few tenths of a micron in diameter. Normally these particles would not be a problem but because of their agglomeration they will cause difficulty. Toward the lower left is a droplet which also contains smaller particles. This again could be a problem but does not necessarily have to be.

[Figure 2-3] is a selected sample of dust collected from a building ventilation system. The particle on the right is approximately 100 microns in diameter. Again, particles which would not cause problems individually might do so when agglomerated.

Only when a device is operated at an energy level which is sufficiently high to destroy any agglomeration without interference is the agglomerate not a problem. If the device operates at a lower energy level then the same agglomerate produces a cleanliness problem. In some cases it has been found necessary to increase the available energy[3] for device actuation as a means of reducing contamination problems.

From the above discussion, it follows that the action of contaminants can be delayed or prompt. Prompt action is the most common effect of a contaminant and appears almost immediately. Such contaminants do not require that any contributory mechanism (which will be discussed shortly) be involved. Prompt-action contaminants can be classified as hard or soft particles.

Hard particles are defined as those capable of damaging the surface of the component. This may be done by removal of material from the surface of the component by grinding action, or by embedding of a relatively undistorted particle. In this action the component surface is plasticly deformed, whereas only elastic deformation takes place in the hard particle. Referring to typical stress-strain

[3] See Chapter 4 for more detailed discussion of this subject.

curves of materials, and noting both the elastic deformation range and the plastic deformation range, we see that hard particles will have a tensile strength at least 10% greater than the component material.

Soft particles will not cause damage to the surface of the component. They are collected and retained on this surface. These particles may be smeared over the surface to produce a coated section. Since soft particles have a lower tensile strength than the component material, they are subject to continual breakdown. Although they do not damage the surface of the component, they interfere with the operation of the device.

Prompt-action contaminants can further be classified by size. The size of the particle should be considered in relation to the critical dimension and regardless of particle consistency. Such a classification will result in particles larger than and smaller than the critical dimension. The contaminant effects of particles are reasonably straightforward for particles larger than critical clearances or spacings. Typically, these effects are either that the critical dimension will not permit the entrance of the contaminant, or that the critical dimension will close upon the particle in some manner. Particles may be smaller than the clearance and still be large enough to cause problems. The critical particle diameter is generally believed to be one-half of the critical dimension. There has been some discussion on this point, with one school suggesting that the critical particle diameter is one-third of the critical spacing. Particles in a device smaller than the critical dimension can cause serious difficulty if they agglomerate or if more than one particle is collected at a critical position. The rate of agglomeration for particles in air with and without electric charge can be determined. Agglomeration of particles in clean room air is of little concern, however, since in determining the level at which the clean room is maintained this agglomeration rate has been considered.

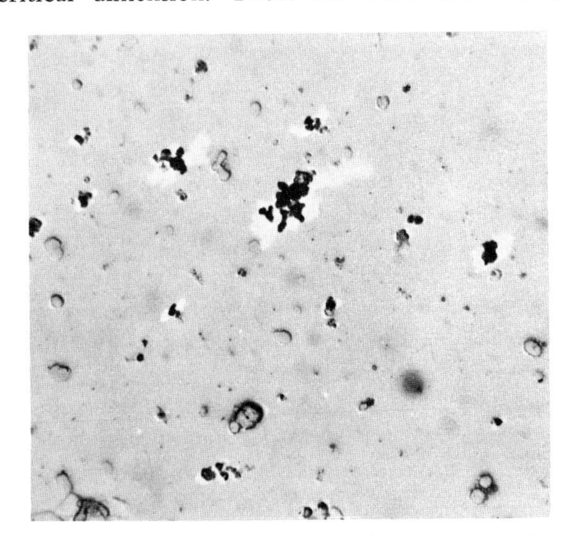

FIGURE 2-2. Electron micrograph of material collected in a laboratory atmosphere. *Courtesy Armour Research Foundation*

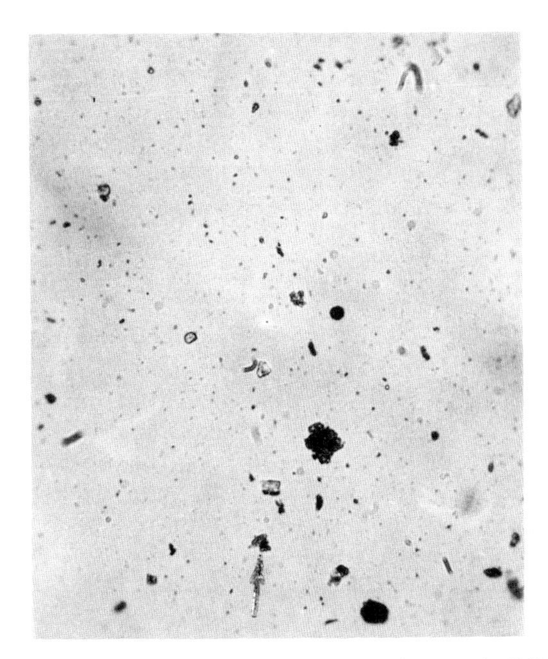

FIGURE 2-3. Sample of dust collected from a building ventilation system. Arrow marks particle approximately 100 microns in diameter. *Courtesy Armour Research Foundation*

Normally, this rate is not significant enough to bias the size distribution of particles in the clean room. The size distribution of particles is maintained by Stoke's law (to be discussed shortly), which is a function of particle size. Agglomeration results in an increase in the effective size of the particle, which allows it to fall out at a faster rate. Agglomeration of particles after deposition has a low but finite probability. Deposition of more than one small particle at a critical area over a short period of time has a probability high enough to be important. A mathematical model of this agglomeration and its effect on the critical dimension needs to be developed.

A primary cause of contamination may be a material that does no harm until reaction, diffusion, or other processes take place. This type of contaminant can be labeled as a delayed-action contaminant. Such a contaminant requires a contributing mechanism or material before it can cause damage. Delayed action contaminants can be either gases or particles. Gaseous contaminants are capable of reacting directly with metals. Their reaction rates are increased greatly in the presence of water vapor. These gases include oxygen, sulfur dioxide, sulfur trioxide, and other acid gases. The reaction products are mainly oxides or salts of the metal base. If an adherent, uniform film is formed in noncritical areas, no great problems arise. If the reaction products do not adhere, however, a protective coating does not form, and a new surface is continuously exposed to reaction. The particle size of the reaction products can cover the range from submicron particles to millimeter-size flakes. In addition to the damage caused by removal of substrate by reaction, these materials can be transported into critical areas where subsequent damage may occur. The same considerations apply to the organic vapor–noble metal reaction product described as brown polymer in many references.

Having discussed gaseous contaminants, let us consider other delayed-action contaminants. Delayed-action contaminants that can be classified as particles do not cause immediate damage. Such particles may be present on the surface of a component. These particles may have formed as a result of reaction with a gas, or they may have been deposited by other means. Pressure and/or heat may cause the particles to be forced into the surface of the component. This intimate contact may then permit diffusion of the material of the particle into the component material. Depending on the composition of the particle and of the component, the products formed (alloys or compounds) as a result of such diffusion may result in serious loss of structural strengths of a sensitive component.

Particles may be present in a system in sizes too small to cause any physical damage by action of individual particles. The repetitive action of numbers of particles may cause damage, however. A good example of such action is the erosion of orifices, nozzles, etc., in servo valves. The particles causing damage do so only after a period of time during which the damaged part has been exposed to these particles. Another similar effect is suspected in some failures of air bearings or gas-lubricated bearings. In this case organic vapors in the compressed lubricating gas cool rapidly while expanding through orifices. When this occurs, condensation of high-molecular-weight organic materials may produce particles that can grow to a size capable of causing damage.

Deposition of particles on the surface of a sensitive device may be of no consequence if the particles remain at an innocuous location. If they are shaken loose during transit or storage and fall into a critical location, damage will occur. Particles produced by wear from normal operation of one part of the device may be transported to a critical zone, causing damage. Migration may occur as a result of tangential (thrown off rotating parts, as belt pulleys), aerodynamic (blown from one point to another), or mechanical (wiped from one part by another) forces, as well as the usual electrostatic, gravitational, or inertial forces.

Energy Relationships of Particles[4]

The relative energy level between a particle and a probable point of deposition controls the rate at which the particles are collected and retained. The types of energy gradients of most importance for particle deposition are electric, kinetic, and thermal. Electrical gradients which cause electrostatic precipitation are capable of effecting the collection of particles in almost any size range. Once the particles have been charged, they will be strongly attracted to grounded or oppositely charged surfaces. After deposition, the effects of the initial electrification may alter the adhesive forces, but no quantitative data are available. Normal aerosols are composed of charged particles with a charge distribution dependent on composition and centering around zero net charge. The particles pick up a charge during their generation process by exposure to ionizing radiation, by contact with or collection of other charged particles, etc. The variation in the

[4] The material discussed under this heading is abstracted from reference *4*, pp. 19 and 20.

electric field surrounding the component surface will depend to some extent on the conductivity of the component.

The term kinetic energy gradient is used to summarize inertial forces depending on velocity difference between the contaminant particles and the component surfaces. Direct gravitational effects and impaction effects are included. The latter effects are not considered separate, whether they arise from motion of the particles (as wind-carried) or of the component (as on a fan blade). The controlling parameters of device, particle, and air flow determine whether the particle will deposit on the surface or will follow the air streamlines around the surface.

Thermal energy gradients cause thermal precipitation to take place when the substrate is at a lower temperature than the surrounding air. If this is the case, submicron particles will be deposited and may agglomerate to particles large enough to cause damage.

Chemical and Physical Properties

Chemical and physical properties of contaminants are outlined by Lieberman(*4*). He states:

> Essentially all the chemical and physical properties of contaminants are of importance. The degree and kind of damage produced will depend upon these properties.

The rate at which damage occurs will also depend on the chemical and physical properties of the contaminants. Lieberman continues:

> The hardness and friability of the particles will play a part in determining whether the particles are broken up or whether the device is damaged. The electrical properties affect the deposition and collection rates of contaminants. Chemical properties, including crystal structure will affect the damage rate after collection. Diffusion rates and resulting compound are a function of the composition characteristics of both the contaminant and the substrate.[5]

In addition to the normal properties considered, a few of special concern should be mentioned.

Many salts have the property of growing by absorption of water vapor from the air. This action is called nucleating. In some cases, a salt crystal not large enough to deposit may be exposed to highly humid air. In this environment it will grow to a substantial or collectible size. After deposition the particle can then produce damage by physical means or by formation of salt solutions. It can be considered a type of delayed-action contaminant.

Another property of concern is tackiness. Tacky particles may be collected and deposited in an area where they will collect other contaminating material over a period of time.

Representative sizes of typical particles are listed in Figure 2-4(*5*).

Contaminant Sources[6]

Manufacture

Contaminant sources are present in the manufacture and assembly of components. Normally, single-component items are manufactured and placed together or assembled into pieces called subassemblies. Contaminant sources are present in both operations. Manufacturing sources present in the preparation of a single-component item will be considered first.

A component may consist of a cast, stamped, rolled, or molded part. Machining operations may have been performed as part of initial fabrication, but not as a final dimensional adjustment for fit purposes. The component may be metallic, plastic, nonmetallic chemical, or a combination of materials.

Casting inclusions is the term used to define inhomogeneities within the component. These may range from air bubbles to sand grains for metal castings. They may include dissolved impurities that will recrystallize metal, glass, or plastic when the casting cools. Pressed or molded parts may contain inadvertent inclusions of any nature.

Carry-over contamination occurs mainly when the component of interest is part of a small batch. A previous batch may have left similar or dissimilar material as a particulate or film contaminant in or on the fabricating machine. This material may be picked up by the component during fabrication.

A type of contamination that occurs mainly when the component is part of a large batch is due to cutting operations. The contaminating material may

[5] Reference *4*, p. 20.

[6] The material discussed under this heading is abstracted from reference *4*, pp. 21–34.

be chips from machining operations, foreign material circulated in the cutting fluid, or combinations of the two. The contamination from this source may be chemically identical to the component.

Assembly

A number of contamination sources are associated with assembly operations. Lieberman states in his report(*4*):

Although the major labor involved is assembling of parts and installation of fasteners, some fitting operations are involved. These may require either removal of material (as in drilling or tapping) or addition of material (as in soldering or welding). During the assembly process the possibility of contaminant introduction is probably greatest because of exposure to the highest levels of contaminant sources. Some typical assembly operation sources are soldering, brazing, welding, adhesives, wire drawing, grinding, fitting, handling and deformation of component by tools.

Soldering, brazing, and welding are commonly used in making metal-to-metal assemblies without the use of fasteners. In all of these operations, flux is used to remove oxide films from the base metal, and molten metal is used to join the work pieces. In many cases one or more of the elements is heated above its boiling point; mostly this occurs with flux. On vaporization, the material escapes into the surrounding air, cools, and condenses as droplets on a nearby cold surface. The condensed material can act as a contaminant, either immediate or delayed, depending on the location of the particles and the forces applied to them. In addition to condensed and deposited fragments, careless assembly or fabrication may result in excess bead, which can be a source of difficulty.

Adhesive particles can be a serious source of contaminants. Joints between dissimilar materials utilize an adhesive of one sort or another. The adhesive may be a resin, a glue, or a solvent for one or both of the materials being joined. In addition to problems of the type mentioned with flux and solder fragments, the adhesive may contain vapors (plasticizer or solvent) which can migrate to other portions of the assembly and act as a delayed-action contaminant.

Assembly of components using threaded or mortised joints can produce fragments as a result of wire drawing. The fragments, whether metal or plastic, are mainly fiber-shaped, unless the component material is friable. Repeated assembly may result in fatigue at threads, producing flakes as well as fibers of material.[7]

Grinding and other fitting operations are sources of contamination. Lieberman reports(*4*):

For extremely close fit or for balance, it may be necessary to fit individual components together by grinding, lapping, or honing operations. In any such case, it is assumed that the installation is sufficiently sophisticated to allow for removal of fragments thrown into the air or suspended in fluid. However, the operation may result in imbedding of abrasive particles into the surface of the component. In addition, particles can be held on the component surface quite strongly without imbedding. Subsequently, damage can occur to mating parts.

Assembly of components in jigs or while being handled or supported by tools may result in deformation of surfaces. Normally this is not a serious problem unless slippage occurs. Mainly deformation and particle production will occur as a result of tool action on fasteners. Even without slipping, bolthead deformation during closure will result in some particle production from the bolt head and the threaded end as well as from the components being fastened together. The danger of contaminant production as a result of careless application or of poor selection of tools is obvious.[8]

Storage

Storage is another source of contamination. Lieberman reports(*4*):

Sometime during or after assembly or subassembly, a device will be stored for periods of time ranging from a few hours to several years. During this time, several possibilities exist for contamination of the device, even though it is completely passive and, in fact, may have a protective covering. In the case where shipping or transfer of devices from one location to another is involved, one additional contamination possibility exists. This is one example of delayed-action contamination. If contaminating particles are present within the device or its casing at an innocuous location, vibrations produced during shipping may cause the particles to be transported to a critical location.

Deposition of particles from the air occurs at all times. . . . Deposition during storage, however, occurs when the device is in a zone with little or no airflow that could cause impaction of particles. The particles may be deposited as a result of gravitational settling, with some additional collection resulting from electrostatic collection after the airborne materials have been carried close to the device surface. Mainly, the particles depositing from the air will be the larger ones (larger than 5 microns), since the smaller particles will tend to remain suspended because of turbulence in the air.

Improperly cleaned containers or covers used to hold devices during storage may transfer particles to the devices. This is especially true of padded con-

[7] Reference *4*, pp. 22-24.

[8] Reference *4*, pp. 22-24.

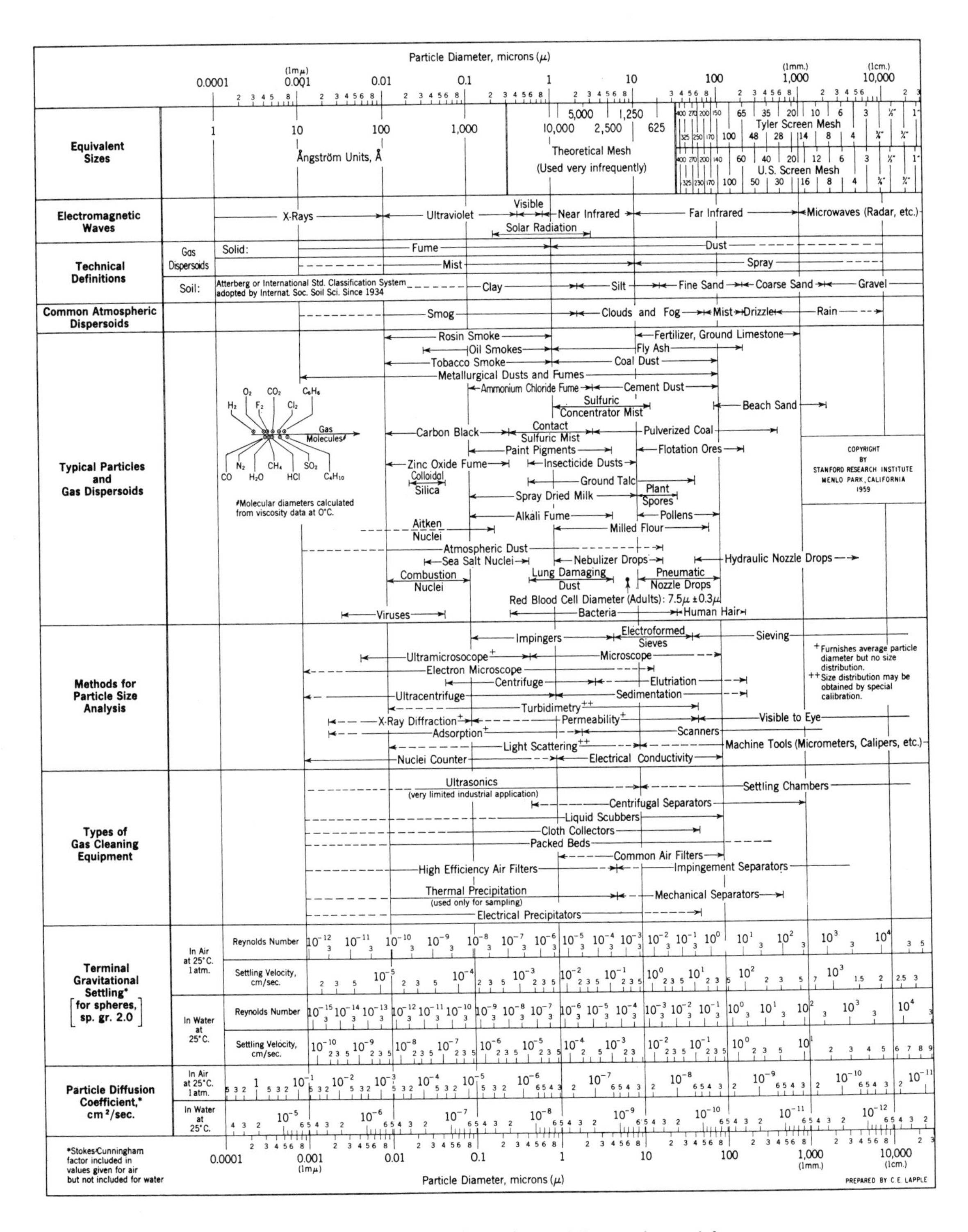

FIGURE 2-4. Characteristics of particles and particle dispersoids. *Reprinted by permission of Stanford Research Institute*

tainers and plastic containers. In the first case, the contours of the container may trap particles which are not released until the device causes deformation of the padding. In the second case, because of their normal electric charge, plastic containers may pick up particles from the air and hold them until removal onto the device. This can be a serious problem when repeated overnight storage is required for small components or for large devices. With small components the use of plastic boxes with pressed-on tops or soft bags leads to particles of plastic being removed from the container interiors. With large devices repeated creasing and folding of "dust-covers" may cause damage at the folds, which will produce particles.

[Breathing of the container] exists when long-term storage is required. If the container is not hermetically sealed, it will "breathe" as the temperature of the container cycles with day and night. During the intake portion of the cycle, any particles in the air surrounding the container can be drawn into a position where they can contaminate the devices.[9]

The danger of formation of corrosion products comes about because the personnel responsible for storage are often not aware of requirements to avoid the possibility of reacting gases in the storage areas. Indoctrination of these personnel is often needed.

Cleaning

Lieberman states:

It is sometimes difficult to realize that a cleaning process may be a source of contamination. Consideration of the extreme levels of cleanliness required for successful operation of precise devices reveals that a cleaning process is actually a process of transfer of dirt from a higher concentration to a lower one. If the lower concentration contains contaminants above acceptance levels (size or concentration), it is impossible to produce a clean device.[10]

Both dry and wet transfer of contaminants may be used in a cleaning process:

The mechanisms involved in cleaning precise devices are the following: (1) The bond between the contaminant particle and the device must be broken. This bond may be physical or electrical. Chemical bonding is not considered. (2) The particle must be physically removed from the surface of the device. (3) The possibility of redeposition or recontamination must be avoided.

Dry transfer occurs when a very large amount of contamination is being removed. The means for doing so usually involves wiping or polishing with an absorbent or collecting material. The fibers may be removed from the wiper as a result of poor initial retention within the fabric. After some use, the wiper will have a particle concentration sufficiently high so that as much contamination will be left on the device as is removed. The ways in which dry transfer can contaminate include the following: (1) The strength of the bond between the particle and the device may be too much to be overcome by the wiping action alone. (2) The wiping action may cause triboelectric charging either of a portion of the wiper or the device. The charged portions may produce very high electrostatic bonds. (3) The wiping action may move particles about on the surface but does not necessarily lift them from the surface.

Wet cleaning is done by exposing the contaminated surface to a clean fluid which will wet the particles and the surface, agitating the fluid or the device so as to pull particles from the surface, sweep dirt-laden fluid from the vicinity of the surface, and dry the surface. Problems exist in each of these processes. Normally a chlorinated hydrocarbon solvent is used as the transfer fluid. A serious problem exists in obtaining clean fluid and in keeping it clean when handling it. Wettability is not a serious problem, since any of several fluids can be used. Ultrasonic cleaners are mainly used to agitate the fluid. The effectiveness of the energy distribution throughout the cleaning tank often varies. The choice of frequency and energy level may not be optimum. Of greater importance is the fact that the amplitude of the agitation is not large enough to remove particles an appreciable distance from the surface of the part being cleaned. The possibility of recontamination is very great. The rate at which fluid is circulated through the clean-up filter is not high enough to keep the fluid clean in the tank. Because of surface tension effects, any particles in the fluid will be collected on the device when it is removed from the tank. Until the device is dried, any air-suspended particles will collect on the wet surface and remain after drying. Often, a wet surface may have particles in the liquid layer that can easily be moved laterally over the surface but are removed from the liquid layer only with great difficulty.

Much of the discussion above does not deal with a contaminant source as such but with removal of previously acquired contaminants. It is believed that the problems of cleaning are sufficiently serious to include the process in this discussion.[11]

Air

Air is a gigantic source of contamination. Lieberman reports(*4*):

[9] Reference *4*, pp. 24 and 25.

[10] Reference *4*, p. 26.

[11] Reference *4*, pp. 26-28.

The air which continually surrounds the components and the device can be thought of as a contamination storehouse. The air contains both organic and inorganic vapors. The air contains particles large enough to cause damage to the device if they are deposited on or in the device. Because of the constant exposure to airborne contaminants, the greatest precautions have been made to minimize the contaminant concentration in the air. Some particles will always be present in the air because of the multiplicity of sources to which the air is exposed. The ways in which the air can be contaminated will be considered later. At this time, the ways in which contaminated air can affect the device are of interest, i.e., the mechanism of transfer from the air to the device.

When particles are placed in a region where there is an energy gradient, they will travel to that part of the region where the energy level is lowest. The most familiar example is the phenomenon of gravitational settling in which particles move only vertically and down. Thus particles moving under gravitational forces only will settle on surfaces with a horizontal component.

Electrical fields can produce movement in aerosol particles also. Charged particles will move in uniform electric fields, while either charged or uncharged particles will travel in nonuniform fields. Particles in an area where a thermal gradient exists will move to the cooler part of the zone. The mechanisms involved in causing particle motion are not discussed here. The net result is that particles are moved in an appropriate direction, resulting in deposition on surfaces that do not necessarily have a horizontal component.

The energy gradient forces are directed toward the particles suspended in the air; they are independent of any inertial forces resulting from air currents; they cause no interaction between particles. Because of these factors, these forces are probably the most important in causing contamination.

When an airstream containing particles is forced to change direction because an obstacle is in its path, those particles which have sufficient inertia will continue on in their original trajectories until they impact on the surface of the obstacle. Smaller or lighter particles will continue to move around the obstacle. Depending upon the shape of the obstacle, some collection may occur on the downstream face as a result of turbulent eddy formation. This oversimplified description pictures the two extremes of the impaction processes.

Diffusion, coalescence, nucleation, and other similar type processes are primarily the result of interparticle forces. They have no direct effect upon contaminant deposition. They change the particle characteristics sufficiently so that the deposition pattern will change. Diffusion produces random particle motion, resulting in translation of particles from an expected narrow trajectory to a broad path. Brownian motion of the particles may also result in coalescence and growth of particles. If growth occurs, more material will be impacted than if it had not grown. Coalescence and growth may occur as a result of electric fields, gravitational effects, and turbulence. If the particle is capable of absorbing water vapor (of initiating droplet growth by nucleation), it may grow to a size which would be collected under conditions that would not normally permit collection of the dry particle alone. In short, the interparticle forces may lead to a change in the particle characteristics that will change its normal deposition probability.[12]

Assembly Environment

The air provided for the environment in which precise devices are assembled is cleaned and conditioned as well as possible. The cleaning is normally done by a superinterception filter capable of efficient collection of particles 0.3 micron and larger. Even so, the assembly environment often contains appreciable quantities of particles which are large enough to be collected completely by the filter. It is apparent, then, that the assembly environment is adding contaminants to the air which is especially cleaned for that environment.[13]

As an example of this process, the contaminants expected from normal operations in a general-purpose clean room or Air Force standard clean room are summarized for three general source types:

A well-designed air handling system for a clean room will not permit material over approximately 0.5 micron in diameter to enter the air in the room. However, faulty installation or damaged filters will permit oversize particles to enter the room. The need for placing the filter downstream of the air conditioning system is sufficiently well documented so that contamination from conditioner components is not considered here. A well-installed filter system including an effective prefilter will nevertheless permit penetration of approximately 5 out of 10,000 particles. When the intake of dust is quite high, excessive particle penetration may take place before the filter retention and pressure drop increases.

The types of contaminants which can enter the clean room through the air cleaning system are many and varied. They include silica, rubber, spores, seeds, microbes, fungi, and oil droplets pulled in from the outside environment. Asbestos, cellulose, or glass fiber fragments can be removed from the filter medium, especially in new filters. Metal and oxide fragments can be produced from the surface of the conditioning system.

The mechanisms by which particles are removed from clean room surfaces are complex and are dis-

[12] Reference *4*, pp. 28-30.

[13] Reference *4*, p. 30.

cussed only superficially. The particles are dislodged by air currents from the surfaces on which they have been trapped. The force required for dislodging depends upon the physical and chemical characteristics of the surface and of the particles. Either sliding or rolling occurs, depending on the particle shape. As the air velocity increases, the velocity difference between the upper and lower portions of the particle produces aerodynamic lift. Eventually the particles are carried out of the laminar flow region close to the surface and into the space where random air currents can lift and keep suspended the particles which have been entrained. This process can occur for particles which have been deposited on the surface or which have been generated at the surface.

The types of contaminants which can be re-entrained depend upon their original generation process. Particles which have been transported to the surface from the air cleaning system will be of the type outlined above. In addition, the various surfaces can produce other types of particles. For example, plastic, wall, ceiling, or floor surfaces on abrasion or impact can produce flakes of plastic that are highly charged. Metal walls do not produce particles, but the solvents and cleaners used to keep them clean usually produce particles as a result of evaporation; i.e., the solvent will contain a residue of high-boiling material and dirt that is left on the surface when the solvent evaporates. A similar situation exists when tap water is used. The splashed water evaporates, leaving a residue of scale which can be entrained into the air.

When drawers or sliding door cabinets are used, a metal strip usually slides on plastic rollers. Abrasion of the metal and of the plastic produces particles which can be ejected into the air as the rollers flex. In addition, droplets of lubricant can be emitted from bearings at such rollers and at door hinges.

Normal operations in the assembly environment involve operations with jigs and tools. If they have been adequately cleaned before they are brought into the room and if the moving parts of the tools do not require lubrication, no particles will be generated by the tools. However, the force necessary to hold, join, or otherwise manipulate the device is usually enough to deform parts of the device. During this deformation, particles can be produced from either the device or the tools. The nature of the particles will depend on the deforming materials.

Any mechanical operation which is carried on with a tool will produce particles. Metalwear particles will be produced by wrenches or screw drivers. The particle production capabilities of grinding, soldering, welding, etc., are well enough known so that these tools are expected to be used in an exterior space or be properly vented. The use of electrical devices cannot be avoided in assembly environments; the contamination produced by electric arcs begins in the form of nuclei of less than 0.1 micron in diameter. These particles consist of hygroscopic and metal oxides, which can grow by nucleation or coalescence. The spray generated by ultrasonically agitated baths may contain particles removed from cleaned components. When the spray droplets evaporate, the suspended small particles may form a single agglomerate.

The activity of personnel in the assembly environment is probably the greatest single cause of contamination. Personnel moving about in an otherwise clean atmosphere leave a trail of particulate and gaseous contamination behind them. This contamination arises from several sources. The act of walking produces transient air currents which result in much re-entrainment. In addition, the usual foot coverings do not adequately prevent "pumping" of dust from the shoes. Mainly, personnel activity results in re-entrainment and brushing off of particles from many surfaces.

Another contaminant source is the tendency to shed skin and hair particles. The outer layers of skin flake off almost continuously. The flake rate and size depend on the amount of abrasion to which the skin is exposed and its prior condition. Exhaled air is another source of contamination. The breath is saturated with water vapor at body temperature and also contains some particles. Perspiration is usually quite acid. Thus all normal body exudations are contaminants.

The clean-room uniform may provide fibrous contamination and, unless carefully cleaned, will carry dirt particles from previous operations into the area. Most uniforms permit passage of at least small amounts of body hair or material from normal clothing worn under the uniform.[14]

Normal Operation

From time to time, a device which has been carefully cleaned, assembled, and checked will fail prematurely. One of the causes for such failure is the generation of particulate contamination during normal operation of the device. The processes controlling such generation will be discussed shortly. In addition to the processes of particle generation as a result of normal wear or of overspeed or overstress or a component, vibration during operation may accelerate migration of particles to a critical area. Particles which appear as a result of normal operation include rubber or similar plastic from wear on "O" rings or from belt drives. Nylon and metal particles are produced during operation of miniature gear assemblies. The "brown polymer" is produced by operation of noble metal electrical contacts in an atmosphere containing hydrocarbons. Epoxy resin particles often drift around in the interior of devices sealed with this material. These materials generally constitute a problem which can be best controlled during the design of the device.[15]

[14] Reference *4*, pp. 30-34.

[15] Reference *4*, p. 34.

Stokes' Law

So far, the nature of particles, what they are, their shape, their size, some of their characteristics, how they are identified, and how they possibly affect the product have been discussed. This chapter will now delve further into an understanding of particulate matter by explaining some theory about the forces acting on these airborne particulates. This can be done by going back to Newton's second law, which governs the motion of a particle settling under the influence of gravity. This relationship can be expressed by the equation(*6*)

$$m\frac{du}{dt} = mg = m'g - F \qquad (2\text{-}1)$$

where m and m' are the masses of the particle and the fluid displaced by the particle, du/dt is the acceleration of the particle, g is the acceleration of gravity, and F is the force resisting the particle's motion. If the particle is spherical and the only significant forces acting on the particle are frictional forces, then its motion is governed by Stokes' equation:

$$F = 3\pi\mu ud \qquad (2\text{-}2)$$

where μ is the viscosity of the fluid, and d is the diameter of the particle. If m and m' are expressed in terms of volume and density, $(\pi d^3/6)\ \rho$ and $(\pi d^3/6)\ \rho_o$, respectively, then the above equation becomes

$$\frac{\pi d^3}{6}\rho\frac{du}{dt} = \frac{\pi d^3}{6}(\rho - \rho_o)\,g - 3\pi\mu ud \qquad (2\text{-}3)$$

If the velocity or motion of the particle is constant —that is, if $du/dt = 0$—and x is the distance moved in the time t, an expression for the equivalent diameter, d_e, can be written:

$$d_e = \left[\frac{18\mu u}{(\rho - \rho_o)\,g}\right]^{1/2} = \left[\frac{18\mu}{(\rho - \rho_o)\,g}\right]^{1/2}\left[\frac{x}{t}\right]^{1/2} \qquad (2\text{-}4)$$

By so arranging Stokes' law and equating all values to d_e, particles that are not spherical can be handled. Thus, if the terminal velocities of settling under the influence of gravity can be determined, it may be assumed that their diameters are equivalent to those of spherical particles of equal density which settle with equal velocity. The term d_e applies to an irregular particle. It is the diameter equivalent to that of a spherical particle of equal density which settles at the same rate as does the irregular particle.

Equation (2-4) can be rearranged to allow the direct computation of the settling velocity of a particle in air. The symbol V_s is substituted for x and is the particle terminal settling velocity.

$$V_s = \frac{gd_e^2\,(\rho_p - \rho_g)}{18\mu} \qquad (2\text{-}5)$$

The particle and gas densities (mass) are expressed by ρ_p and ρ_p, respectively.

For particles within the range 0.3 to 1.0 micron in diameter, Cunningham's correction factor must be applied to the settling velocity to allow for the increased speed of settling owing to the tendency of these particles to slip between molecules of air with little or no drag. The correction factor is given by equation (2-6):

$$V_c = V_s\left(\frac{1 + 0.172}{D}\right) \qquad (2\text{-}6)$$

where

V_c = corrected settling velocity.
V_s = settling velocity computed in *a* above.
D = particle diameter in microns.

Table 2-1 shows some settling velocities of spherical airborne particles having a specific gravity of 1.0. Figure 2-4 shows values for settling velocities of spheres having a specific gravity of 2.0.

Size-Distribution Relationships

Having discussed the properties of contaminants and their sources, we shall now consider the presence of these contaminants within the clean room environment. Recently improved automatic particle-counting equipment, along with improved manual counting techniques, have shown more defined characteristics for airborne particulate matter. Experimental data(*7*) taken throughout the United States in various outdoor and indoor locations tend to substantiate the fact that there is a definite size-distribution relationship for airborne particulate matter. Recent investigations(*8*) by Philip R. Austin, Clifford F. Frith, and Stewart W. Timmerman,

TABLE 2–1

SETTLING RATES OF AIRBORNE PARTICLES*

Diameter of particles (microns)	*Velocity of Settling*		
	Feet per Minute	*Inches per Hour*	*Centimeters per Second*
0.1	0.00016	0.115	0.000081
0.2	0.00036	0.259	0.00018
0.4	0.0013	0.936	0.00066
0.6	0.002	1.44	0.0010
0.8	0.005	3.60	0.0025
1.0	0.007	5.04	0.0036
2.0	0.024	17.3	0.012
4.0	0.095	68.4	0.048
6.0	0.21	151	0.11
8.0	0.38	274	0.19
10	0.59	425	0.30
20	2.4	1,728	1.2
40	9.5	6,840	4.8
60	21.3	15,320	10.8
80	37.9	27,250	19.2
100	59.2	42,600	30.0
200	352	253,500	179
400	498	360,000	253

* This table has been compiled from "Size and Characteristics of Airborne Solids," by W. G. Frank, published in the Smithsonian Meteorological Tables. Rates are for particles in the shape of spheres, having a specific gravity of 1.0 and settling in still air at a temperature of 70° F.

within various facilities at Cape Kennedy further substantiate this size-distribution relationship. This relationship can be defined by Stokes' law and is essentially a logarithmic function. Stokes' law, as discussed previously, gives the rate of fall of a small sphere in a viscous fluid. When a small sphere falls under the action of gravity through a viscous medium, it ultimately acquires a constant velocity; see equation (2-5).

Figure 2-5[16] shows the curve titled Particulate Time Settling (PTS). This curve is taken from data of Figure 2-4, which gives the terminal gravitational settling for spheres of specific gravity of 2.0. The values presented are settling velocity, in centimeters per second, versus particle diameter. The atmospheric conditions are air at 25°C and 1 atmosphere pressure. The Stokes-Cunningham factor is included for these values. These data have been plotted in Figure 2-5 as the inverse function of settling velocity—that is, time required for a sphere to settle 1 cm. This scale is shown on the right-hand vertical axis of Figure 2-5, in seconds per centimeter. Also plotted in Figure 2-5 is the curve AF Standard Clean Room—Operational Limit (AFSCR) (*9*). The slope of this curve is essentially parallel to the slope of the particulate time settling curve for particles 2 microns to 25 microns in size. Future references will be made to the particulate time settling curve as PTS and to the Air Force standard clean room operational curve as AFSCR. In further figures in which size-distribution relationships for various locations are shown, they will be compared to the straight-line curve, AFSCR, for clarity. The slope of this line represents Stokes' law with a high degree of accuracy in the particle size range of interest for clean rooms.

It is acknowledged that the particle time settling curve is but one of many curves that can be drawn representing the settling time of particulate matter, but Stokes' equation shows that this slope is representative of settling time for particulate matter within air. If particulate matter is of such a shape and configuration that it has a greater projected drag area than the spheres used for the PTS curve, a shifting of the curve will take place, but the relationship of particles of one size to those of another will remain essentially the same. This curve represents to a high degree of accuracy the settling relationship for particulate matter.

The slope of the AFSCR curve is a generalized relationship of a theoretical air sample that has been analyzed for its size distribution of airborne particles. The best monitoring equipment takes 20 seconds to analyze an air sample. In this period of time the total quantity of particles does fluctuate; however, the size-distribution relationship should not materially change. This fluctuation accounts for part of the irregular shape of the experimental curves. Further, an operation that is generating particles in a selected size range will bias the experimental curves. Lastly, the accuracy of the monitoring equipment

[16] Figures 2-5 through 2-54 are reproduced through the courtesy of MAMES (Middletown Air Materiel Area, Directorate of Maintenance Engineering, Industrial Engineering Division, Special Projects Branch) Olmsted Air Force Base, Pennsylvania.

and techniques can cause variations in experimental curves.

The following experimental data were obtained by both manual and automatic counting techniques[17] throughout the United States.

Curve MA-M1 (Figure 2-6)

Date: 23 Nov. 1962

Time: 1349 to 1359 hours

Length of Sample: 10 minutes

Place: Clean Room Lab Area, Bldg. 137, Olmsted AFB, Pa.

Person Performing Sampling: 1st Lt. C. F. Frith

Instrument Used: Millipore sampling kit—0.8-micron membrane filter. Sample taken 32 inches from floor.

Temperature and Humidity: Similar to Air Force Class I requirements.[18]

Limitations of Test: Background count on membrane filter is appreciable for particle size range less than 2.0 microns.

Reason for Test: To determine contamination level of clean room lab for particle size range greater than 5.0 microns.

Observations: Note that curve M-1 is essentially

[17] See Chapter 9 for discussion of these techniques.

[18] Air Force Class I, II, III and IV Clean Rooms were defined in USAF Technical Order 00-25-203 dated 1 Mar. 61. These definitions were illogically stated and have been eliminated.

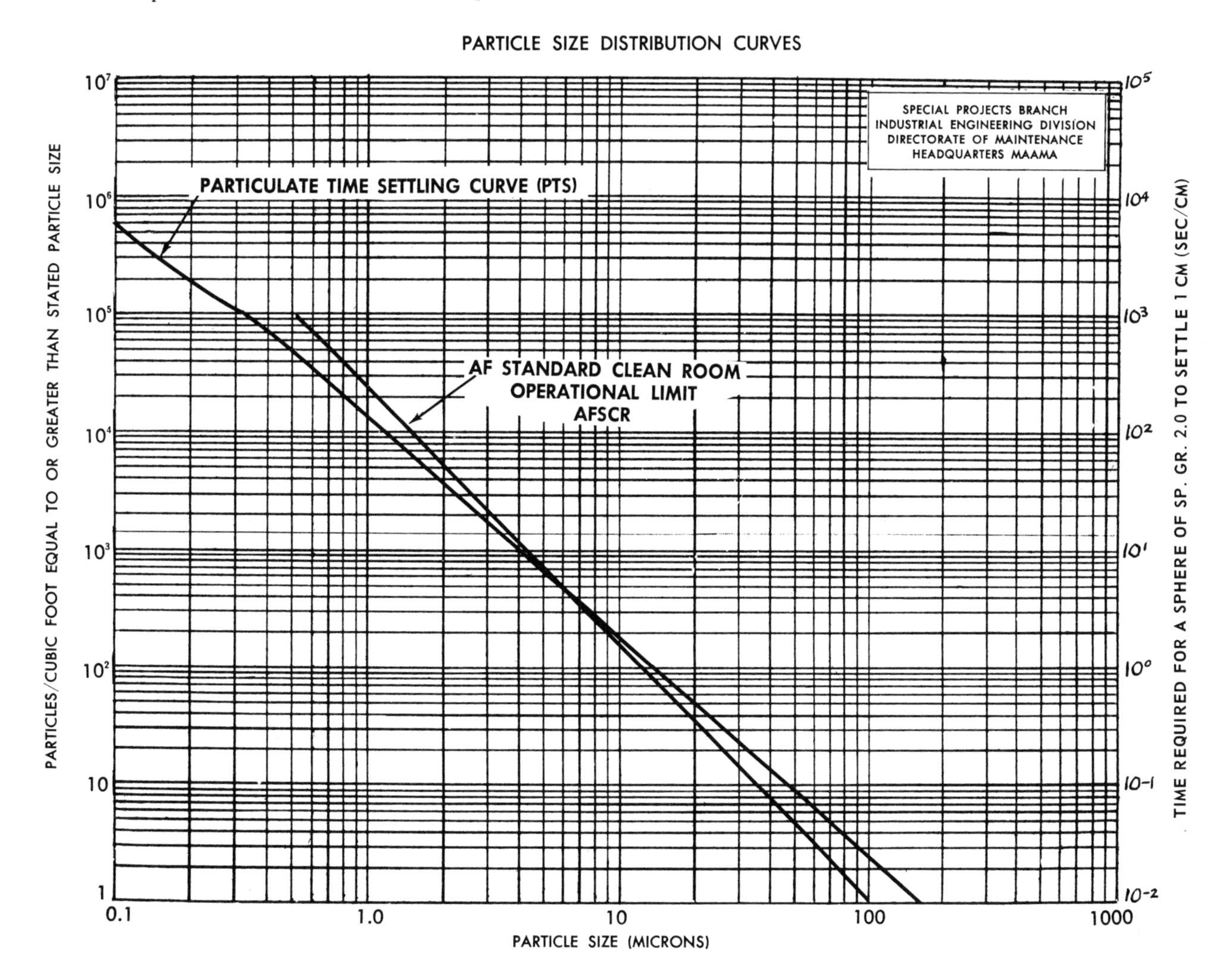

FIGURE 2-5.

linear when plotted on log-log paper and is parallel to the slope of the particulate time settling curve (PTS) and AFSCR curve of Figure 2-5.

Curve MA-M2 (*Figure 2-6*)
Date: 23 Nov. 1962
Time: 1401 to 1411 hours
Comments: All other conditions and observations the same as for MA-M1.

Curve MA-R1 (*Figure 2-6*)
Date: 5 Feb. 1963
Time: Afternoon
Place: Center of Bldg. 137—No. A Clean Room, Olmsted AFB, Pa.
Persons Performing Test: Clean room lab technicians
Instrument Used: Royco particle counter
Height of sample: 32 inches from floor
Sample rate: 0.0025 cfm (cubic feet per minute)
Dilution rate: 0.01 cfm (dilution ratio = 4–1)
Counter was operating on total mode, recording all particles equal to or greater than selected channel size. Each sampling was of 1-minute duration.

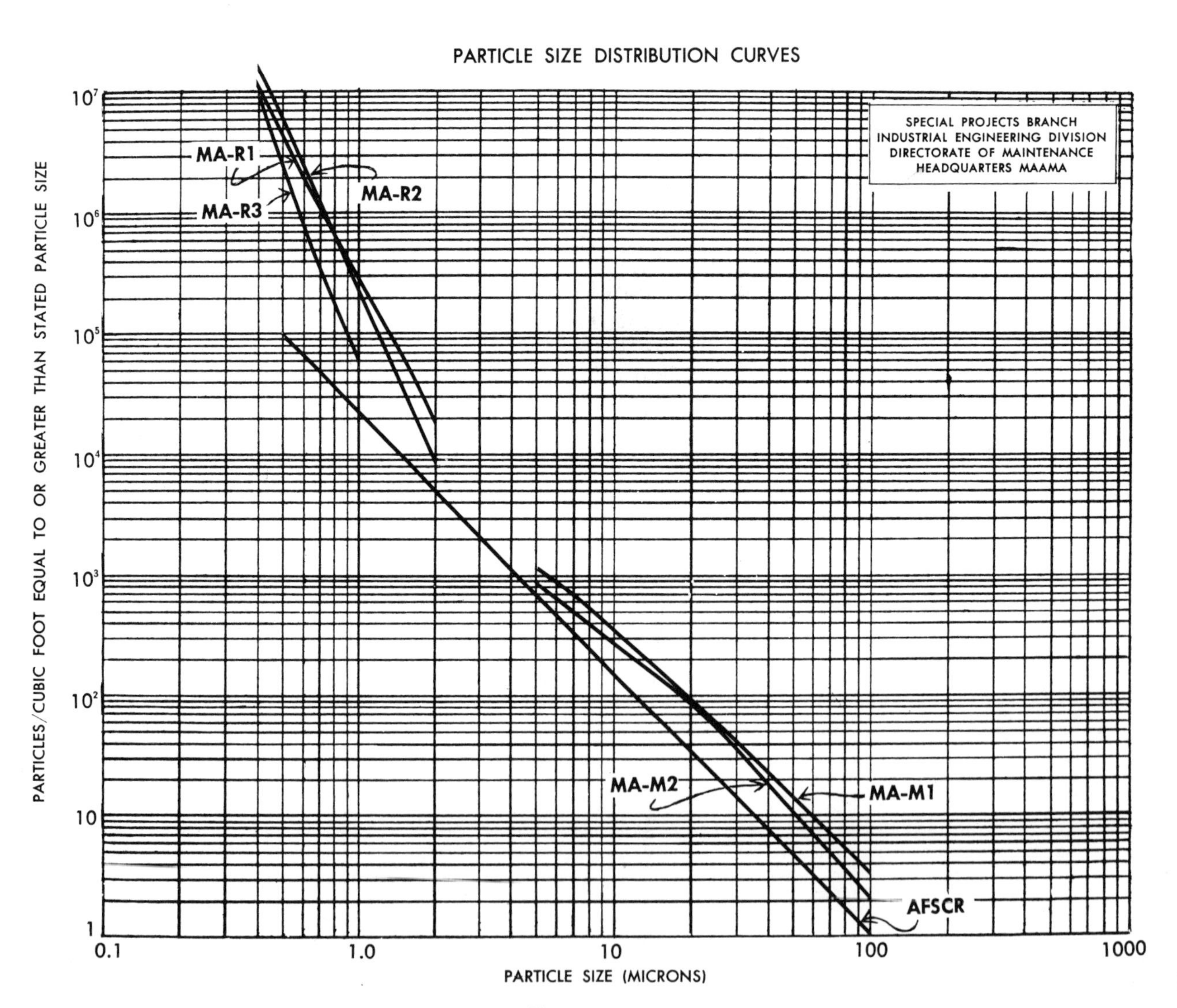

FIGURE 2-6.

Temperature and Humidity: Similar to Air Force Class I conditions.
Limitations of Test: High concentrations of airborne particulates dictated the initial dilution ratio which limited the data to the 0.4-micron to 2.0-micron range.
Reason for Test: To determine contamination level of small-size particles in area sampled.
Observations on Curve: This curve is essentially linear in nature. The indications here are that particles in this size range are deviating from the PTS and AFSCR slopes, since they are accumulating in the air and are not settling out, owing to the long interval of time required for settling of particles of this size.

Curve MA-R2 (Figure 2-6)
Date: 5 Feb. 1963
Time: 1 hour after MA-R1
Comments: All other conditions and observations similar to those for MA-R1.

Curve MA-R3 (Figure 2-6)
Date: 31 Jan. 1963
Time: Afternoon
Place: West exit of Bldg. 137 (outdoors), Olmsted AFB, Pa.

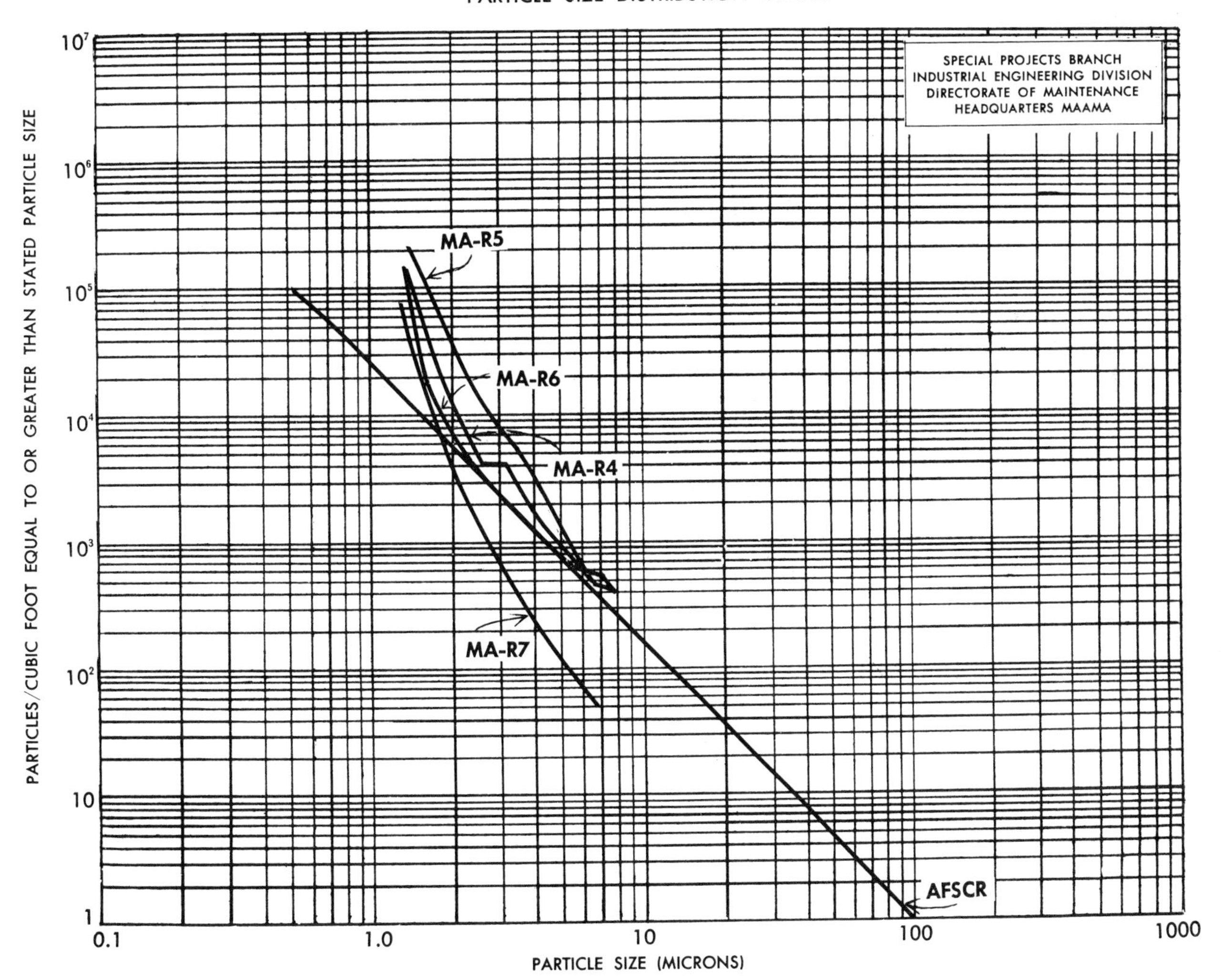

FIGURE 2-7.

Person Performing Test: Clean room lab technician

Instrument Used: Royco particle counter

Height of sample: 24 inches from road level

Sample rate: 0.0025 cfm

Dilution rate: 0.02 cfm (dilution ratio = 8–1)

Counter was operating on total mode. Each channel was operating for 1-minute sample.

Atmospheric Conditions: Clear day, 35°F.

Limitations of Test: High concentrations of airborne particulates dictated the initial dilution ratio which limited the data to the 0.4-micron to 2.0-micron range. Only random counts were recorded with this dilution ratio for the channels above 1.0 micron, however.

Reason for Test: To determine the ambient contamination level for the particle size range between 0.4 and 2.0 microns.

Observations on Curve: Same as for MA-R1.

Curve MA-R4 (Figure 2-7)

Date: 5 Mar. 1963

Time: 1000 to 1230 hours

Place: Clean Room Lab Area, Pillar H19, Bldg. 137, Olmsted AFB, Pa.

Person Performing Test: Clean room lab technician

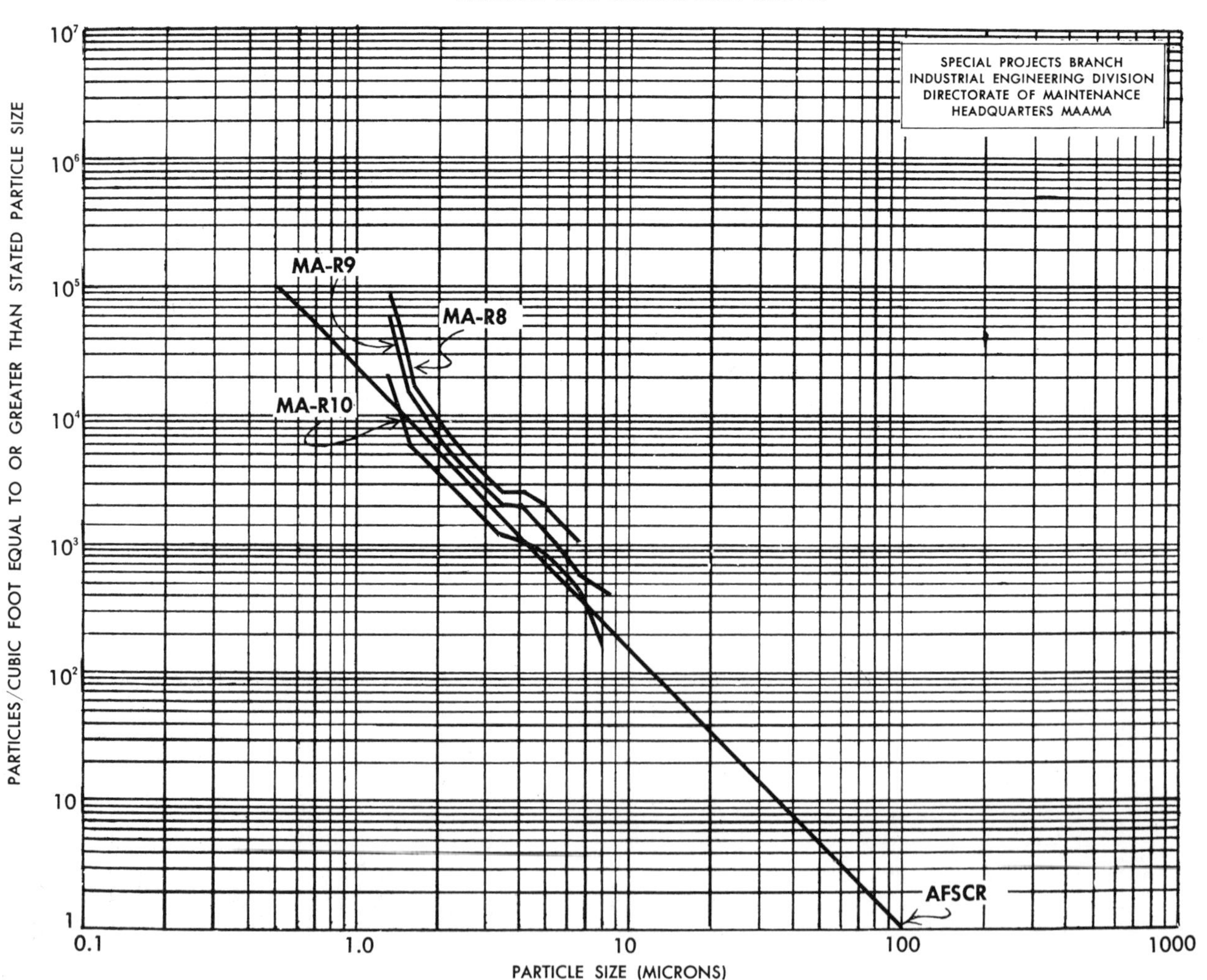

FIGURE 2-8.

Instrument Used: Royco particle counter
Height of sample: 32 inches from floor
Sample rate: 0.01 cfm
Particle counter was operating on total mode, taking 1-minute samples per channel.

Limitation of Test: Size range between 1.3 and 8.0 microns was investigated. This curve is an average of ten complete tests of nine channel readings each for the above time period.

Reason for Test: To investigate the relationship between curves MA-R1, MA-R2, and MA-R3, and curves MA-M1 and MA-M2.

Observations on Curve: There is a predominant curvature to the slope of the curves averaged for MA-R4. At the point of particles greater than 2.3 microns, the slope of the curve is essentially the same as that for MA-M1 and MA-M2. For particles 1.3 microns and smaller, the slope of the curve is essentially the same as that for MA-R1 and MA-R2. These empirical data indicate that in the range of 2.0 microns there is a predominant change of slope for the curve of size-distribution relationship for airborne particulate matter.

Curve MA-R5 (*Figure* 2-7)
Date: 5 Mar. 1963
Time: 1036 to 1045 hours
Person Performing Test: Clean room lab technician
Instrument Used: Royco particle counter
Limitations of Test: All other conditions the same as for MA-R4, except that this curve is an individual run of nine channels for all particles equal to or greater than 1.3, 1.6, 2.0, 2.5, 3.2, 4.0, 5.0, 6.4, and 8.0 microns.

Curve MA-R6 (*Figure* 2-7)
Limitations of Test: All conditions the same as for MA-R5, except that these nine readings were taken from 1055 to 1103 hours.

Curve MA-R7 (*Figure* 2-7)
Date: 5 Mar. 1963
Time: 1345 to 1415 hours
Place: Clean Room Lab Area, Pillar H19, Bldg. 137, Olmsted AFB, Pa.
Person Performing Test: Clean room lab technician
Instrument Used: Royco particle counter
Height of sample: 13 feet above floor level at ceiling air intake.
Sample rate: 0.01 cfm
Dilution rate = 0 cfm
Counter was operating on total mode, taking 1-minute samples on each channel.

Temperature and Humidity: Similar to Air Force Class I conditions.

Limitations of Test: The last channel of the Royco counter used was 8.0 microns. No particles were recorded on this channel during this test. This could be attributed to the low air flow and the short duration of sampling time. Curve MA-R7 is an average of ten complete sets of nine readings during the above time interval, representing ninety 1-minute samples. The channels recorded were 1.3, 1.6, 2.0, 2.5, 3.2, 4.0, 5.0, 6.4 and 8.0 microns.

Observations on Curve: Notice that the slope of the curve at 1.3 microns is essentially the same as the slope of MA-R1 and MA-R2. Notice that in the larger particle size ranges the slope of this curve is approaching the slope of the PTS and AFSCR curves.

Curve MA-R8 (*Figure 2-8*)
Date: 6 Mar. 1963
Time: 1030 to 1038 hours
Place: Rear of Bldg. 137 between pillars L16 and L19, Olmsted AFB, Pa.
Persons Performing Test: Clean room lab technician
Instrument Used: Royco particle counter
Height of sample: 32 inches from floor
Sample rate: 0.01 cfm
Dilution rate = 0 cfm
Particle counter was operating on total mode, taking 1-minute samples for each channel.

Atmosphere and Humidity: Similar to Air Force Class I requirements.

Limitations of Test: No cumulative count for particles greater than 8.0 microns could be obtained with this model of the Royco counter.

Reason for Test: To investigate area between 1.3 and 8.0 microns.

Observations on Curve: The slope of the curve after 2.0 microns is essentially parallel to the slope of the PTS and AFSCR curves.

Curve MA-R9 (*Figure 2-8*)
Date: 6 Mar. 1963
Time: 1030 to 1200 hours
Limitations of Test: All conditions the same as for MA-R8, except that ten runs of nine readings apiece were averaged over this time duration. The curve is essentially parallel at each point to MA-R8.

Curve MA-R10 (*Figure 2-8*)
Date: 6 Mar. 1963
Time: 1300 to 1430 hours
Place: East end of Clean Room B, Bldg. 137, Olmsted AFB, Pa.
Person Making Test: Clean room lab technician
Instrument Used: Royco particle counter
Height of sample: 32 inches from floor
Sample rate: 0.01 cfm
Dilution rate: 0 cfm
Counter was operating on total mode, taking 1-minute samples for each channel.
Limitation of Test: Same as for MA-R8.
Reason for Test: To investigate curves in size range between 1.3 and 8.0 microns for another area in the same building.
Observations on Curve: Curve MA-R10 is an average of ten runs of nine channel readings,

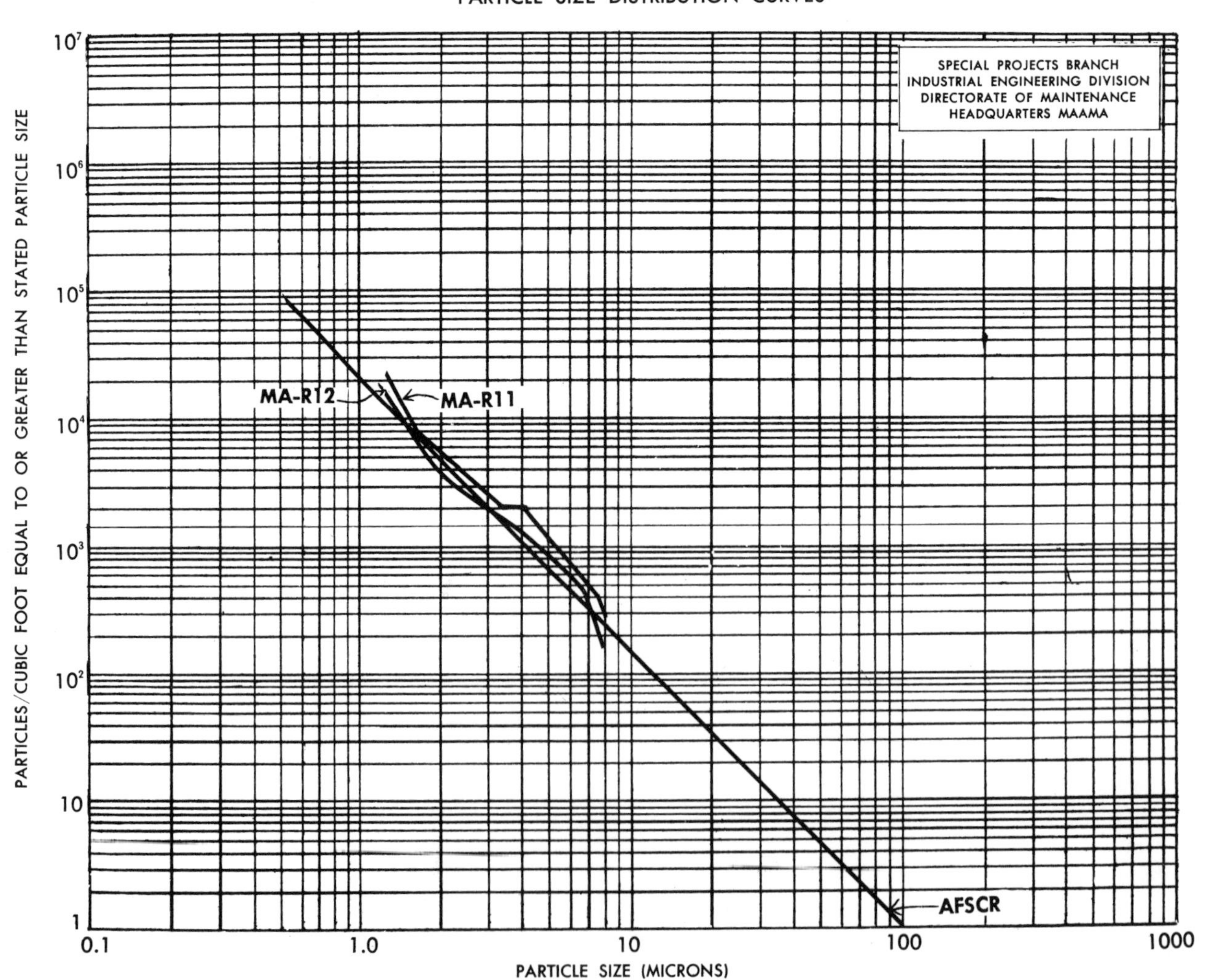

FIGURE 2-9.

each representing ninety 1-minute samplings. This curve is similar to MA-R8 and MA-R9. It is essentially parallel to the slope of the AFSCR and PTS curves.

Curve MA-R11 (*Figure 2-9*)
Date: 7 Mar. 1963
Time: 0800 to 0930 hours
Place: Center of Clean Room B, Bldg. 137, under intake vent, Olmsted AFB, Pa.
Person Performing Test: Clean room lab technician
Instrument Used: Royco particle counter
Height of sample: 32 inches from floor
Sample rate: 0.01 cfm (no dilution)
Counter was operating on total mode, taking 1-minute samples on each channel.
Temperature and Humidity: Similar to Air Force Class I requirements.
Limitations of Test: Same as for MA-R8.
Reason for Test: To investigate area between 1.3 and 8.0 microns under cumulative counting conditions.
Observations on Curve: This curve represents an average of ten runs of nine channel readings each. The curve is essentially parallel to the slope of the AFSCR and PTS curves. The slope of the curve at 1.30 microns approximates the slopes of MA-R1 and MA-R2.

Curve MA-R12 (*Figure 2-9*)
Date: 7 Mar. 1963
Time: 1000 to 1130 hours
Place: West end of Clean Room B, Bldg. 137, Olmsted AFB, Pa.
Limitations of Test: All conditions of this test the same as for MA-R11. This curve is an average of ten individual runs of nine channels each.
Observations on Curve: The observations are the same for as MA-R11.

Curve MA-R13 (*Figure 2-10*)
Date: 7 Mar. 1963
Time: 1354 to 1403 hours
Place: West side of Bldg. 137 (outdoors), 8 feet from building, Olmsted AFB, Pa.
Persons Performing Test: Clean room lab technician
Instrument Used: Royco particle counter
Height of samples: 32 inches from roadway
Sample rate: 0.01 cfm
Dilution rate = 0 cfm
Counter was operating on total mode, taking 1-minute samples on each channel.
Atmospheric Conditions: Temperature 42°F. Winds up to 25 mph, predominantly from the northwest.
Limitations of Test: Same as for MA-R8.
Observations on Curve: Curve is essentially linear when plotted on log-log paper and parallel to the AFSCR and PTS slopes.

Curve MA-R14 (*Figure 2-10*)
Date: 7 Mar. 1963
Time: 1300 to 1430 hours
Limitation of Test: All conditions the same as for MA-R13. This curve was an average of ten readings of nine channels each, representing ninety individual samplings of which MA-R13 is part.
Observations on Curve: Same as for MA-R13.

Curve MA-R15 (*Figure 2-10*)
Date: 7 Mar. 1963
Time: 1430 to 1436 hours
Place: Same as for MA-R13
Observations on Curve: Same conditions for this test as for MA-R13 and MA-R14. Notice that the slope at 1.0 micron is directly in line with the slope of the line at 1.3 microns on MA-R14. This curve is a continuation of MA-R14. The slope of this curve is essentially the same as that of MA-R1 and MA-R2.

Curve MA-R16 (*Figure 2-10*)
Date: 7 Mar. 1963
Time: 1430 to 1438 hours
Place: Same as for MA-R13
Observations on Curve: Same as for MA-R15.

Curve MA-R17 (*Figure 2-10*)
Date: 8 Mar. 1963
Time: 0909 to 0915 hours
Place: Clean Room Lab Area, Bldg. 137, Olmsted AFB, Pa.

Person Performing Test: Clean room lab technician

Instrument Used: Royco particle counter
Height of sample: 32 inches from floor
Sample rate: 0.005 cfm
Dilution rate: 0.01 cfm (dilution ratio = 2–1)
Counter was on total mode, taking 1-minute samples for each channel.

Temperature and Humidity: Similar to Air Force Class I conditions.

Limitation of Test: The low dilution ratio obscured the exact counts on channels for 0.32 and 0.4 micron. Readings on these channels were 11,676 for 0.32 micron and greater, and 14,112,000 for 0.4 micron and greater. The reading at the 0.5 micron channel was 14,454,000 particles equal to and greater than 0.5 micron.

Reason for Test: To investigate small-particle range in the clean room lab area.

Observations on Curve: This curve shows a linear nature when plotted on log-log paper.

Curve MA-R18 (*Figure 2-10*)
Date: 8 Mar. 1963

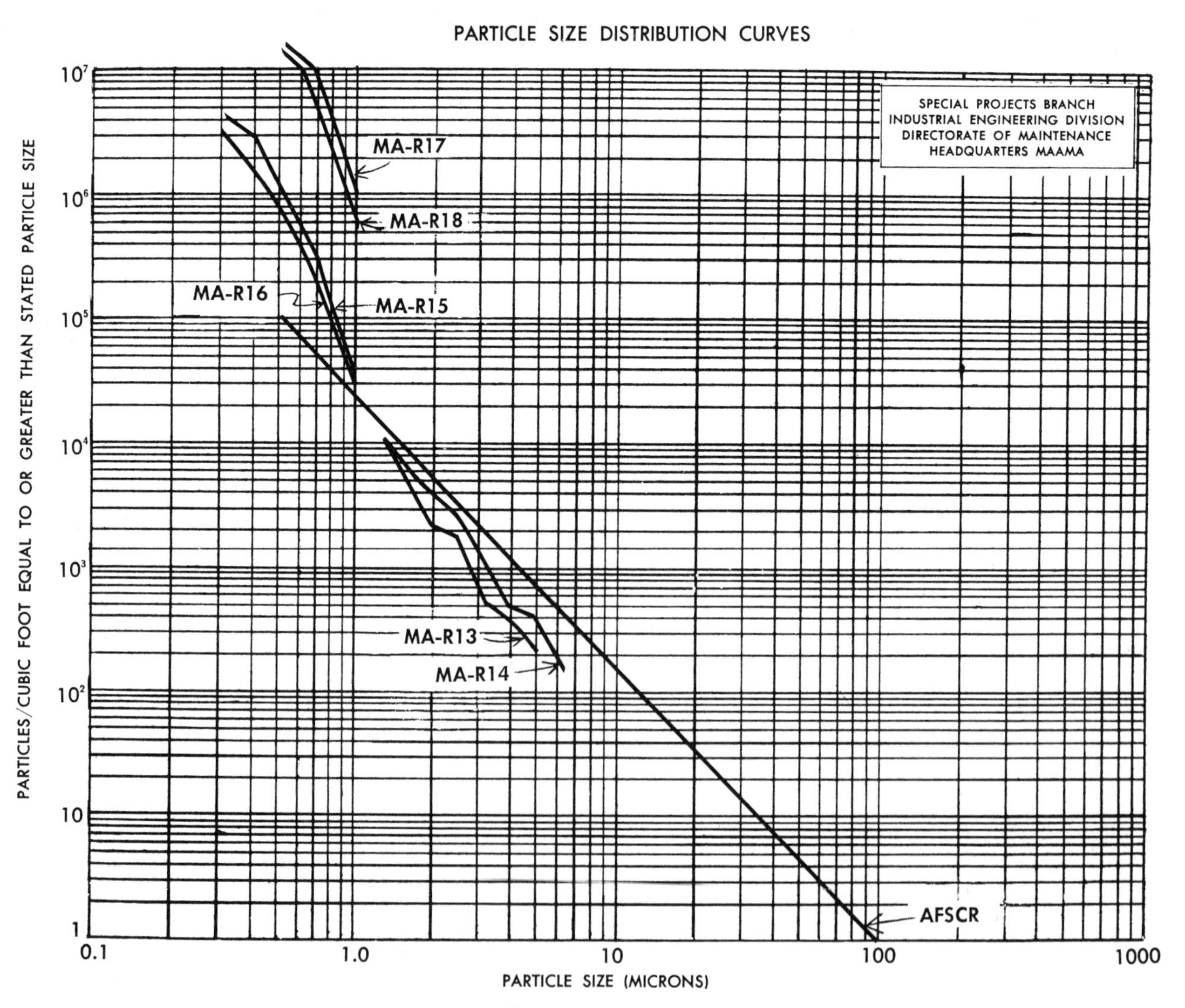

FIGURE 2-10.

Time: 0927 to 0933 hours
Limitations of Test: All other conditions and observations the same as for MA-R17.

Curve MA-R19 (Figure 2-11)
Date: 8 Mar. 1963
Time: 1400 to 1415 hours
Place: 8 feet from west exit of Bldg. 137 (outdoors), Olmsted AFB, Pa.
Person Performing Test: Clean room lab technician
Instrument Used: Royco particle counter
Height of sample: 32 inches from roadway
Sample rate: 0.01 cfm
Dilution rate = 0 cfm
Counter was operating on total mode, taking 1-minute samples per channel.
Temperature and Humidity: Clear day, temperature 45°F.
Limitations of Test: All channels on Royco counter were used.
Reason for Test: To establish ambient contamination level for outside air.
Observations on Curve: Slope of the curve from approximately 2.5 microns and larger is essentially parallel to the AFSCR and PTS slopes.

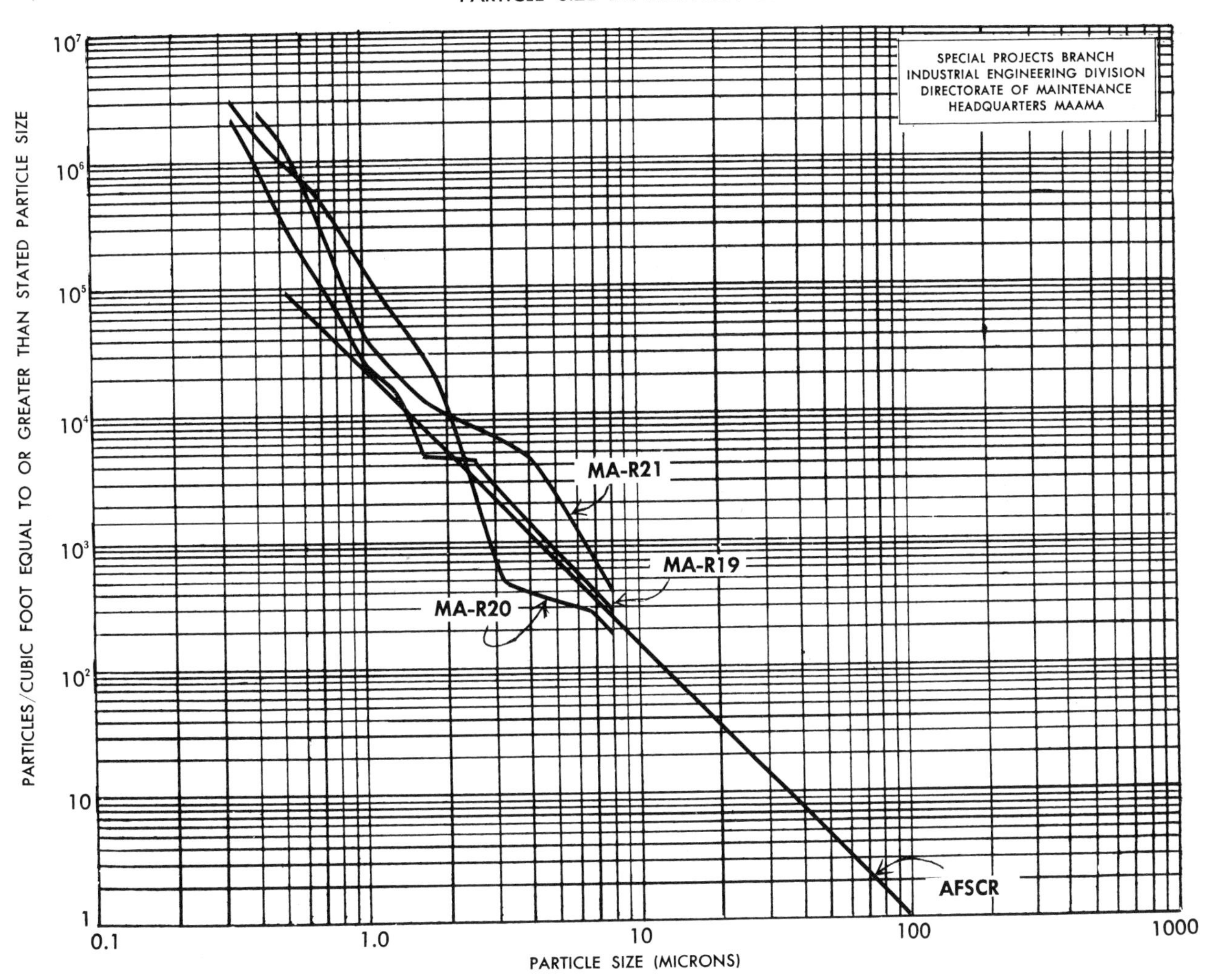

FIGURE 2-11.

At approximately 1.0 micron and smaller, the slope of the curve begins to move away from the PTS slope.

Curve MA-R20 (Figure 2-11)

Date: 8 Mar. 1963

Time: 1415 to 1430 hours

Person Performing Test: Clean room lab personnel

Limitations of Test: Same conditions as for MA-R19.

Observations on Curve: Curve MA-R20 is following the general pattern of MA-R19. Light vehicle traffic upstream of the counter may account for irregularities of curve.

Curve MA-R21 (Figure 2-11)

Date: 8 Mar. 1963

Time: 1500 to 1515 hours

Limitations of Test: Same conditions as for MA-R19.

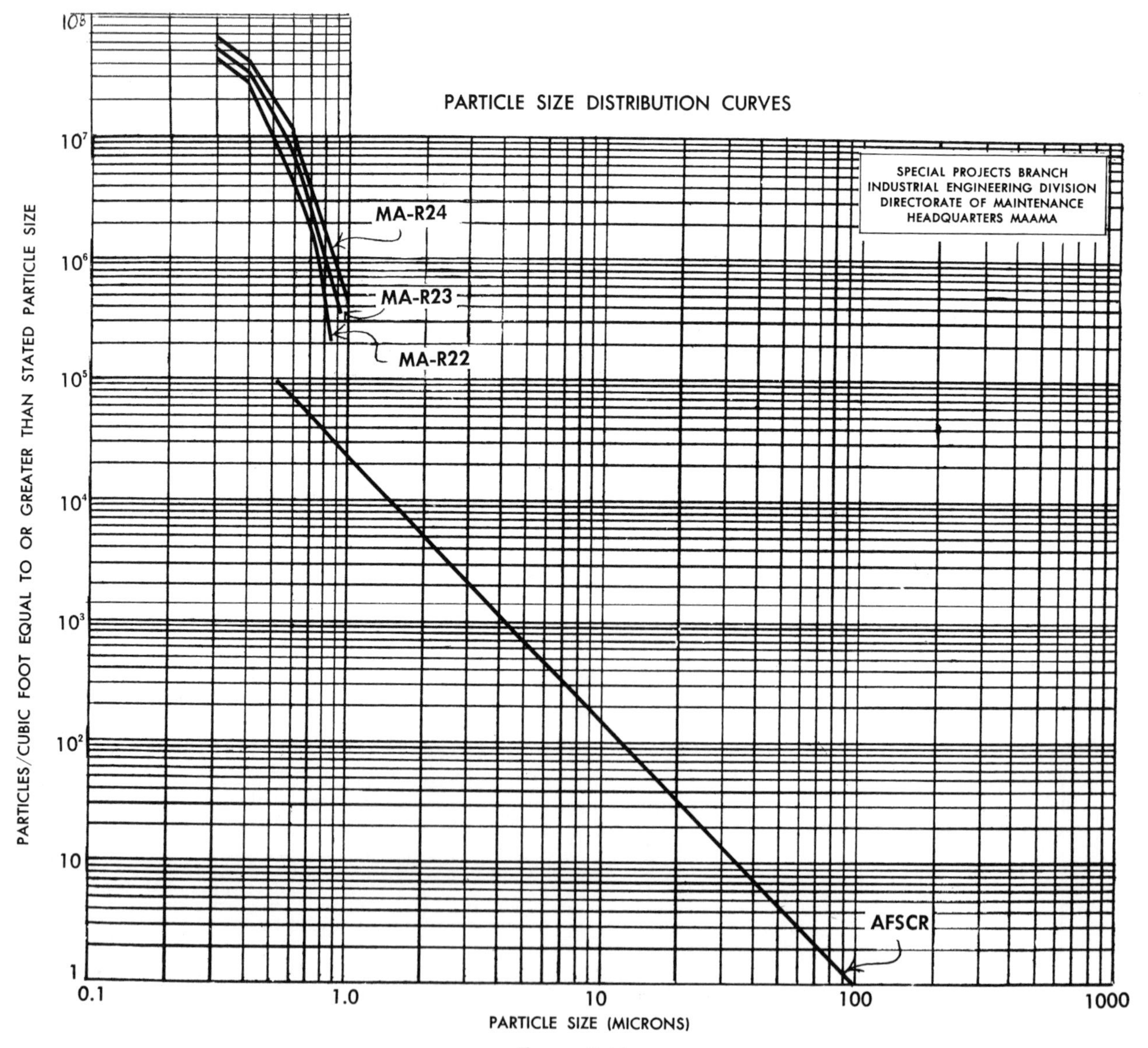

FIGURE 2-12.

Observations on Curve: This curve is similar to MA-R19. During the time period in which tests MA-R19, MA-R20, and MA-R21 were performed, there was light foot traffic upwind of the counter, and an occasional materiel-handling truck passing by. This may account for some of the sharp peaks and dips of the curves.

Curve MA-R22 (Figure 2-12)
Date: 27 Feb. 1963
Time: 0830 to 0836 hours
Place: Northwest corner of Bldg. 137, Olmsted AFB, Pa.
Person Performing Tests: Clean room lab technician
Instrument Used: Royco particle counter
Height of sample: 32 inches from floor
Sample rate: 0.00125 cfm
Dilution rate: 0.01 cfm (dilution Ratio = 8–1)
Counter was operating on total mode, taking 1-minute samples per channel.
Temperature and Humidity: Similar to Air Force Class I conditions.
Limitation of Test: The range between 0.32 and 1.0 micron was investigated with this dilution ratio.
Reason for Test: To determine the effect of highly contaminated air on the counter. To determine the counter reaction and curve established for highly contaminated air in the low size ranges.
Observations on Curve: A marked bowing of the curve is present. During the test it was noticed that in the lower size range there were slight hesitations in the counting cycle. This could be attributed to either coincidence loss or jamming of the counting zone.

Curve MA-R23 (Figure 2-12)
Date: 8 Mar. 1963
Time: 1130 to 1136 hours
Place: Clean Room Lab Area, Olmsted AFB, Pa.
Limitations of Test: All other conditions the same as for MA-R22.
Observations on Curve: Same as for MA-R22.

Curve MA-R24 (Figure 2-12)
Date: 8 Mar, 1963
Time: 1224 to 1230 hours
Limitations of Test: This was the tenth run in this area and was a continuation of MA-R23; MA-R23 was the first run in the series.
Observations on Curve: Same as for MA-R23.

Curve W-M1 (Figure 2-13)
Date: 27 Sept. 1962
Place: Bldg. 160, Robins AFB, Ga.
Person Performing Tests: 1st Lt. Clifford F. Frith
Instrument Used: Millipore sampling kit—0.2-micron membrane filter
Temperature and Humidity: Similar to Air Force Class III conditions.
Reason for Test: To determine contamination level of the room with manual technique in conjunction with developing correlation data with automatic counters.
Observations on Curve: Curves are linear in nature but diverge from the PTS slope. These tests were performed in conjunction with calibration of other instruments, and there was excessive movement in the area. This may account for large-size particles being present.

Curve W-M2 (Figure 2-13)
Date: 20 Sept. 1962
Limitations of Test: Same as for W-M1, but taken ½ hour later.

Curve W-M3 (Figure 2-13)
Date: 20 Sept. 1962
Limitations of Test: Same as for W-M1, but taken 1 hour later.

Curve W-M4 (Figure 2-14)
Date: 21 Sept. 1962
Limitations of Test: Same as for W-M1.

Curve W-M5 (Figure 2-14)
Date: 21 Sept. 1962
Time: ½ hour after W-M4
Limitations of Test: Same as for W-M1.

Curve W-M6 (Figure 2-14)
Date: 21 Sept. 1962
Limitations of Test: Same as for W-M5, but taken ½ hour later.

Curve W-M7 (Figure 2-14)
Date: 25 Sept.1962
Limitations of Test: Same as for W-M1.

Curve W-R1 (Figure 2-14)
Date: 14 Jan. 1963
Place: Bldg. 160, Robins AFB, Ga.
Person Performing Test: 1st Lt. Clifford F. Frith
Instrument Used: Royco particle counter
Height of sample: 32 inches from floor
Sample rate: 0.01 cfm
Particle counter was operating on total mode, taking 1-minute samples on each channel.
Temperature and Humidity: Similar to Air Force Class III conditions.
Reason for Test: Monitoring of Class III Area.
Observations on Curve: Curve is essentially linear in nature and similar to MA-R1.

Curve W-R2 (Figure 2-14)
Date: 14 Jan. 1963
Place: Bldg. 160, Robins AFB, Ga.
Person Performing Test: 1st. Lt. Clifford F. Frith
Limitations of Test: Same as for W-R1.

Curves W-M8 and W-M9 (Figure 2-15)
Date: 15 Jan. 1963

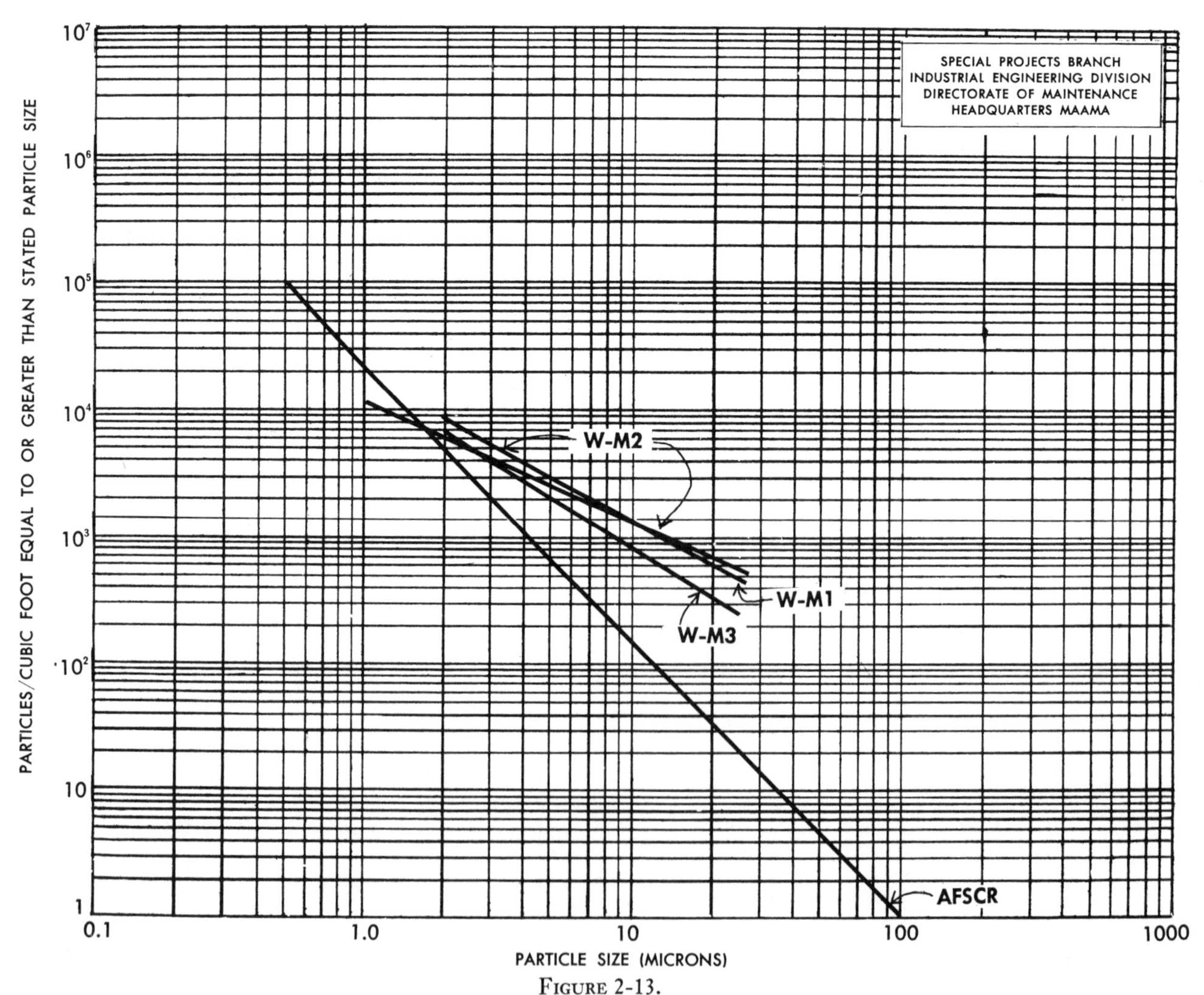

FIGURE 2-13.

Time: 1400 hours

Place: Bldg. 160, HIG side of Gyro Shop, Robins AFB, Ga.

Person Performing Tests: Quality-control technician

Instrument Used: Millipore sampling kit, 0.8-micron membrane filter, and ASTM F25-63T counting method

Temperature and Humidity: Similar to Air Force Class III conditions.

Reason for Test: Standard monitoring procedure.

Observations on Curve: The curve is essentially linear and is approaching conditions parallel to the AFSCR and PTS slopes for the larger-size particles.

Curves W-M10 and W-M11 (Figure 2-15)

Date: 28 Jan. 1963

Time: 0830 hours

Place: Bldg. 160, lab side of Gyro Shop, Robins AFB, Ga.

Person Performing Test: 1st Lt. Clifford F. Frith

Instrument Used: Millipore sampling kit, 0.8-micron membrane filter, and ASTM F25-63T counting method.

Temperature and Humidity: Similar to Air Force Class III conditions.

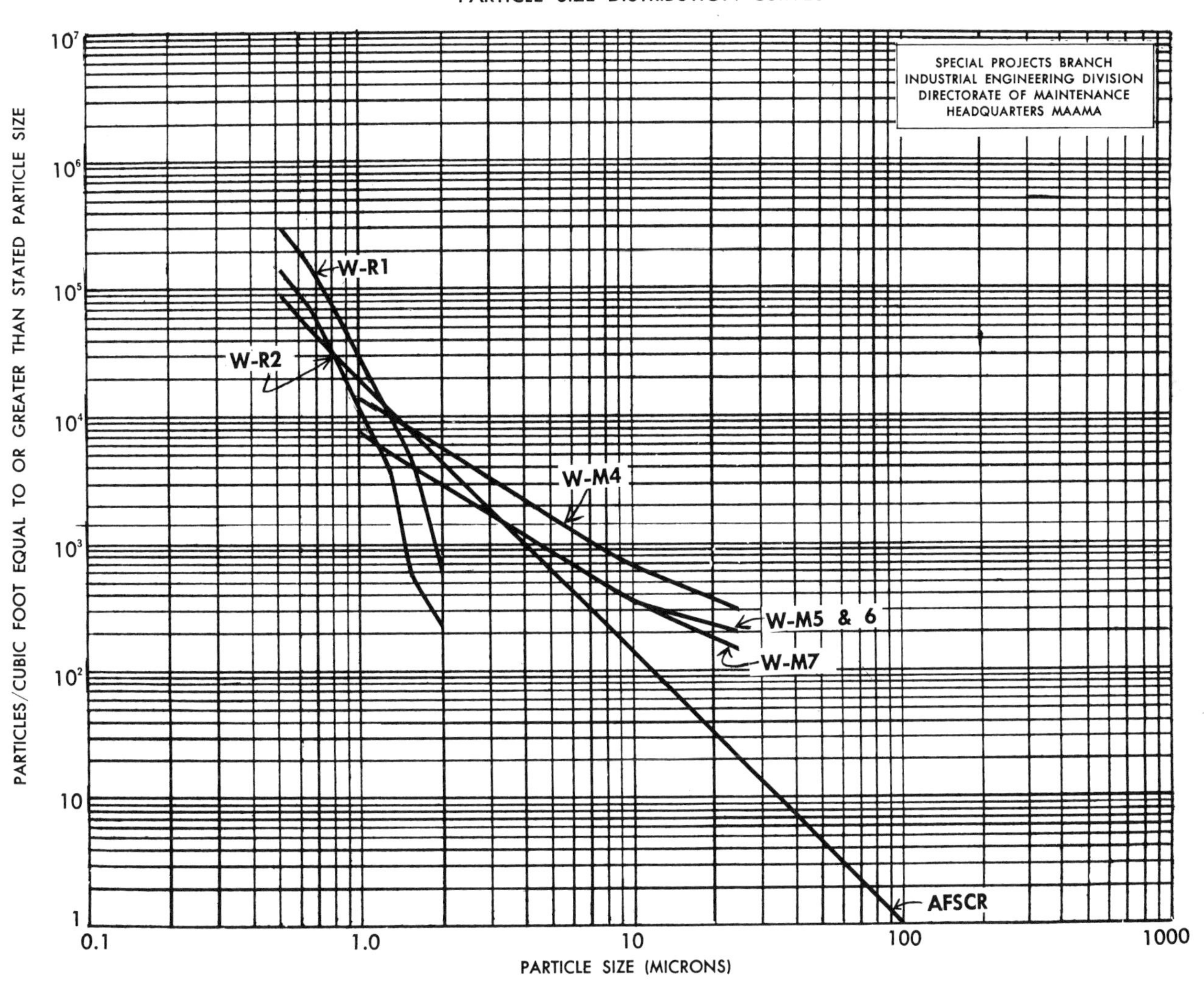

FIGURE 2-14.

Reason for Test: Increased contamination was noticed, and a split filter was discovered as a result of these tests.

Curves W-M12 and W-M13 (Figure 2-15)
Date: 28 Jan. 1963
Time: 0830 hours
Place: Bldg. 160, Robins AFB, Ga.
Limitations of Test: All conditions the same as for W-M10 and W-M11.

Curves W-M14 and W-M15 (Figure 2-15)
Date: 28 Jan. 1963
Time: 1300 hours
Place: Bldg. 640, Memory Drum Area, Robins AFB, Ga.
Person Performing Test: Quality-control lab technician
Instrument Used: Millipore sampling kit, 0.8-micron membrane filter, and ASTM F25-63T counting method
Temperature and Humidity: Similar to Air Force Class III conditions.
Reason for Test: Standard monitoring procedure.
Observations on Curve: The slope of the curve

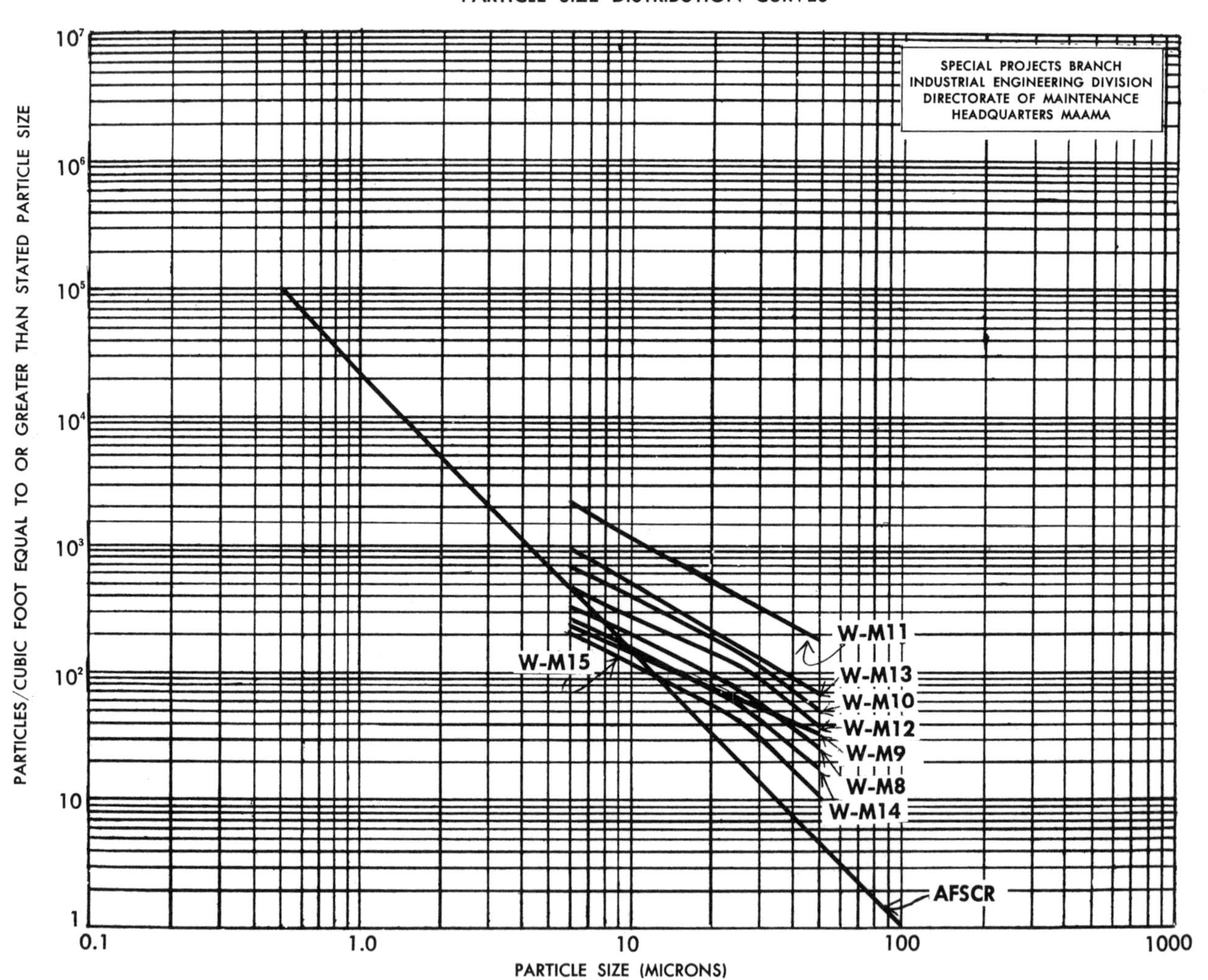

FIGURE 2-15.

for larger-size particles approaches conditions parallel to the slope of the AFSCR and PTS curves.

Curve W-M16 (Figure 2-16)

Date: 7 Mar. 1963

Place: East side of Bldg. 160 (outdoors), Robins AFB, Ga.

Person Performing Test: 1st Lt. Clifford F. Frith

Instrument Used: Millipore sampling kit, 0.8-micron membrane filter, and ASTM F25-63T counting method

Relative Humidity: 52%.

Reason for Test: To determine ambient contamination level outside Bldg. 160.

Observations on Curve: Curve W-M16 is essentially parallel to the slope of the AFSCR and PTS curves.

Curve W-M17 (Figure 2-16)

Date: 8 Mar. 1963

Place: Same as for W-M16

Person Performing Test: 1st Lt. Clifford F. Frith

Instrument Used: Millipore sampling kit, 0.8-micron membrane filter, and ATSM F25-63T counting method

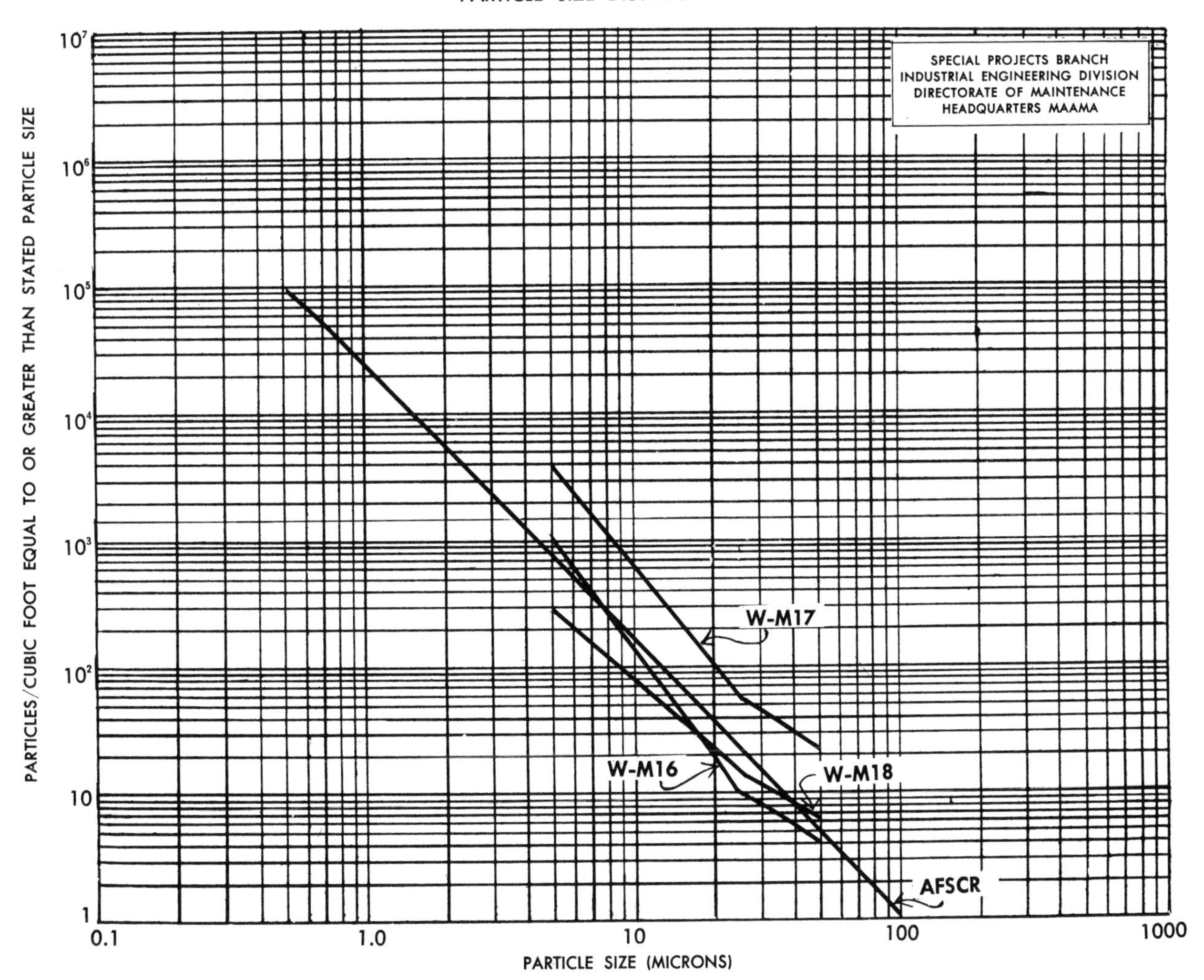

FIGURE 2-16.

Relative Humidity: 61%.
Reason for Test: To determine ambient contamination level outside Bldg. 160.
Observations on Curve: Curve is essentially parallel to the slope of the AFSCR and PTS curves.

Curve W-M18 (Figure 2-16)
Date: 12 Mar. 1963
Time: Afternoon
Place: Same as for W-M16.
Instrument Used: Same as for W-M16.
Relative Humidity: 94%.
Reason for Test: Same as for W-M16.
Observations on Curve: Same as for W-M16.

Curve W-R3 (Figure 2-17)
Date: 8 Mar. 1963
Time: 0946 to 1100 hours
Place: West side of Bldg. 160, intake tube, outside door, Robins AFB, Ga.
Person Performing Test: 1st. Lt. Clifford F. Frith
Instrument Used: Royco particle counter
Height of sample: 32 inches from ground
Sample rate: 0.01 cfm

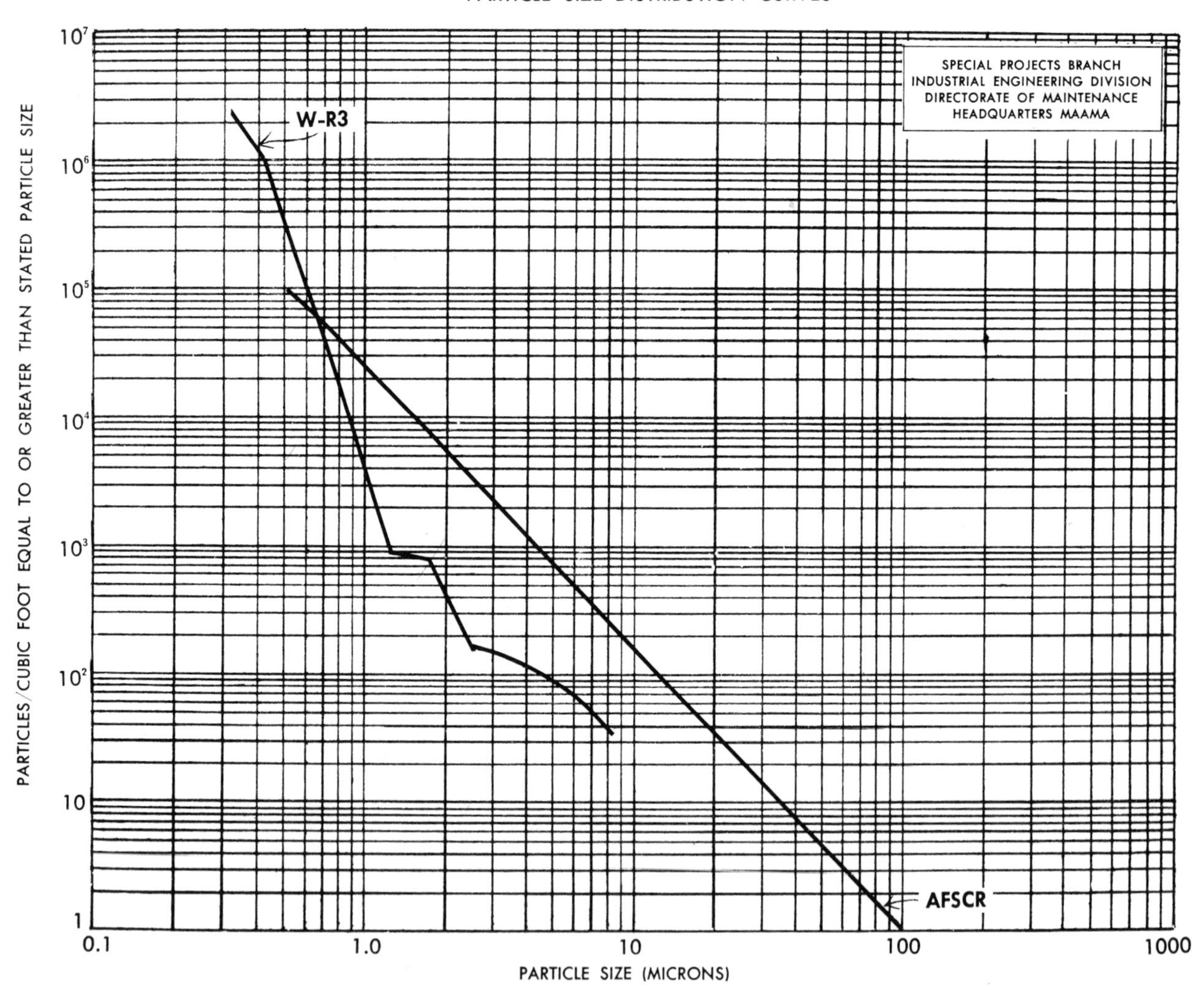

FIGURE 2-17.

Counter was operating on total mode, taking 1-minute samples.

Reason for Test: To determine ambient contamination level for outdoor air. This curve represents a series of three complete runs, each run fifteen channels between 0.3 and 8.0 microns in size.

Observations on Curve: The slope of the curve for the small-size particles is essentially parallel to that of MA-R1. After particles reach 2.5 microns in size, the slope of the curve is essentially parallel to the slope of the AFSCR and PTS curves. A change in slope is noted between 1.3 and 2.50 microns.

Curve N-R1 (Figure 2-18)

Date: 1 Mar. 1963

Time: 1245 hours

Place: Newark AFS, Ohio

Person Performing Test: James R. Klein, Olmsted AFB, Pa.

Instrument Used: Royco particle counter

Height of sample: 32 inches from floor

Sample rate: 100 cc/min.

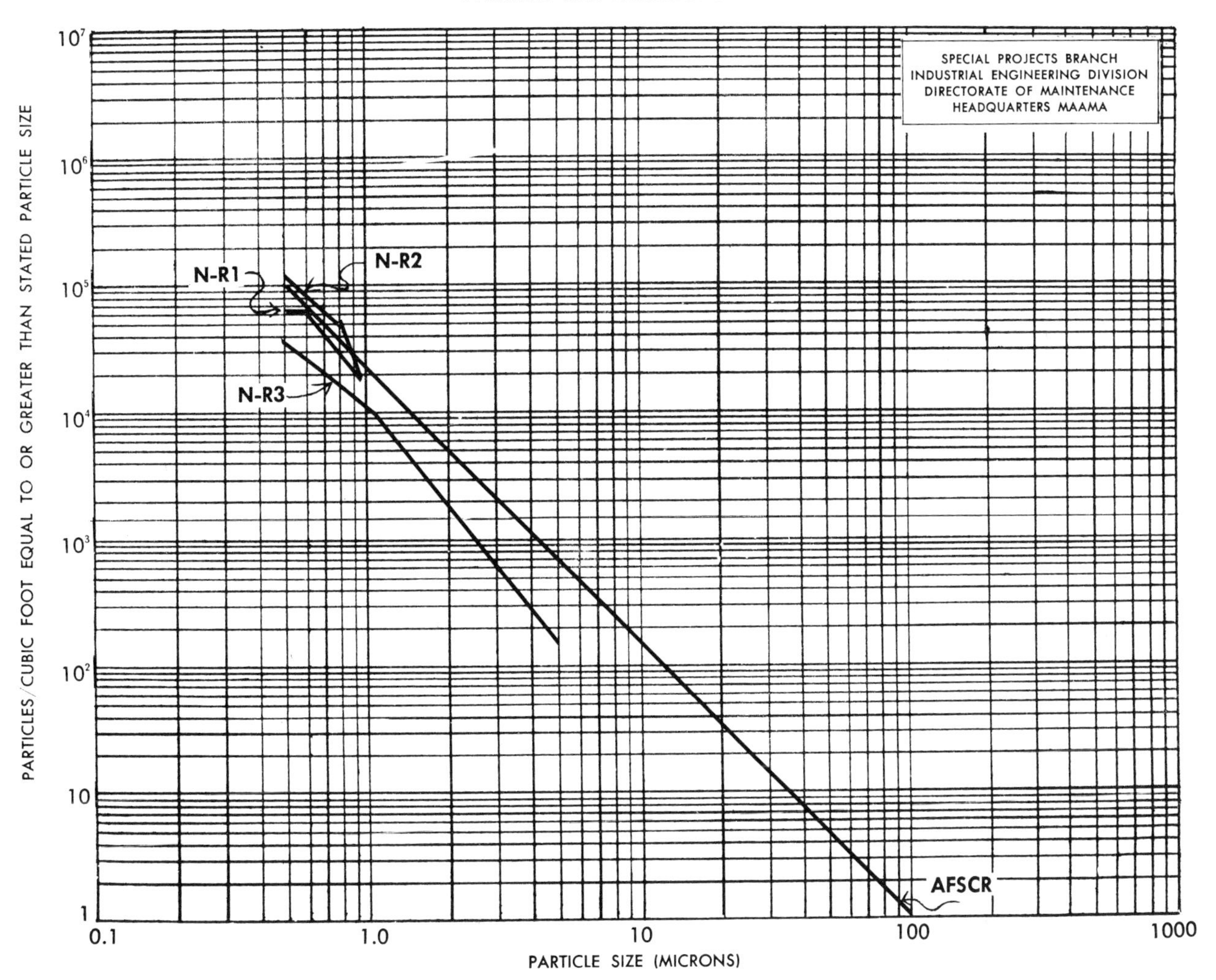

FIGURE 2-18.

Counter was operating on total mode, taking 0.3-minute samples for each channel.

Temperature and Humidity: Similar to Air Force Class IV conditions. (See footnote 18)

Reason for Test: To determine contamination level of room.

Observations on Curve: Curve is essentially parallel to the slope of the AFSCR and PTS curves.

Curve N-R2 (Figure 2-18)

Date: 1 Mar. 1963

Time: 1250 hours

Limitations of Test: All other conditions and observations the same as for N-R1.

Curve N-R3 (Figure 2-18)

Date: 1 Mar. 1963

Place: Air Force Class IV Clean Room, 25 by 30 by 8 feet, Newark AFS, Ohio

Person Performing Test: Charles Johnson

Instrument Used: Royco particle counter

Height of sample: 32 inches from floor

Sample Rate: 100 cc/min.

Counter was operating on total mode, taking 10-minute samples on each channel.

Temperature and Humidity: Similar to Air Force Class IV conditions.

Reason for Test: Monitoring contamination lev-

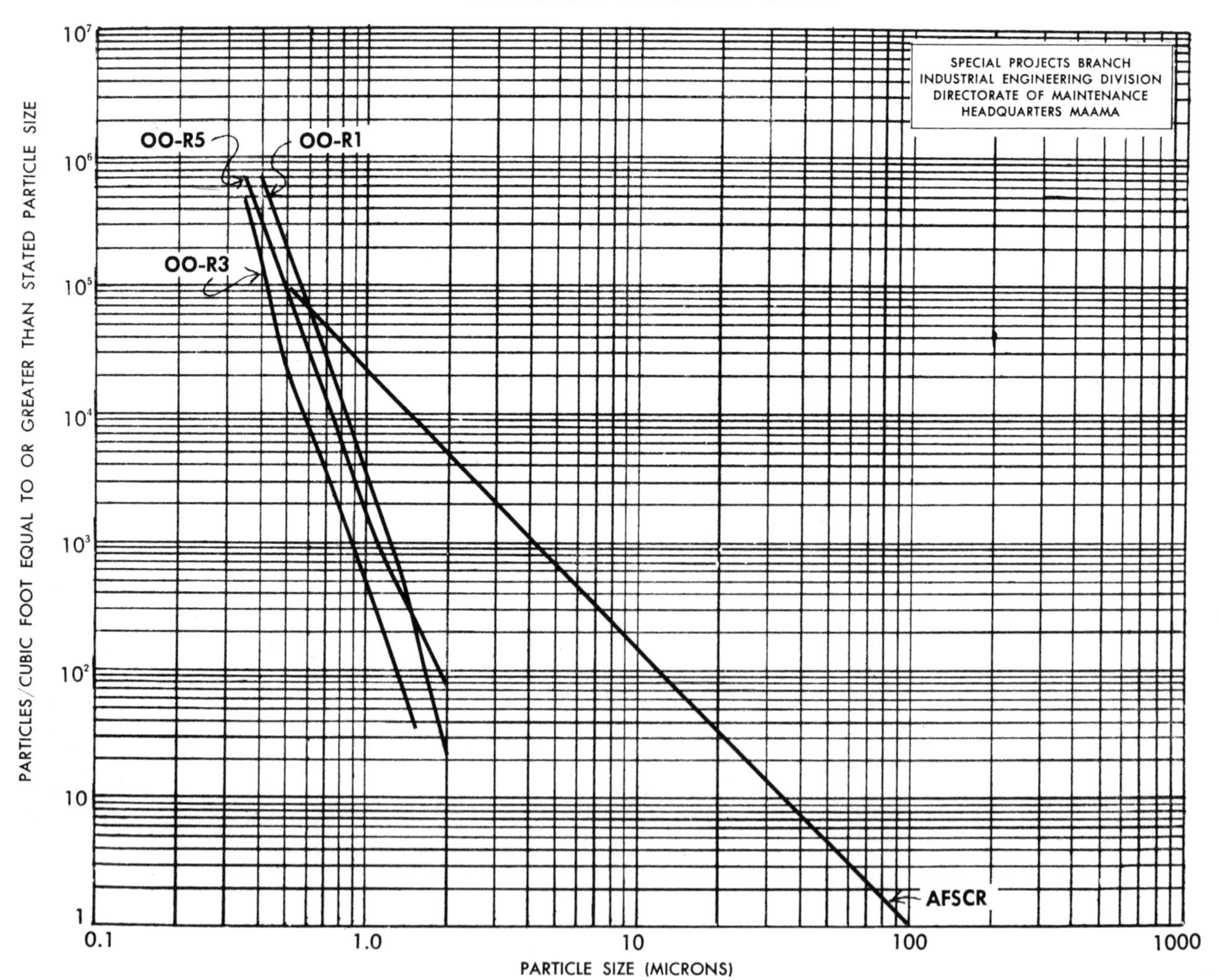

FIGURE 2-19.

els. This curve represents three complete runs of three channels each, a total of 90 minutes sampled.

Observations on Curve: Curve is essentially linear and parallel to the slope of the AFSCR and PTS curves.

Curve 00-R1 (*Figure 2-19*)

Date: 3 Dec. 1962

Place: Bldg. 103A, Hill AFB, Utah

Person Performing Test: Bruce Hampel

Instrument Used: Royco particle counter

Height of sample: 32 inches from floor

Temperature and Humidity: Similar to Air Force Class II conditions.

Reason for Test: Monitoring of room "at-rest" conditions.

Observations on Test: The slope of this curve is essentially parallel to MA-R1.

Curve 00-R3 (*Figure 2-19*)

Date: 4 Dec. 1962

Limitations of Test: All conditions and observations the same as for 00-R1, except that the room is not "at rest."

Curve 00-R5 (*Figure 2-19*)

Date: 5 Dec. 1962

Limitations of Test: All other conditions and ob-

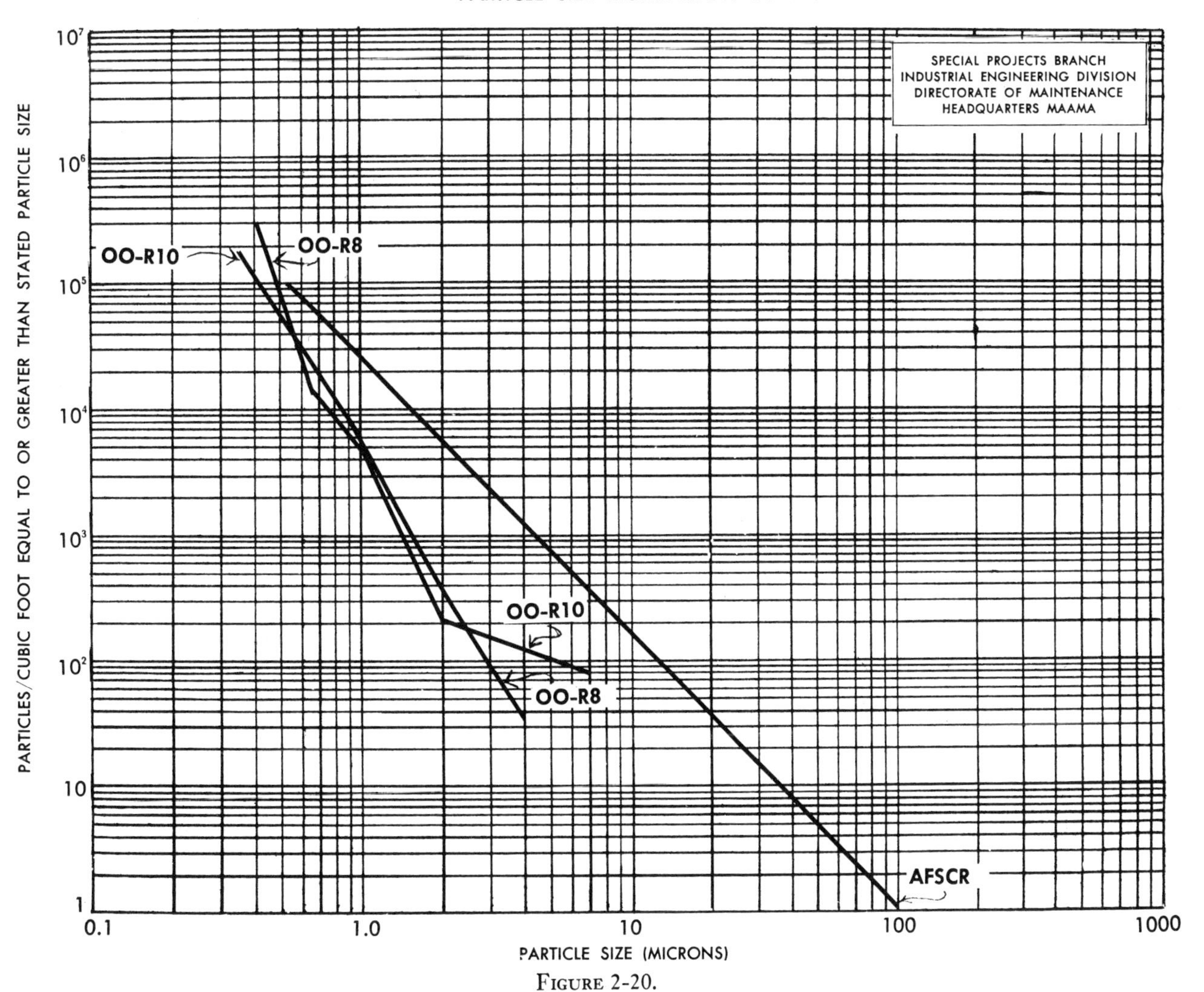

FIGURE 2-20.

servations are the same as for 00-R1, except that the room is not "at rest."

Curve 00-R8 (*Figure 2-20*)

Date: 6 Dec. 1962

Limitations of Test: All conditions and observations the same as for 00-R1.

Curve 00-R10 (*Figure 2-20*)

Date: 7 Dec. 1962

Limitations of Test: All conditions and observations the same as for 00-R1.

Curve R-1 (*Figure 2-21*)

Date: 28 Jan. 1962

Time: 1400 hours

Place: Palo Alto, Calif.

Person Performing Test: William R. Zinky of Royco Instruments, Inc. This curve appeared in a paper entitled "A New Tool for Air Pollution Control: The Aerosol Particle Counter," presented at the 55th Annual Meeting of Air Pollution Control Association by William R. Zinky, Sheraton-Chicago Hotel, May 20-24, 1962, Chicago, Ill. Notice the linear nature of this curve when plotted on log-log paper.

Curve R-2 (*Figure 2-21*)

Date: 21 Mar. 1962

Time: 1700 hours

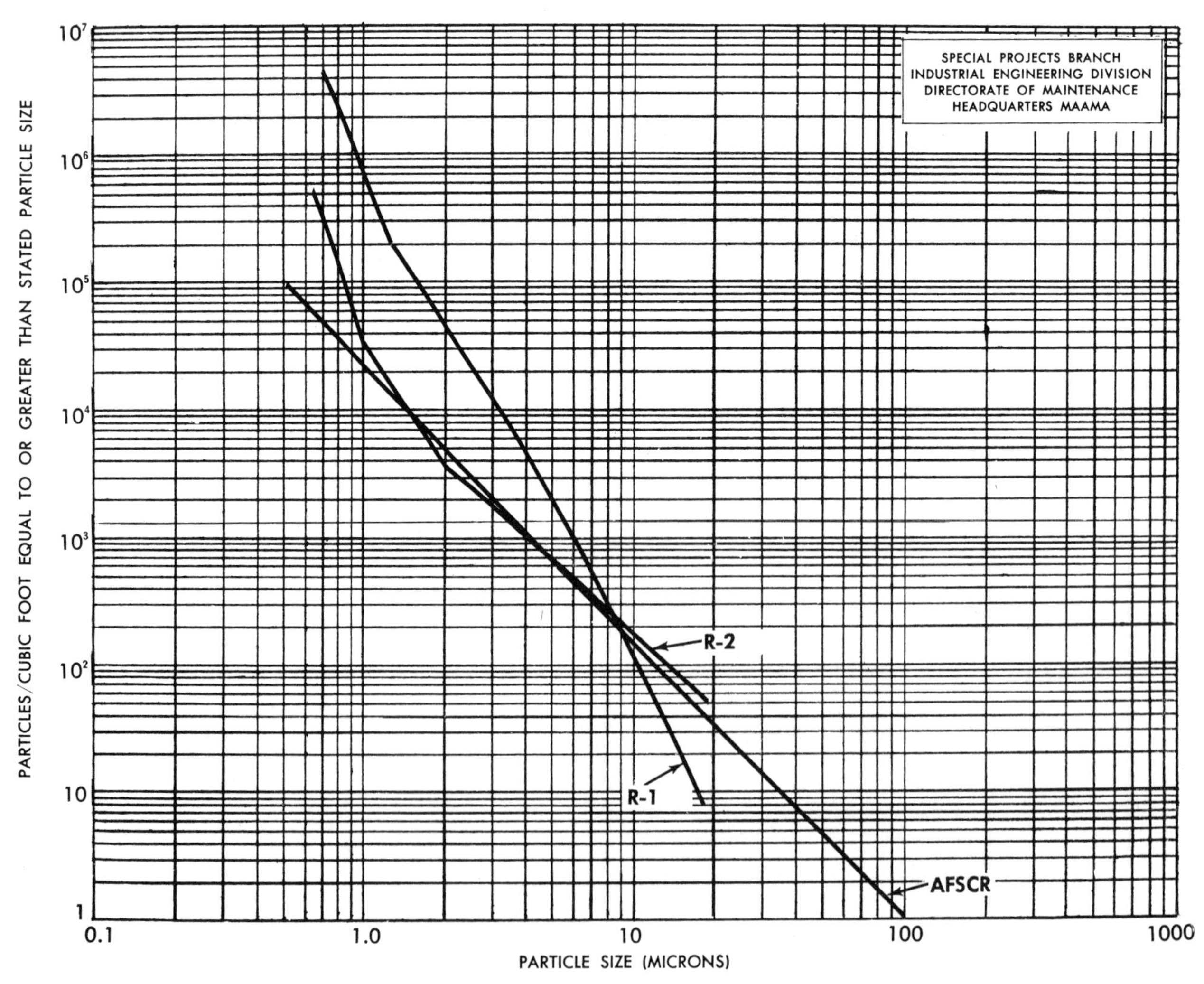

FIGURE 2-21.

Place: Eagle Rock, Calif. (N.E. Los Angeles)
Person Performing Test: Keith Linn of Royco Instruments, Inc.
Instrument Used: Royco particle counter
Atmospheric Conditions: Clear day, elevation 600 feet.
Observations on Curve: Notice that the slope of the curve between 0.64 and 1.0 micron is essentially parallel to MA-R1. The curve from 2.0 to 15 microns is parallel to the slope of the AFSCR and PTS curves.

Curve G-1 (Figure 2-22)
Date: 21 Sept. 1962
Place: Bldg. 160, Robins AFB, Ga.
Instrument Used: General Computer/Electronics particle counter.
One-minute samples for all three channels sampled concurrently. Particle size ranges: 0.5 to 1.0 micron; 1.0 to 4.0 microns; 4.0 to 8.0 microns.
Temperature and Humidity: Similar to Air Force Class III conditions.
Reason for Test: Demonstration test of instrument.
Observations on Curve: The curve between 0.5 and 1.0 micron is essentially parallel to MA-

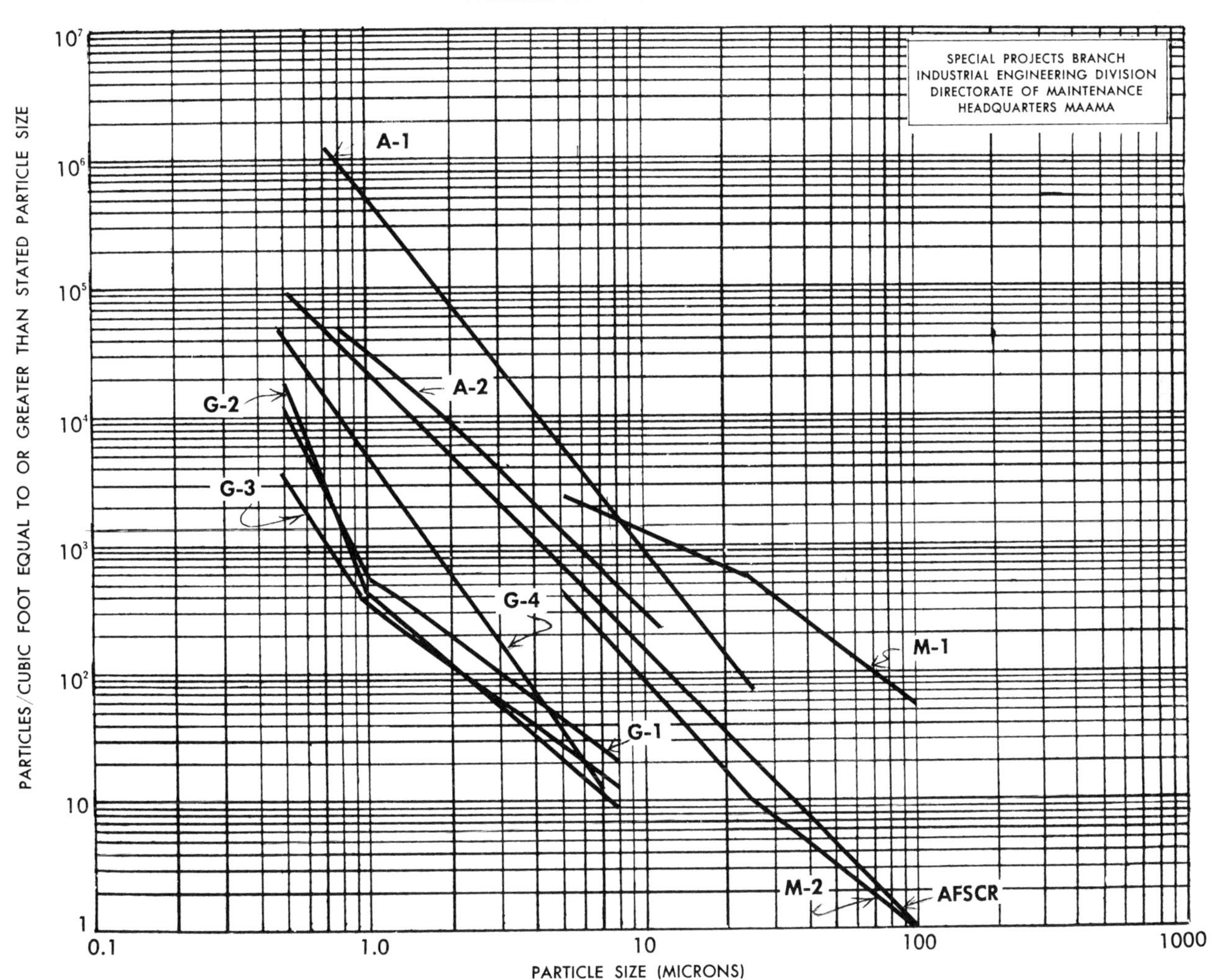

FIGURE 2-22.

R1. The slope of G-1 between 1.0 and 8.0 microns is parallel to the slope of the AFSCR and PTS curves.

Curve G-2 (*Figure 2-22*)
Date: 21 Sept. 1962
Limitations of Test: All conditions and observations the same as for G-1.

Curve G-3 (*Figure 2-22*)
Date: 21 Sept. 1962
Limitations of Test: All conditions and observations the same as for G-1.

Curve G-4 (*Figure 2-22*)
Date: 25 Sept. 1962
Limitations of Test: Same conditions as for G-1.
Observations on Curve: Curve is linear in nature throughout.

Curve A-1 (*Figure 2-22*)
Date: 1957
Place: Chicago lakefront
Person Performing Test: Armour Research Foundation of Illinois Institute of Technology
Instrument Used: Armour Research Institute particle counter
Observations on Curve: Curve is essentially linear in nature and approaches conditions parallel to the slope of the AFSCR and PTS curves.

Curve A-2 (*Figure 2-22*)
Place: Remote Illinois rural areas
Person Performing Test: Armour Research Foundation of Illinois Institute of Technology
Instrument Used: Armour Research Institute particle counter
Observations on Curve: Curve is essentially parallel to the slope of the AFSCR and PTS curves.

Curve M-1 (*Figure 2-22*)
Place: City air
Person Performing Test: Millipore Filter Corp.
Instrument Used: Millipore sampling kit
Observations on Curve: Curve is essentially parallel to the slope of the AFSCR and PTS curves.

Curve M-2 (*Figure 2-22*)
Place: Country air
Person Performing Test: Millipore Filter Corp.
Instrument Used: Millipore sampling kit
Observations on Curve: Curve is essentially parallel to the slope of the AFSCR and PTS curves.

Curve GA-R1 (*Figure 2-23*)
Date: 10 Sept. 1962
Time: 0945 hours
Place: Controlled-Environment Room, Grumman Aircraft Engineering Corp., Bethpage, N. Y.
Person Performing Test: C. T. Williamsen
Instrument Used: Royco particle counter
Height of sample: 34 inches from floor
Sample volume: 200 cc
Sample time: 10 minutes per channel
Reason for Test: To determine ambient contamination level of room.
Observations on Curve: Curve GA-R1 is essentially parallel to the slope of the AFSCR and PTS curves.

Curve GA-R2 (*Figure 2-23*)
Date: 10 Sept. 1962
Time: 1300 hours
Place: Controlled-Environment Room, Grumman Aircraft Engineering Corp., Bethpage, N. Y.
Person Performing Test: C. T. Williamsen
Instrument Used: Royco particle counter
Height of sample: 32 inches from floor
Volume of samples: 100 cc, 150 cc, 200 cc.
Sample time: 3 minutes per channel
Reason for Test: To determine the variation in particle count with change in sampled volume. The points for this curve are an average of three samples at three different flow rates.
Observations on Curve: Notice that the slope of this curve is essentially parallel to the slope of the AFSCR and PTS curves.

Curve GA-R3 (*Figure 2-23*)
Date of Test: 13 Mar. 1963
Place: OAO Room, Grumman Aircraft Engineering Corp., Bethpage, N. Y.
Person Performing Test: C. T. Williamsen
Instrument Used: Royco particle counter
Height of sample: 32 inches from floor
Sample rate: 0.01 cfm
Counter was operating on single-channel count with a 3-minute cycle per channel.

Reason for Test: To determine contamination level of the room at this particular time.

Observations on Curve: This curve generally follows the slope of the AFSCR and PTS curves.

Curve GA-R4 (*Figure 2-23*)

Date: 13 Mar. 1963

Limitations of Test: Same observations and conditions as for GA-R3, except that each channel was operating on a 10-minute cycle.

Curve GD-R1 (*Figure 2-24*)

Date: 16 Oct. 1962

Time: 1100 hours

Place: Laminar/Cross-Flow Room, General Dynamics, Pomona, Calif.

Persons Performing Test: Jim Henri, Royco Instruments, Inc., Palo Alto, Calif., and Boyd Agnew, Agnew-Higgins, Inc., Stanton, Calif.

Instrument Used: Royco particle counter

Height: 32 inches from floor

Sample rate: 283 cc/min.

Counter was operated on individual channels. Each channel was recorded for the period of 1 minute.

Atmospheric Conditions: 74°F dry bulb

Relative humidity: 37%

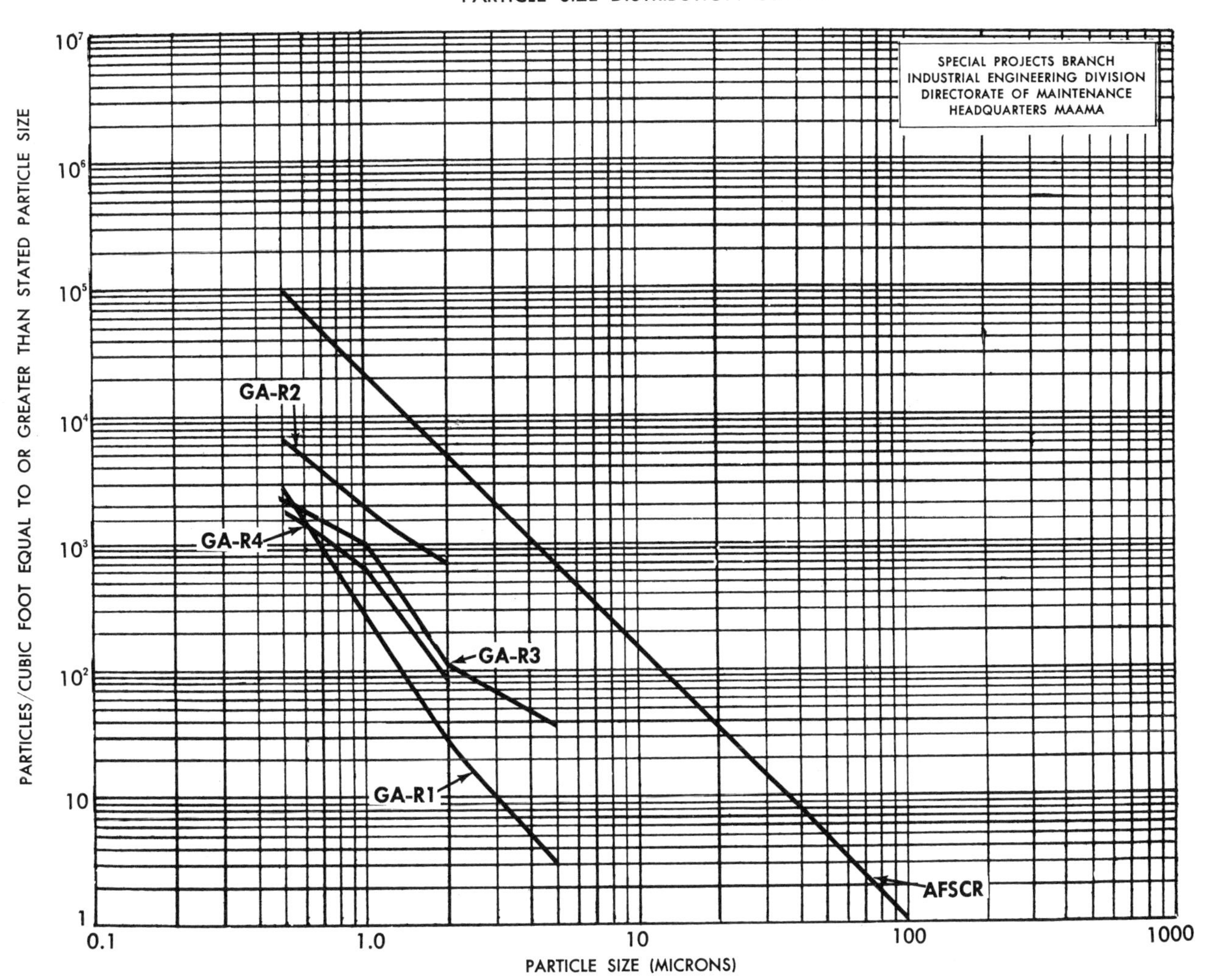

FIGURE 2-23.

Limitations of Tests: Initial prove-in of laminar/cross-flow room. This curve is linear in nature when plotted on log-log paper.

Observations on Curve: There were 7 persons active within this room during the test.

Curve GD-R2 (Figure 2-24)

Date: 16 Oct. 1962

Time: 1300 hours

Limitations of Test: The same conditions existed with this curve as for GD-R1, except that there were 5 persons in the room during this test.

Observations on Curve: The slope of this curve for particles 0.5 micron and smaller approaches the slope of MA-R1. The slope of the curve for particles greater than 1.0 micron approaches the slope of the PTS curve. Each section of the slope of this curve is linear in nature when plotted on log-log paper.

Curve GD-R3 (Figure 2-24)

Date: 16 Oct. 1962

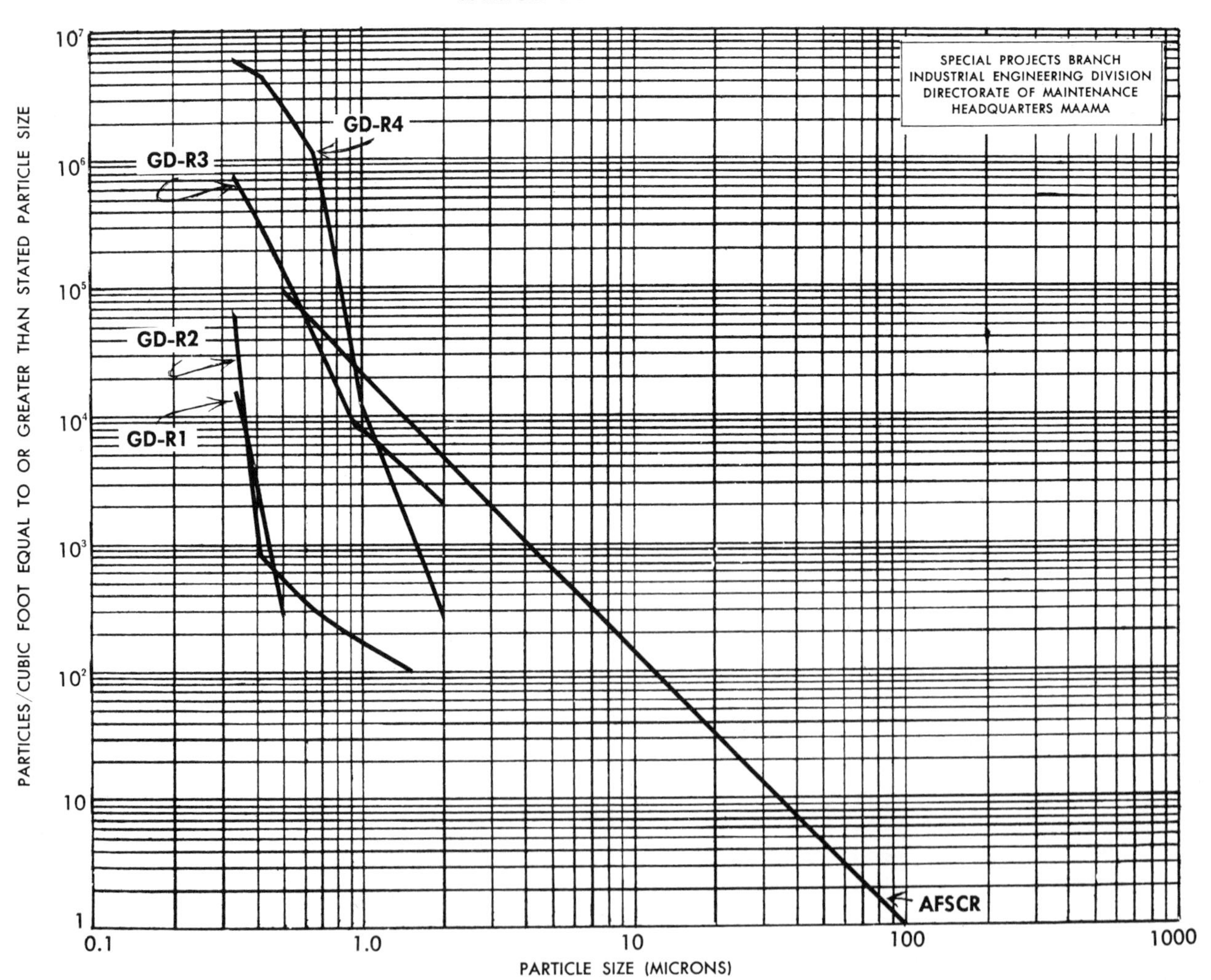

FIGURE 2-24.

Time: 1435 hours
Place: Anteroom of Laminar/Cross-Flow Room, General Dynamics, Pomona, Calif.
Persons Performing Test: Jim Henri, Royco Instruments, Inc., Palo Alto, Calif., and Boyd Agnew, Agnew-Higgins, Inc., Stanton, Calif.
Instrument Used: Royco particle counter
Height of sample: 32 inches from floor
Rate of sample: 283 cc/min.
One-minute samples were taken on each channel.
Atmospheric Conditions: Similar to conditions for GD-R1.
Reason for Test: Same as for GD-R1.
Observations on Curve: The slope of the curve for particles 1 micron and smaller approaches the slope of MA-R1. For particles 1 micron and larger, the slope of the curve is similar to the slope of the AFSCR and PTS curves. Both sections of the curve are linear in nature.

Curve GD-R4 (*Figure 2-24*)
Date: 16 Oct. 1962
Time: 1510 hours
Place: Computer Room, Bldg. 1, General Dynamics, Pomona, Calif.
Person Performing Test: Jim Henri, Royco Instruments, Inc., Palo Alto, Calif.
Instrument Used: Royco particle counter
Height of sample: 32 inches from floor
Sample rate: 283 cc/min.
One-minute samples were taken on each channel.
Reason for Test: To determine contamination level in another area of the General Dynamics facility.
Observations on Curve: The curve in the small-particle range has a pronounced curvature. This could very likely be caused by too highly contaminated air being sampled by the Royco counter. The curve for particle sizes greater than 8 microns is linear in nature when plotted on log-log paper and approaches the slope of MA-R1. At the point 1.0 micron and greater, a new slope is noitced which is less steep than for particles of smaller size range of the same curve.

Curves GD-R1 through GD-R4 were taken from the report titled "Airborne Particle Counts," written by Mr. Boyd Agnew of Agnew-Higgins, Inc., Stanton, Calif. Data were taken in Agnew-Higgins Laminar Flow/Ultra Clean Room located in Bldg. 4, General Dynamics, Pomona, Calif.

Curve GD-R5 (*Figure 2-25*)
Date: 20 Feb. 1963
Time: 1100 hours
Place: Laminar/Cross-Flow Room, General Dynamics, Pomona, Calif.
Person Performing Test: 1st Lt. Philip R. Austin
Instrument Used: Royco particle counter
Height of sample: 32 inches from floor
Sample rate: 300 cc/min.
Counter was operating on total mode, taking 1-minute samples for each channel.
Atmospheric Conditions: Same as for GD-R1.
Limitations of Test: This test was used as a control for GD-R6. The ambient contamination level for a spot 6 feet downstream of a bench location was monitored by this curve within the laminar/cross-flow room.
Reason for Test: To determine the feasibility of a cross-flow room with essentially laminar-flow characteristics for Air Force use. More particularly, to determine the contamination level downstream of a high-particle-generation operation within such a room.
Observations on Curve: Curve on GD-R5 is essentially linear in nature when plotted on log-log paper. It is essentially parallel to the AFSCR and PTS curves.

Curve GD-R6 (*Figure 2-25*)
Date: 20 Feb. 1963
Time: 1115 hours
Place: Same as for GD-R5.
Person Performing Test: 1st Lt. Philip R. Austin.
Instrument Used: Royco particle counter
Height of sample: 32 inches from floor
Sample rate: 300 cc/min.
Counter was operating on total mode with 1-minute samples being taken on each channel.
Atmospheric Conditions: Similar to those for GD-R1.
Limitations of Test: Three technicians were performing a gyro opening and assembly operation 6 feet upstream of the Royco particle counter.

This operation included removal of the assembly from a shock-absorbing package, which was a particularly dirty operation.

Reason for Test: To determine the increased contamination level under GD-R5 when this operation was performed.

Observations on Curve: This curve is linear in nature when plotted on log-log paper. It is essentially parallel to the slope of the AFSCR and PTS curves but shows a higher contamination level than GD-R5.

Curve GD-M1 (Figure 2-25)

Date: 20 Feb. 1963

Place: Laminar/Cross-Flow Room, General Dynamics, Pomona, Calif.

Person Performing Test: Physicist, in conjunction with 1st Lt. Philip R. Austin

Instrument Used: Gelman sampling kit

- Sample height: 32 inches from floor
- Sample rate: 15 liters/min.
- Sampling time: 20 minutes
- Sample size: 10 cu ft

Atmospheric Conditions: Similar to those for GD-R1.

Reason for Test: To determine contamination level at exit of laminar/cross-flow room with normal activity.

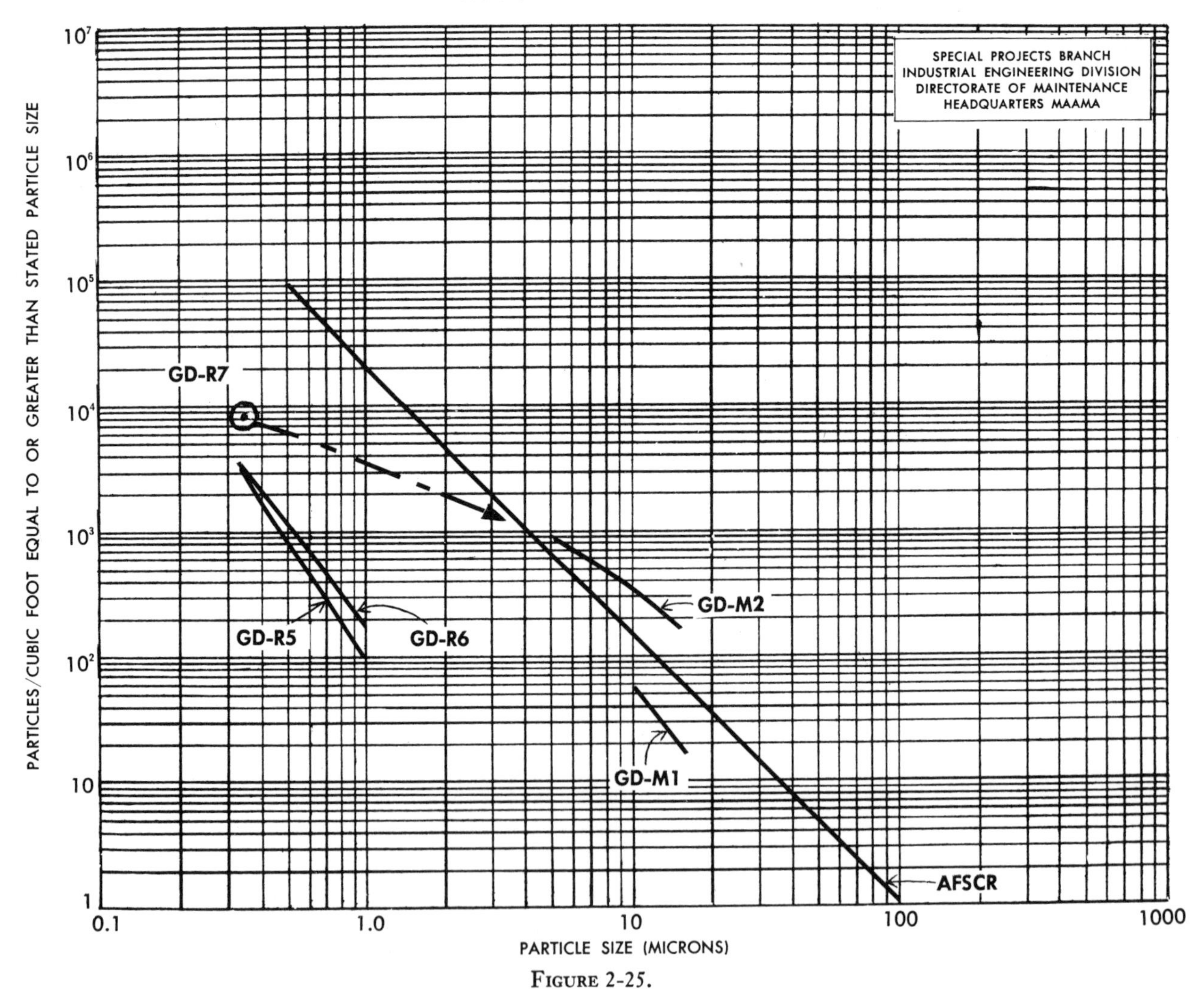

FIGURE 2-25.

Observations on Curve: Slope of the curve is essentially parallel to the slope of the AFSCR and PTS curves.

Curve GD-M2 (Figure 2-25)

Date: 20 Feb. 1963

Time: 1333 hours

Place: Laminar/Cross-Flow Room, General Dynamics, Pomona, Calif.

Person Performing Test: Physicist in conjunction with 1st Lt. Philip R. Austin

Instrument Used: Gelman sampling kit

Height of sample: 30 inches from floor

Sample rate: 15 liters/min.

Sample time: 2 minutes

Sample size: 1 cu ft

Atmospheric Conditions: Similar to those for GD-R1.

Limitations of Test: This test was performed with abnormally high activity being performed upstream of the sampler (Lt. Austin performing calisthenics for 2 minutes, approximately 8 feet from the Gelman sampler).

Comment on Curve: Slope of this curve is essentially parallel to the slope of the AFSCR and PTS curves. Point GD-R7 was taken in conjunction with this test.

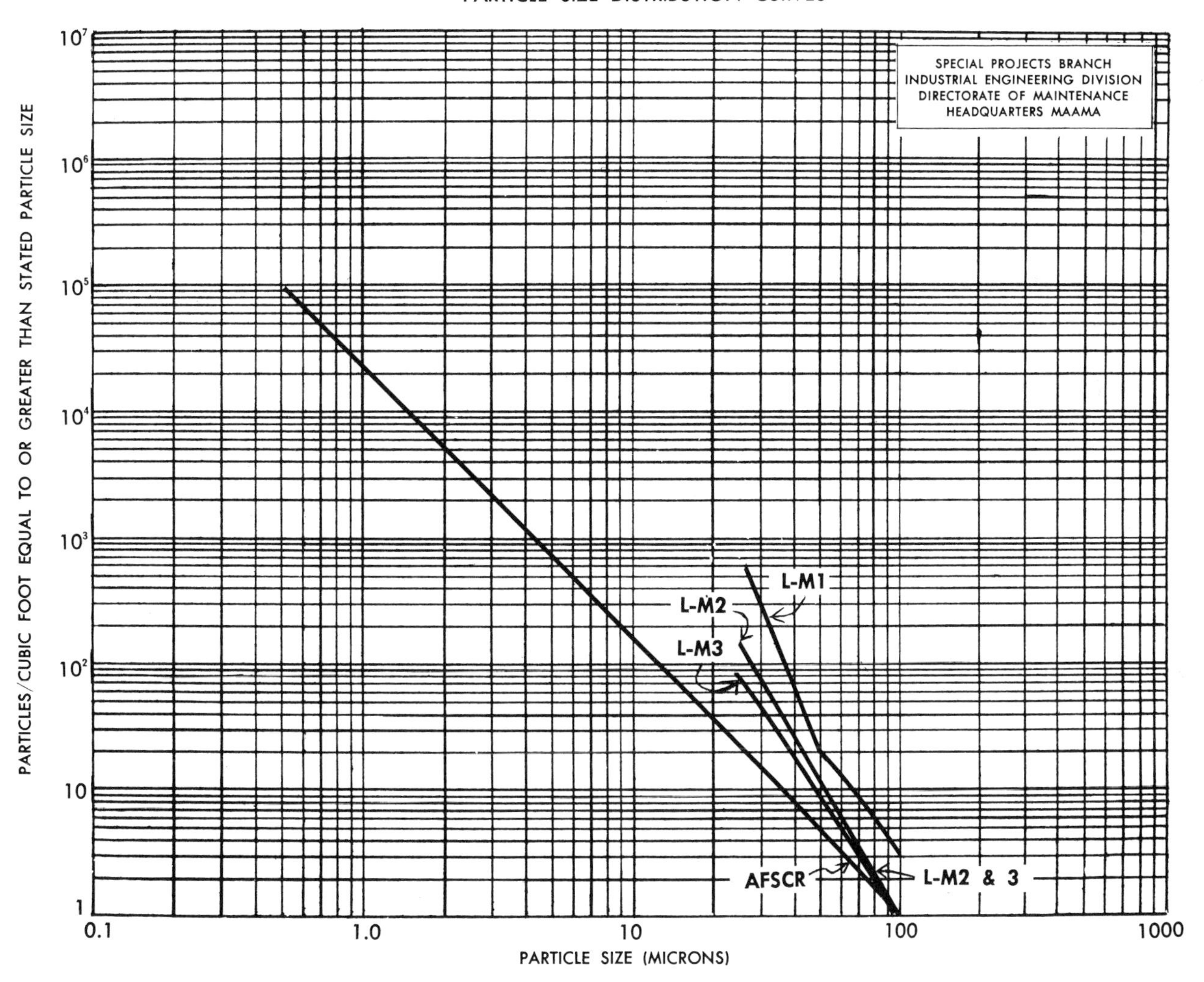

FIGURE 2-26.

Curve GD-R7 (*Figure 2-25*)
Date: 20 Feb. 1963
Time: 1333 hours
Limitations of Test: All conditions for this test were the same as for GD-M2, except that a Royco counter was positioned 10 feet from the abnormally high activity. This test was run concurrently with GD-M2. Two 1-minute readings were taken on all particles greater than or equal to 0.32 micron.
Comment on Curve: The projection of point GD-R7 to GD-M2 gives a slope not too much different from the slope at 5 microns for the curve of GD-M2.

Curve L-M1 (*Figure 2-26*)
Date: 31 Jan. 1963
Place: Air-Conditioned Room 1 (Class I), Lockheed Missiles and Space Co., Van Nuys, Calif.
Person Performing Test: E. Kreeger
Instrument Used: Manual sampling and counting technique.
Temperature and Humidity: Similar to Air Force Class I conditions.

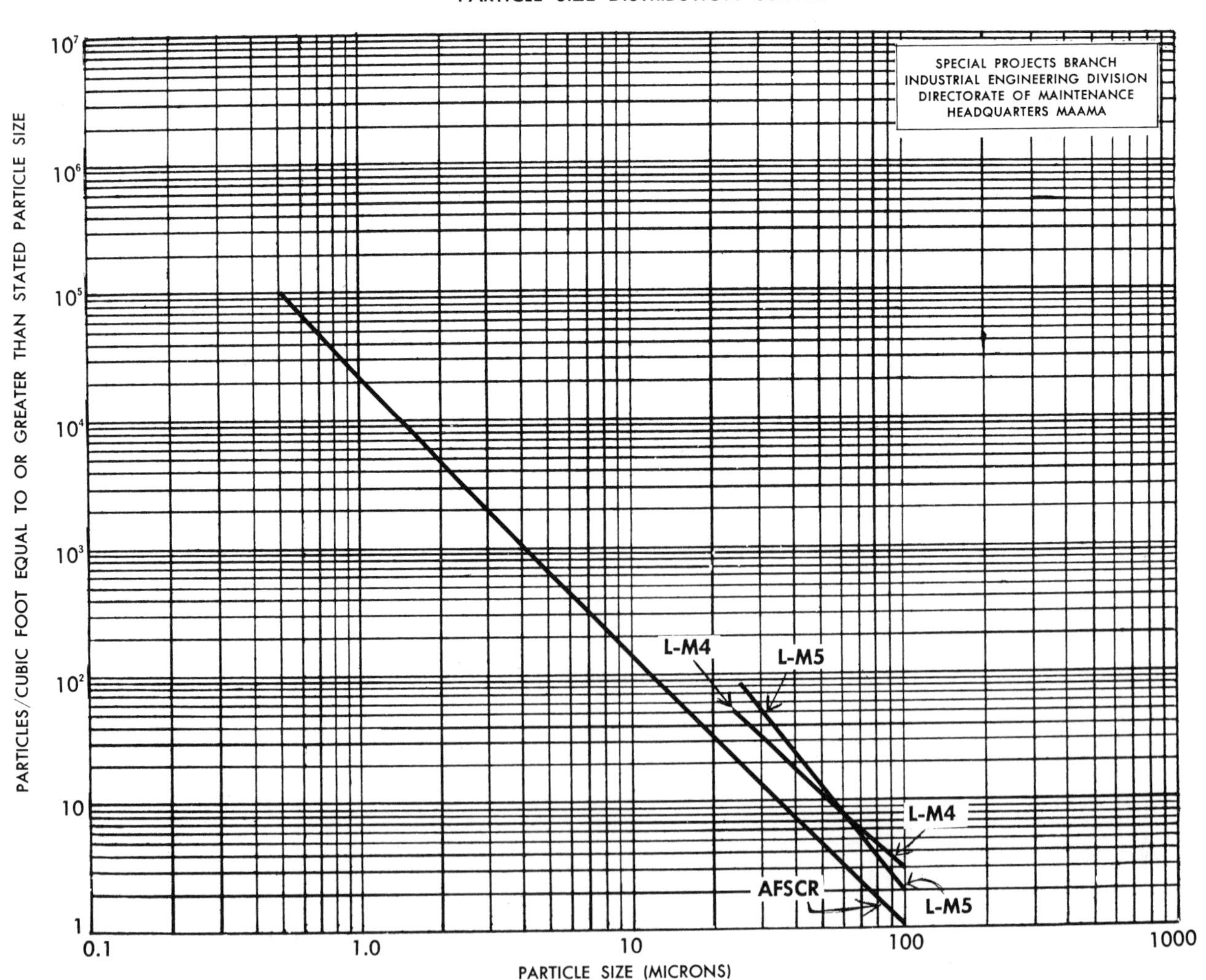

FIGURE 2-27.

Reason for Test: Standard monitoring procedure.
Observations on Curve: In the higher ranges this curve is essentially parallel to the slope of the AFSCR and PTS curves.

Curve L-M2 (*Figure 2-26*)
Date: 31 Jan. 1963
Place: Air-Conditioned Room 2 (Class I), Lockheed Missiles and Space Co., Van Nuys, Calif.
Person Performing Test: E. Kreeger
Instrument Used: Manual sampling and counting technique.
Atmospheric Conditions: Similar to Air Force Class I conditions.
Reason for Test: Standard monitoring procedure.
Observations on Curve: Same as for L-M1.

Curve L-M3 (*Figure 2-26*)
Date: 31 Jan. 1963
Place: Air-Conditioned Room 3 (Class 1), Lockheed Missiles and Space Co., Van Nuys, Calif.
Person Performing Test: E. Kreeger
Instrument Used: Manual sampling technique.
Atmospheric Conditions: Similar to Air Force Class I conditions.
Reason for Test: Standard monitoring procedure.
Observations on Curve: Same as for L-M1.

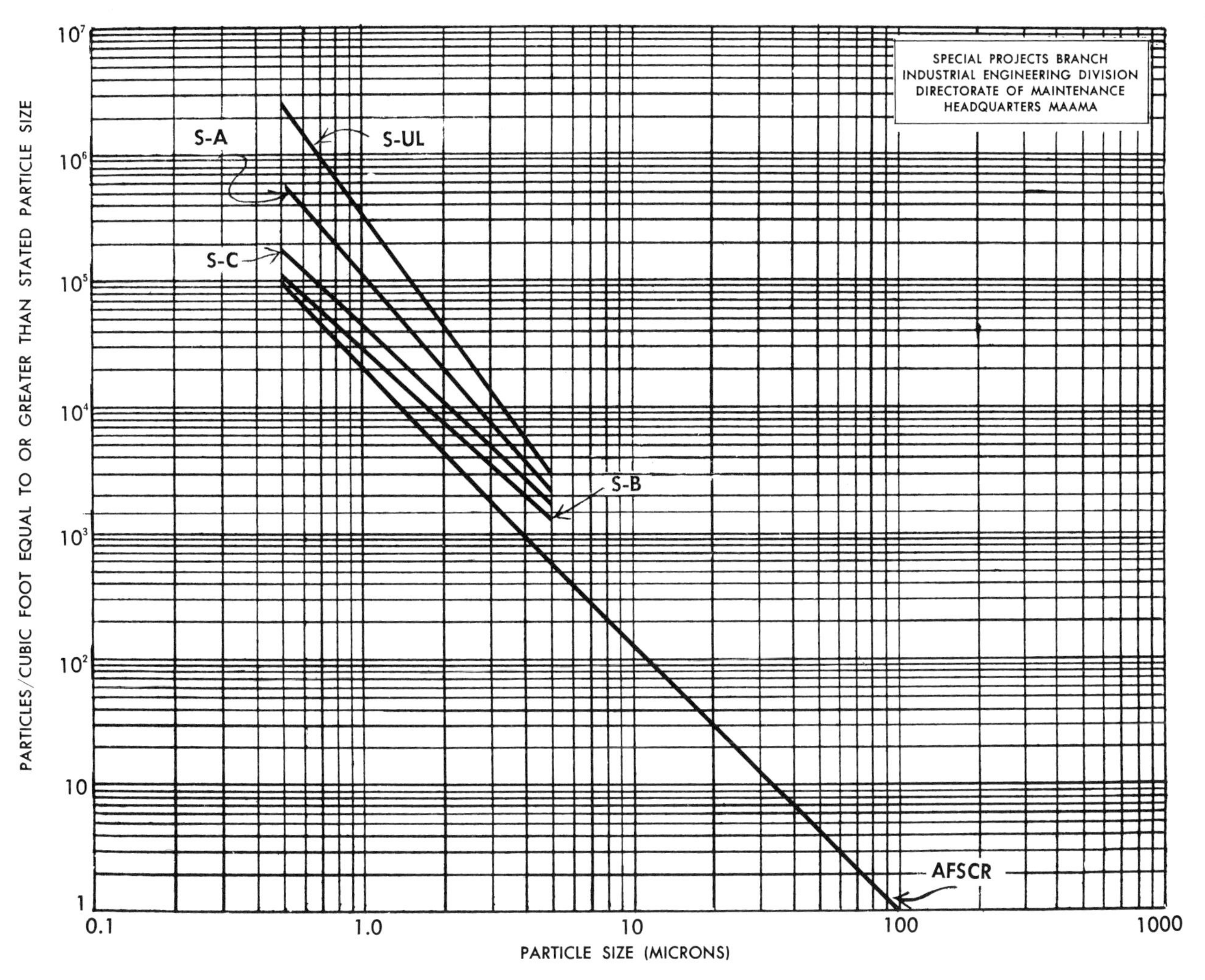

FIGURE 2-28.

Curve L-M4 (Figure 2-27)
Date: 22 June 1962
Place: Air-Conditioned Package and Assembly Room (similar to Class I), Lockheed Missiles and Space Co., Van Nuys, Calif.
Instrument Used: Manual sampling technique.
Atmospheric Conditions: Similar to Air Force Class I conditions.
Reason for Test: Standard monitoring procedure.
Observations on Curve: The curve is essentially parallel to the slope of the AFSCR and PTS curves.

Curve L-M5 (Figure 2-27)
Date: 25 June 1962
Place: Air-Conditioned Package and Assembly Room (Class I), Lockheed Missile and Space Co., Van Nuys, Calif.
Person Performing Test: F. Pickel
Reason for Test: Standard monitoring procedure.
Observations on Curve: Same as for L-M4.

Curve S-A (Figure 2-28)
Date: 1962

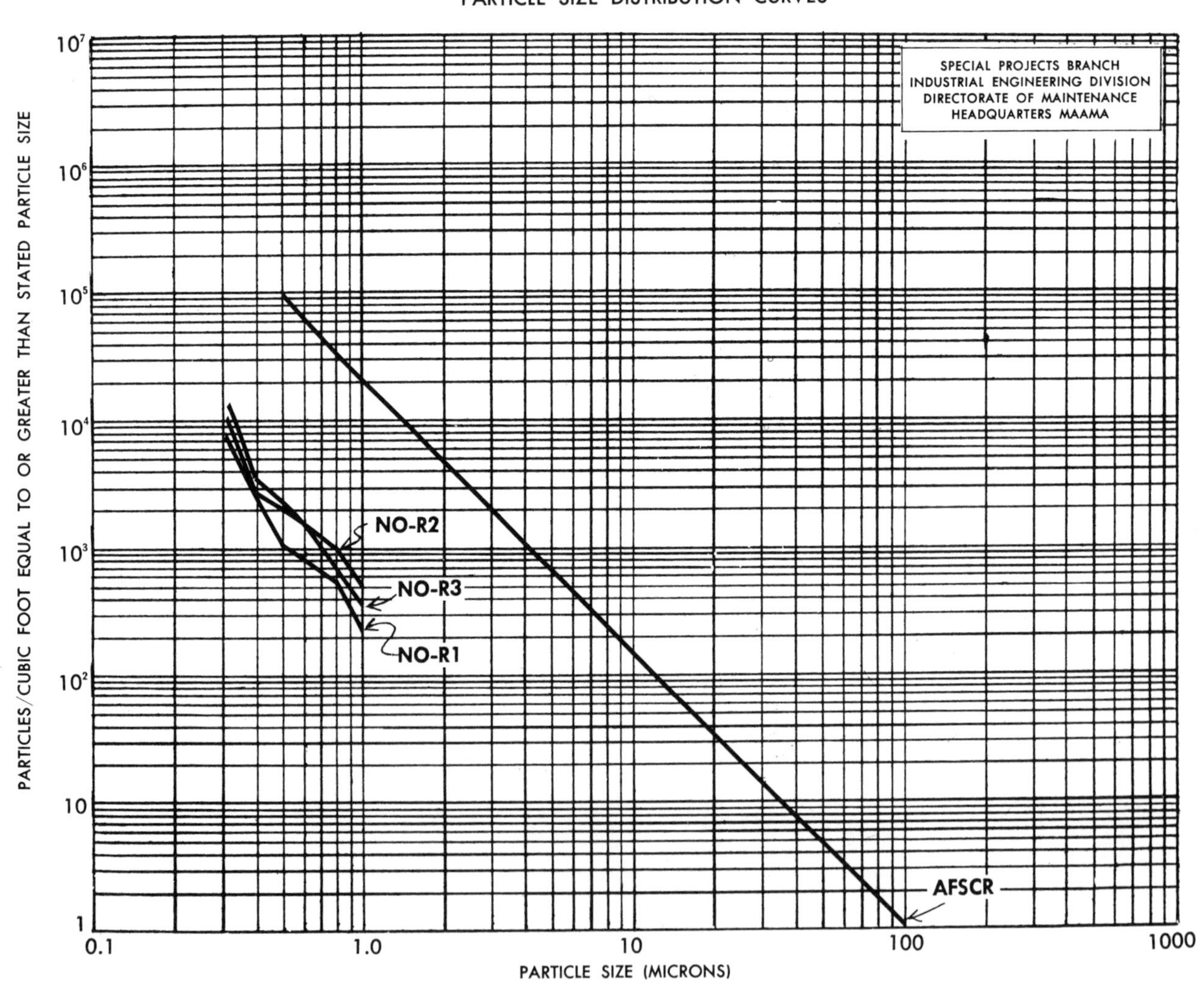

FIGURE 2-29.

Place: Clean Room A, Sandia Corp., Albuquerque, N. Mex.

Instrument Used: Royco particle counter and manual sampling technique, counting all particles greater than 0.5 micron in size.

Limitations of Test: This test was taken over a period of time and represents four individual samples, by both the Royco particle counter and the manual sampling technique.

Reason for Test: To determine the contamination level of Clean Room A by different sampling methods.

Observations on Curve: By joining the two points, we get a slope of a line essentially parallel to the slope of the AFSCR and PTS curves.

Curve S-B (Figure 2-28)

Date: 1962

Place: Clean Room B, Sandia Corp., Albuquerque, N. Mex.

Instrument Used: Royco particle counter and manual sampling technique, counting all particles greater than 0.5 micron in size.

Limitations of Test: Same as for S-A.

Reason for Test: Same as for S-A.

Observations on Curve: By joining the two

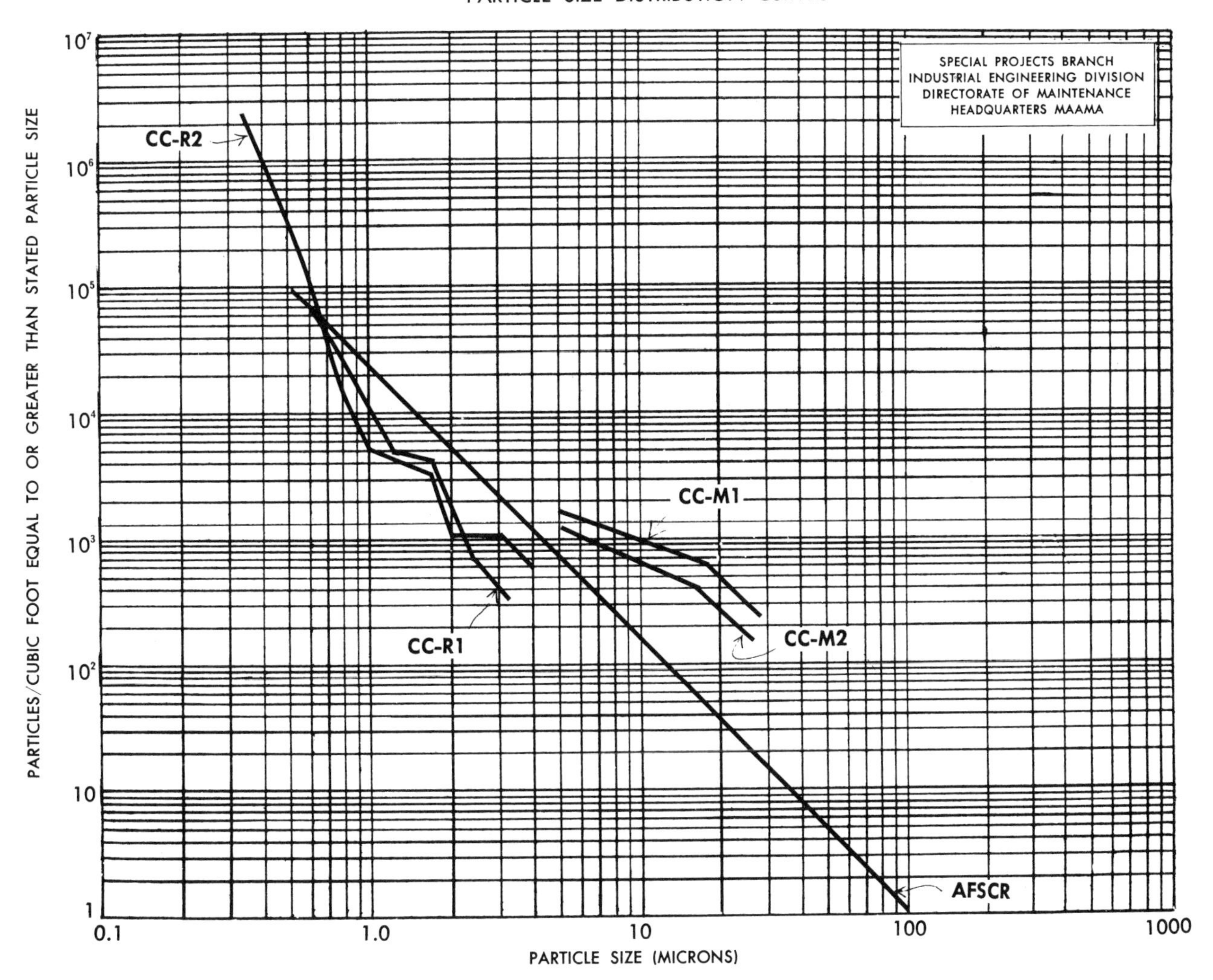

FIGURE 2-30.

points, we obtain a slope essentially parallel to the slope of the AFSCR and PTS curves.

Curve S-C (Figure 2-28)
Date: 1962
Place: Clean Room C, Sandia Corp., Albuquerque, N. Mex.
Limitations of Test: Same conditions and observations are made as for S-A.

Curve S-UL (Figure 2-28)
Date: 1962
Place: Uncontrolled Lab Area, Sandia Corp., Albuquerque, N. Mex.
Limitations of Test: Same conditions and observations are made as for S-A.
Comment: Curves S-A, S-B, S-C, and S-UL were compiled from the report "A Comparison of Dust Count Data Obtained from Different Measuring Methods," by R. C. Marsh, Staff Member Physicist, Advanced Manufacturing Development Division, Sandia Corp., Albuquerque, N. Mex.

Curve NO-R1 (Figure 2-29)
Date: 21 Mar. 1963
Time: 1020 hours

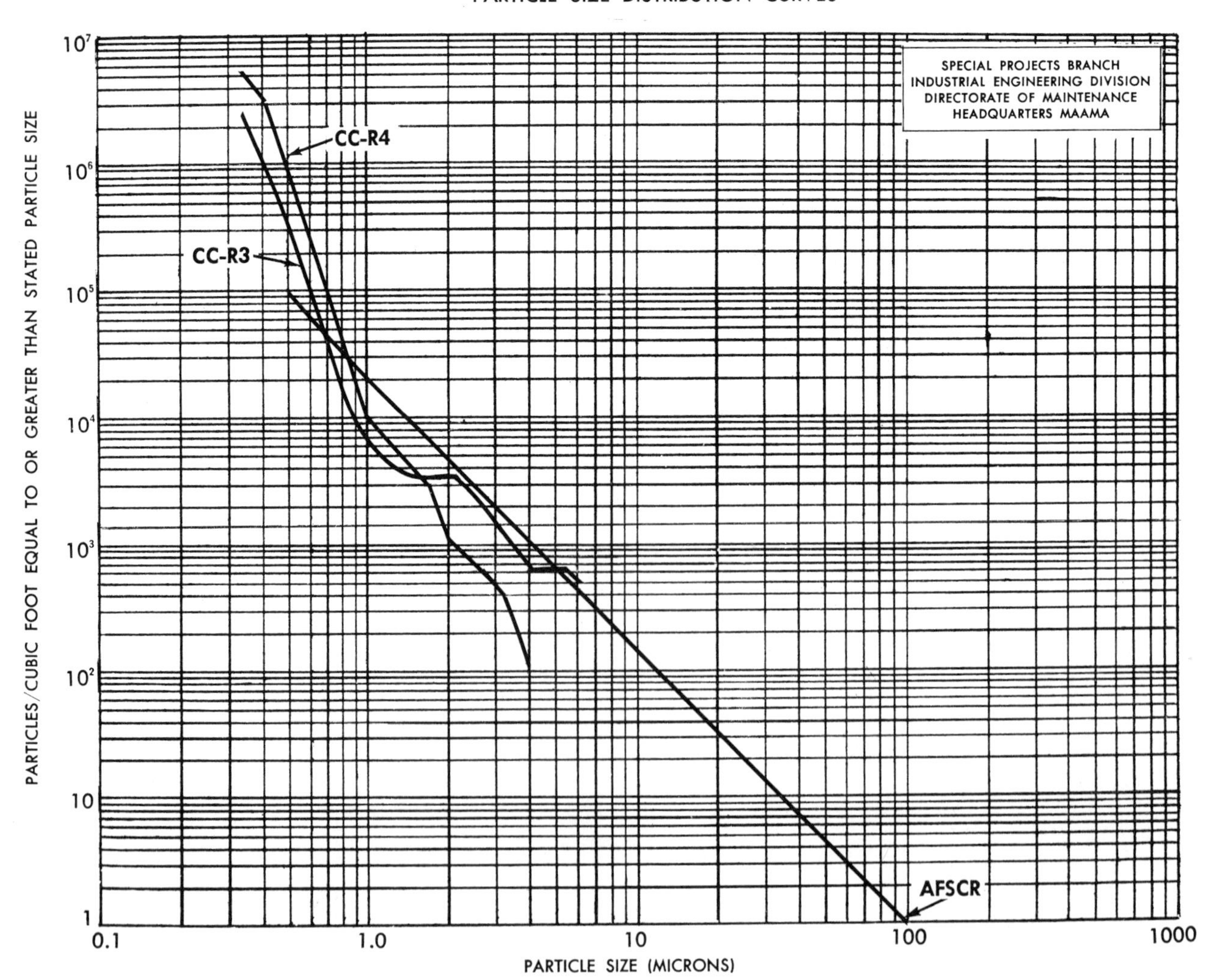

FIGURE 2-31.

Place: Norden, Division of United Aircraft Corp., Norwalk, Conn.
Persons Performing Test: Norden personnel
Instrument Used: Royco particle counter
Height of sample: 32 inches from floor
Sample volume: 1 liter
Counter was operating on individual channels. Each channel was reported for a period of 10 minutes.
Limitations of Test: Each point represents a 10-minute sample. The entire curve represents a period of 50 minutes. Each point is taken 10 minutes after the last point. The channels monitored were 0.32, 0.4, 0.5, 0.8, and 1.0 micron.
Observations on Curve: The general slope of this curve approaches conditions parallel to the slope of the AFSCR and PTS curves.

Curve NO-R2 (*Figure 2-29*)
Date: 21 Mar. 1963
Time: 1100 hours
Limitations of Test: Same conditions exist for NO-R2 as for NO-R1.
Comments on Curve: Same as for NO-R1.

Curve NO-R3 (*Figure 2-29*)
Date: 21 Mar.1963
Time: 1330 hours

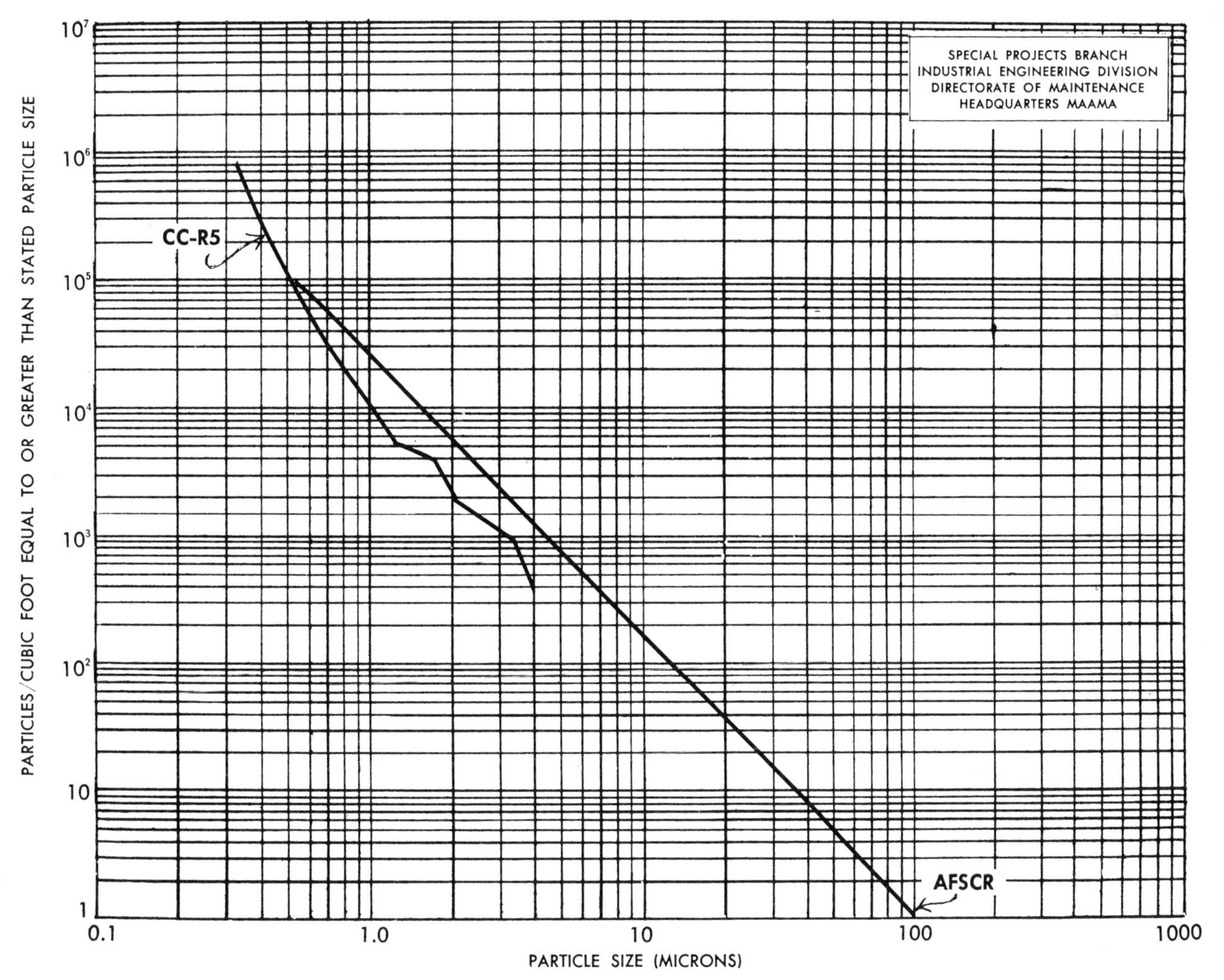

FIGURE 2-32.

Limitations of Test: Same conditions exist for NO-R3 as for NO-R1.

Observations on Curve: Same as for NO-R1.

Comments: Curves NO-R1, NO-R2, and NO-R3 are representative of data taken during the days March 20 through 23. The data presented are sample data taken from standard monitoring procedure for the area involved.

Cape Kennedy Data

The ensuing descriptions present experimental data obtained by both automatic and manual counting techniques at Cape Kennedy. The following data are common to curves CC-R1 through CC-R29 and curves CC-M1 through CC-M5:

Date: 4 June 1963

Place: Manned Spacecraft Center, Cape Kennedy, Florida

Persons Performing Tests: 1st Lt. Philip R. Austin, 1st Lt. Clifford F. Frith, and Stewart W. Timmerman. (Keith V. Kelly assisting)

Instruments Used: All curves designated by "R," as CC-R1, were obtained by a Royco particle counter modified to the newest configuration by Royco Instrument, Inc., in May 1963. All curves designated by "M," as CC-M1, were ob-

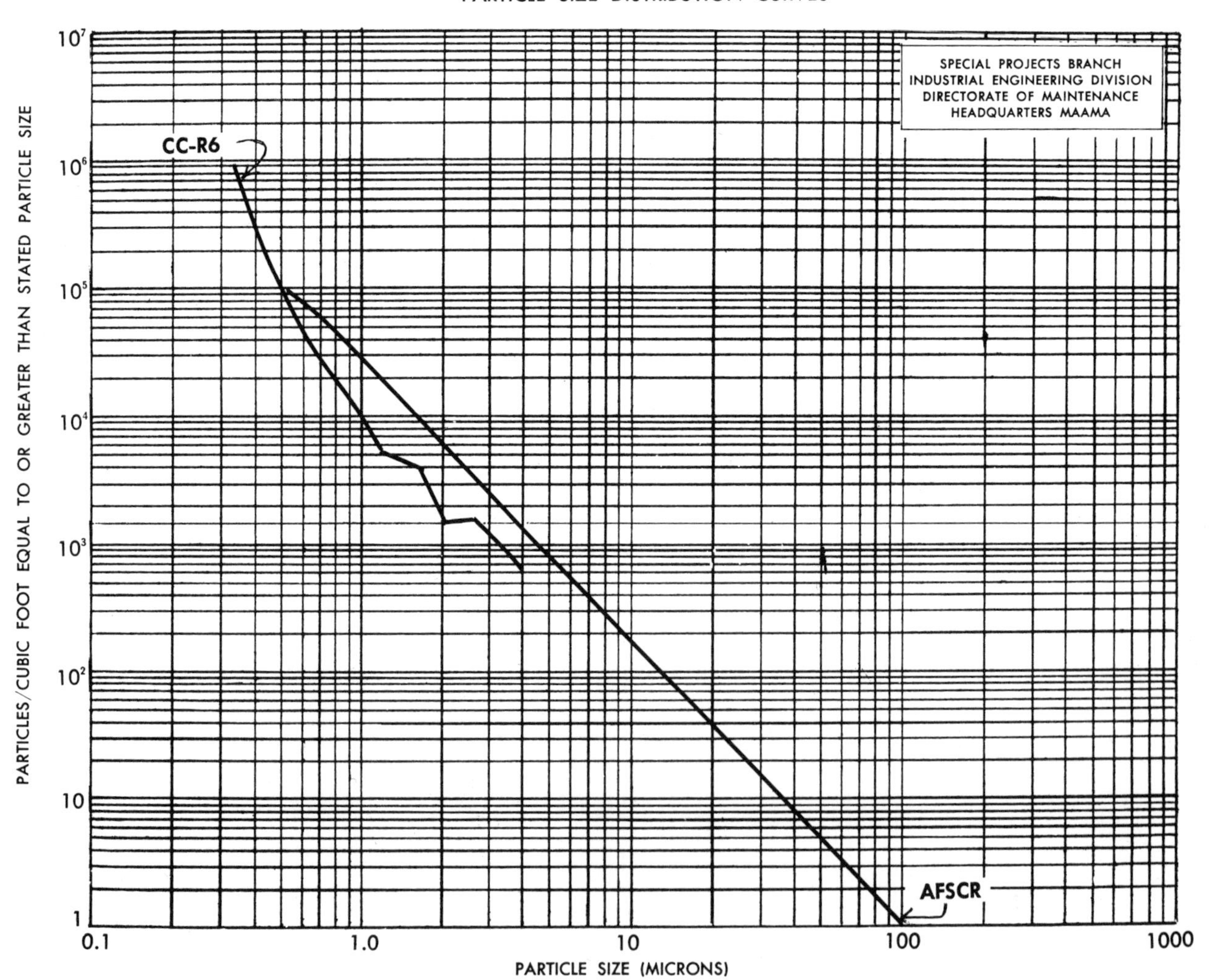

FIGURE 2-33.

tained by a Millipore sampling kit with 0.8-micron 47-mm membrane filters.

The following data are common to curves CC-R30 through CC-R47, and curve CC-M6:

Date: 5 June 1963

Place: Various facilities at Cape Kennedy, Florida

Persons Performing Tests: 1st Lt. Philip R. Austin, 1st Lt. Clifford F. Frith, and Stewart W. Timmerman

Instruments Used: All curves designated by "R" were obtained by a Royco particle counter modified to the newest configuration by Royco Instrument, Inc., in May 1963. All curves designated by "M" were obtained by a Millipore sampling kit with 0.8-micron 47-mm membrane filters.

Reviewing the data taken within facilities and at ground level outdoors, we note a definite change in slope for particles less than 2.0 microns in size. This change in slope is toward increased numbers of particles in the smaller size range of less than 2.0 microns. This occurrence was expected as a result of previous similar tests. One explanation which has been offered is that cigarette smoke, being predominately of this size range, causes this deviation in slope. In curves CC-R5, 6, 7, 30, and 31, outdoor

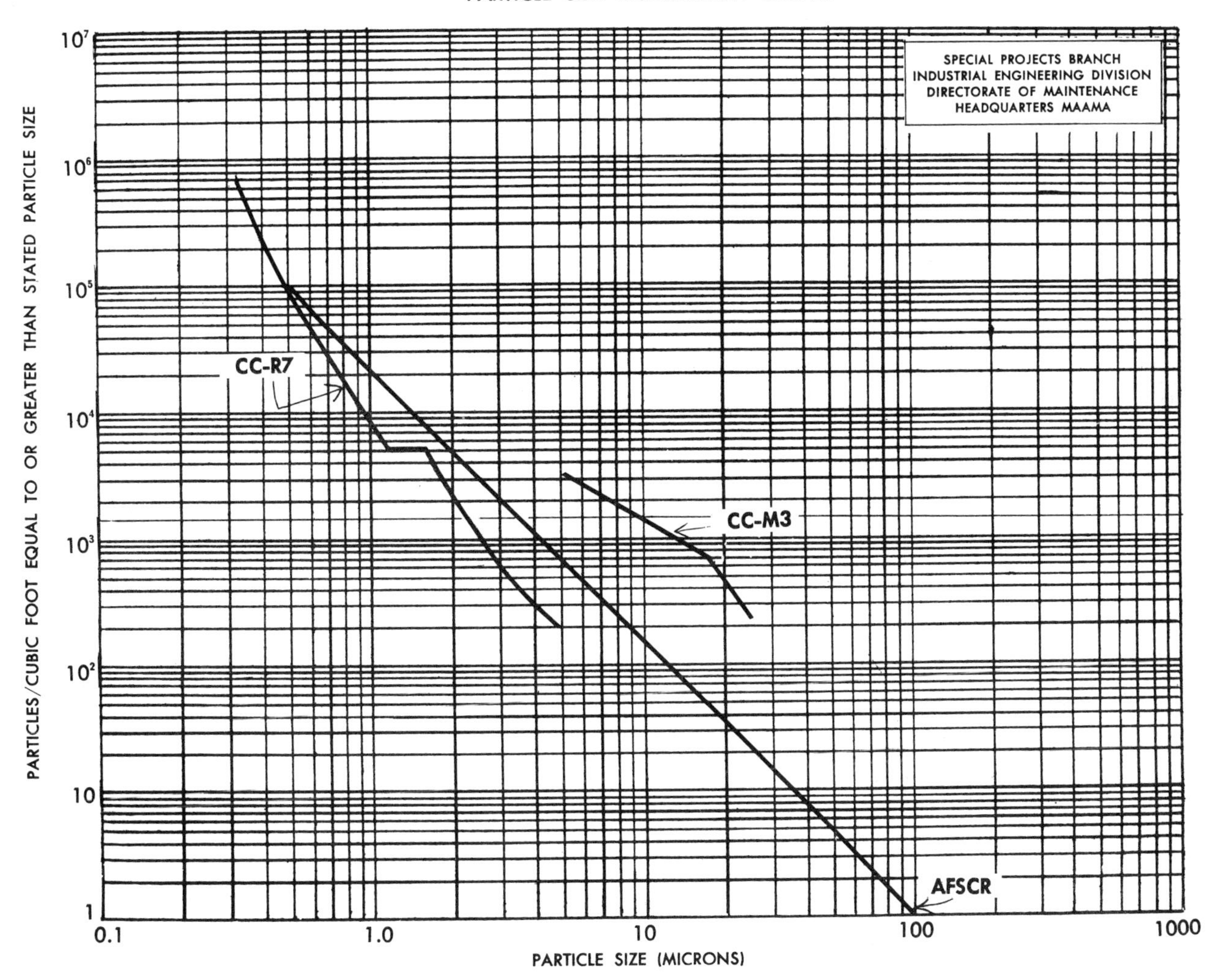

FIGURE 2-34.

air was sampled. Because of the wind direction and the location of the sampled area, the closest cigarette smoke generation would be at least several miles away. Curves CC-R26, 27, 28, and 29 were taken in such a location that the nearest cigarette smoke generation would have been several hundred yards away. Yet in all these curves a deviation from Stokes' law exists in the small particle sizes, similar to that deviation observed within facilities as in curves CC-R1, 2, 3, 4, 8, 9, 10, 11, 12, 13, 14, 15, 16, 17, 18, etc. From the observations made during this study and previous studies it appears that the gravitational forces are not the most significant forces on these small particles.

In analyzing the following data taken at ground level and at 116 feet above ground level outdoors, it appears that there is no increase of smaller particles of the small-size range at the elevated sampling point. That is, the size-distribution relationship for airborne particulate matter at the 116-foot level seems to follow Stokes' relationship in all size ranges sampled. This indicates that, for all size ranges sampled, gravitational forces are the most significant forces on these particles.

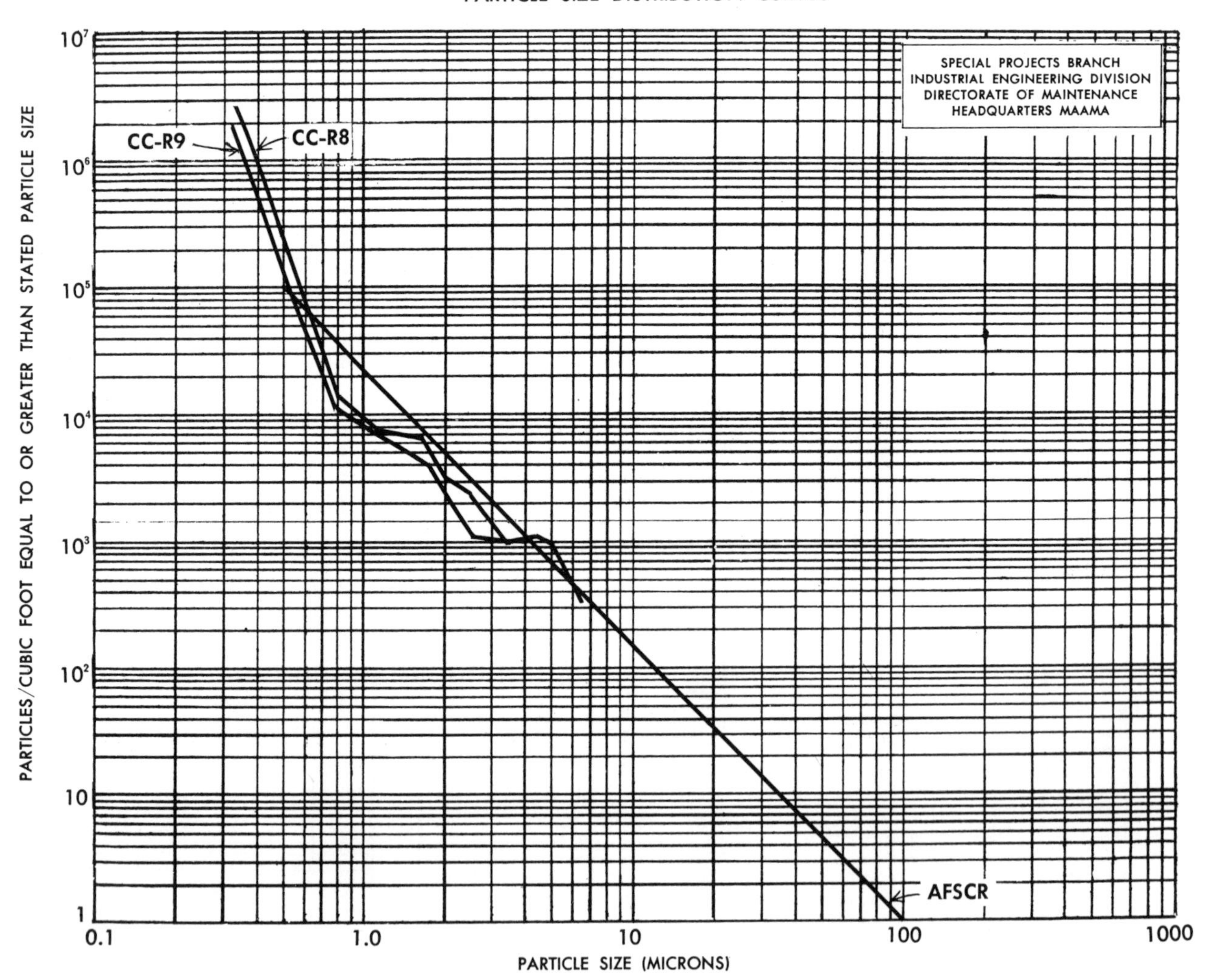

FIGURE 2-35.

Curve CC-R1 (Figure 2-30)
Time: 0925 hours
Place: Reaction Control Systems Bldg., Room W126 (This room had a grated floor with a water bath below the floor.)
Sample Characteristics
Height of sample: 32 inches from floor
Length of sample: Each of thirteen channels was sampled on total mode for 0.3 minute.
Sample rates: 0.01 cfm or 283 cc/min
Temperature and Humidity
Indoor ambient conditions: dry bulb 69°F; wet bulb 62°F; ∴ 68% relative humidity outdoor ambient conditions: dry bulb 82°F; wet bulb 74°F; ∴ 70% relative humidity
Observations on Curve: There is a predominant curvature to the slope of this curve between 0.8 and 1.6 microns. The slope for the larger particle size range is essentially parallel to the PTS curve or AFSCR curve as shown in Figure 2-5. The slope of CC-R1 deviates from the Stokes' law in the smaller particle size range. It appears that the significant force on particles of this size is no longer gravity but other types

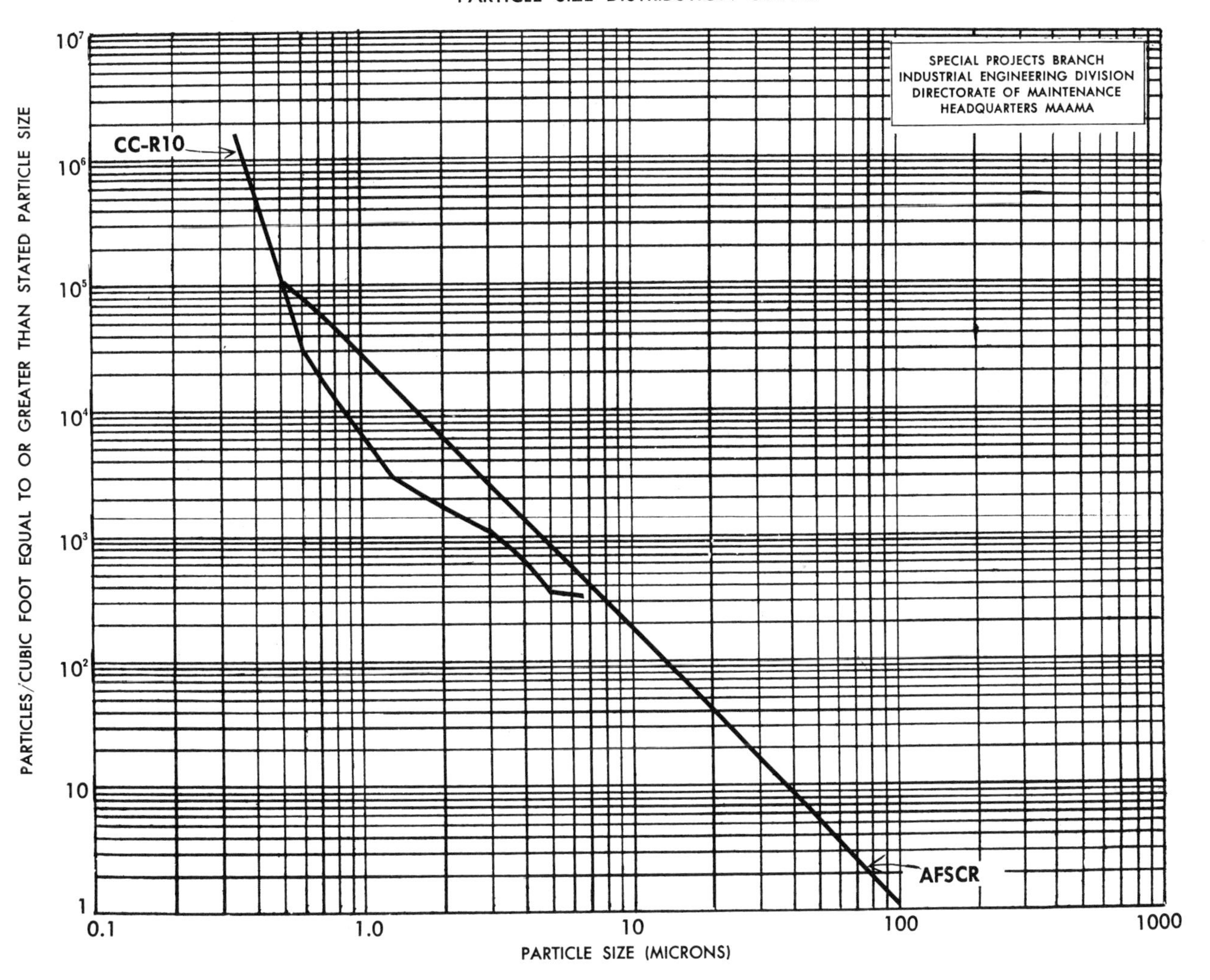

FIGURE 2-36.

of forces. Aerodynamic forces on particles in this size range are significant, which would account for the accumulation of smaller particles in this range.

Curve CC-R2 (Figure 2-30)
Time: 0928 hours
Place: Reaction Control Systems Bldg., Room W126. All conditions similar to those for CC-R1.

Curve CC-M1 (Figure 2-30)
Time: 0945 hours
Place: Reaction Control Systems Bldg., Room W126. This test was performed adjacent to those for CC-R1 and CC-R2.
Sample Characteristics
Height of sample: 12 inches from the floor
Length of sample: 10 minutes at a flow rate of 0.5 cfm
Humidity: Same as for CC-R1.
Observations on Curve: In the larger particle size range, this curve is parallel to the PTS curve. The smaller particles observed by this method seemed less than expected. This could possibly be due to particles missed during

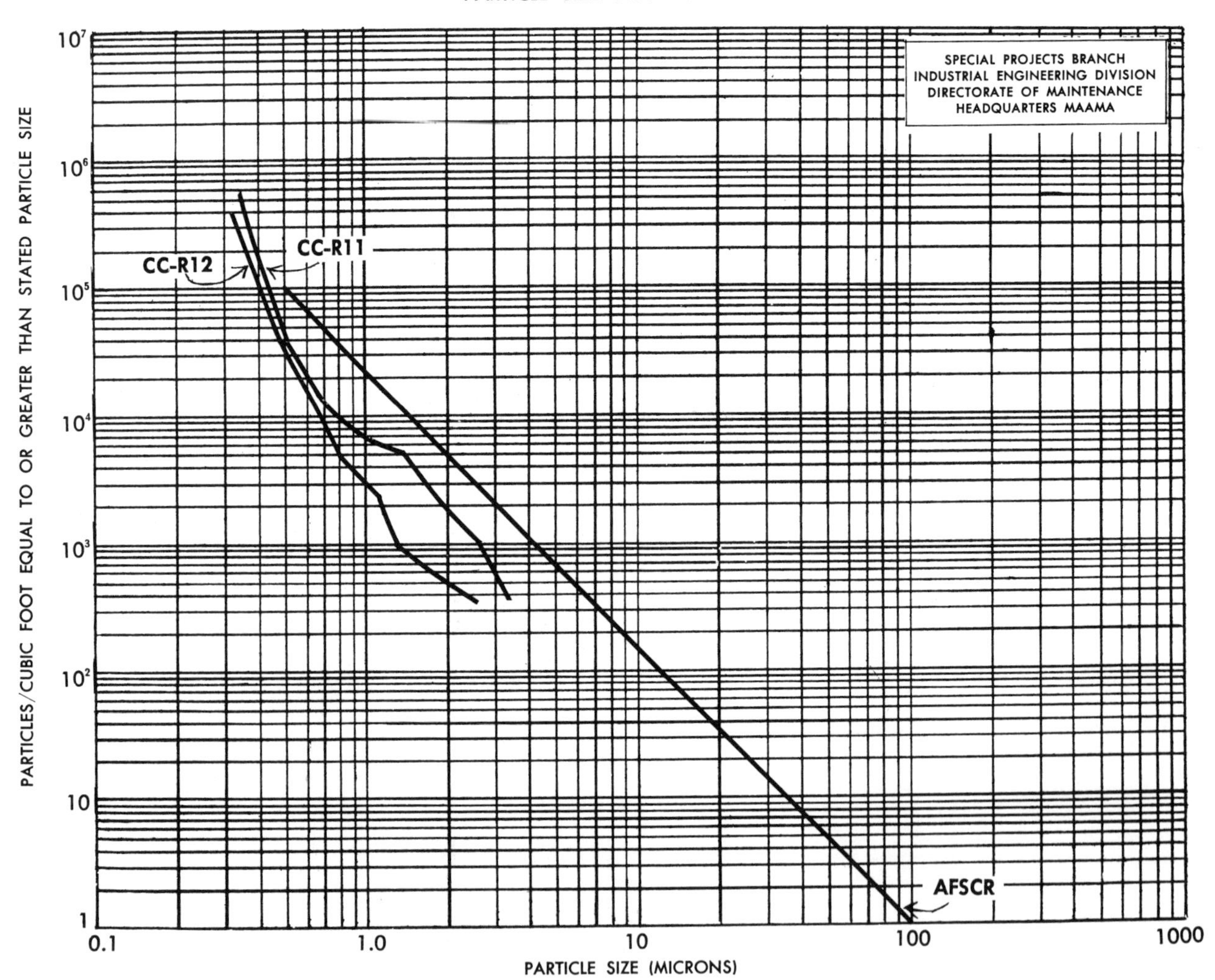

FIGURE 2-37.

counting of the membrane filter. This curve should show linearity throughout its length and conditions parallel to the AFSCR curve.

Curve CC-M2 (*Figure 2-30*)
Time: 1000 hours
All observations are the same as for CC-M1.

Curve CC-R3 (*Figure 2-31*)
Time: 0931 hours
Place: Reaction Control Systems Bldg., Room W126
Sample Characteristics
Height of sample: 32 inches from the floor
Length of sample: Each of thirteen channels was sampled on total mode for 1 minute
Sample rate: 0.01 cfm or 283 cc/min
Temperature and Humidity: Same as for CC-R1.
Observations on Curve: Same as for CC-R1.

Curve CC-R4 (*Figure 2-31*)
Time: 0948 hours
All observations are the same as for CC-R3, except that several people were moving about the area of the counting at the start of the sample.

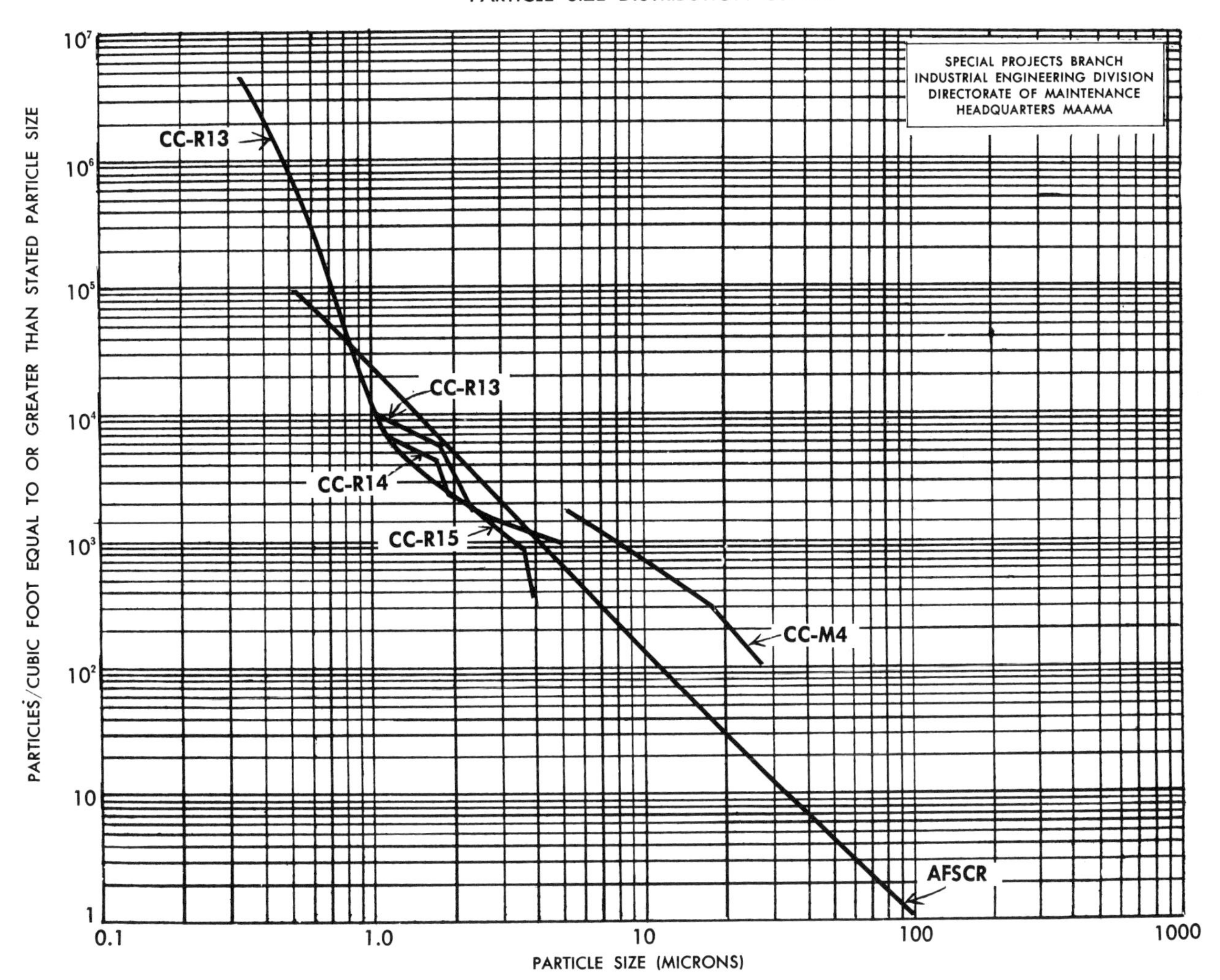

FIGURE 2-38.

Curve CC-R5 (*Figure 2-32*)

Time: 1055 hours

Place: Outside rear of Reaction Control Systems Bldg. (facing west)

Sample Characteristics: Same as for CC-R1, except that a 5- to 10-mph wind from the west was evident.

Temperature and Humidity: Dry bulb 82°F; wet bulb 74°F; • • • 70% relative humidity

Observations on Curve: For particles less than 1.0 micron in size, there is a pronounced deviation from the PTS curve. In the larger particle size range, the curve follows Stokes' relationship very well. Notice that the curve is quite smooth as compared to previous curves shown. This can be attributed to undisturbed sampled air. The air being sampled had a fairly constant but low velocity over constant land mass with no human or man-made disturbance upstream of the sampled air. Notice also that in the larger particle size range the curve closely parallels the AFSCR curve.

Curve CC-R6 (*Figure 2-33*)

Time: 1105 hours

All observations are the same as for CC-R5.

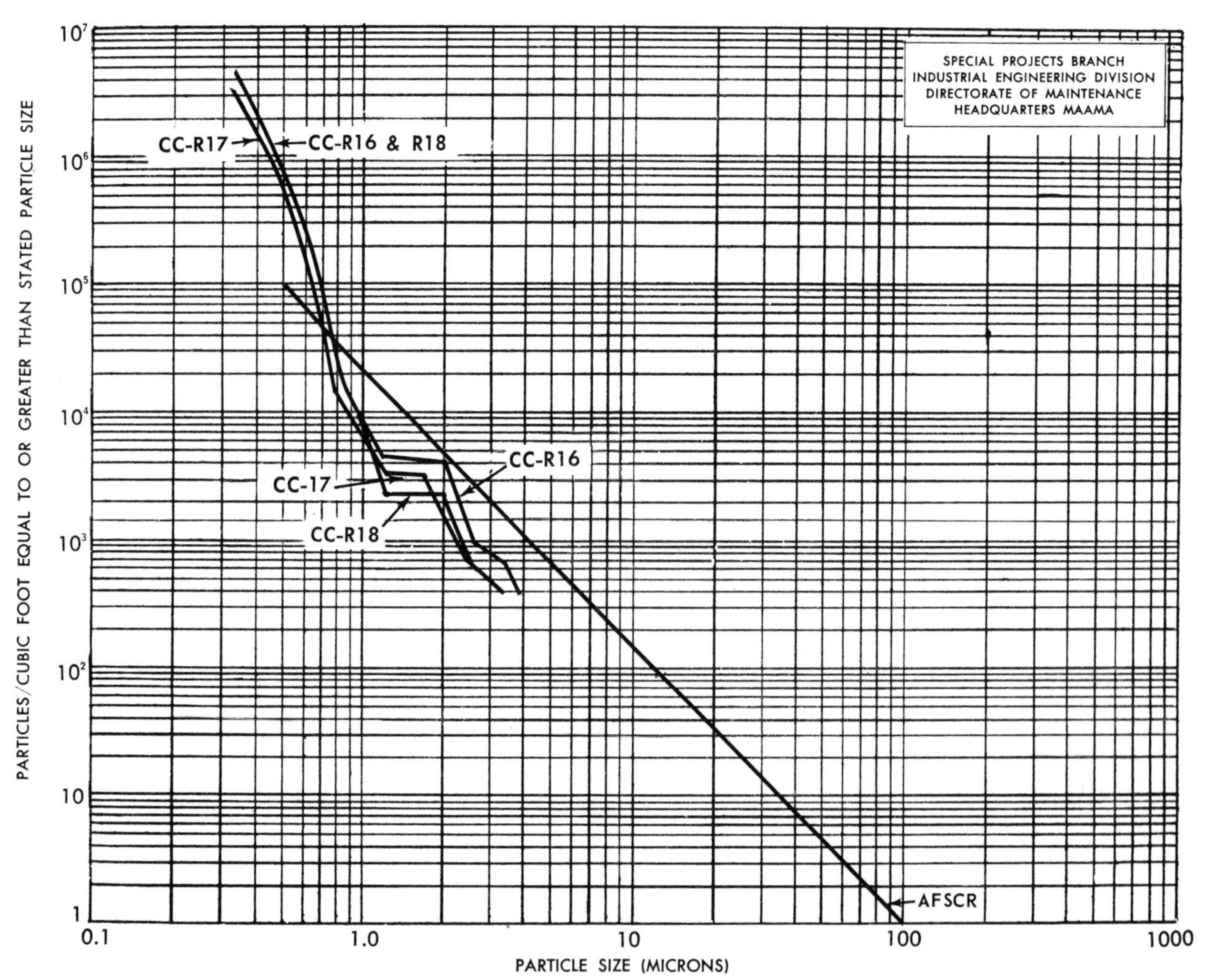

FIGURE 2-39.

Curve CC-R7 (Figure 2-34)
Time: 1110 hours
All observations are the same as for CC-R5, except that 1-minute samples were made on each channel.

Curve CC-M3 (Figure 2-34)
Time: 1120 hours
Place: Same as for CC-R5. The Millipore apparatus was placed on top of the Royco counter.
Sample Characteristics
Height of sample: 44 inches from floor
Length of sample: 10 minutes at a flow rate of 0.5 cfm
Flow rate: Same as for CC-R5
Temperature and Humidity: Same as for CC-R5
Observations on Curve: This curve is essentially parallel to the PTS and AFSCR curves.

Curve CC-R8 (Figure 2-35)
Time: 1320 hours
Place: Environmental Control Systems Bldg., Test Control

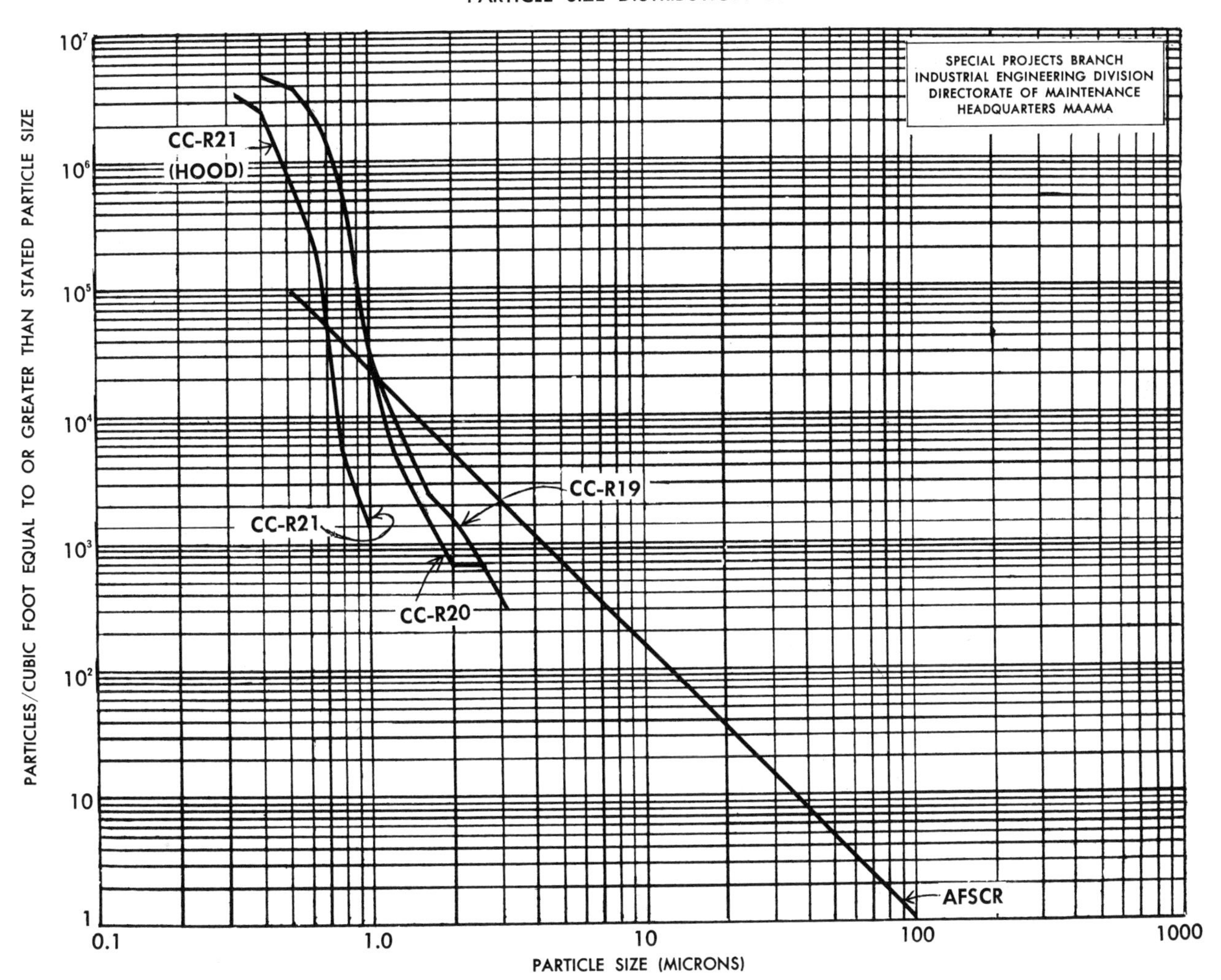

FIGURE 2-40.

Sample Characteristics
Height of sample: 32 inches from floor
Length of sample: Each of thirteen channels was sampled on total mode for 0.3 minutes.
Sample rate: 283 cc/min
Temperature and Humidity
Indoor ambient conditions: dry bulb 75°F; wet bulb 62°F; • • • 47% relative humidity
Outdoor ambient conditions: dry bulb 85°F; wet bulb 73°F; • • • 57% relative humidity
Observations on Curve: This curve changes slope in the 1.0-micron particle size range. The slope of the curve for the smaller particles deviates from the PTS and AFSCR curves. For particles in a larger size range, the slope of the curve is essentially parallel to the AFSCR curve.

Curve CC-R9 (Figure 2-35)
Time: 1331 hours
All observations are the same as for CC-R8.

Curve CC-R10 (Figure 2-36)
Time: 1335 hours
All observations are the same as for CC-R8.

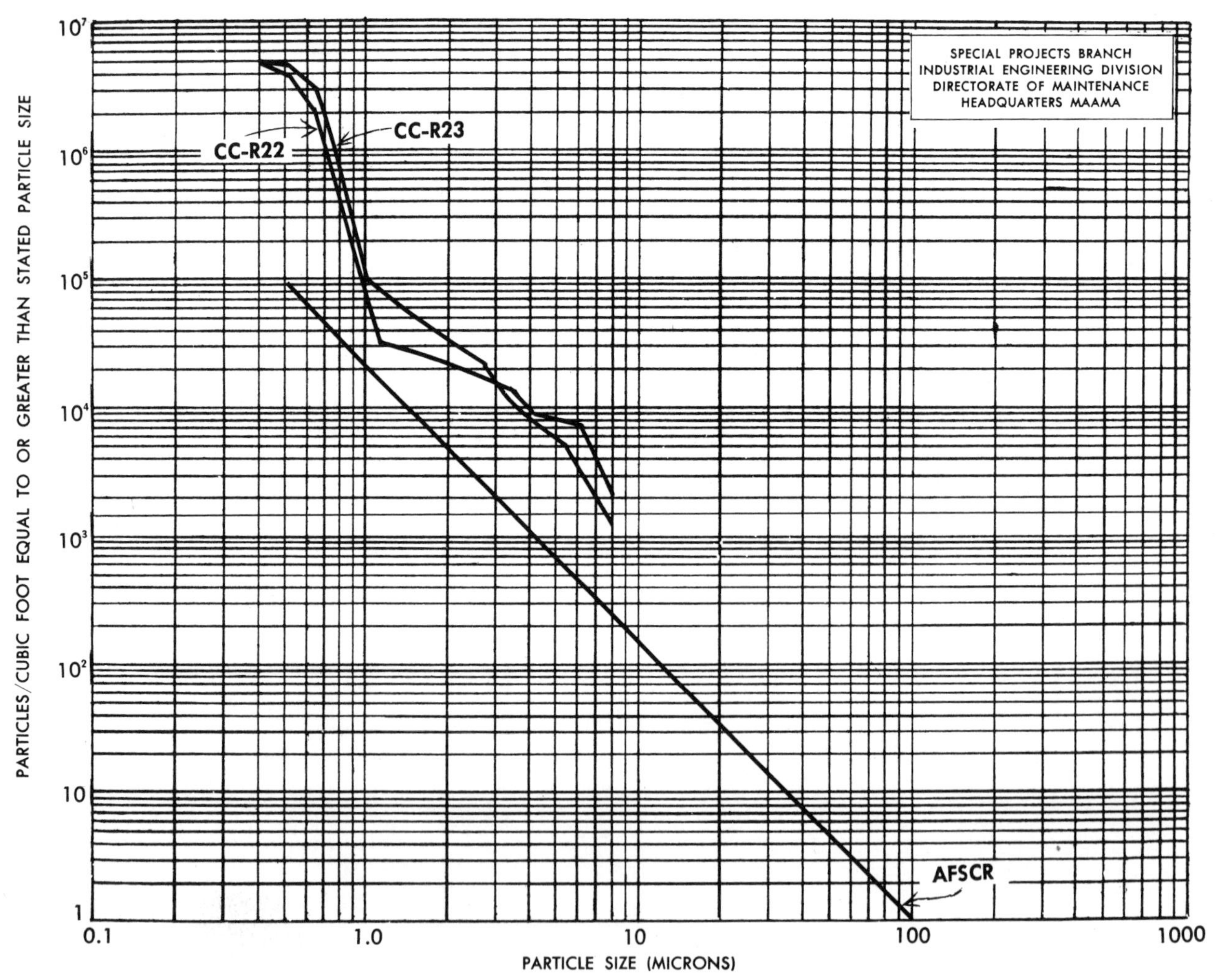

FIGURE 2-41.

Curve CC-R11 (*Figure 2-37*)
Time: 1402 hours
Place: Environmental Control Systems Bldg., (Pre-Installation Acceptance) Room.
Sample Characteristics: Same as for CC-R8. For the smaller particle sizes, the slope of the curve deviates from the PTS and AFSCR curves. For the larger particle size ranges, the slope of the curve is essentially parallel to the AFSCR curve.

Curve CC-R12 (*Figure 2-37*)
All observations are the same as for CC-R11.

Curve CC-R13 (*Figure 2-38*)
Time: 1446 hours
Place: Hangar S, McDonnell Aircraft, Class 6 White Room (Mercury Capsule Preparation and Build-up Room). The Royco counter was located 6 feet from the wall at approximately the lengthwise center of the room.
Sample Characteristics
Height of sample: 32 inches from floor
Length of sample: Each of thirteen channels was sampled on total mode for 0.3 minute.
Sample rate: 283 cc/min

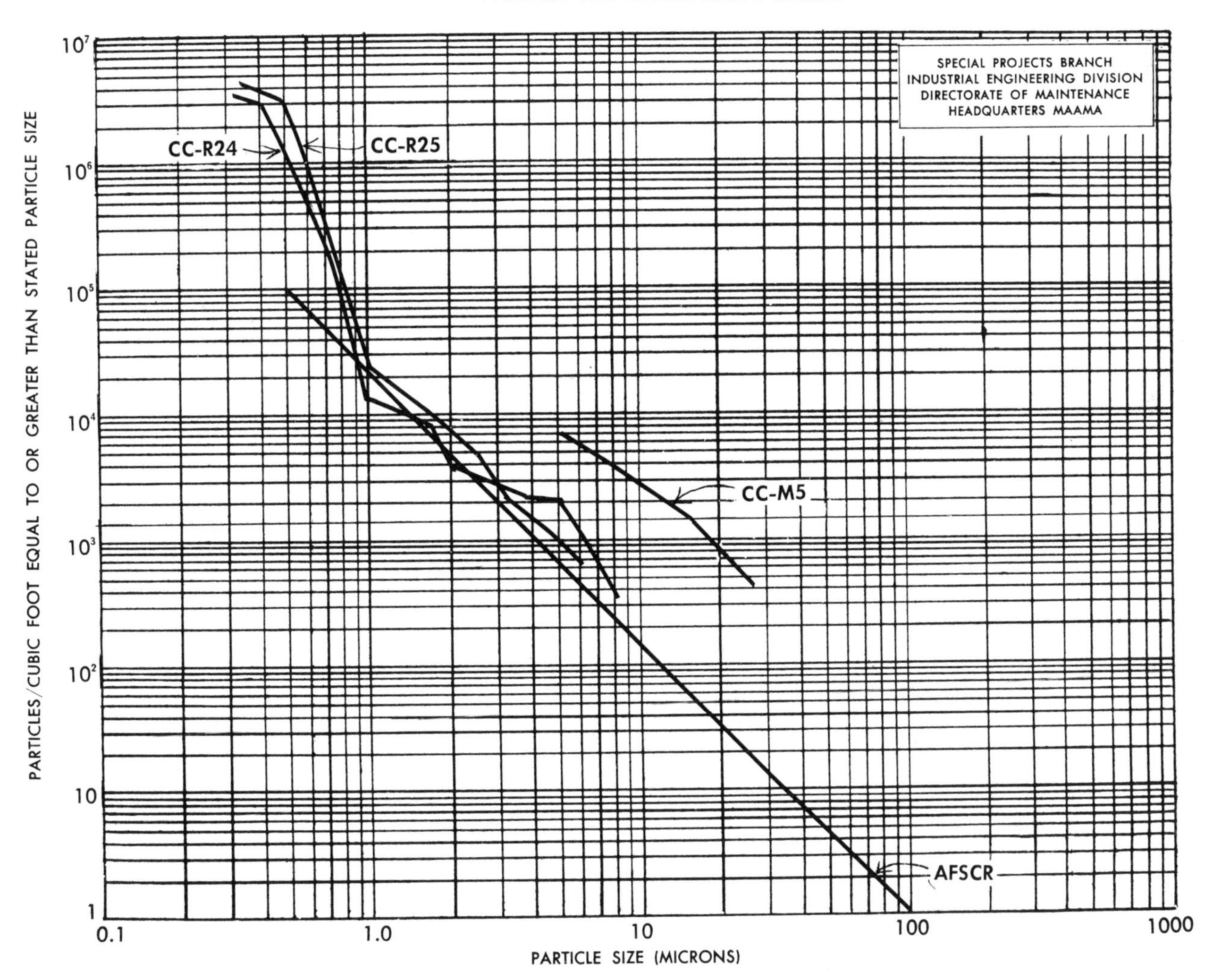

FIGURE 2-42.

Observations on Curve: The slope of the curve for the smaller-size particles is a linear function which deviates from the slope of the AFSCR curve. The slope of this curve in the small particle-size ranges is parallel to that of CC-R11 and CC-R12. There is a predominant change in slope in the 1.0- and 2.0-micron particle size ranges. The slope of the curve for particles in the larger size range is essentially parallel to the AFSCR curve.

Curve CC-R14 (Figure 2-38)

Time: 1451 hours

All observations are the same as for CC-R13.

Curve CC-R15 (Figure 2-38)

Time: 1458 hours

All observations are the same as for CC-R13.

Curve CC-M4 (Figure 2-38)

Time: 1450 hours

Place: Hangar S, McDonnell Aircraft, Class 6 White Room (Mercury Capsule Preparation and Build-up Room). The Millipore filter sampler kit was located adjacent to the Royco counter on the work bench.

Sample Characteristics

Height of Sample: 42 inches from floor

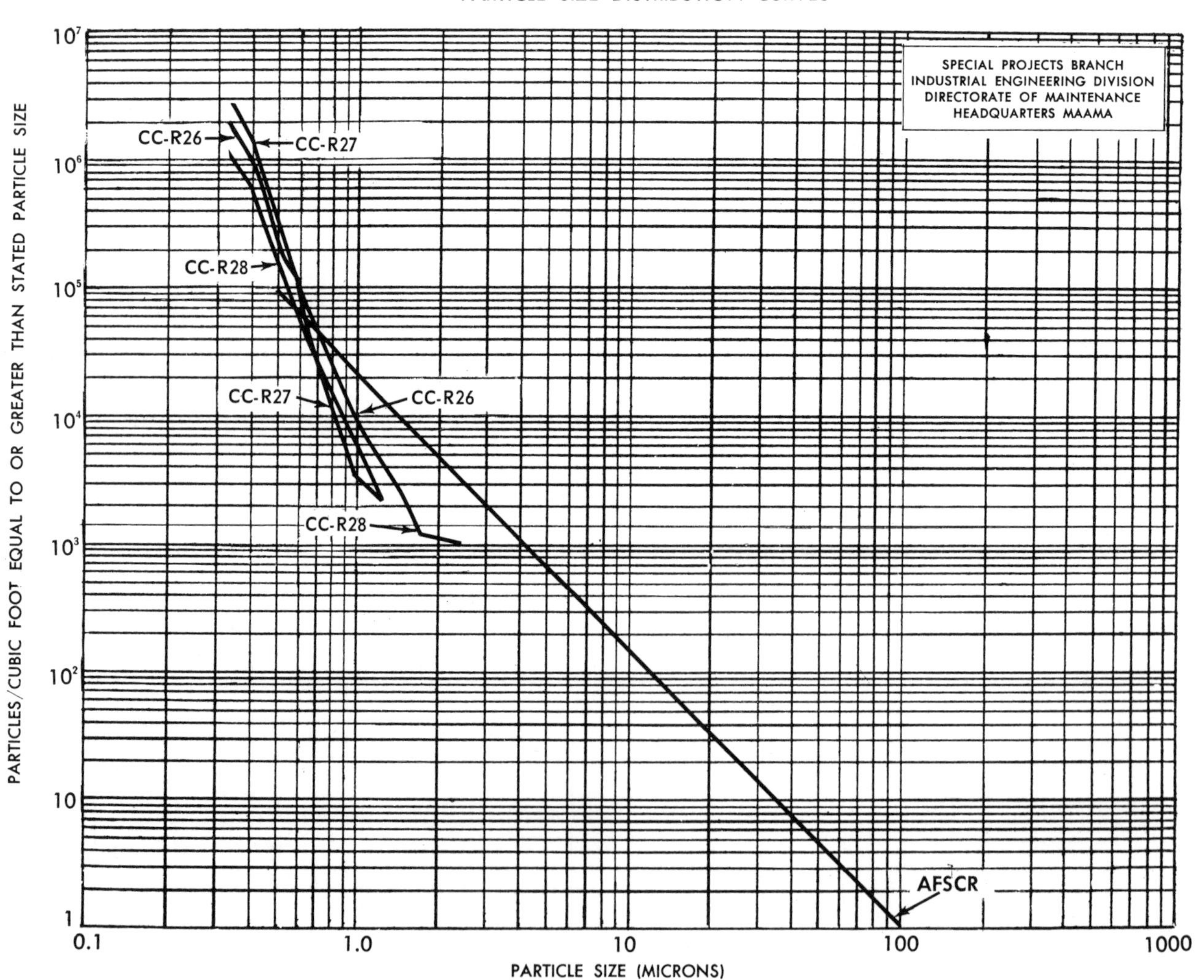

FIGURE 2-43.

Length of sample: 10 minutes at a flow rate of 0.5 cfm

Observations on the Curve: The curve is essentially parallel to the slope of the AFSCR curve.

Curve CC-R16 (*Figure 2-39*)

Time: 1515 hours

Place: Hangar S, McDonnell Aircraft, Class 6 White Room (inside Mercury Capsule 15B)

Sample Characteristics

Height of sample: 2 feet above technician lying prone inside Mercury capsule; technician was tracing wires and tightening bolts. Only one man was working inside the capsule.

Length of sample: Each of thirteen channels was sampled on total mode for 0.3 minute.

Rate of sample: 283 cc/min

Observations on Curve: This curve was essentially parallel to CC-R13, CC-R14, and CC-R15. Notice that a peaking function appears between 1.3 and 2.5 microns. This indicates generation of particulates inside the capsule of this size.

Curve CC-R17 (*Figure 2-39*)

Time: 1525 hours

All observations are the same as for CC-R16.

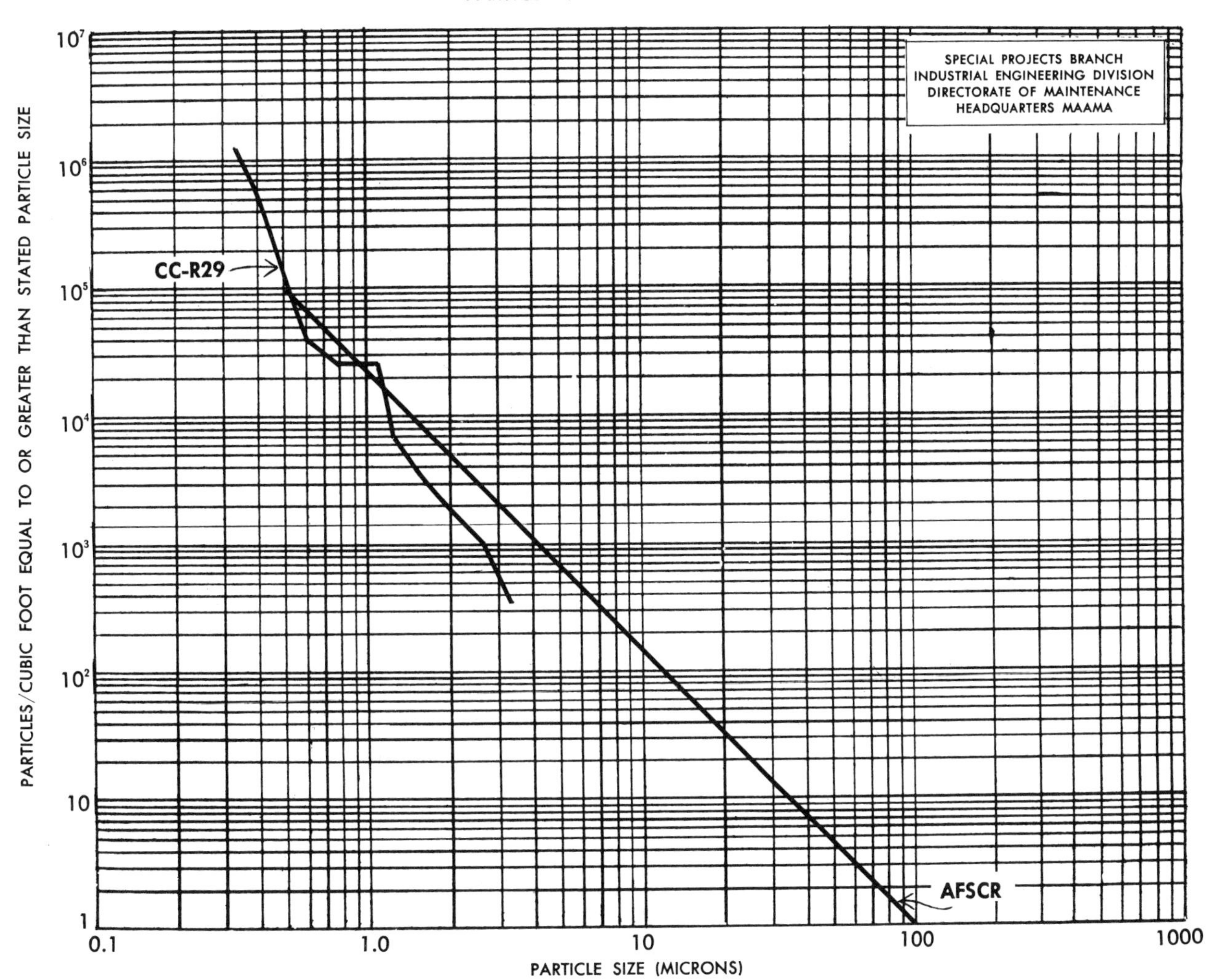

FIGURE 2-44.

Curve CC-R18 (*Figure 2-39*)
Time: 1535 hours
All observations are the same as for CC-R16.

Curve CC-R19 (*Figure 2-40*)
Time: 1545 hours
Place: Hangar S, McDonnell Aircraft, Class 10 Clean Room (The room is currently not being used except for storage.)
Sample Characteristics
Height of sample: 32 inches from floor
Length of sample: Each of thirteen channels was sampled on total mode for 0.3 minute.
Sample rate: 283 cc/min

Observations on Curve: In a small particle size range, a prominent deviation from the AFSCR curve was noted. A change in slope appears to take place between 1 and 2 microns. It was noted that within the common wall dividing the Class 10 clean room and change room an air duct joining the two rooms was installed. This allowed air to travel freely between the change room and the Class 10 room. The high values of particles in the small size range in-

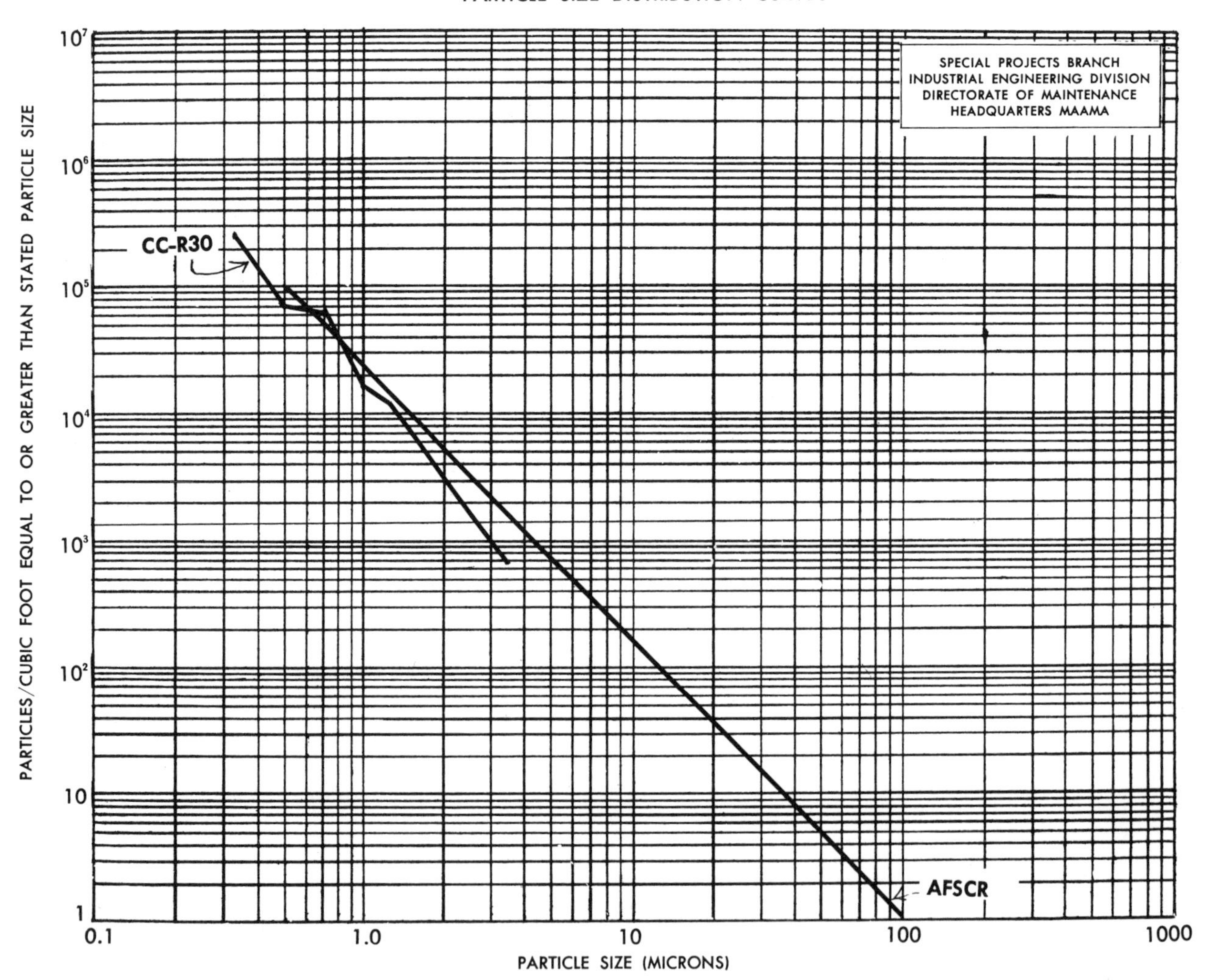

FIGURE 2-45.

dicates overloading of the counting mechanism of the Royco counter. It also indicates that a very large amount of contaminants from the change room was entering into the Class 10 room through the joining duct.

Curve CC-R20 (*Figure 2-40*)
Time: 1550 hours
All observations are the same as for CC-R19.

Curve CC-R21 (*Figure 2-40*)
Time: 1555 hours

Place: Hangar S, McDonnell Aircraft, Class 10 Clean Room (Sample was taken inside dust-free hood.)

Sample Characteristics

Height of sample: 2 inches from the working surface of dust-free hood and 2 inches inside the hood. High-efficiency particulate air filters (HEPA), which are 99.97% efficient on 0.3-micron dioctyl phthalate smoke, were not used in this dust-free hood.

Length of sample: Each of thirteen channels was sampled on total mode for 0.3 minute.

Sample rate: 283 cc/min

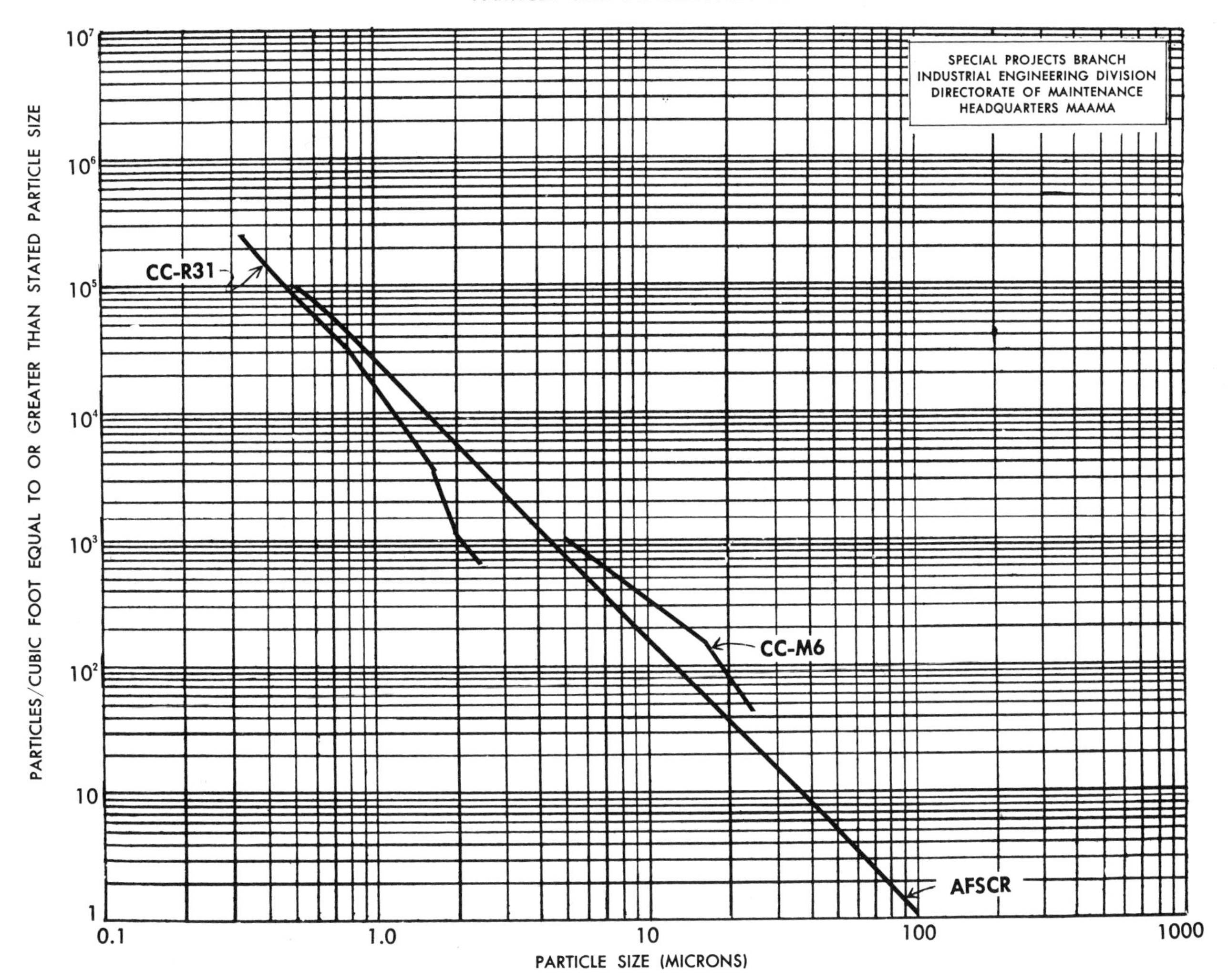

FIGURE 2-46.

Observations on Curve: This curve is essentially parallel to CC-R19 and CC-R20.

Curve CC-R22 (Figure 2-41)

Time: 1603 hours

Place: Hangar S, Change Room leading to Class 6 and Class 10 Clean Rooms

Sample Characteristics

Height of sample: 32 inches from floor

Length of sample: Each of thirteen channels was sampled on total mode for 0.3 minute.

Sample rate: 283 cc/min

Observations on Curve: There is a definite change in slope of the curve between 1.0 and 2.0 microns. The curve is essentially linear and parallel to the AFSCR curve in the larger particle size range. The curve is essentially linear and deviates from the AFSCR curve in the smaller particle size range. This slope of the curve is similar to the slope of previous curves.

Curve CC-R23 (Figure 2-41)

Time: 1610 hours

Place: Same as for CC-R22, except that two peo-

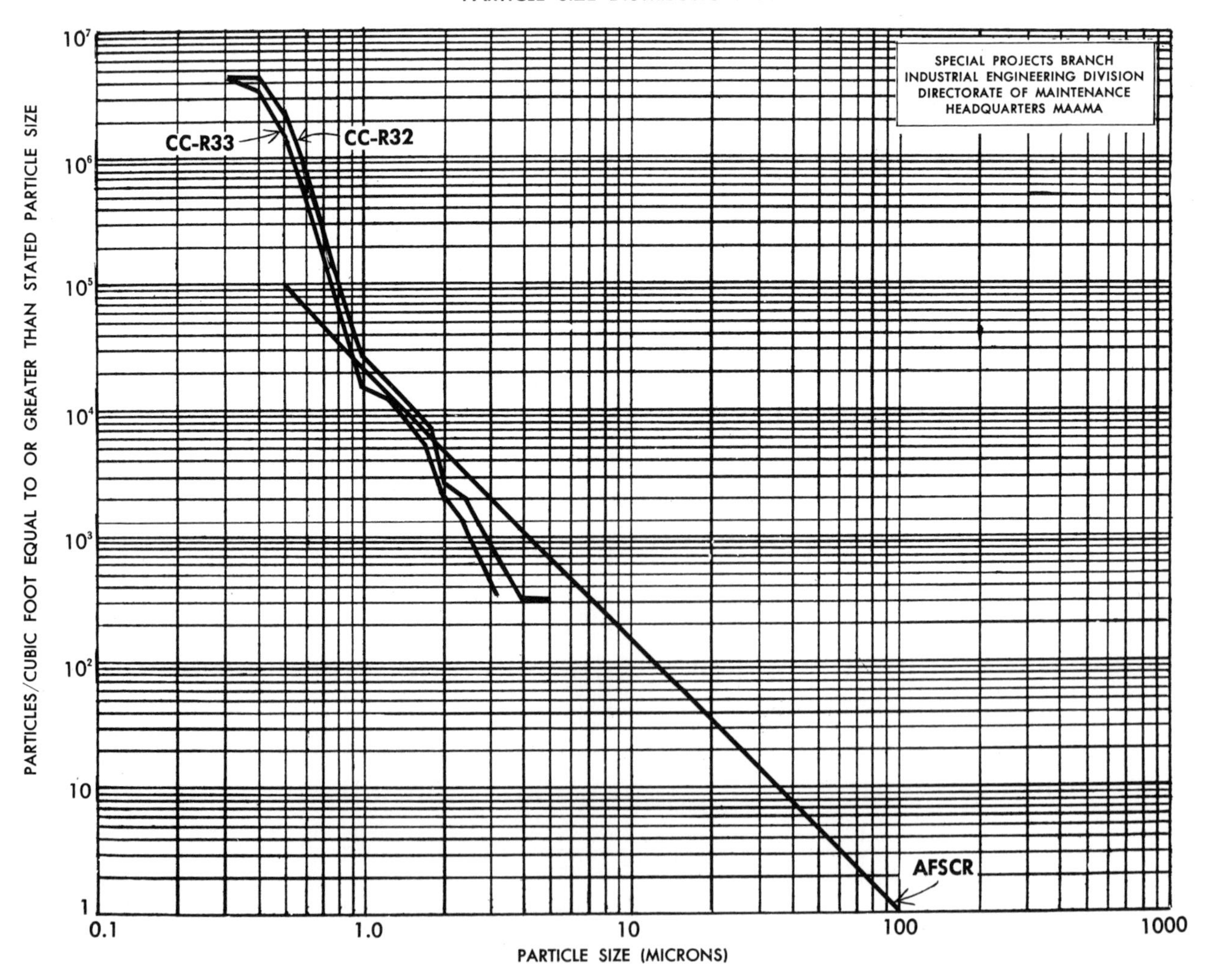

FIGURE 2-47.

ple were changing near the particle counter. All other observations are the same as for CC-R22.

Curve CC-R24 (Figure 2-42)

Time: 1626 hours

Place: Hangar S, hallway outside the Change Room and Class 6 Clean Room. There was continual traffic within 2 feet of the counter. The hallway has no ceiling except the roof of the hangar. There is a continuous outside air flow through the hangar and hallway.

Sample Characteristics: Same as for CC-R22.

Observations on Curve: There is a definite change in the slope of the curve in the range of 1.0 to 1.3 microns. The slope of the curve for the larger particles is exactly parallel to the AFSCR curve. The slope of the curve for the smaller particles is exactly parallel to CC-R22.

Curve CC-R25 (Figure 2-42)

Time: 1631 hours

All observations are the same as for CC-R24.

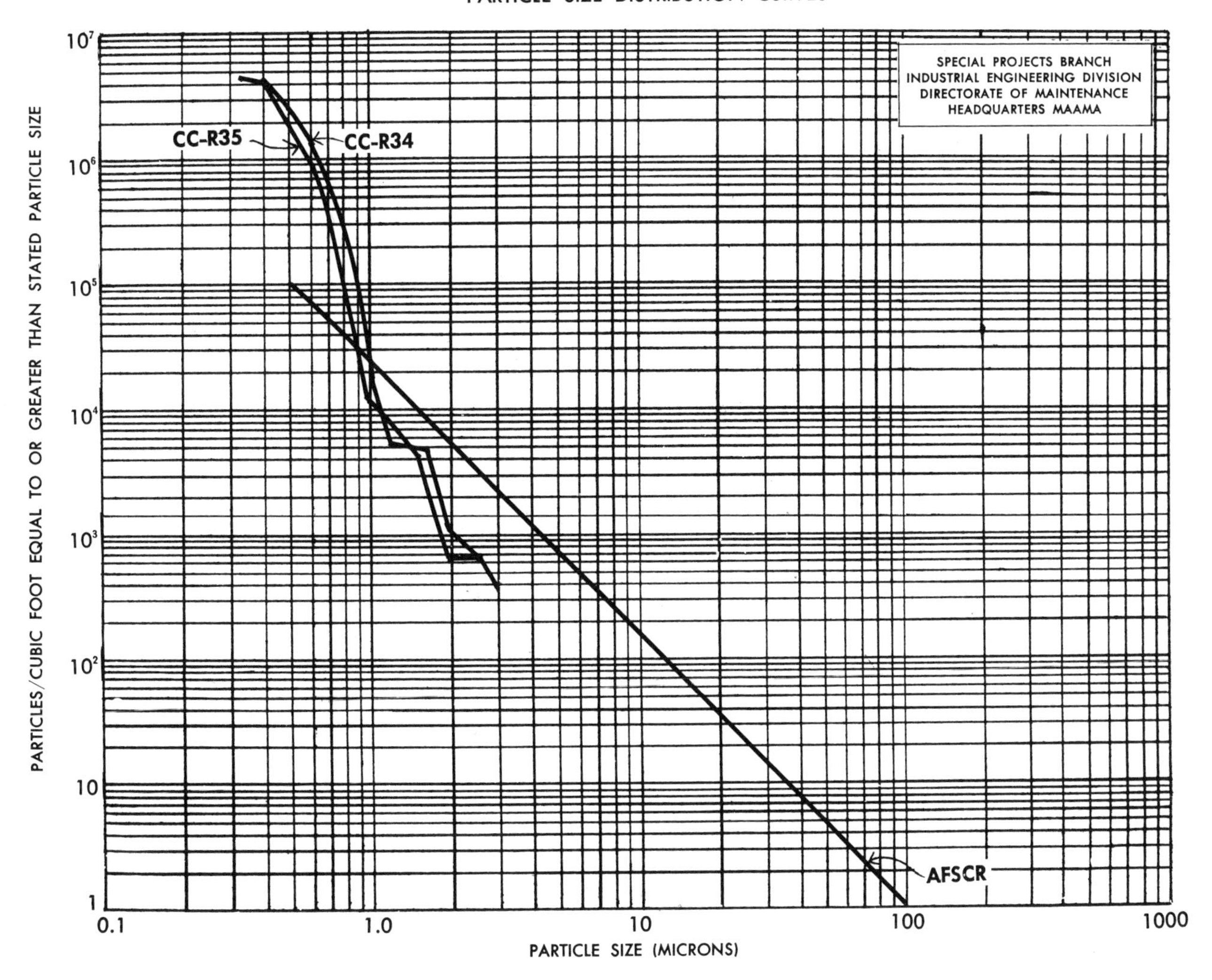

FIGURE 2-48.

Curve CC-M5 (Figure 2-42)
Time: 1615 hours
The particle count sample was taken at the same location as for CC-R24 and CC-R25.
Sample Characteristics: Same as for CC-M4.
Observations on Curve: This curve is essentially parallel to the AFSCR curve.

Curve CC-R26 (Figure 2-43)
Time: 1650 hours
Place: East apron of Hangar S, wind direction approximately 10 to 15 mph from the north.

Sample Characteristics
Height of sample: 32 inches from ground
Length of sample: Each of thirteen channels was sampled on total mode for 0.3 minute.
Sample rate: 283 cc/min
Observations on Curve: There appears to be a definite trend toward a changing slope in the 1.0- to 2.0-micron particle size range. The low count in this range plus the high multiplication factor being used for the short time duration for each sample did not allow full estimation of the curve on the large particle size

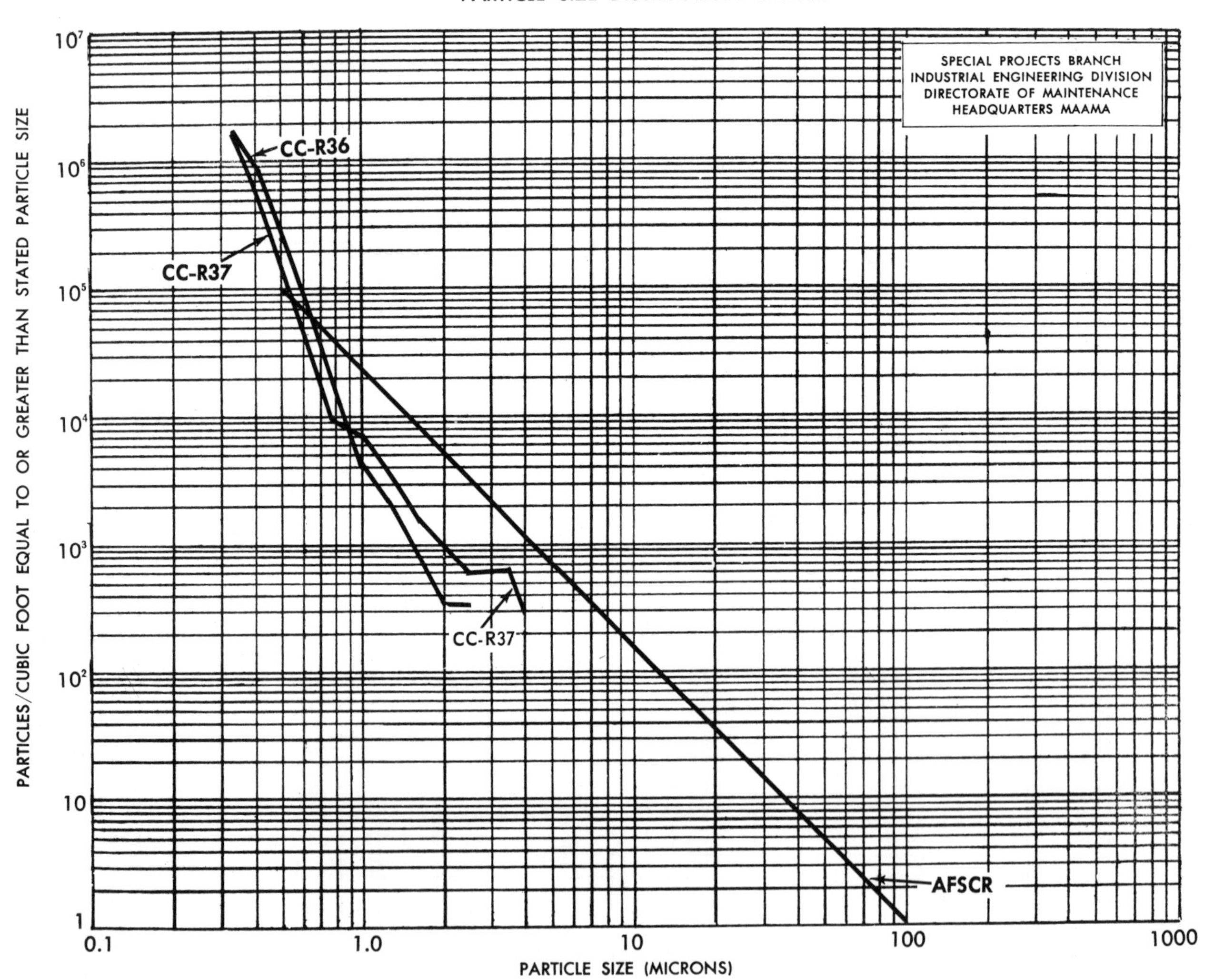

FIGURE 2-49.

range. The curve from 1.6 to 2.5 microns tends to be essentially parallel to the AFSCR curve. The slope of the curve in the smaller particle size range is essentially linear and deviates from the AFSCR curve.

Curve CC-R27 (*Figure 2-43*)
Time: 1655 hours
All observations are the same as for CC-R26.

Curve CC-R28 (*Figure 2-43*)
Time: 1700 hours
All observations on this curve are the same as for CC-R26.

Curve CC-R29 (*Figure 2-44*)
Time: 1707 hours
All observations are the same as for CC-R26.

Curve CC-R30 (*Figure 2-45*)
Time: 1030 hours
Place: Complex 34 Saturn Gantry (Service Structure) at 116-foot level. There was a 15- to 20-mph wind from the northeast (wind direction parallel to beach).

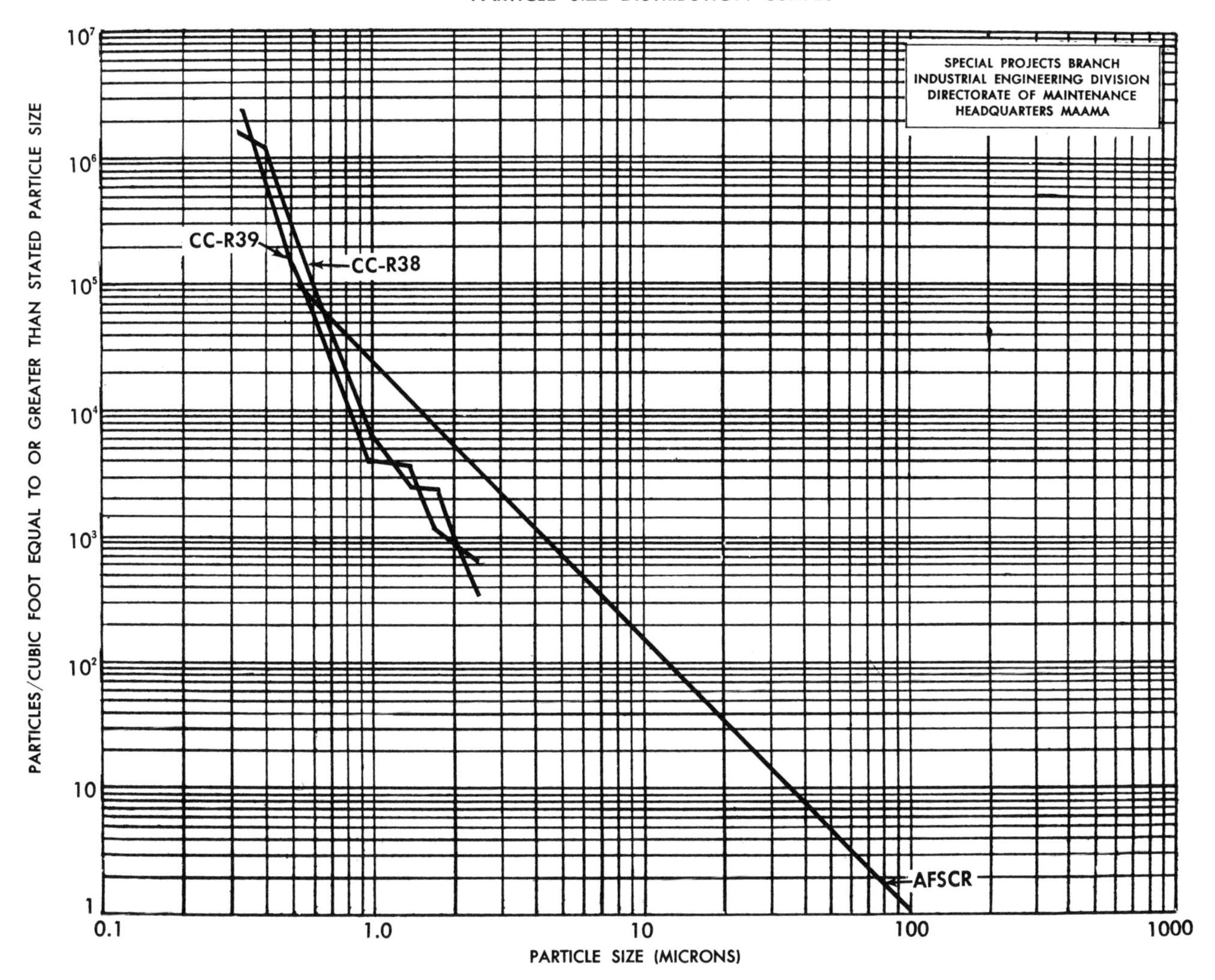

FIGURE 2-50.

Sample Characteristics
Height of sample: 32 inches from the deck
Length of sample: Each of thirteen channels was sampled on total mode for 0.3 minute.
Sample rate: 283 cc/min
Observations on Curve: This curve is essentially linear and parallel to the PTS and AFSCR curves in all particle size ranges. No deviation from Stokes' law is noted in the smaller particle size ranges.

Curve CC-R31 (*Figure 2-46*)
Time: 1035 hours
All observations are the same as for CC-R29.

Curve CC-M6 (*Figure 2-46*)
Time: 1035 hours
Place: Same as for CC-R30 and CC-R31
Sample Characteristics: Same as for CC-M4
Observations on Curve: Same as for CC-M4

Curve CC-R32 (*Figure 2-47*)
Time: 1130 hours
Place: Complex 34 Block House Control Center (10 feet from entrance stairway).
Sample Characteristics: Same as for CC-R30.
Observations on Curve: There is a definite change in the slope of the curve at approxi-

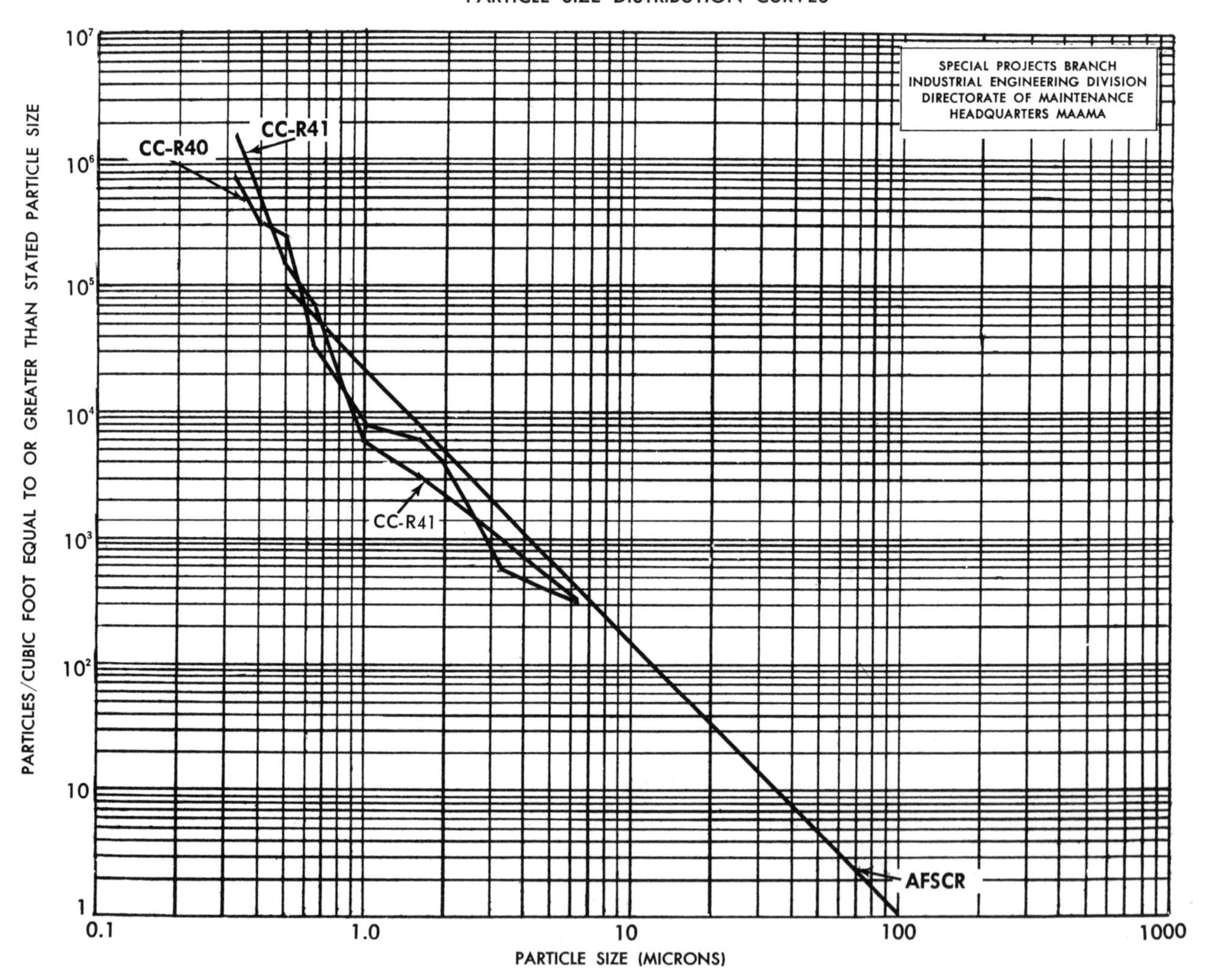

FIGURE 2-51.

mately 1.0 micron. The slope of the curve for particles larger than 1.0 micron is essentially linear and parallel to the AFSCR curve. The slope of the curve for the smaller particle size range is essentially linear but deviates from the AFSCR curve.

Curve CC-R33 (*Figure 2-47*)
Time: 1137 hours
All observations are the same as for CC-R32.

Curve CC-R34 (*Figure 2-48*)
Time: 1145 hours
Place: Complex 34 Block House Control Center (data tapes non-operative)
All observations are the same as for CC-R32.

Curve CC-R35 (*Figure 2-48*)
Time: 1155 hours
All observations are the same as for CC-R32.

Curve CC-R36 (*Figure 2-49*)
Time: 1415 hours
Place: Physical Standards Bldg., Dimensional Lab

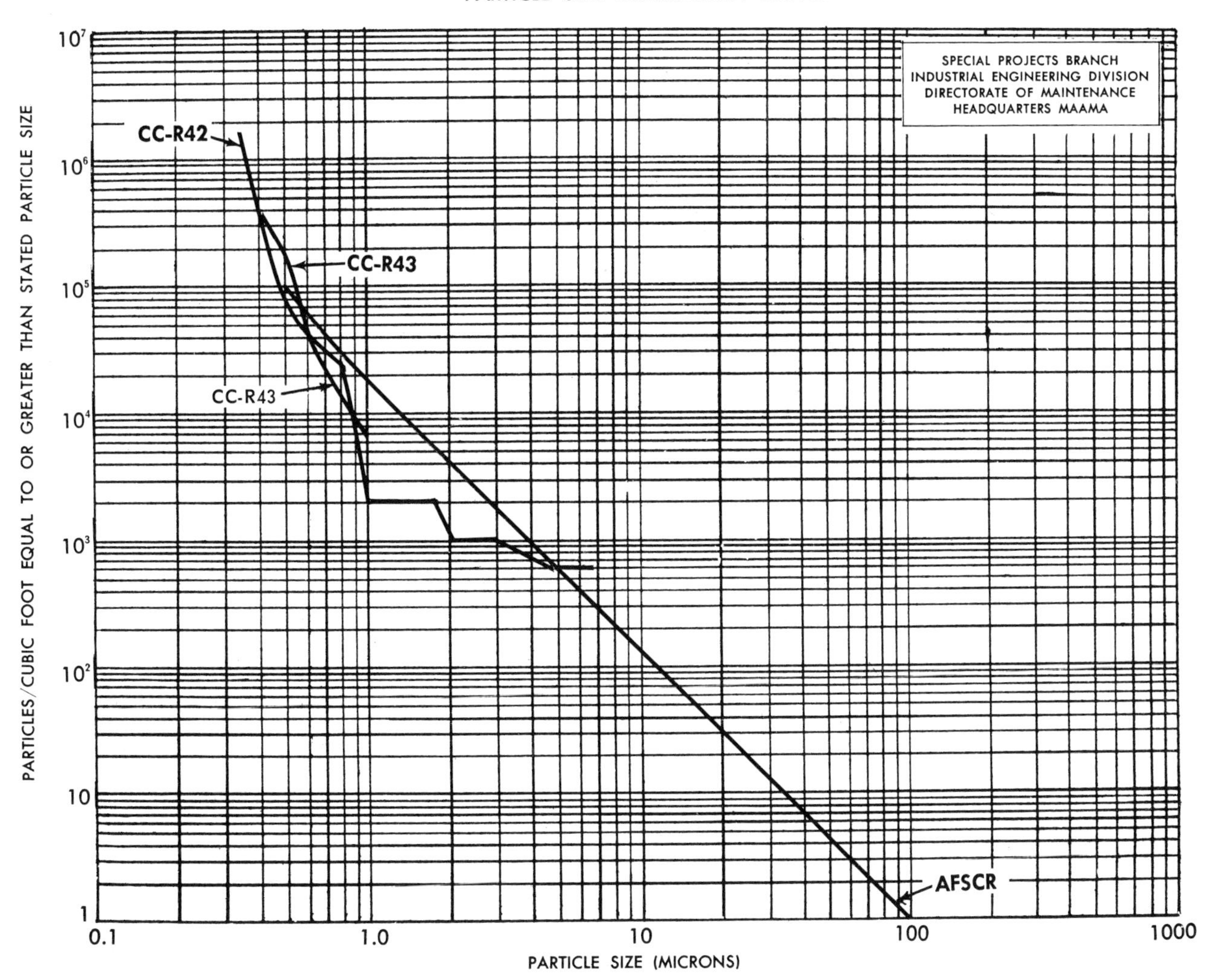

FIGURE 2-52.

Sample Characteristics

Height of sample: 32 inches from floor

Length of sample: Each of thirteen channels was sampled on total mode for 0.3 minute.

Sample rate: 283 cc/min

Observations on Curve: There is a definite change in the slope of the curve at approximately 1.0 micron. The slope of the curve is essentially parallel to the AFSCR curve in the larger particle size range. The curve is essentially linear and deviates from the AFSCR curve in the smaller particle size range.

Curve CC-R37 (*Figure 2-49*)

Time: 1420 hours

All observations are the same as for CC-R36.

Curve CC-R38 (*Figure 2-50*)

Time: 1430 hours

Place: Physical Standards Bldg., Electromechanical Lab

All observations are the same as for CC-R36.

Curve CC-R39 (*Figure 2-50*)

Time: 1440 hours

All observations are the same as for CC-R36.

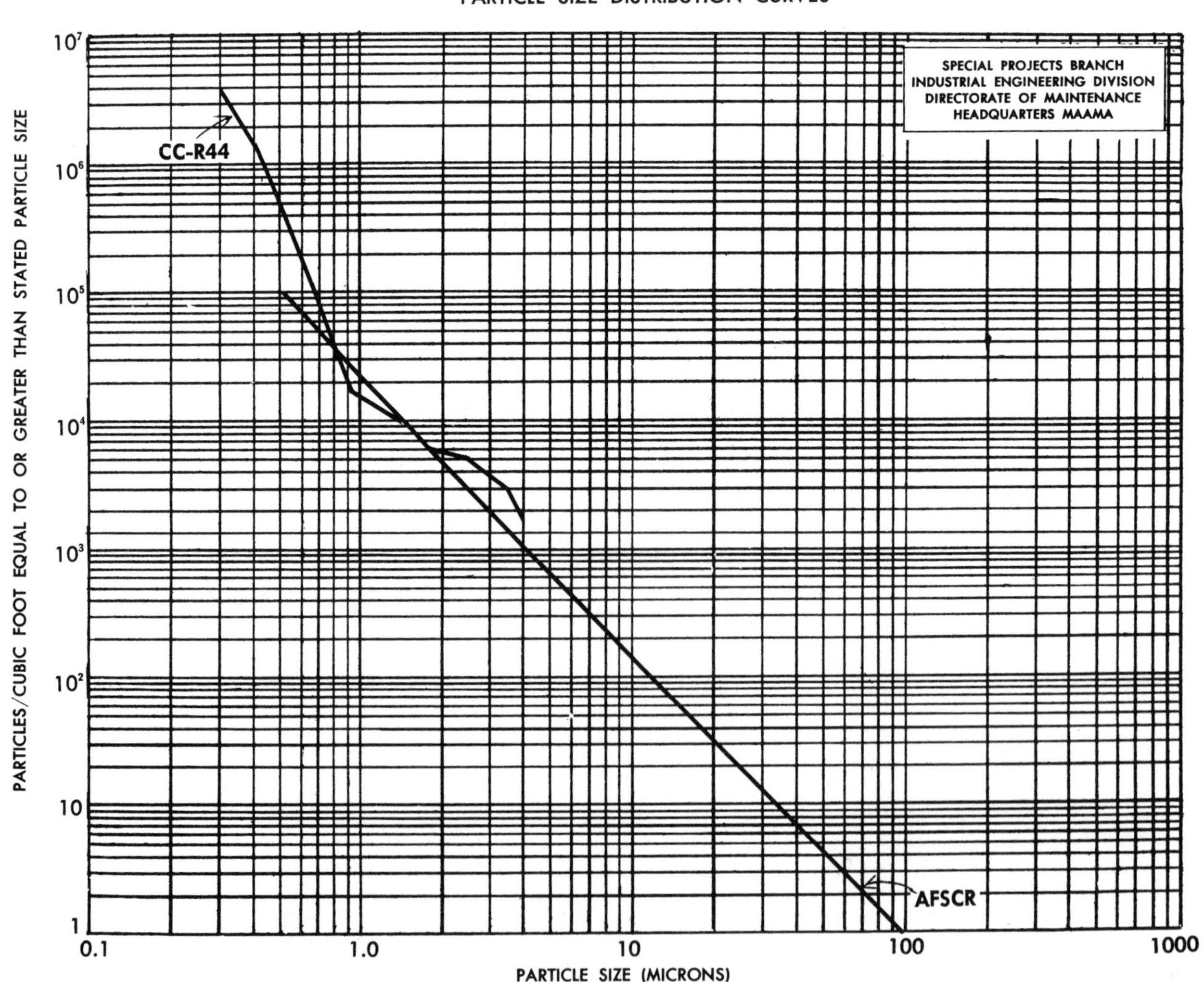

FIGURE 2-53.

Curve CC-R40 (*Figure 2-51*)
Time: 1455 hours
Place: Physical Standards Bldg., Fuel and Chemical Lab (14 by 20 feet with a partition between, two Whitfield benches operating)
Sample Characteristics: Same as for CC-R36.
Observations on Curve: There is a definite change in the slope of the curve at approximately 1.0 micron. The curve is essentially parallel to the AFSCR curve in the larger particle size range. The curve is essentially linear and deviates from the AFSCR curve in the smaller particle size range.

Curve CC-R41 (*Figure 2-51*)
Time: 1500 hours
All observations are the same as for CC-R40.

Curve CC-R42 (*Figure 2-52*)
Time: 1505 hours
All observations are the same as for CC-R40.

Curve CC-R43 (*Figure 2-52*)
Time 1510 hours
All observations are the same as for CC-R40.

Curve CC-R44 (*Figure 2-53*)
Time: 1520 hours

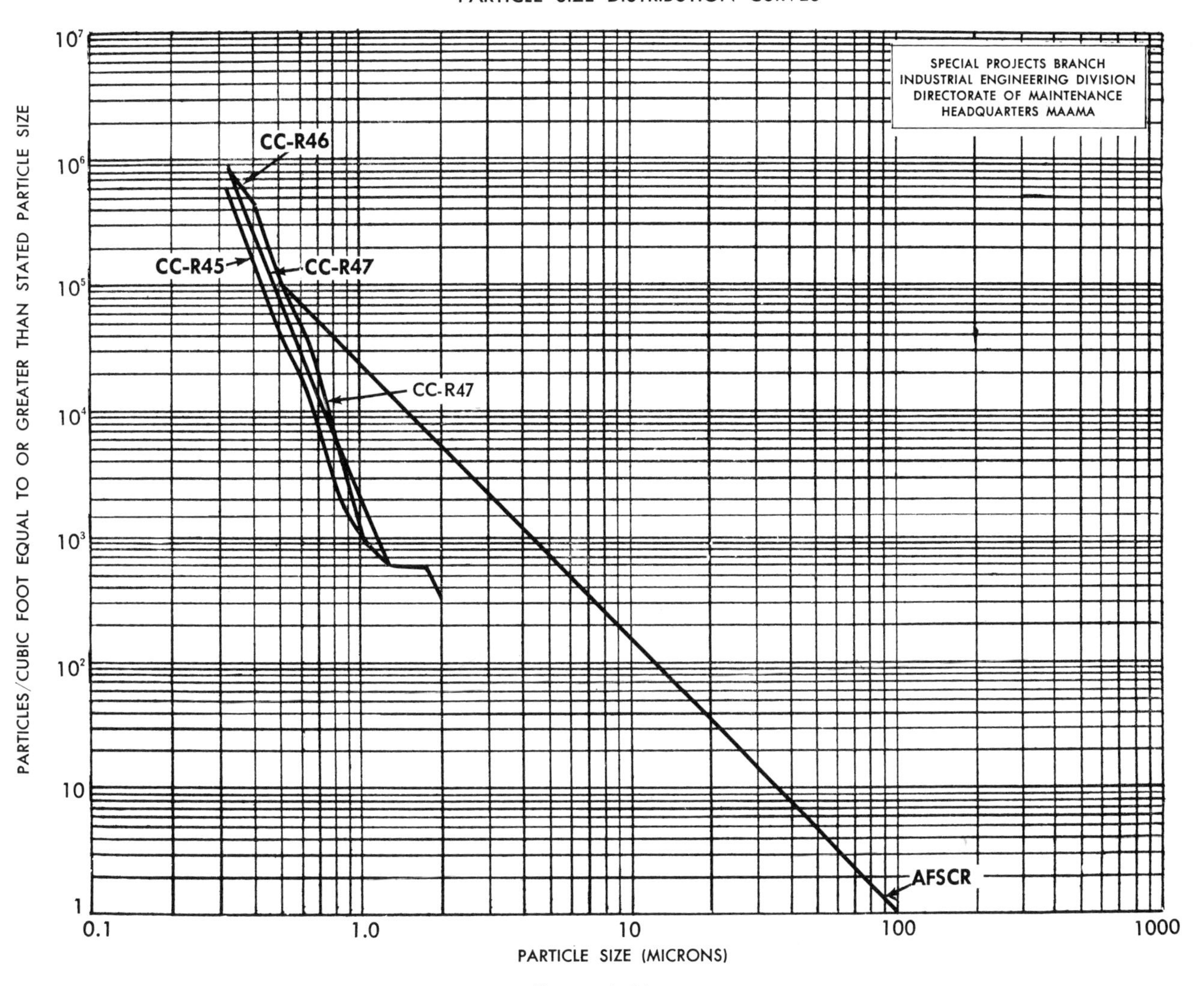

FIGURE 2-54.

Place: Physical Standards Building, Test Oxidizers, Room 5
Sample Characteristics: Same as for CC-R40.
Observations on Curve: There is a definite change in the slope of the curve at 1 micron. The curve is essentially parallel to the AFSCR curve in the larger particle size range. The curve is essentially linear and deviates from the AFSCR curve in the smaller size range.

Curve CC-R45 (*Figure 2-54*)
Time: 1600 hours
Place: Water Pump Station No. 1, LOX Cleaning Clean Room (room was "at rest" prior to sampling)
Sample Characteristics
Height of sample: 32 inches from floor
Length of sample: Each of thirteen channels was sampled on total mode for 0.3 minute.
Sample rate: 283 cc/min
Observations on Curve: There was a definite change in the slope of the curve in the 1.0- to 1.3-micron size range. The slope of the curve for the larger particles was essentially parallel to the AFSCR curve. The curve for the smaller particles was essentially linear and deviates from the AFSCR curve.

Curve CC-R46 (*Figure 2-54*)
Time: 1605 hours
All observations are the same as for CC-R45.

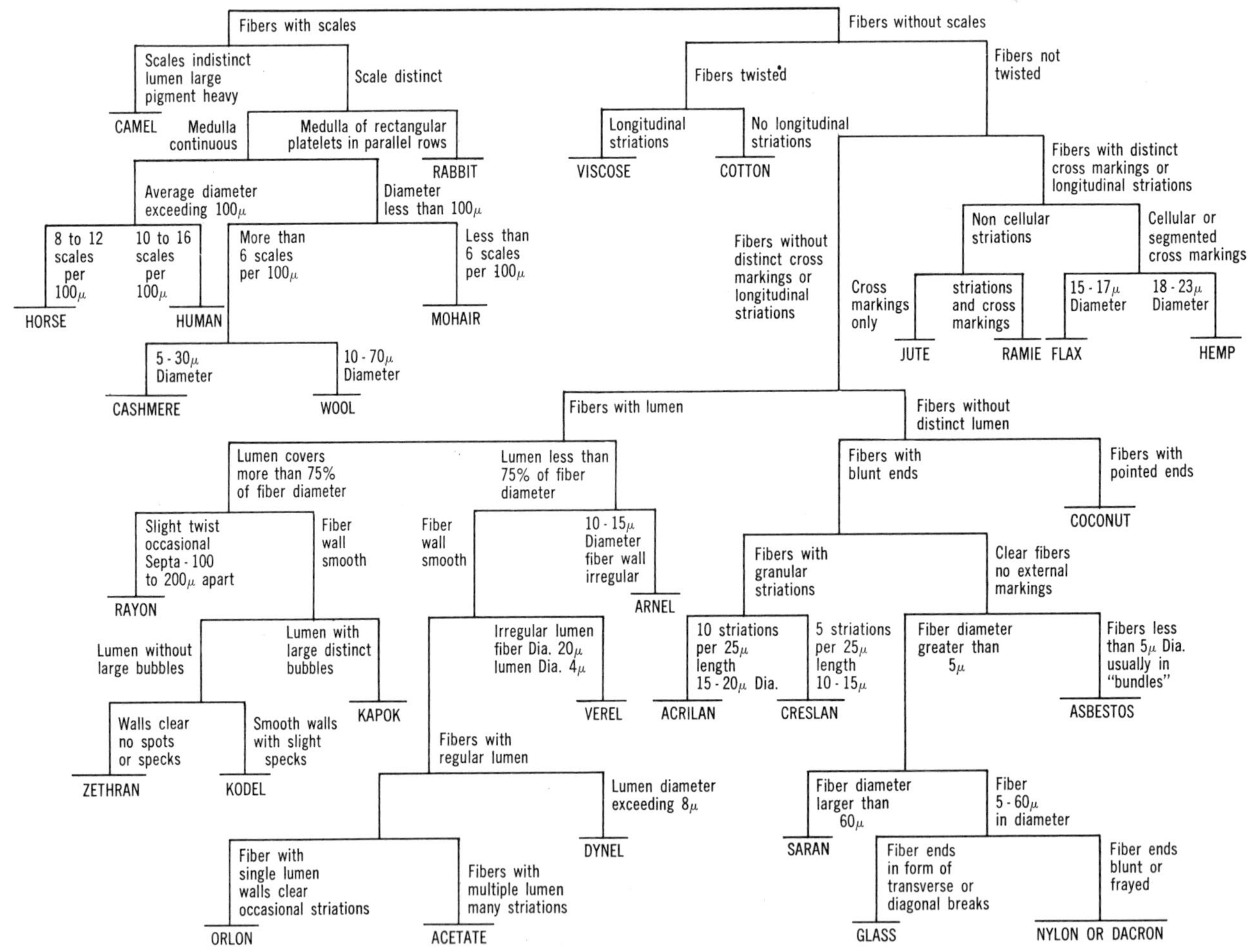

FIGURE 2-55. Relationship between aerosol concentration and rate of particle deposition. *Courtesy Armour Research Foundation*

Curve CC-R47 (Figure 2-54)
Time: 1610 hours
All observations are the same as for CC-R45.

Other Studies

The normal content of particle contamination in the air may vary from a few hundred particles per cubic foot to several million particles per cubic foot. The size of particles can reach approximately 50 microns even in a controlled clean room. Figure 2-55 shows some expected deposition rates on horizontal surfaces. This curve will give an idea of what type of deposition one might expect once he has a reasonable idea of the concentration of the material in the air. This particular curve was drawn for particles covering the general atmospheric dust size distribution of 1 to 6 microns. When parts are exposed for any appreciable period of time, the fallout can increase by a very sizable amount. Note that the abscissa on this curve describes a logarithmic scale in number of particles per square millimeter per minute. The usefulness of the clean air supply is obvious from the data shown.

Oral Emissions from Personnel

Personnel can contribute as sources of contamination. Oral and nasal emissions present serious problems to corrodible products when these vapor droplets deposit on sensitive parts. As an example, consider the emissions shown in Figures 2-56, 2-57, and 2-58. It can readily be seen that such emissions should be prevented from reaching sensitive items. They are but a small part of the total airborne contaminants present in clean rooms.

The Contamination Index (10) for various personnel activities ranges anywhere from 100,000 particles per minute to 30,000,000 particles per minute 0.3 microns in size and larger. An individual standing or sitting with no movement emits 100,000 particles per minute. A person sitting with light head, hand and forearm movement emits 500,000 particles per minute. Sitting with average body and arm movement and some toe tapping produces 1,000,000 particles per minute. Changing positions from sitting to standing gives off 2,500,000 particles per minute. Slow walking, two miles per hour, emits 5,000,000 particles per minute while average walking at 3.57 miles per hour produces 7,500,000 particles per minute and fast walking at five miles per hour produces 10,000,000 particles per minute. Climbing stairs produces particles at the same rate as fast walking. Calisthenics will produce from 15,000,000 to 30,000,000 particles per minute. These indices are estimations from collected data.

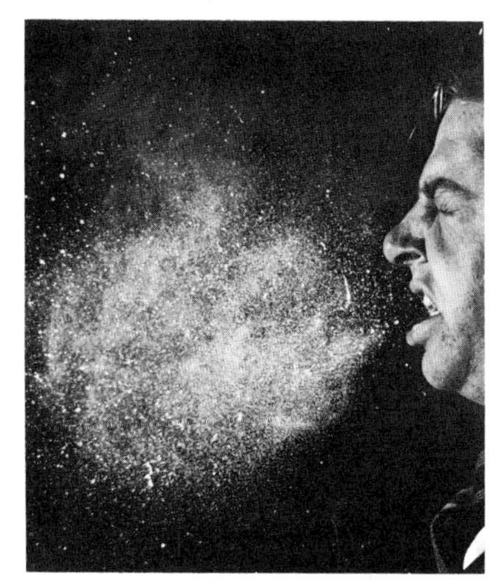

FIGURE 2-56. A violent, unstifled sneeze, completed, shows droplet dispersion. Photos taken with intense 1/30,000-second flash against dark background. *Courtesy Air Engineering*

FIGURE 2-57. Enunciating the letter "F." Consonants are more difficult than vowels to pronounce without forming droplets. Note larger droplets. *Courtesy Air Engineering*

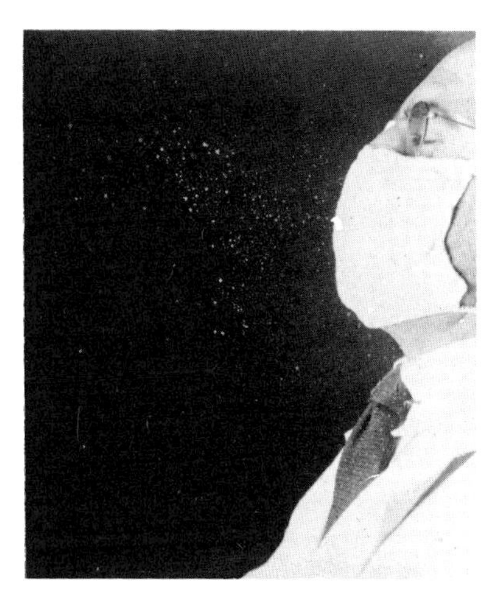

FIGURE 2-58. A sneeze through a mask of the type worn by surgeons. Mask was constructed of a layer of cotton flannel between two layers of muslin. *Courtesy Air Engineering*

REFERENCES

1. RILLINGS, K. W. and WILLIAMSEN, C. T. *Micro Particle Contamination in Aerospace Components and Facilities.* ADR-13-04-61.0. Bethpage, N.Y.: Grumman Aircraft Engineering Corp., December 1961.

2. AUSTIN, 1/LT. PHILIP R. *Contamination Control Is Your Job.* Olmsted AFB, Pa.: MAMES, April 1963.

3. LIEBERMAN, ALVIN. "Cleanliness versus Need." *Conference on Clean Room Specifications.* SCR-652, pp. 18-19. Office of Technical Services, Department of Commerce, Washington, D.C., April 1963.

4. LIEBERMAN, ALVIN. *Contamination Effects Study.* ARF 3216-4. Chicago, Ill.: Armour Research Foundation, October, 1962. Prepared for Sandia Corp., Albuquerque, N. Mex.

5. LAPPLE, CHARLES E. "The Little Things in Life." *Stanford Research Institute Journal,* Vol. 5, pp. 94-102 (3rd quarter, 1961).

6. ORR, CLYDE, JR., and DALLA VALLE, J. M. *Fine Particle Measurement.* New York, N.Y.: Macmillan, 1960.

7. AUSTIN, 1/LT. PHILIP R. *Size Distribution Relationships for Airborne Particulate Matter.* Report 17.0002.04.01. Olmsted AFB, Pa.: MAMES, April 1963.

8. AUSTIN, 1/LT. PHILIP R. *Size Distribution Relationships for Airborne Particulate Matter.* Report 17.0003.04.02. Olmsted AFB, Pa.: MAMES, July 1963.

9. *U. S. Air Force Technical Order 00-25-203, Standards and Guidelines for the Design and Operation of Clean Rooms and Clean Work Stations.* Office of Technical Services, Department of Commerce, Washington, D.C., July 1963.

10. AUSTIN, PHILIP R. *Austin's Contamination Index.* Middletown, Pa.; Contamination Control Lectures, August 1964.

Chapter 3. *Filtration*

Introduction

Many different types of air-cleaning equipment are available. In most cases this equipment has been designed for special purposes, such as the removal of zinc fumes with particle sizes of less than 0.1 micron or particles of chemical sprays such as acid mists. Physical methods involved in air cleaning include (1) gravitational methods, (2) inertial methods, (3) filtration, (4) washing, and (5) electrostatic precipitation. In general, most air-cleaning equipment will remove a good portion of the total weight of particulate matter present. With gross contamination this type of removal is adequate, but for clean rooms it will hardly suffice. On a weight basis, 0.1-micron particles account for less than 1% of all the particulate matter in the air. On a particle-count basis, however, they account for roughly 65% of the number of particles(*1*). Recent studies, as shown in Figures 2-6 through 2-54, indicate this per cent value to be higher. The requirements of clean rooms can hardly be satisfied by capturing a good percentage of the weight of particles in the air. In a clean room we wish to obtain the cleanest air possible. Everything that enters a clean room is dirty. The people, the tools, and the equipment are dirty. Even if our critical components are packaged, the package is dirty. Since air makes up the greatest volume of the clean room, it would seem logical to get it as clean as possible. The obvious solution is to get the most efficiently filtered air possible.

Since maximal removal of micron-size particles from the air is required in clean rooms, filtration should be used. It is by far the most efficient and practical method of removing small particles from the air. The savings from the purchase of a less-efficient filtering system are not enough to justify less than the best filtration. If it is desired to limit particles in a clean room by specifying a maximum count, high-efficiency particulate air (HEPA)[1] filters are a must. Air Force experience pointed out that, when other types of filters were employed, the count of particles in the submicron and low-micron ranges reached gigantic porportions (see Figures 2-6 through 2-54). The larger particles held to the size-distribution relationship. This was due to the generation and reintroduction of the smaller particles into the clean room. These particles were never captured by the filtration system. Had high-efficiency particulate filters been employed, it would have been possible to remove these particles and hold the count to the particle size-distribution relationship.

The general principles of air filtration will now be discussed briefly. For more detailed presentation of theory, the publications of La Mer *et al.*(*2*) and of Green and Lane (*3*) are recommended.

Very few practical air filters depend on screening or sieving action to remove the suspended material. Since the interstices of a screening-type filter must necessarily be smaller than the smallest particle to be removed, the resistance to air flow is high. As the surface becomes covered with collected material, resistance rises, and ultimately air flow stops as all the interstices become plugged. All practical aerosol filters consist of randomly oriented fibers of various materials placed in such a manner that most of the open spaces or interstices are much larger than the diameter of the particles to be removed. The filtering action depends on the particles

[1] The name coined by the U. S. Atomic Energy Commission for filters that are at least 99.97% efficient by volume on 0.3-micron particles (dioctyl phthalate test).

contacting and adhering to the fibers or collecting surface.

Mechanisms of Filtration[2]

There are several mechanisms that may cause suspended particles to impact on the fibers. These include (1) direct interception, (2) deposition in accordance with Stokes' law, (3) inertial effect, (4) diffusion, and (5) electrostatic effect. Direct interception and deposition have less effect in removing particles in filter than the latter three mechanisms.

The first mechanism, direct interception, is restricted to particles whose centers remain in a given streamline. It occurs if the particles are too large to show appreciable Brownian motion but are also too small to be appreciably subject to Stokes' law. Brownian motion is the motion imparted to submicron particles by the random motion of gas molecules of air. This motion will cause some of the particles to collide with filter fibers.

The second mechanism is settling according to Stokes' law governing rate of fall. If a particle is large enough, it will not coincide with any streamline in the air flow but will be deposited on the upper surfaces of the filter fibers. The rate of deposition will vary with particle size, concentration, and the total area that the upper surfaces of the fibers project into the horizontal plane. The rate of fall of particles less than 0.3 micron in diameter is so low that this mechanism is probably negligible in removing small particles in filters.

The third mechanism that will cause particles to collect on the filter fibers is the inertial effect. The forces of impaction are generally more effective for collection of particles 1 micron in diameter and larger. As air flows through a filter, it must continually change direction to permit flow around the randomly oriented filter fibers. As a result of inertial effects, those particles with sufficient mass continue in their original paths and strike the filter fiber despite the change in the path of the air flow. Other micro-aerodynamic forces may also be involved in this method of impaction. Tests with particulates 1 to 5 microns in diameter have shown that impaction of these sizes on fibers is somewhat improved as air velocity is increased through the filter material(*5*). This is true because the inertial force is directly proportional to the square of air velocity and inversely proportional to the radius of curvature of the air stream. It also has been found that decreasing the fiber diameter increases the collection efficiency(*6*).

The fourth mechanism, diffusion, pertains primarily to small-particulate aerosols. It accounts for the impaction of almost all particles having a diameter of less than 0.3 micron. Fine particles of this magnitude diffuse in a manner similar to molecular diffusion, and in the case of passage through a filter they are further subject to the laws governing isotropic turbulence which occurs when the eddying motion is randomly distributed(7). Contrary to the action with larger particles, a decrease in air velocity through the filter increases the deposition of small particles, since they remain within the filter configuration a long time. This results in greater opportunities for impaction by the diffusion process.

Still another process by which particles are deposited is by the electrostatic charge which may be present on the filters and particles when air at low humidity passes over the fibers. Certain types of filters may acquire both positive and negative electrostatic charges in various areas of the filter mass. These charges may be strong forces in the removal of particles from an air stream.

For the most efficient filter, it is desirable to have the fiber diameter less than the diameter of the smallest particles to be removed from the air. The use of small-diameter fibers increases greatly the deposition area of a filter and at the same time increases the free space, thereby reducing resistance to air flow. Small fibers require support to prevent their being packed together, causing increased resistance. This is usually overcome by the use of a binder which holds the fibers in position. This allows the particles to deposit on the inner fibers of the filter, thereby providing greater loading capacity.

After particles are deposited, they are held in place by electrostatic and adhesive forces between the particles and the fibers. The ability of particles to remain on fibers depends more on the nature of the adhesive force than on fiber size or particle size, until particle agglomerates become large enough that their cross sections produce air resistance sufficient for detachment.

[2] Abstracted and condensed from reference *4*.

A plot of efficiency versus particle size for submicron and micron-size particles will produce two curves. The point at which these curves intersect would be the size most difficult to collect. This point appears to be around 0.3 micron. Investigations have also shown that the most numerous particles in air of a given size occur in this range.

Development of the CWS[3] Filter

Prior to 1930, little thought had been given to air filtration. Since no market existed for air-filtering devices, research in the field was meager. Filtration of larger particles (above 5 microns) was not considered a problem. The majority of particles in the air are in the range from 0.2 to 1 micron, however. Removal of these particles first became necessary for protection of personnel against poisonous dusts and mists. This was a result of advanced developments in chemical and bacteriological warfare. High removal efficiency was essential, since a relatively small dose could harm or kill an individual.

After extensive research by the Chemical Warfare Service during World War II to develop an improved gas mask filter, a filter paper was developed which was almost 100% efficient by volume on submicron-size particles. (Out of this work came a formulation containing short-fiber asbestos and cellulose, later known variously as CWS-6, CC-6, and AEC-1.) Since it was classified as defense information, its use was limited to gas masks and associated types of filtration equipment. During the development of the first atomic bomb, the Manhattan Project found itself with a similar filtration problem, the capture of radioactive dust. Almost all this dust had to be captured so that a lethal radiation dose would not be generated. The Manhattan Project investigated the Chemical Warfare Service filter and was the first to use it for area filtration. With additional research the Atomic Energy Commission developed it into a high-efficiency filter for removal of fine particles from large volumes of air. In order to evaluate the filter and to establish production standards, a 0.3-micron-diameter dioctyl phthalate (DOP) aerosol penetration test was adopted as standard test.

In recent years, filter of a glass fiber and asbestos has been favored because of improved fire resistance. This filter also has improved moisture resistance, greater strength, and equal or better retention efficiency when compared to the former filters.

High-efficiency filters are constructed of a frame, the filter medium (filter paper), separators, adhesive, and gasket material. The filter paper is pleated accordion fashion, and a corrugated separator is inserted in each fold. These separators allow air to flow up into the pleats and through the filter medium. The original Atomic Energy Commission filter was constructed of a wooden frame with cardboard separators and cellulose filter material. The chief disadvantage of this construction was that it was not fireproof. New fireproof filter designs are available that have metal frames and separators and glass fiber filter material. Various special types of filters are available which resist extreme conditions of temperature, humidity, corrosion, and pressure.

The key to efficient filtration is the filter paper which contains submicron-size asbestos fibers evenly distributed throughout the paper. This paper has the ability to capture submicron-size particles with low air-flow resistance. A filter 2 feet square and 11½ inches deep has approximately 250 sq ft of filtering surface. This unit is rated at 1000 cfm.

Filter efficiency will be greater if the filter is operated at less than rated capacity. A good filter installation will allow this. The exact life of the filters depends on the amount of particulate matter being filtered and on the degree of prefiltering employed. In general, prefiltered systems run for 8000 to 20,000 hours between changes. High-efficiency particulate filters are also referred to in the trade as absolute, super-interception, and HEPA filters.

Methods for Rating the Efficiency of Air Filters[4]

Methods for testing the efficiency of air filters vary widely. These tests are not directly comparable, and therefore care must be exercised in evaluating filters on the basis of uncorrelated test ratings. Any efficiency test for air filters measures the percentage of particulate matter in air which is collected by the filter. This percenage may be ex-

[3] Chemical Warfare Service.

[4] Abstracted from Brochure No. 710A, dated November 25, 1958, prepared by the Cambridge Filter Corp., Syracuse, New York.

pressed on the basis of weight, number, discoloration effect, or by other means.

The size and composition of the particulates in air may have as much effect on the efficiency as does the manner in which the test is conducted. When a particular type of dust or dirt is employed, it must be specified. Any test on prepared test dusts is only as good as the means employed to disperse the dust during the test. Fine dust, particularly carbon black, tends to conglomerate into much larger particles. No matter what the ultimate particle size of the dust, the test filter will be required to remove only agglomerates if the dispersal mechanism is not adequate.

One fundamental objection to tests employing prepared dusts is that air filters normally are called upon to remove atmospheric dust, which is much finer than any test dust yet devised.

Weight Tests[5]

Filter weight efficiency or arrestance tests compare the weight of a test dust which passes through a filter with the weight of dust fed into the duct ahead of the filter. In considering any weight test, it must be remembered that, spherical particles being assumed, the weight of a solid particle varies as the cube of its diameter. Therefore, when filtering a dust in which the size of particle varies widely, as it does in almost all natural materials, it is necessary to remove only a few of the larger particles in order to show high weight efficiency. For example, suppose that a certain dust is made up of particles 10 microns and 1 micron in diameter, in the ratio of one 10-micron particle for each one hundred 1-micron particles. Then it will be necessary to remove only the few 10-micron particles in order to be 90% efficient on a weight test, although the filter is only 1% efficient on a particle count basis.

ASHRAE[6] Code Tests

The ASHRAE Code Test was adopted in 1933 (*ASHRAE Transactions,* Vol. 39, 1933, p. 225). Although many modifications have been suggested in the ASHRAE literature, none of these have been approved by the Technical Air Cleaning Committee of the ASHRAE. The 1933 test consists in injecting a known quantity of a prepared dust (containing 50% by weight of powdered lampblack and 50% by weight of ashes from a Pocohontas coal, screened to pass 200 mesh) into the air supplied to the filter. The quantity of dust in the cleaned air is determined by extracting (by filtration through a porous crucible) the dust from a known quantity of air and weighing it.

AFI Code Test

Section 1 of the Air Filter Institute Code Test is somewhat similar. In this test a prepared dust is employed containing 72% by weight of "Standardized Air Cleaner Test Dust Fine" (Arizona road dust), 25% by weight of "K-1 Carbon Black," and 3% by weight of "No. 7 cotton linters ground in a Wiley mill with 4-millimeter screen." A known weight of this dust is aspirated into the air stream ahead of the filter being tested, and the entire air stream beyond the filter is passed through what AFI calls the "absolute filter." This is not a true absolute filter but a glass mat which is approximately 80% to 85% efficient on a particle-count basis. It is assumed that all the dust passing the test filter is captured by the glass mat, and the weight gain of this filter is therefore a measure of the penetration of the test filter.

Atmospheric Dust Weight Test

Weight tests can also be performed on air filters with atmospheric dust, although these values for efficiency are almost never found in manufacturers' literature. One reason is that, because of the low weight concentration of dust in the atmosphere, days or weeks are necessary in order to collect enough dust to weigh accurately. Perhaps a more important reason is that, because of its extremely small particle size, all air filters show much lower weight efficiencies on atmospheric dust than they do on the prepared test dusts. This test is normally conducted by drawing equal quantities of air from ahead of and behind the test filter through weighed disks of high-efficiency chemical filter paper. The weight gain of these disks over an extended period of time is accurately determined, and from these values the weight efficiency of the filter on atmospheric dust may be determined.

Weight tests may also be performed by the same

[5] *Ibid.*, pp. 1 and 2.

[6] American Society of Heating, Refrigeration and Air-conditioning Engineers.

general method with any dust or dirt which it may be necessary to remove in any particular application.

Discoloration Test[7]

The discoloration test, also known as the dust-stop, photometric, or blackness test, was developed by the National Bureau of Standards as an improved method of testing air filters. The method of performing this test has several variations, but they appear to give comparable results, providing that atmospheric dust is employed.

The most convenient way to conduct this test is to employ a device known as the Dill dust-spot tester. Samples of the cleaned and uncleaned air are drawn through two filter papers in the tester, one on each side of a light chamber. Light passes through each of these papers and falls on photocells which are connected so that their potentials oppose each other. There is also a sensitive galvanometer in the electrical circuit. If one filter paper becomes dirtier than the other, the photocells receive unequal light intensity, and the galvanometer deflects. By adjusting the relative flow rates of cleaned air samples, the galvanometer is kept on zero, showing that the filter papers are becoming dirty at equal rates. The two sampling rates are registered by flowmeters, and the filter efficiency is calculated from the relative sampling rates. Thus, if 1 cfm of uncleaned air produces as much dirt as 4 cfm of cleaned air, the filter is 75% efficient. Several variations of this procedure are possible and have certain advantages under particular conditions. For example, samples of cleaned and uncleaned air may be drawn one at a time at equal flow rates, and the times measured for the filter papers to reach equal discoloration as shown by a certain amount of deflection of the galvanometer.

The principal advantage of the discoloration test is that it answers the question: How well does the filter being tested remove the dirt which will smudge or blacken light-colored objects? For supply air systems this question is inherently much more important than what percentage of the weight of dirt present the filter removes. Most of the blackening effect of atmospheric dirt is due to extremely small particles which may, however, form only a very small percentage of the dirt by weight. Another important advantage of this test is that it forms a rapid way of testing filters with atmospheric dust, since the equipment is sufficiently sensitive that determinations may be made in about 10 minutes. These advantages have led to the adoption of the discoloration test as the primary means of rating the efficiency of air-conditioning filters and electrostatic precipitators.

Special Efficiency Tests[8]

Additional air-filter tests employed for specific purposes include the dioctyl phthalate smoke test, the jet impinger test, and special tests employing radioactive materials or microorganisms.

DOP Test

The dioctyl phthalate (DOP) smoke test was developed by the Chemical Warfare Service during World War II as the ultimate test for the particulate filters in respirator canisters. The equipment (see Figures 3-1 and 3-2) consists of a special generator for the DOP smoke and a smoke penetrometer (a photoelectric light-scattering instrument) for determining the amount of smoke that penetrates the filter. The generator of DOP smoke is closely controlled to maintain the particle diameter of the smoke at 0.3 micron, which is usually considered to be the most difficult size to remove with strainer-type filters. When the smoke is mixed with the proper amount of diluting air, a concentration of approximately 40 grains per cubic foot results. The penetration meter consists of a chamber containing a photocell through which either the filtered or unfiltered smoke may be drawn. A beam of light shines into the chamber but is prevented by a shield from striking the photocell directly. If the smoke enters the chamber, however, light is refracted by the smoke around the shield and falls on the photocell. The electrical impulse is amplified and registers directly in percentage of penetration. Several scales are provided, the most sensitive of which will show penetrations of a few thousandths of 1%. The DOP test has been adopted as the standard by which the Atomic Energy Commis-

[7] Abstracted from Brochure No. 710A, dated November 25, 1958, prepared by the Cambridge Filter Corp., Syracuse, New York.

[8] *Ibid.*, pp. 3 and 4.

sion and its contractors purchase all high-efficiency particulate air filters. Each filter is individually tested by this method, and the penetration is marked on the filter. Unfortunately this test is limited in its general application by the size and cost of the equipment required.

Jet Impinger

The jet or cascade impinger is a test device which permits the determination of the number of particles of various sizes passing through the filter being tested. Cleaned air and uncleaned air are pumped in turn through a series of nozzles in which the air reaches progressively higher velocities and then impinges on plates coated with a sticky material. The higher the velocity, the finer the particles that are captured. The number of particles caught on the plates must be counted by observation through a microscope. Since the latter is obviously a laborious operation, the use of this test is limited, being employed mostly as a method of calibrating other test methods.

Other Tests

Air filters have been tested on occasion by introducing known amounts of radioactive dust or mists into the air stream ahead of the filter. The penetration can then be determined by collecting all the radioactive material in a known volume of cleaned air and counting its activity by electronic means.

The same general scheme has been employed with bacteria in order to determine the degree of sterility provided to the air by high-efficiency filters. In this case, the number of microorganisms passing the filter is determined by growing cultures.

Comparative Filter Efficiencies[9]

The accompanying table furnishes typical examples of the efficiencies provided by various air filters according to some of the different tests previously described.

The device used in the evaluation of high-efficiency particulate air filters is the DOP smoke penetrometer. It is of interest to understand the workings of this unit, since the ratings for clean room filters are based on its operation. MIL-STD-

[9] *Ibid.*, p. 4.

Type of Filter	ASHRAE (weight test)	NBS Test* (atmospheric dust)	DOP Test (0.3-micron smoke)
HEPA Filters Micretain(R)†	†	†	99.97% min‡
Cambridge AEROSOLVE(R) 95	†	99%	95%
Cambridge AEROSOLVE(R) 85	99%	80–85%	50–60%
Cambridge AEROSOLVE(R) 45	96%	30–35%	20–30%
Electric precipitator	99%	85–90%	60–70%
Pleated paper	94%	25–30%	15–20%
2-inch clearable	76%	8–12%	2–5%
2-inch throwaway	76%	8–12%	2–5%

(Prepared by Cambridge Filter Corp.)

* National Bureau of Standards Discoloration Test.

† Practically 100%. Test not practical for more accurate reading.

‡ Maximum allowable penetration of dioctyl phthalate smoke, 0.05%. Every filter individually tested.

282 describes the operating procedure for the E18 smoke penetrometer (see Figure 3-1) in evaluating the smoke penetration and air resistance of filters. By this method, air is drawn through a filter precleaner at *A* and divided into three streams. A vapor stream flows at approximately 85 cfm through duct

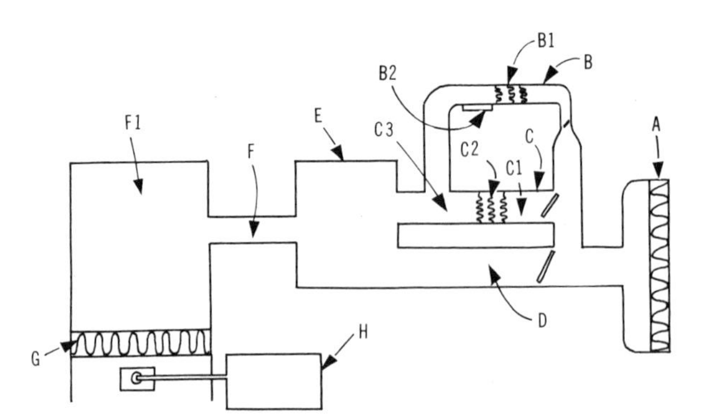

FIGURE 3-1. Smoke penetrometer schematic. See text for description.

B, where it is heated, *B1*, and passes over the surface of liquid DOP, *B2*. A second stream (quenching) flows at approximately 265 cfm through duct *C*, where it is cooled, *C1*, and then slightly heated, *C2*. The mixing of the vapor and quenching streams, *C3*, forms an aerosol of DOP, the particle size of which is relative to the temperature differential of the vapor and quenching air streams. A third stream, *D* (diluent, main dust), flows at approximately 850 cfm into the mixing chamber, *E*, where it dilutes and uniformly disperses the smoke-laden air passing from its vapor and quenching air streams.

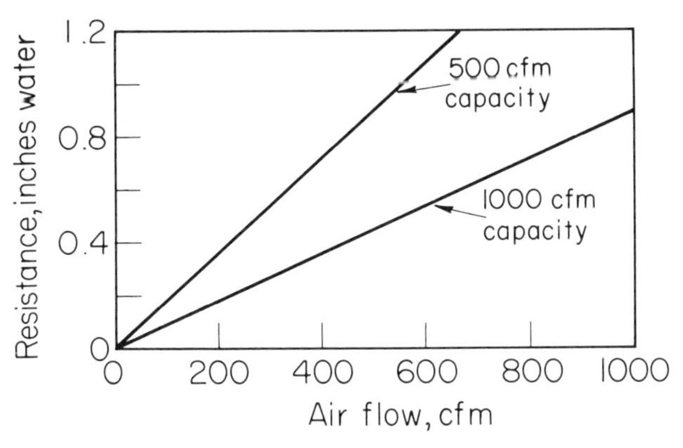

FIGURE 3-2. Resistance versus air flow (70°F, 29.9 inches Hg) for clean high-efficiency filters. *Courtesy Air Engineering*

During the filter test, the smoke is taken from the mixing chamber through a test air stream, *F*, into the test plenum, *F1*, at a rate of flow equal to the rated capacity of the test filter. The smoke passing through the test filter, *G*, is measured by the per smoke through the particle-size meter, *H*, and noting the degree of polarization of a light beam.

Typical plots of resistance versus flow for two cent penetration indicator. The particle size of the smoke is determined by passing a sample of the sizes of high-efficiency filters are shown in Figure 3-2. According to the specification at rated flow, the initial resistance or static pressure differential across the filter shall not exceed 0.90 inch (water gauge) (*8*). All filter sizes will have substantially the same resistance at rated flow because the filter area is adjusted proportionally to the designed capacity to provide for a face velocity of 5 fpm through the medium.

Figure 3-3 shows a portable test setup for testing super-interception filters at Lawrence Radiation Laboratory, Livermore, California.

High-Efficiency Particulate Air Filters *(9)*

Filter Unit Construction[10]

Some acquaintance with filter unit components and with manufacturing steps in fabricating the high-efficiency particulate filter unit can be helpful in understanding the necessity for handling and installing it properly.

As previously mentioned, components of the filter unit normally consist of a frame, filter medium (fil-

[10] Abstracted from reference *9*, pp. 1 and 2.

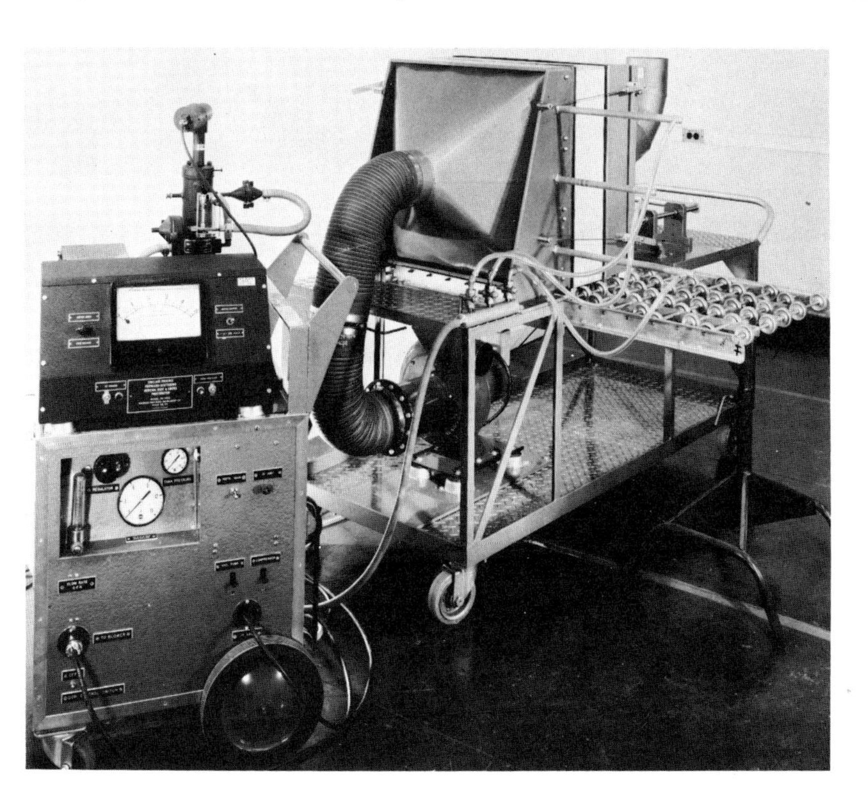

FIGURE 3-3. Portable test setup for testing super-interception filters at Lawrence Radiation Laboratory. Equipment on cart, at left, is air-operated DOP generator and light-scattering photometer. Test stand is at right. *Courtesy Air Engineering*

ter paper), separators, adhesive, and gasket. Contrary to a frequent misconception, high-efficiency filters are not constructed of multiple layers of filter medium in the direction of air flow. Rather, a single layer, 8 to 20 mils thick, is accordion-pleated to a conventional height. During the pleating, a separator is inserted between each fold. The usual separator is a rectangular sheet of material corrugated along its width. Its purpose is to separate each lap of filter medium and, in operation of the assembled filter unit, to allow air to flow along the channels formed by the corrugations and through the medium. With separators inserted and the filter medium pleated to height, this assembly is known as the filter pack. The filter pack is held in a jig, and edges at the ends of pleats are trimmed evenly with a bandsaw, trimmings are removed with compressed air, and adhesive is applied fully over both trimmed sides. The jig is removed when the adhesive has cured sufficiently to keep the pack from springing apart.

The inner face of four frame members and their ends are then coated completely with adhesive, and the frame members are assembled around the pack to contain it. More adhesive is beaded along the exposed junctions of the frame and the trimmed sides of the pack on both faces of the filter unit. These beads of adhesive are placed for additional assurance that air will not leak through the adhesive bond between the pack and frame. A gasket is supplied along the frame edge, around one or both faces, as desired. The gasket is formed of four strips of material, usually ¾ inch in width, which are adhered for their full length to the frame edge. Adhesive should be applied to ends of gasket strips, and the ends should abut and adhere tightly to prevent air leakage through the gasket during operation of the filter unit. Ends of gasket pieces cut for dovetail mating are recommended to prevent gasket leakage at these points.

A variety of materials has been used for components of the high-efficiency filter unit. Some of these are listed here.

Frame

a. Plywood, exterior, both standard and fire-retardant-treated
b. Steel
c. Aluminum
d. Asbestos combinations
e. Plastic

Filter Medium (0.007- to 0.040-inch thicknesses)

Fibrous filter papers made of:
a. Glass
b. Glass and asbestos
c. Ceramic material
d. Esparto (cellulose) and asbestos

Separator

a. Asbestos paper
b. Aluminum alloy
c. Aluminum–asbestos (laminated)
d. Kraft paper
e. Plastic

Adhesive or Cement

a. Rubber-base adhesive (normal and self-extinguishing)
b. Asbestos furnace cement
c. Epoxy resin
d. Polyester resin (self-extinguishing)
e. Silicates

Gasket

a. Latex sponge rubber
b. Neoprene sponge (open and closed cell)
c. Neoprene and cork
d. Mineral wool

This list of materials is far from complete. New materials are introduced occasionally to increase fire-resistive qualities, efficiency, strength, or resistance to chemical attack, or to reduce the cost of fabrication. Variations in filter unit construction have been made. For example, one filter unit is fabricated entirely without separators. Another contains a pad of fine glass fibers, instead of adhesive, to seal between the filter pack and frame. Cylindrical filter units are being produced instead of the conventional square or rectangular shapes, and the unit can be enclosed and fitted with nipples to receive and exhaust the air. The latter two variations are designed for special application.

High-efficiency filter units, all with an efficiency of 99.97% or better in the removal of particles from air streams, can be purchased to meet varying degrees of moisture and humidity resistance, exposure to temperature, and resistance against solvents, alkalies, and acids.

Packaging and Shipping[11]

Packaging practice varies among the filter unit manufacturers. Normally, units are packaged in cardboard cartons, with various approaches existing for internal strengthening and impact-resistance of the container. Usually a carton will contain one of the larger units, such as a 1000-cfm unit, 24 by 24 by 11½ inches in size; or it may have two 500-cfm units, each 24 by 24 by 5⅞ inches. The smaller sizes, 50 cfm, 8 by 8 by 5⅞ inches, and 25 cfm, 8 by 8 by 3 1/16 inches, frequently are packaged in multiple.

When a filter unit is placed in the carton, it is inserted so that the pleated folds are vertical, a position essential to prevent damage in shipment. To prevent sagging of the pleats, it is important that vertical positioning of the pleats be maintained in handling and storage. Moreover, the vertical position is the one in which the filter unit should be installed for operation. Pleats of a filter unit installed in horizontal position form shelves for collection of entrapped material, the accumulated weight of which causes sagging and leads to a shorter life for the unit.

When a filter unit is shipped with pleats in the horizontal position, the vibration to which it is subjected in transportation, and the jarring which usually accompanies handling, occasionally cause the filter medium to break at the adhesive line. This can be identified as a hairline crack. Separators infrequently break at this line, depending on the material of which they are made. In radical cases—for example, when the filter pack is pleated loosely—separators will lose their corrugation, will sag (Figure 3-4),[12] and the medium will break along the full edge of one or more separators (Figure 3-5). This also can occur when the separators absorb moisture (Figure 3-6).

FIGURE 3-4. Corrugated separators stretched and sagging from shipment of filter unit with pleats in horizontal position. *Courtesy U. S. Atomic Energy Commission*

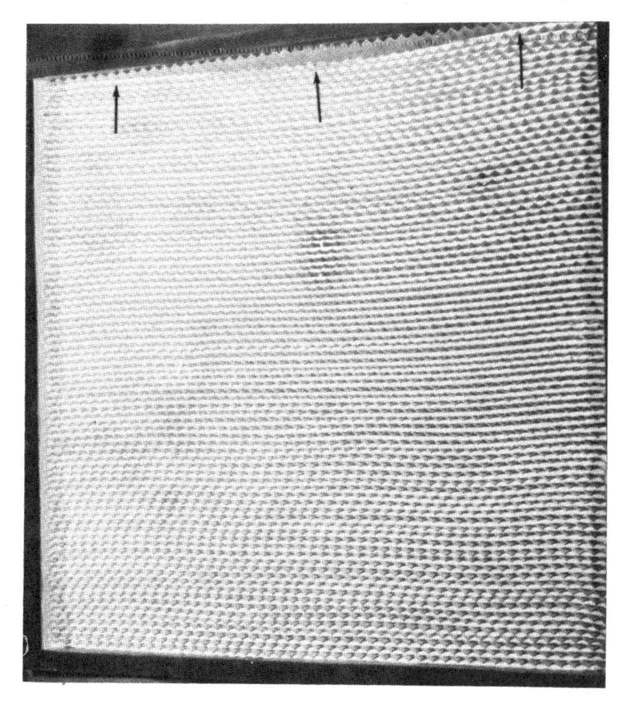

FIGURE 3-5. Filter medium broken along edge of topmost separator. *Courtesy U. S. Atomic Energy Commission*

Inspection and Testing[13]

Inspection starts when a delivery of filter units reaches the purchaser, even while the load still is aboard the carrier. As the shipment is being unloaded, every carton should be inspected for external damage and improper positioning in the cargo space. Damaged cartons, including those with corners dented and those improperly positioned, should

[11] *Ibid.*, p. 3.

[12] Figures 3-4, 3-5, and 3-6 and Figures 3-9 through 3-18 were abstracted from reference *9* and are reprinted by permission of the U. S. Atomic Energy Commission.

[13] Abstracted from reference *9*, pp. 3, 6, 9, and 10.

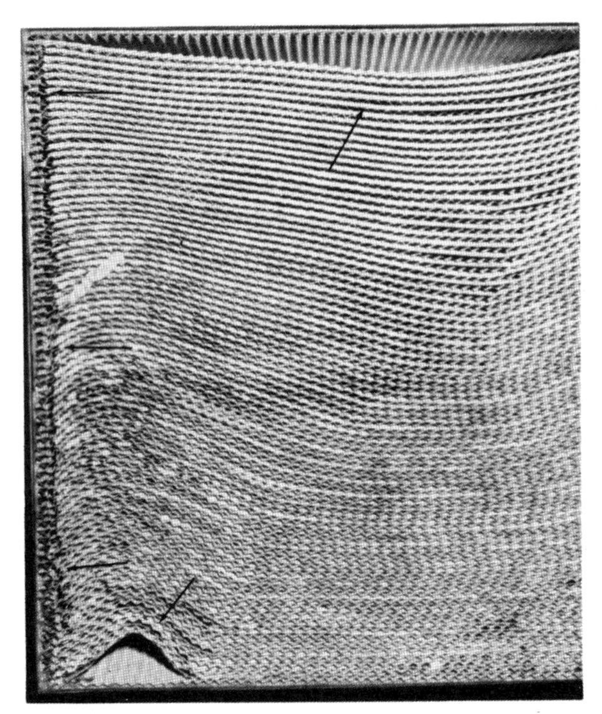

FIGURE 3-6. Separators in filter unit absorbed moisture. Damage aggravated by shipment. *Courtesy U. S. Atomic Energy Commission*

be set aside for particularly careful inspection of the filter unit contained. Damage will be more prevalent when filter units are loaded with mixed cargoes or are shipped in a partially loaded carrier.

The filter unit must be removed carefully from its carton. The acceptable method for removal is to open the top flaps (Figures 3-7 and 3-8) of the container after removing the sealing tape. With flaps folded back, the carton should be inverted or upended gently to place the exposed end of the filter unit or, in one manufacturer's package, the face of the filter unit, on a flat surface, preferably the floor. The surface must be clear of nuts, bolts, and similar protrusions which would damage the face of the unit. Then the carton is withdrawn from the filter unit. Any attempt to remove the filter unit from the carton by grasping the unit below the exposed filter frame can result in irreparable damage if fingers puncture the delicate, soft filter medium attached immediately below the frame.

Visual inspection of the filter unit to detect physical damage is necessary. A strong lamp should be used to examine the exposed areas of both faces to assure that no breaks, cracks, or pinholes are evident. In addition, a less intense light, such as a flashlight, can be employed in a darkened room. The inspector should look for visible defects, with the light projected along the full length of each channel created by the separators (see Figure 3-9).

Translucent spots may not necessarily indicate holes or cracks. More likely, these will prove to be variations in thickness which occur during manufacture of the filter medium. Breaks or cracks in the medium usually show up on the surface edges of the filter pleats but often are not detected readily. Minor cracks can be of major importance. If the filter unit is installed with this surface-edge damage, the cracks can be extended by air movement through the unit. After examining each channel, the inspector should examine critically the adhesive seal around the filter unit face, to be sure that the seal is complete and unbroken (Figure 3-10). When one face of the filter unit has been inspected, the

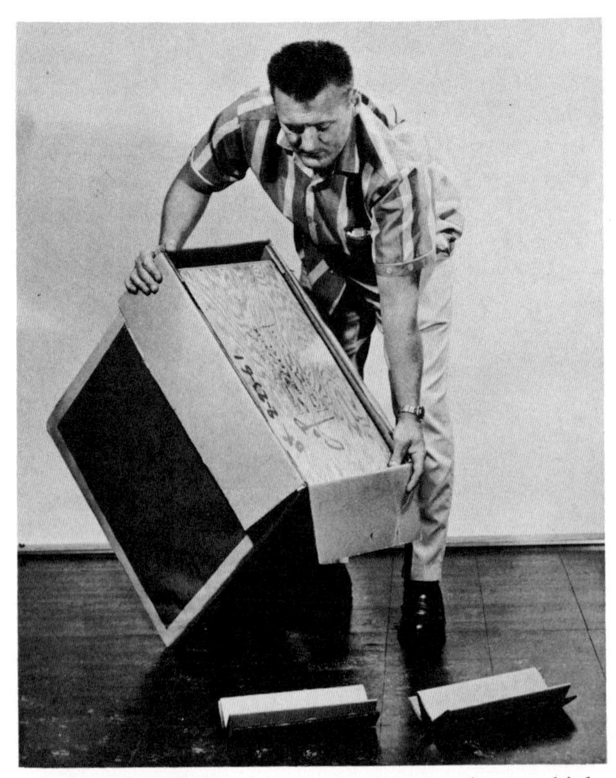

FIGURE 3-7. Filters of the super-interception or high-efficiency type as shown should always be carefully unpackaged. Box flaps should be folded back first. *Courtesy Air Engineering*

other face should be examined in the same manner and with the same care.

After the inspector has completed a thorough scrutiny of both faces, he should check the corner joints of the frame for adhesive sealing and tightness. Gasketing about the edge of the frame should be inspected for tight abutment or mating of gasket strips (Figure 3-11) and its physical condition (Figure 3-12). Gasket strips should be examined also for full adhesion to the frame.

Cartons showing damage or dented corners and those found loaded in improper position should be inspected very carefully. The filter unit should be examined at all corners, particularly at the point of carton impact, for damage to separators and the filter medium. Exterior damage to several protruding separator edges in a small area will not influence filter unit efficiency as long as the medium is not mashed, punctured, or broken (Figure 3-13). Even though the medium may not be broken on one face,

FIGURE 3-8. After box has been turned over, it should be removed from the filter as shown. *Courtesy Air Engineering*

FIGURE 3-9. Inspecting filter unit with strong lamp to detect breaks, cracks, and holes near face. *Courtesy U. S. Atomic Energy Commission*

it is possible to find it damaged at the opposing point on the other face. Large areas of mashed separator edges, even though the medium is not damaged, will obstruct the passage of air through the filter unit and reduce its life (Figure 3-14). Im-

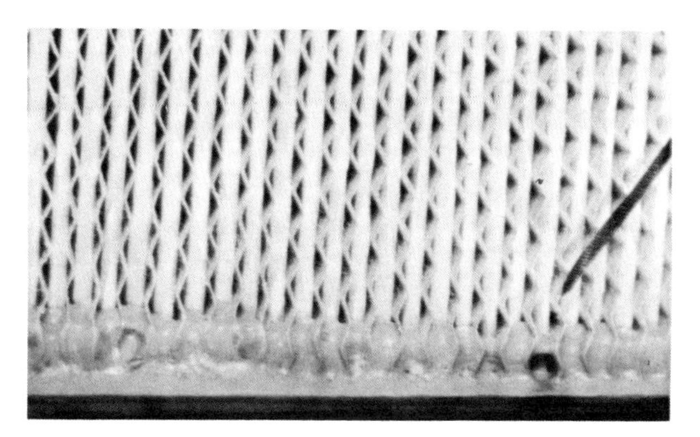

FIGURE 3-10. Defect in adhesive seal (U. S. Army photo). *Courtesy U. S. Atomic Energy Commission*

FIGURE 3-11. Enlarged photo showing improper butting of gasket strips. Unfiltered air can leak through this gap when filter unit is installed. *Courtesy U. S. Atomic Energy Commission*

properly stowed filter units should be inspected for cracks alongside the adhesive seal (Figure 3-15), for extreme sags in pleats and separators, and for slits or breaks in the medium.

Repair of a damaged filter unit, particularly the medium, should not be attempted by the user. Any unit so repaired must be retested with the DOP penetrometer to assure that hidden damage does not exist which will reduce filtering efficiency. Repair and retest thus become uneconomical for most users.

Standard practice for manufacture of the high efficiency filter unit requires that the manufacturer's test air flow and test findings of penetration and resistance be marked on the frame of the filter unit. These will be found in a stamp bearing the manufacturer's name, or vendor's name, together with the model number and serial number of the filter unit. If not specified, DOP penetration should not exceed 0.05 of 1%, and air resistance should be not more than 1.0 inch (water gauge) at rated air flow.

Purchasers should be aware that filter units 500

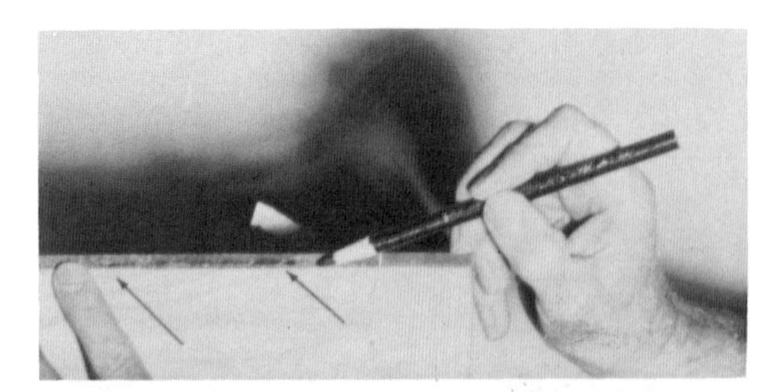

FIGURE 3-12. Defective gasket strip. Air can leak through this slit if filter unit is mounted loosely in installation. *Courtesy U. S. Atomic Energy Commission*

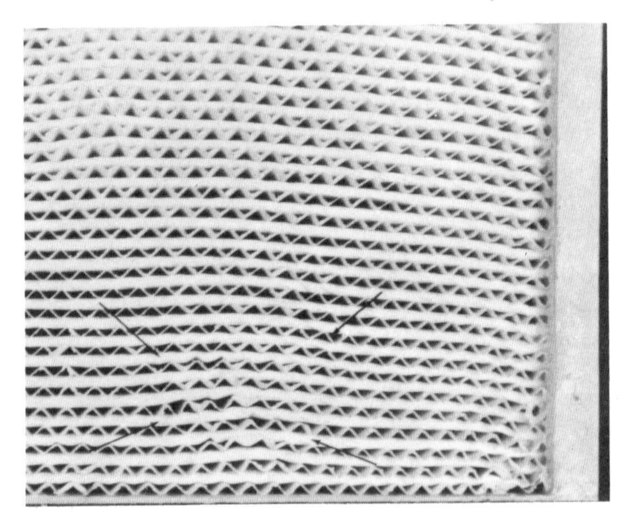

FIGURE 3-13. Separator edges damaged in small area, lower center. This should not reduce filter unit efficiency. Distortion of pleats requires very careful inspection of filter unit (U. S. Army photo). *Courtesy U. S. Atomic Energy Commission*

FIGURE 3-14. Large area of separator edges damaged. This location on the opposite face of the filter unit also requires inspection (U. S. Army photo). *Courtesy U. S. Atomic Energy Commission*

FIGURE 3-15. Pleats cracked in a line roughly paralleling the adhesive seal. A filter unit so damaged cannot give high-efficiency service. *Courtesy U. S. Atomic Energy Commission*

cfm and larger in size which were manufactured in 1960 of combustible cellulose–asbestos medium exceeded 1.0 inch (water gauge) in resistance. The reason has been attributed to the quality of asbestos fibers available for manufacture of the cellulose–asbestos medium. Purchasers of a filter unit containing this medium should be prepared to accept a shorter life for use of the unit.

Storage[14]

After inspection, the filter unit should be repacked carefully in the carton in which it was shipped and received. All packing material for internal strengthening of the carton and for protection of the filter unit should be replaced properly. Pleats of the filter unit should conform to the vertical arrow on the carton. This step should be taken routinely, whether the filter unit will be installed at an early date or whether it will be stored.

Cartons of filter units should be positioned in storage to conform to the vertical arrow. Manufacturer's recommendations for storage heights should be followed. When these are not available, filter units 24 by 24 by 11½ inches and 24 by 24 by 5⅞ inches should be stacked not more than three filter units high.

Mixing of other items and materials with filter units in storage should be avoided to prevent damage to the filter units. Recommended aisle widths consistent with good warehousing practice should be provided to reduce damage of filter units from materials-handling equipment and other traffic. Filter units should not be stored in locations where they will be exposed to dampness, excessive heat or cold, or rapidly changing temperatures.

Filter units should be inverted (180°) after every storage period of six months. This will equalize the strain between opposing adhesive seals which bond the filter pack to the frame.

Handling[15]

Mechanical warehousing equipment is recommended for handling quantities of filter units. Such equipment preferably will provide a flat bed for movement of the units. Chains, slings, and hooks obviously are not to be used. Filter units must be loaded on pallets when forklift trucks and similar equipment are employed. The cartons should be placed on the pallet so that the arrow on the carton points vertically.

In handling a packaged filter unit physically, a person must make certain that the carton is tilted on one corner, picked up at opposing corners, and deposited carefully on the floor or other surface. The carton should not be dropped or jarred (Figure 3-16). Any filter unit dropped, whether or not in the carton, should be re-examined for damage, as previously discussed.

When a filter unit is lifted, it must be grasped only along the outer surface of the frame. Even

FIGURE 3-16. Visible damage from dropping filter unit. Break shows in form of a line immediately above and parallel to dark rubber gasket. *Courtesy U. S. Atomic Energy Commission*

[14] *Ibid.*, p. 10.

[15] *Ibid.*, p. 15.

slight contact of fingers at almost any point within the frame can puncture the filter medium. Placing around the frame a strap equipped with handle and slide fastener is suggested where a unit 24 by 24 by 11½ inches or larger will be handled extensively.

A handle or grip may be attached permanently to the wood filter frame at some locations for ease of installation and removal of the filter unit. In such instances, care must be taken in attaching the handle. Screws should not be pounded for starting, and nails should never be used. The recommended method is to drill starting screw holes, making certain that the drill and the length of screws do not penetrate through the frame and pierce the filter medium attached. (Screws must not be longer than the thickness of the wood frame, usually ¾ inch.) Pounding will subject the filter medium to cracking and possibly will loosen the adhesive seal which bonds the filter pack within the frame. Attachment of a handle to a metal-frame filter unit is not recommended, and in no case should this be attempted after the filter unit has been assembled by the manufacturer.

Filter units should be kept in shipping cartons when being moved from one location to another. When being transferred for installation, the units should be unloaded at a point that, so far as is practicable, will reduce physical handling. Filter units should remain in cartons until ready for installation and then should be unpacked as discussed in "Inspection and Testing." If for any reason an unpackaged filter unit must be placed with its face on the floor or other surface, the surface must be cleared of every object or irregularity that might damage the filter pack.

Installation[16]

Craftsmen responsible for installation of the filter unit must be informed of the high-efficiency performance required of it. Moreover, they should know that the filter pack within the frame is delicate and must not be damaged during installation (Figure 3-17). Equally imporant, the filter unit must be installed so that unfiltered air will not leak past the unit (*10*).

The surface to which the filter unit is applied must be true, clean, smooth, flat, free of weld

[16] *Ibid.*, p. 16.

FIGURE 3-17. Filter unit damaged severely at two points during installation. *Courtesy U. S. Atomic Energy Commission*

spatter, and sufficiently rigid to compress fully all the gasket surface. The following procedure is recommended.

1. Carefully remove filter unit from shipping carton, following the procedure described under "Inspection and Testing."
2. Carefully inspect both faces of the filter unit for cracks in the filter medium, for damage of separators, and for separation of the filter pack at the frame.
3. See that the gasket is cemented firmly to the frame and that the gasket pieces are butted or mated at the joints.
4. If gasketing of both faces is not needed for mounting the filter unit, remove one gasket and clean the edges of the filter frame at the points of clamp contact.
5. The gasket must be compressed firmly, to approximately 30% of its original thickness. Apply compression evenly and equally at all points in increments of 5 foot-pounds or less, with the filter frame completely covering the opening.
6. Always install the filter unit with pleats and separators in the vertical position. This will eliminate sagging of pleats from accumulated weight of materials stopped by the filter unit.
7. In locations where a filter unit is subject to physical damage after installation (intakes to hoods,

duct systems, etc.), protect it by a wire mesh screen or expanded metal shield.

8. Use an "in-place test" to check a filter unit for proper installation. Portable equipment similar in principle to the DOP penetrometer can be employed. With the ventilation system in operation, particles of DOP generated by air pressure(*11*) are sprayed on and about the upstream face of the mounted filter unit. A probe moved over the downstream face picks up DOP particles that penetrate through the filter unit or leak around the gasketing owing to faulty mounting. Particles picked up by the probe are drawn through tubing to the photoelectric detection unit which indicates their presence by meter or audible signal. The "in-place test" is not a substitute for quality assurance testing by the DOP penetrometer, which determines the total efficiency of the filter unit. It is, however, an excellent method to assess performance of the installed filter unit and is recommended for this purpose. An alternative test employs an analog light-scattering photometer and the use of a cigarette smoke generator. Such a technique will uncover faults and leaks in the filter or about the filter sealing edges.

Filter Unit Replacement[17]

The resistance, or pressure drop, across the filter unit is usually the determining factor for replacement of the unit. This is normally accomplished when the air resistance equals 2 inches (water gauge).

Replacement of the filter unit may be required for reasons other than resistance. A number of the factors for replacement of the unit are considered below.

1. Loss of efficiency, determined from air-sampling measurements made downstream of the filter unit.
2. Visible damage or rupture of the filter medium in a unit.
3. Excessive build-up of lint or combustible particle matter on the filter unit from the environment.
4. Change in production method, in laboratory operation, in hood application, or from dry-air to moist-air exposure (a filter unit suitable for dry air is not necessarily adaptable to moist air).

[17] *Ibid.*, p. 19.

Design Recommendations for Systems of Filter Units[18]

Particulate filter units, including prefilters, should be readily accessible and easily removable. The ease with which a filter unit can be reached and changed will reduce maintenance costs and cut down the introduction of contaminant into the clean room.

High-efficiency filter units are normally designed for horizontal air flow and should be mounted accordingly. In this type of installation, the internal pack of the filter unit is supported by one side of the filter frame. In contrast, a system designed so that air passes vertically through the filter unit allows a horizontally designed filter pack to sag of its own weight and with the pressure of the air stream. Such a pack is retained in place only by the strength of the adhesive attaching it within the filter frame. When the vertical air draft is downward, the pressure of the air stream also is imposed on the unsupported filter pack. In vertical air filtration, sagging of the filter pack will be more prevalent in a high-humidity atmosphere, and this will be aggravated by loading with the accumulated weight of materials caught by the filter unit.

Currently filter manufacturers are considering improved design of these filters to allow for vertical-flow installations. Proper structural modifications will prevent sagging of the filter medium in the vertical-flow applications. Horizontal filter installations should use filters with aluminum frames and separators, since the aluminum separators will give more rigid support to the filter medium. Where aluminum cannot be used because of chemical attack, plastic should be substituted.

Various methods are used for mounting a filter unit. Whatever method is selected, the high-efficiency filter unit must be held firmly and the gasket compressed sufficiently and evenly to prevent air from bypassing the unit. A design that requires calking or taping to seal between units placed side by side or one above the other in a filter bank is not recommended.

It is recommended that the design require a metal mounting to receive the filter unit. This mounting should provide a framework of proper dimension to accommodate the frame of the filter unit. The open-

[18] *Ibid.*, pp. 19 and 20.

ing formed by this framework should not be smaller than the filter frame, as this would impede the passage of air through the filter pack of the unit. The metal mounting should have a bearing surface that is rigid, true, flat, smooth, clean, and free of weld spatter. The mounting may have quick-acting clamps, hold-down bolts, or rods. Hold-down rods may be tapped into the bearing surface or toe-welded. Tolerance should be provided between rod centers, to allow easy replacement of the filter unit. Where rods are welded to the bearing surface (Figure 3-18), spacing between rods must permit the welding bead as well as the rod to clear the outside edge of the filter unit. Leakproof installation of the filter unit cannot be assured when its rubber gasketing must be compressed over welding beads. Wing nuts or other easily handled fasteners may be used with hold-down rods.

When a housing rather than an open-surface mounting is to be provided to receive the filter unit, it similarly should be of such dimensions that the filter unit can be installed readily without forcing and that easy replacement of the unit can be made.

Prefilter[19]

Life of a high-efficiency particulate filter unit normally will be extended if the air-handling system includes a prefilter to remove larger particles before the air reaches the high-efficiency unit. This will prevent premature loading of the filtration medium with large air-stream material and thereby eliminate early replacement of the high-efficiency unit. The prefilter should be selected with due regard to efficiency required, fan capacity, and fire resistance.

The point selected for location of the prefilter should be easily accessible but should not endanger the basic operation of the clean room. Prefilter should be located as close to the high-efficiency filters as is economically practical. Replacement or cleaning of the prefilter is required much more frequently than replacement of the high-efficiency unit.

FIGURE 3-18. Mounting arrangement designed for vertical air flow through filter bank. Note welding bead at base of holddown rods. *Courtesy U. S. Atomic Energy Commission*

Fire Extinguishment[20]

A high-efficiency filter unit constructed of combustible medium is readily ignited and extremely difficult to extinguish. Once ignited, the fire in a typical cellulose–asbestos medium and Kraft paper–separator unit progresses through the depth of the filter pack and spreads laterally until the entire pack is consumed. In applications where these filter units are banked, it is possible for fire to spread from one unit to another. Tests have shown that the cellulose–asbestos unit often will ignite with explosive force and set fire to adjacent units from the exit (downstream) side of a bank, particularly when there is insufficient air replacement on the downstream side. This indicates that air flow should not be damped off completely in the event of fire. Sufficient air movement to remove explosive or combustible gases should be maintained. This should be preplanned so that a regular procedure can be followed in a fire.

Water that contains a wetting agent is the only extinguishing material effective on fire in a combustible high-efficiency filter unit. On occasion, a fine spray of plain water can control the lateral spread of fire within the filter unit, but the fire can be expected to continue its path through the pack.

Fire Involving the Fire-Resistive Unit

A fire in a fire-resistive filter unit containing glass fiber filter medium is much easier to combat than one in a cellulose–asbestos high-efficiency unit. The components contribute only negligibly to

[19] *Ibid.*, p. 22.

[20] *Ibid.*, pp. 23 and 25.

combustion. Fire rapidly melts and ruptures the glass filter medium, but, once the source of ignition is extinguished or is removed from the filter unit, combustion of the filter unit ceases quickly, usually without too much damage to the separators and wood frame. Noncombustible separators, especially in filter units of larger depth, such as units 24 by 24 by 11½ inches, serve reasonably as flame arrestors. Owing to fire-retardant treatment of the wood frame, the likelihood of flame spread from this source is small. With the fire-resistive unit, as in the cellulose–asbestos unit, air similarly should not be damped off completely in case of fire. If it is necessary to damp off the air, precaution should be taken against collection of explosive or combustible gases.

REFERENCES

1. NORTHRUP, DAVID H. "The A.E.C. or C.W.S. Air Filter." *Chemical Engineering Progress*, Vol. 49, No. 10, pp. 513-517 (October 1953).

2. LA MER, V. K., DROZIN, V. G., KRUGER, J., and CATSON, S. *Filtration of Monodispersed Solid Aerosols.* N.Y.Q. 4526. U. S. Atomic Energy Commission, 1953.

3. GREEN, H. L., and LANE, W. R. *Particulate Clouds: Dusts, Smokes, and Mists.* London: E. & F. N. Spon, 1957.

4. DECKER, H. M., BUCHANAN, L. M., HALL, L. B., and GODDARD, K. R. "Method of Air Cleaning." *Air Filtration of Microbial Particles.* Public Health Service Publication 953. U. S. Government Printing Office, Washington, D.C., 1962.

5. RODEBUSH, W. H. "Filtration of Aerosols." *Handbook on Aerosols*, pp. 117-122. U. S. Atomic Energy Commission, U. S. Government Printing Office, Washington, D.C., 1950.

6. RAMSKILL, E. A., and ANDERSON, W. L. "The Inertial Mechanism in the Mechanical Filtration of Aerosols." *J. Colloid Science*, Vol. 6, pp. 416-428 (October 1951).

7. DALLAVALLE, J. M. "Diffusion of Particles." *The Technology of Fine Particles.* New York, N.Y.: Pitman, 1948.

8. "Recommended Minimal Specifications Revised for High Efficiency Filter Unit." *Health and Safety*, Issue 120. U. S. Atomic Energy Commission, Washington, D.C., January 1961.

9. GILBERT, HUMPHREY, and PALMER, JAMES H. *High Efficiency Particulate Air Filter Units.* TID-7023. Office of Technical Services, Department of Commerce, Washington, D.C., August 1961.

10. RICHARDSON, W. J., and PALMER, J. H. *The Installation, Handling and Storage of High-Efficiency Filters.* TID-7593. Sixth AEC Air Cleaning Conference. Office of Technical Services, Department of Commerce, Washington, D.C., July 1959.

11. *An Air-Operated Aerosol Generator.* Report of Progress. U. S. Naval Research Laboratory, Washington, D.C., July 1956.

Chapter 4. *Product Requirements*

Introduction

The need for controlling contaminants in both civilian and military products is not new, as has been emphasized. Prior to development of current-day weapon systems, producers of these commercial items devised many shop methods to minimize contaminants in their products. One of their principal aides in this work was feedback information from the users. When failures occurred that could be attributed to contamination, this information was fed back into the production line. The result in many cases was an improved product.

Today, however, military requirements demand that every component of a weapon system perform perfectly each time it is called on to act. A component in an atomic weapon system or missile system must perform flawlessly the first and only time it is required to perform as a part of that system. There is little, if any, feedback from these systems when field failures occur because of contamination. Irving M. Kodel, while employed by Sandia Corporation, manufacturer of atomic weapons, made the following statement(*1*):

> While Sandia's testing program prior to field use is extensive and carefully planned, it can never guarantee 100 percent reliability; this is due to several factors, one of which is the transportation of the component after testing and prior to field use. Travel by truck, train, or plane, can easily cause a foreign particle which had remained dormant and harmless through all the testing to move into a critical position the one and only time the unit is used in the field.

Several particular examples can be given to emphasize the need for clean room control for such products. Dust or moisture entrapped between optical cover glass and solar cells will affect the response of the solar cells and hence their efficiency. In the case of a space program called Advent, a solar cell has a surface area of 0.31 square inch. Contaminants can both block off the energy path and scratch the top surface of the cells (the *p*-layer) which is only 0.001 inch thick. If this happens, the efficiency of the cells is reduced. In this example, a loss of 1% in efficiency would be equivalent to the loss of power from fifty solar cell submodules.

Gross contamination such as dirt and impurities in solder can cause a local hot spot because of an increase in resistance. The temperature rise, in turn, can cause a rapid deterioration of adjacent electronic components.

Water vapor is ever present in air, and the amount is a function of the humidity. Too much moisture interferes with potting and allows the formation of leakage paths that result in arc-over or corona discharge in rarified atmospheres.

The accuracy of an inertial guidance system is dependent on the quality of construction and assembly of the elements making up the guidance system. The most important of the factors in determining accuracy is the degree of perfection of mechanical balance within the gyros themselves. For a typically floated precision gyroscope, an unbalanced mass of approximately 0.00001 of an ounce located at a distance of 3 inches from the center of the float assembly will cause the gyro to precess or drift, at about 1 minute of arc per hour. A speck of dandruff, a thumb print, a tiny garment fiber, or a small part of an eyelash will cause enough imbalance to make the gyro virtually useless in today's guidance systems. It takes only one 10-millionth of an inch of axial shift of a gyro spin axis bearing to make a space craft miss the moon by milcs(*2*). The allowable error for planetary missions will be even less.

Another problem area is the measurement of the critical mechanical tolerances required by gyro assemblies. For instance, on the bombing navigation system that one manufacturer has been producing for the Air Force, fit tolerance varied from 0.0002 to 0.0008 inch. However, some of the fits required on the 2 FBG gyro as quoted from the specification are as follows: Shaft to bearing, 0.000035 to 0.000075 inch; shaft to upper fixed spacer, 0.000005 to 0.000065 inch; shaft to lower fixed spacer, 0.000050 to 0.000065 inch.

Today this industry is measuring to plus or minus 10 millionths on bore and shaft measurements and is presently investigating methods of measurement that will increase this capability to plus or minus 5 millionths.

An important measurement made in gyro testing is the gyro unbalance. This is measured in dyne centimeters. An analogy for this unit of measurement would be the difference in force exerted by a lit and an unlit match held between two fingers.

In conjunction with this discussion, it might be well to define an arc second. Mathematically it can be expressed as 0.000058 inch of arc on a circle having a radius of 1 foot. An analogy is the amount of eye motion that a man standing in Philadelphia would have to make to read across a newspaper held by another man in New York City approximately 100 miles away. Errors in gyros of the magnitude of arch seconds can cause incompleted missions in many sophisticated systems.

An example of a subminiature ball bearing is shown in Figures 4-1 and 4-2. This New Departure bearing has tiny balls only 0.01 inch in diameter, and an inside diameter of 0.01 inch. Figure 4-3 shows other examples of small and miniature ball bearings.

The concept of dust control and its omnipresent importance in tube manufacturing production has received ever-increasing concern and attention in the last few years. Studies indicate that contamination cannot be wholly eliminated but can be effectively controlled by means of an efficient high-performance filtration system.

The tube industry is concerned with the minutest dust particles in vacuum. Particulate matter 0.5 micron in diameter and 1 micron in length is able to produce 1.3×10^{15} molecules (*3*) of gas at a vacuum level of 10^{-7} mm Hg. The presence of numerous particles within this size range would have serious consequences.

One company faced with this problem was the Hughes Microwave Tube Division of Los Angeles,

FIGURE 4-1. Subminiature ball bearing produced by New Departure. *Courtesy New Departure Division, General Motors Corp.*

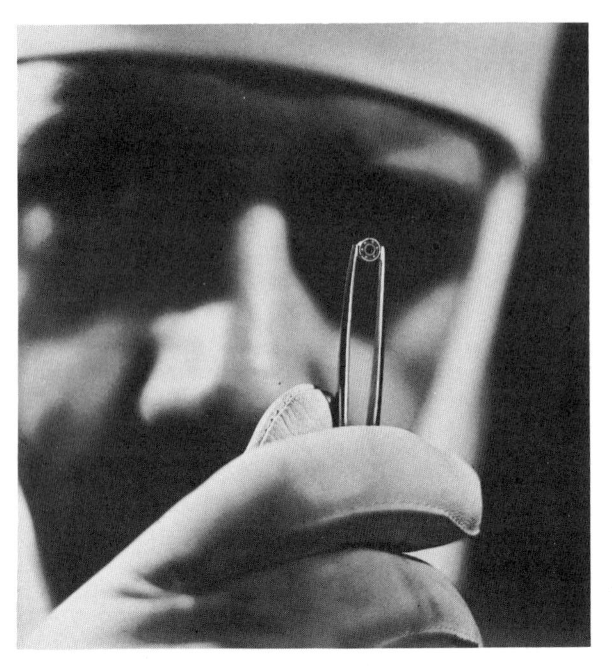

FIGURE 4-2. New Departure's subminiature ball bearing has tiny balls only 0.01 inch in diameter, and an inside diameter of 0.01 inch. *Courtesy New Departure Division, General Motors Corp.*

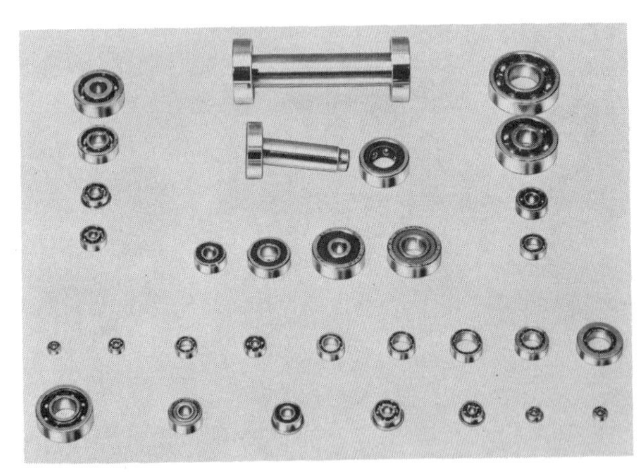

FIGURE 4-3. Examples of miniature ball bearings. *Courtesy New Departure Division, General Motors Corp.*

California. After careful evaluation of various filter media, this company selected a high-efficiency particulate air filter for their air-conditioning system. It has been reported as extremely successful, with average sampling tests under operating conditions indicating a level of 200 to 225 particles in the 5- to 25-micron particle size range. Other areas of the building average 1200 particles in this range.

An example of the microcircuitry used by Lear, Grand Rapids, Michigan, is shown in Figure 4-4. Conductive as well as nonconductive contaminants can cause serious problems to these photoetched circuits.

It should be stressed that the need for cleanliness is based on the operational requirements of precise devices. Examples of these devices include electronic, mechanical, hydraulic, and pneumatic assemblies, subassemblies, and individual components. The scope of cleanliness covers the entire range of manufactured objects, for each precise device must operate correctly within narrow ranges of performance and with extreme reliability. For a precise device to operate according to its specifications, the component, subassembly, or device must be free and clean of contaminants, since contamination may interfere with the motion of its parts. It is immaterial whether the interference affects the rate of motion or the energy required to produce the motion. The motion can be sliding, rolling, uniform, intermittent, or any combination of these. Contamination may affect the position requirements of timers, switching devices, etc. Contaminants can also interfere with energy transmission when mechanical or fluid energy transmission is considered. This, in turn, can affect the flow rate of fluids and the pressure capability of fluid systems. Lieberman states:

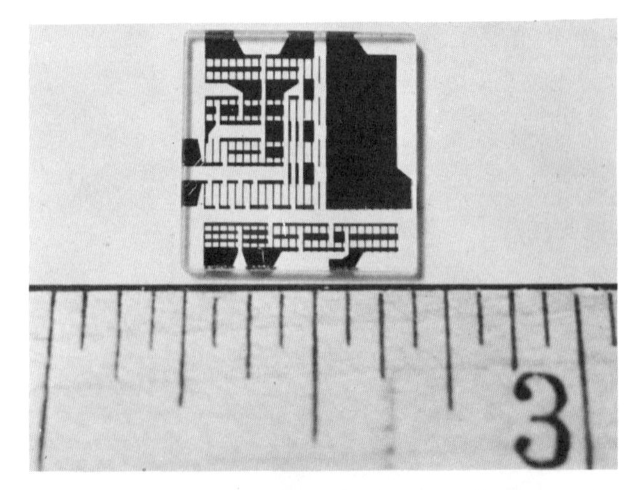

FIGURE 4-4. Microcircuitry used by Lear-Siegler in the production of instruments. *Courtesy Lear-Siegler, Inc.*

The mechanism with which contaminants interfere with required operation are many and varied. Dimensional changes can result from wear and friction effects over an adequate period of time. These minute changes can result in subcomponent degradation due to galling, seizing, blockage, or slip-stick phenomena in moving devices.

Catastrophic failure can also occur when increased friction causes local heating which then can result in thermal expansion and subsequent seizure. In high-speed devices structural failure usually occurs; in low speed devices welding sometimes happens. In electrical systems, arcing across heated conductive materials which were not conductive before they were heated is a potential outcome.

The fusion of particulates or of gaseous contamination into the surface of a component is sometimes responsible for the formation of a compound or alloy whose physical properties differ from those of the substrate. Some years back there was a problem known as the brown polymer formation. This is one very familiar example of such an effect due to gaseous contamination. Localized failure of the substrate due to change in tensile strength, creep rate, brittleness or conductivity is a common occurrence when this happens.

A device which is to operate correctly cannot tolerate any of these phenomena. This means that the device must be clean or at least the unavoidable contaminants must not produce harmful effects. This, in essence, is the definition of cleanliness itself. Bluntly stated, cleanliness is "just short of the amount of dirt that causes the problem."[1]

Unfortunately the amount of dirt that can cause a problem varies from device to device and from requirement to requirement. The type of dirt or contaminant that is harmful to the device also varies. The major criterion, however, is the ability of the contaminant to cause damage. This means that any material must be in a defined and harmful physical location and must have physical properties that result in damage in order to be considered a contaminant.

Sometimes a device is stored during or after assembly. The storage period may range from minutes to years. During this time, contamination of the device can occur even if it has a protective covering. Shipping of the device from location to location creates additional problems. Particles present within a device, or on the interior of the case, can be moved from a harmless to a critical location by vibration. Although the concentration of particle contamination in a sealed case may be very low, the contamination level can be maintained over a fairly long period of time. This is due in part to the device's breathing as a result of temperature changes. Continual diffusion of contaminants to surfaces of the device can occur. Improperly cleaned containers will transfer particles to the device also. This is especially true of padded containers and plastic containers. Contours of padded containers trap particles which are not released until the device causes deformation of the padding. Plastic containers pick up particles from the air and retain these particles as a result of electric charge. After surface discharge, the plastic surfaces deposit the particles on the components of the device. One of the possible causes of device failure is the generation of particulate contamination during normal operations. The necessary stresses involved in the normal operation cause wear and friction, which produce particulate contamination. During the past decade a series of articles has appeared in the journal *Wear*, describing the rate of contaminant production as a function of materials of construction and stresses. These articles may be of special interest to designers. The problem of particles migrating to a critical location can best be controlled by properly designing the device, if adequate knowledge is available on particle effects. By "design" is meant correct selection of mating surface materials and of mating surface clearances. Knowledge in this field is meager, however, compared to what is needed.

As an example of the need for reliability, consider certain military weapons that use explosive actuators where single-shot, high-reliability action is required. Lieberman states(*4*):

In general, contamination problems are inversely proportional to the amount of energy available for device actuation. In this same way, transmission of large amounts of energy is not sensitive to contamination to the degree that transmission of small energy levels is. At first glance it appears that almost every problem must be considered individually, each device, each application, each subcomponent, and so forth, but this is not necessarily the case. Careful observations of the requirements and problems of individual devices show that type classification within the device and across device types is possible. Classes of cleanliness

[1] Reference *4* of Chapter 2, p. 7.

vary from those required for assembly and preparation of thin film devices to those involved in the manufacture of heavy rotating electrical machinery.

The need for cleanliness must be examined on an economic basis—that is, the cost for attaining a desired degree of cleanliness must be weighed against expected benefits and requirements. Costs invariably rise with the necessity for eliminating the possibility of contamination effects.

General Literature Survey[2]

Pauly(*4*) surveyed the existing literature in 1956 to determine what characteristics of a dust environment could serve as a basis for recommending new test procedures to evaluate the resistance of military equipment to dust infiltration. The literature was organized according to the effects of dust, the components of the dust environment, and the factors affecting the dust conditions. It was found that particulate matter generated as a result of operation of equipment in the dust environment was more severe on equipment operation than was the climatic type of dust storm. The data listed in the literature were insufficient to predict the effect of a given dust condition in promoting dust penetration. It was possible to describe only in general terms the dust environment to which equipment types are subjected. Pauly initiated a research program to study the infiltration of dust under various dusty environments in which exposure time, dust concentration, air velocity, temperature, type of dust, and relative humidity could be investigated. Reproducibility of results was difficult, and only general trends were observed. His work was not involved with system failures.

McKee(*5*) investigated the effects of atmospheric contaminants in missile systems after the equipment had been exposed at the launching sites for about 2 years. The particular problems that he studied were influenced by the presence of atmospheric contaminants. The sources of these contaminants were within the system itself, rather than due to external corrosive material. The decomposition of insulation and plastic materials and the volatilization of fuel and oxidizer and other materials in the system represented the primary sources of atmospheric contaminants which had affected the deterioration of the equipment. It was observed that, regardless of the source, atmospheric contaminants change deterioration patterns. It was also found that atmospheric humidity exerts a considerable influence on these effects. The missile systems investigated showed evidence of fungus growths, electrolytic corrosion, corrosion of electronic parts and coatings, and corrosion of valves and fittings on the fuel system.

In a study made by Carter(*6*), fatigue life of balls ½ inch and 9/16 inch in diameter was found to vary inversely with the tenth power of stress. Dry powders, molybdenum disulfide, and graphite with a maximum particle size of 25 microns were tested in an effort to discover lubricants usable at temperatures beyond 450°F. These powders gave poor fatigue life, however, and occurrence of failure indicated that lubricant particles probably acted as minute stress raisers.

During the development of the Polaris missile a study was made of acceptable contamination in hydraulic fluid (OS 9196) as purchased, as in a test stand, and as in a control system. In establishing permissible levels, data such as those given in Table 4-1 were used as a guide. A 12-hour service and a 5-year storage life were among the specified parameters. The system under test was a servo valve which would permit passage of a particle 4 microns in diameter maximum and 2.5 microns minimum between the bore and spool clearance.

Briefly, the following conclusions were reached, as quoted from Rillings and Williamsen(7):

1. The design of servo valves must be based upon consideration of the effect of fluid contamination. The best mathematically designed valve may be rendered inoperative by micro particle contamination.
2. The build-up of particles of larger size approaches a saturation point at an early stage of system life. Larger particles are either being filtered out or broken up.
3. The continued increase in the quantity of small particles emphasizes the need for a filtering device capable of removing them from the system.
4. A major source of contamination is the assembly and test bench.[3]

A second test was performed on a pump-motor assembly, reservoir-accumulator assembly, two actuating cylinders, and two servo valves connected

[2] Abstracted from reference *41*.

[3] Reference 7, p. 34.

TABLE 4–1[4]

ALLOWABLE CONTAMINATION LEVELS*

	Particles per 100–Ml Specimen at Size Ranges:					
	5–15µ	*15–25µ*	*25–50µ*	*50–100µ*	*100–µ fiber*	*Notes*
As received						
SAE Panel	100,000	40,000	10,000	1,000	500	
National–56	10,000	4,000	1,000	20	5	
To system						
SAE Panel	20,000	9,000	3,000	300	150	
National–56	2,000	900	300	8	1	
In system						
SAE Panel	50,000	20,000	5,000	600	250	
National–56	1,500	675	225	1	0	
MIL–H–5606B	10,000	4,000	1,000	20	0	
MIL–H–25598	400	200	100	4	0	(This requirement has been abandoned.)
MIL–H–25475	50,000	10,000	500	150	25	
Lockheed–OS–9003	2,500	1,500	150	15	0	
Lockheed (Proposed)	10,000	2,500	500	50	10	
Lockheed (Burbank)	100,000	40,000	10,000	1,000	500	Same as SAE (as received)
Rocketdyne	30,000	300		30	7	300 for 20– to 50–µ range
Autonetics	2,875	1,375		300	100	
Bendix MSD	80,000	—			—	5– to 25–u range only
Bendix Missile (Int.)	250,000			7,500		1 fiber/10 ml
Martin (Denver)			250		10	2 ranges only
Republic	16,000	4,000	1,350	50	50	
Convair (San Diego)	500	300	150	85	35	
MIL–F–8815 (ASG)			15 µ absolute			
OS9196A	10,000	4,000	1,000	100	50	3 over 300 µ
NAV–Tent.	20,000	9,000	2,500	150	—	

* Prepared by Grumman Aircraft Engineering Corp. Abstracted from reference 7, p. 32.

together with tubing. The results of this test reaffirmed the above conclusions.

Another Polaris test program involving eighty-four servo valves from seven different manufacturers was performed. Rillings and Williamsen report that these

> tests related to artificial contamination of the fluid with 90% AC dust and 10% iron carbonyl. Specific quantities of contaminants were periodically introduced as the test progressed toward a condition of malfunction. Some of the causes of failure were collapse of the supply orifice filter, erosion of nozzle target and excessive scoring of slider.[5]

The Industrial Metals Testing Company, working on a contract from the Electric Boat Division, checked and tested a large hydraulic jack system

[4] *Ibid.*, p. 32.
[5] *Ibid.*, p. 35.

for a Mach 5 wind-tunnel project. This test used 800 gallons of hydraulic fluid, six Dennison pumps operating at 35 gallons per minute and 3000 psi, and thousands of feet of welded tubing. Servo-valve openings were limited to ⅛ inch maximum.

The designers were aware of potential problems resulting from contamination. Rapid erosion of valves from any appreciable contamination, especially metallic, was visualized. After this test program, more rigid cleanliness specifications were established. A comparison table of both specifications as stated in the Grumman report(7) is given here.

Contaminant	*Original Specification*	*Revised Specification*
1–25 μ	Less than 40,000	———
10–25 μ metallic	1000 max	20 max
25 μ and greater	500 max	
Nonmetallic	———	3000 max
Nonmetallic greater than 25 μ	———	28 max
Metallic greater than 25 μ	———	2 max

Conclusions from this test work indicate that:

1. Oil must be precleaned to 3 μ.
2. Millipore or equal filters are necessary for preliminary clean-up.
3. Regular 5μ Cuno and 10μ Puralator filters in system will maintain cleanliness for limited time, if no serious contaminant generator develops.
4. Permanent by-pass (3μ Millipore) is advisable for additional safety factor.[6]

Table 4-2 shows microparticle counts from typical field systems determined during the work of three different investigators. Particle-free hydraulic oil appears to be an accomplishment for the future.

One of the most widely accepted standards for evaluation of hydraulic fluid contamination is Aeronautical Recommended Practice No. 598 (ARP 598), prepared by the Society of Automotive Engineers. An extension of ARP 598 has been developed for sizing particles in the range 1 to 5 microns. Automatic counters for monitoring of flowing fluids are being used. These counters operate on the principles of electrical conductivity, light absorption, and ultrasonic beam reflection.

Servo Valve and Hydraulic Fluid[7]

Contaminated fluids can affect the response and service life of every component in a servo system. These contaminants normally originate in the oil, reservoir, valves, accumulators, piping, fittings, hose, actuators, and, most of all, the pump itself(*8*). Some typical examples are oil additives separating from the fluid; silica sand found in the oil reservoir, valves, and pump; tapping compounds still within the valves; and process residue lying in the accumulator, piping, fittings, and rubber tubing. Weld scale and system corrosion products contribute to the valve contamination. Wheeler and Sherrill(*9*) report that the critical points where solid contaminants can cause trouble in a typical flapper nozzle valve are filters, orifices, nozzles, torque motor, drain bleed, and spool clearance. Special attention should be paid to servo valves with parallel filters in the spool end cavities, since these are especially susceptible to the effects of filter clogging. Where these filters clog at different rates, the pressure differential between spool ends shifts the spool gradually and according to the changes in supply pressure. As the pressure drop across the filter rises, gradual loss in valve performance occurs. Ultimately, total failure of the servo control will result.

Servo-valve orifices are normally very small, usually 0.003 to 0.007 inch in diameter. They are especially susceptible to fibrous contaminants. Fibers, because of their random orientation, tend to form a network across the orifice, trapping extremely fine particles. The combination of fine particles and fibers will eventually stop the flow. Nozzles are usually relatively large in size, 0.010 to 0.04 inch. They are also very sensitive, however, to the accumulation of fibers and jagged particles. A build-up of small particles, 2 to 15 microns in diameter, in the metering orifices and nozzles causes a gradual drift or hardover signal in the actuator. This will produce a failure.

Small, hard, fast-moving contaminants do strike orifices, nozzles, and flapper surfaces. The result is erosion of these parts. Erosion changes nozzle and orifice coefficients. The most critical dimension in

[6] *Ibid.*, p. 36.

[7] Abstracted from reference *41*.

TABLE 4–2*

PARTICLE COUNTS FROM TYPICAL FIELD SYSTEMS

(NAA-MC, Cook Research, and GAEC Laboratories)

Fluid	*System*	*Particles per 100 Ml of Fluid at Size Ranges:* 5–15μ	15–25μ	25–50μ	50–100μ	100μ
MIL–H–5606	New Oil A	9,290	2,540	474	146	76
	B	2,590	682	314	82	66
	Aircraft A "High"	203,000	25,700	2,880	454	168
	"Low"	1,700	606	306	86	28
	Aircraft B "High"	69,500	3,700	604	28	28
	"Low"	1,800	408	216	58	6
	Missile A	3,930	726	112	22	0
	Missile B	32,500	4,590	3,600	312	152
	Missile C	2,530	1,040	306	160	170
	G.S.E. A "High"	33,800	1,640	788	108	124
	"Low"	2,520	740	524	38	28
	G.S.E. B	1,190	272	182	82	52
	G.S.E. C	11,400	732	518	132	116
	G.S.E. D	5,660	1,260	768	312	160
	GAEC Test					
	Specimen 1	6,600	2,100	1,300	600	670
	Specimen 2	13,000	5,800	870	290	440
	Specimen 3	43,000	20,000	12,000	6,800	1,710
	NAA–MD					
	Dirty fluid	75,000	25,000	18,000	11,000	125
	Very clean	3,500	660	380	70	30
	Superclean	590	150	100	27	13
MIL–H–8446	New Oil	26,900	2,380	1,060	160	190
	G.S.E.	76,100	632	80	20	64
	Aircraft	65,800	1,560	236	28	80

* Prepared by Grumman Aircraft Engineering Corp. Taken from reference 7, p. 46.

the first stage of a servo valve is the distance between the flapper and the nozzle. This dimension is normally about 0.001 to 0.0015 inch. Under these conditions particles 25 to 38 microns or larger can wedge the flapper hardover and cause servo-valve failure. When the flapper has been inactive for a period of time, this type of failure will occur from an accumulation of particles smaller than 38 microns.

The Armour Research Foundation report[8] further states:

[8] Reference *1* of Chapter 1, pp. 4-6.

Clearance between the torque motor pole pieces and the flapper are usually 0.01 to 0.05 inch. Since the flapper can move approximately 0.0015 inch in either direction this would appear to be sufficient clearance. However, enough magnetic particles can collect on the pole pieces to fill up this space and jam the flapper. Particles which build up on the pole pieces also can change the magnetic characteristics of the torque motor resulting in unstable performance.

The drain bleed, usually 0.012 or 0.026 inch in diameter gives very little trouble from contamination because most contaminants are apparently intercepted by other restrictions before they reach the bleed, which is the last restriction in the first stage. Should the bleed become plugged, full supply pressure would build up inside the valve dome and burst the dome or tear it loose from the housing.

The clearance between the second stage spool and sleeve is usually the smallest in the entire valve assembly. This is done to minimize leakage. The annular clearance between the spool and sleeve normally ranges from 1 to 6 μ. Minute particles wedge themselves between these mating parts when fluid leaks between spool and sleeve. Particles larger than 6 μ are not likely to work their way into the clearance unless they are extremely soft and flexible*(9)*. If the spool remains stationary for any length of time these particles tend to accumulate as silt. Contaminants trapped in this clearance increase the spool and sleeve striction and friction. This results in the valve hunting for the correct spool position, and valve response is lost. This type of contamination increases valve hysteresis and threshold, and is the most common cause of servo valve malfunction. Hysteresis is directly related to the force required to move the slide.

The equation for this force is*(10)*

$$F = \frac{P_1 - P_2}{4} \left[\frac{MK^2}{S} + \pi\, dt \right] \qquad (4\text{-}1)$$

where

$P_1 - P_2$ is pressure on each side of the metering orifice
K is orifice discharge constant
M is the mass of particle
S is the distance the particle moves into the orifice before stopping
d is the circumference of the valve slide
t is the diametral fit.

In apparent contradiction of Wheeler's statements Osgood finds that numerous contamination sensitivity tests have determined that heavy jagged particles that retain their shapes cause the greatest amount of slide to sleeve friction*(10)*. This type of contamination is usually generated by moving parts in the hydraulic system such as motors, pumps, accumulators, valves or actuators. It is generally ferrous. For this reason a high efficiency magnetic filter can often be used to remove the detrimental portion of contamination in the 0 to 10 μ size range. However, removing magnetic particles from a viscous fluid is very difficult. Spool and sleeve wear produce metal contaminants which tend to cause high friction levels in the second stage of the servo valve. They gall and score mating surfaces and greatly decrease the service life of all hydraulic components. Internal leakage increases as wear increases clearances between spool and sleeve.

Silting in the second stage spool is hard to overcome because particles are so small. Silting tends to occur when the spool stands idle or moves through an extremely small amplitude. Greater movement tends to wash the particles away from the spool and prevent silting.

Huggett*(11)* reviewed the fundamental aspects of contaminate silting in low power servo valves. Laboratory tests were conducted with a visual two dimensional flow study model to observe flow characteristics, from which velocity and direction of fluid entrance, vena contracta, and silting were determined. Data are presented to permit the designer to evaluate the need for contamination control in hydraulic system design.

Parker*(12)* discusses hydraulic fluid contamination experience, problems, and possible solutions that relate to Air Force weapon and support systems. He lists the following common contaminants: Iron oxide, silicon, calcium, lead, tin, lint, water, paint, magnetic metals, non-magnetic metals, lapping compounds, pipe seal compounds, rubber, and bacteria.

Electrical Contacts

During the past decade many studies have been made relative to effects of contaminants on electrical contacts. This probably is due to the fact that almost every electrical or electronic device depends on the proper operation of its electrical contacts, and this has been the first major problem attacked.

A second reason for the numerous studies is that electrical contacts lend themselves to contamination studies more easily than do other devices. Since it is felt that electrical contacts are one of the weakest links in product reliability of electromechanical devices, an extensive discussion of this subject will follow.

Maddock*(13)* is one of the few to obtain any quantitative data on dust concentration and failure rate of light electrical contacts. The organic film problem on elecrical contacts has been studied by numerous investigators, including Keefer and Gumley*(14)*, Berry *et al.(15)*, Hermanse and Egan

(*16*), and Chaikin(*17*). It is probably the best example of research applied to the contamination aspect of a specific class of failure mechanisms.

It is felt that the study prepared by Lieberman[po] on this subject can best be expressed in his own words and merits verbatim quotation here. Regarding electrical contacts, he writes:

When certain nonarcing metal contacts, notably palladium and those in the platinum group, are subjected to sliding friction in the presence of an appropriate organic vapor an amorphous colored solid of high molecular weight is formed at the point of slide*(16)*. Molybdenum, tantalum, chromium, gold and rhodium also produce solid products. Silver is the only metal reported not to produce the polymer*(16, 18)*. Chaikin *(17)*, however, states that silver produces polymer one order or magnitude lower than gold. Furthermore, only one of the sliding surfaces needs to be of active metal. Thus, conversion is obtained when palladium slides on quartz or glass. The occurrence of this organic deposit is independent of such environmental factors as airborne dusts and corrosive gases. It requires mechanical but not electrical operation of the contacts. It accumulates in the area immediately surrounding the region of contact slide. Arcing electrical discharges appeared to destroy such deposits completely or in part. These polymer deposits are nonconducting and are quite fragile compared with fibers or other particles to which most persistent opens on operating equipment have been traced. Nevertheless, the polymer has been shown to cause transient effects when an extensive laboratory study was made to compare relay performance with and without dust excluding enclosures. Test circuits were employed which detected all opens, even those of short duration. Despite the absence of dust the relays in the tightest enclosures showed the most opens and the only contaminant found on these contacts was the organic deposit.

Laboratory results have shown that failures caused by polymer formation were more numerous than the dust failures*(14)*. However, dust still appeared to be the main source of failures under service conditions. Polymer formation and carbonaceous deposits on the contacts were found to generate noise when vibrated by the operation of adjacent relays. Polymer failures are not likely to occur on contacts which arc since the arcing burns away the polymer.

It has been found that the contact shapes that tend to maximize contact area produce the smallest failure rates from polymer. Similar results were obtained in which the contact contaminants were limited to dust particles less than 25 μ in diameter. On the other hand, when the contaminating dust was changed to larger particles such as lint and paper fibers, the opposite tendency for the effect of contact shape was observed. It is apparent that arcing produces improvement in contact performance. The arcing burns off the larger irregularities on the contact surfaces, thereby tending to increase the fit or alignment of the contact. It also increases the microscopic roughness, increasing the number of potential conducting areas and possibly reducing the failure rate from fine particles by the mechanism described by Williamson, Greenwood, and Harris*(19)*. Precious metal contacts, when used in a circuit arrangement that results in contact erosion, had a very low failure rate from organic films. For example, the failure rate from dirt and film in a laboratory contact erosion study was only 0.01 failure per 10^9 contact operations. The obvious explanation is that heavy arcing burns away dirt and film, thereby keeping the contacts clean*(14)*.

Humidity has a pronounced effect on failure rate and persistency of failure due to polymer*(14)*. The lower the humidity the higher the rate of failure and persistency. This is because the polymer takes on more water as the humidity increases, becoming less dusty and less likely to fall into the contact area. Conversely, at low humidity the powdery aggregate has a better chance to fall into the contact area and produce contact failure. Tests have shown that the quantity of polymer generated is not affected by humidity. Gebauer*(20)* reports that the mass spectrometer was used to establish the relationship between the oxygen and water vapor content of the atmosphere surrounding the contacts of hermetically sealed relays and the contact resistance. Thus, dust control alone is not sufficient for final relay assembly. In tests on dry reed switches the presence of oxygen invariably caused a rise in contact resistance.

During the first five months of 1957 Bendix reports that of all incoming components employing electrical contacts 75.8% of those rejected were rejected because of excessive or erratic contact resistance*(18)*. Contact problems contributed to over 12% of missed shipping schedules. Nearly every case of contact resistance failure at Bendix has been attributed to contact contamination. The corrective action has been primarily one of improved cleaning techniques and of applying higher contact pressure. This was only partially satisfactory. In very few instances have they been able to positively identify composition of the contaminant. One of Bendix' vendors reduced the contact resistance to an acceptable level by sealing the edges of certain fibrous insulating materials used in a switch to reduce flaking and through the use of Cobehn cleaning process during assembly. The vendor also made 100% contact resistance inspections and packed the snap-action switch individually for shipment.

Berry*(15)* has studied high contact resistance in relays and switching devices in an effort to obtain quantitative information so that charts may be made listing effects of variables versus performance charac-

[po] *Ibid.*, pp. 7-12.

teristics. He found that the most common source of contamination is solder flux. In switching devices not sealed in cans the flux is usually recognized by color, fluorescence, and solubility, and is probably transferred by popping when connections are being soldered. In hermetically sealed relays, the same material is found on contact surfaces, on the side of the cans, and as loose flakes. A second substance found in sealed relays is a white material probably derived from the decomposition or fractionation of rosin. The amount of this material depends on the effectiveness of the mechanical seal, the total amount of solder required, and possibly on the amount of heat evolved. Epidermal scale, often found to cause high contact resistance, results from improper cleaning before sealing the relay. Dirt and dust have been found in various particle sizes and quantities on most of the contacts tested to date. Devices assembled in gray rooms under hoods have smaller and fewer dust particles than devices assembled in open areas.

Berry*(15)* also reports polymer formation as a source of high contact resistance. The formation of polymer is dependent upon contact material, upon a sliding motion in the presence of an appropriate organic vapor, and a condition when no current is made or broken. Once the polymer forms a later current can cause the polymer to carbonize, oxidize, and continue to be a source of high contact resistance. Contacts in a baroswitch operating in the presence of appropriate organic vapors show a greater amount of arcing than do clean contacts of the same material. The reason for this is that the heating of the contacts on closure decomposes the organic material leaving a carbon residue on the periphery or the arc. In repeated operations the arc seeks out the carbon and burns it off. The result is that the arc does not strike in the same spot on successive closures. The erosion brought about by this phenomenon decreases the life of the contact by a factor of 30 to 50. Berry also reports that when roller action is present as the only or final movement of contact much smaller quantities of contaminants will give rise to high resistance. Only rarely has Sandia Corp. encountered high resistance resulting from airborne dusts*(15)*.

Chaikin*(17)* reports a study on electrical contact failure caused by surface contamination. He found that a variety of identifiable particles were shown to be major contaminants but also encountered the organic polymer films. He places the organic films into two classes. Static polymers are formed spontaneously on contact metals in the presence of organic vapors. Frictional polymers are produced when an active metal (of the platinum family particularly) is rubbed against another metal in the presence of an organic vapor. Particles were found in the enclosures of all relays, sometimes in staggering quantities.

In four of seven relays having high contact resistance the cause of the abnormal resistance appeared to be particulate in origin. In the other three, there were no obvious particles in the make area. Chaikin concludes that particle contamination is still a mild-to-severe problem. Penetration of rosin flux during can sealing is a source of particles.

Maddock*(13)* is one of few to obtain a quantitative relationship between dust concentration and contact failure on light electrical contacts operated at contact loadings of less than 20 mg. At the low levels of force used in his study dust played a large part in contact failures. Dust is apparently retained on the contacts and the failure rate is determined by the highest concentration of dust to which the contacts were exposed (subsequent lowering of the concentration does not reduce the failures unless the contacts can be cleaned and sealed at the lower concentration). The contacts studied failed at the rate of 32% in a clean atmosphere presumably because of surface films. The failure rate increased until it was 52% at a dust concentration of 1200 particles/cc. Some tests indicated that, for the apparatus used, the effect of dust is sensibly negligible with contact loads greater than 15 mg.

Sources of Electrical Contact Contamination[9]

The performance of a pair of electrical contacts is changed by the presence of foreign matter on their surfaces. Usually the presence of contamination is associated with contact resistance or reliability; however, contact adhesion and the emission properties are also greatly affected. Changes in adhesion are reflected in variations in the wear and noise level on sliding contacts. The presence of contaminants changes the conditions under which dielectric breakdown of the contact gap occurs, and this in turn results in a different erosion mechanism. Troubles from contact contamination can usually be eliminated by identification of the contaminants, determination of their source, and elimination of the source. If the latter is not feasible, introduction of a properly controlled cleaning process or a change in contact material can assist in reducing the problem. Proper handling during the manufacturing cycle has as much to do with contact performance as proper design and correct choice of materials. Personnel performing the assembling operations should be aware of the contamination problems related to their area of work. They should also be familiar with what happens during the manufacture of the contact and during the lifetime of the finished device.

As mentioned previously, the materials of con-

[9] Abstracted from reference *21*.

struction can contribute greatly to the contamination of the device. Melting usually leaves a scale containing oxides and flux on the cast ingot unless this operation is performed in a vacuum or inert atmosphere. Material from the mold lining also can be left on the ingot surface. These foreign materials are often so deeply embedded that they have to be removed by scalping. During manufacture, operations of rolling, swaging, and drawing result in friction of the contact material against the hard surface of the die or roll. Minute amounts of iron and other steel components are smeared into the material. These small traces could present problems in very miniature units yet to be designed; however, these traces have not been shown to influence present contact performance.

Expensive precious metals are often used in clad forms that have to be annealed with special care to prevent excessive diffusion of base metal into the precious metal, particularly if the precious-metal layer is thin. It is often necessary to pickle clad materials because of oxides formed on the base metal side during fabrication. Pickling tanks can become loaded with copper which in turn can be deposited on a clad material by electrochemical action. This reaction occurs if a critical level of concentration is exceeded and if the material to be cleaned in the tank contains a component less noble than copper (e.g., silver-clad steel).

Every tool wears, and traces of iron, nickel, and other metals can become smeared into the contact surface. Much more dangerous, however, are metal chips or dust particles which can become deeply coined into the contact surface during a coining or welding operation. Welding introduces another source of contaminants. Weld flashes can be coined into the metal surface. Brazing operations performed in air generate oxides. Fluxes used in this operation can become a serious problem when they remain on the contact surface.

To allow proper contact operation, lubricants used in manufacturing operations have to be removed by degreasing. If this operation is done in a liquid phase, the solvents can become loaded with high-boiling components of the lubricant. These will then remain on the parts to be degreased when the solvent is evaporated in the drying operation.

Even minute burrs can cause the breakdown of a contact. Tool wear can result in the formation of burrs on the blanked part. Resharpening the tool every time fins or burrs appear would be expensive, and therefore they have to be removed by abrasive tumbling. Fine particles worn away from the tumbling stones can become embedded in the contact surface and result in difficulties in creep-type (very slow make-and-break) applications(*22*). These particles, generally silicates, also impair the difficult operation of resistance welding of silver or silver alloy contacts directly onto nonferrous base metals.

In discussing the subject of storage as a source of contamination, Freudiger states that gases

> . . . of the ambient atmosphere can react with metals. The first step of the reaction involves the formation of a thin absorbed film. Such a film has a thickness of a few molecular diameters and is formed under any condition except vacuum. Forces between the film and the underlying metal are weak. The reaction can be terminated with this adsorption step. The gold-oxygen system is an example of a reaction which does not go beyond the adsorption step.
>
> If it is thermodynamically possible, metal ions will leave the lattice and react with adsorbed gas ions, representing a chemical reaction involving strong bonding forces between the film and the metal substrate. Whether or not such a film will grow further depends on the particular system. A well-known example is the formation of silver sulfide which can grow to considerable thickness because sulfur ions can diffuse through silver sulfide and react with the metal at the interface. Contrary to belief, silver sulfide is not a good conductor; it belongs to the family of semiconductors with other halides and oxides. The phenomena taking place during the growth of a film are very complex and the time-thickness relationship can follow a variety of function(*23*). Silver sulfide is quite unusual inasmuch as it can creep away from the area where it forms causing trouble if silver is covered with a porous gold plate. The sulfide then forms in the pores and creeps over the gold, defeating the purpose of the gold plate(*24*).
>
> Corrosion of base metals used as supports of contact materials is undesirable. The formation of oxides on a clad welding button can impair its weldability; and contact assemblies consisting partially of copper-based alloys can tarnish severely, a fact which does not necessarily influence contact performance, but does impair the appearance of the contact.[10]

Electrical contacts that perform the operations of closing and opening without sliding can be ex-

[10] Reference *21*, p. 11.

pected to have chemical reactions with the surrounding atmosphere which are speeded up because of an increase in the surface temperature (*25*) of the contact. Particulate matter in the device is hammered into the contact surface. This particulate matter can be present in the assembly before it is enclosed, or it may be generated during mechanical action of the unit. An example is a sharp steel edge rubbing against a piece of pin.

The theory of friction and sliding wear as it applies to electrical contacts is complicated. Surface preparation and ambient conditions have a definite influence on friction, sliding wear, and noise. The influence is such that measurements correlating friction, wear, and noise with variables such as contact force, velocity, contact configuration, and other properties are invalid unless the atmosphere in which the experiments are performed is carefully specified and controlled. Experiments conducted at Bell Laboratories(*26*) which led to the discovery of the frictional polymer show this dependence clearly. The wear area on palladium contacts rubbing against each other in the absence of organic vapor is much larger than the one formed when even small amounts of organic materials are in the surrounding atmosphere.

A thin film of petroleum-based material can be used for lubrication of precious-metal contacts (*27*). Lubricants should not be used in low-energy-level sliding applications if the current is actually broken; under this condition, carbonization and other chemical changes in the oil will increase the noise level(*28*). Modern theory of lubrication stresses the importance of finding lubricants that will form strong bonds with the underlying metal. Achievement of strong bonds with noble metals is difficult because they are relatively inert. For applications in vacuum or in outer-space environs, it is necessary to use solid lubricants such as graphite or molybdenum disulfide, which do not evaporate. Requirements for maintaining the lowest contact resistance are not compatible with good boundary lubrication. Usually a compromise has to be found which often involves tests with a few lubricants.

In discussing chemical effects of an electrical discharge Freudiger states:

Discharges generate heat which raises the temperature of the contact surface and the ambient gas which in turn increases the rate of chemical reactions taking place on the contact such as oxidation of non-noble components of the alloys (copper in a silver-copper alloy). The arc spot itself will usually reach temperatures at which the compounds are not stable. The temperature distribution accounts for the appearance of the contacts after an arc has struck. The outside will generally be too cool for a significant rate of oxidation or other reactions. Nearer the arc, the rate of formation increases due to the increasing temperature so that a ring of compound forms around the arc spot. In the center the temperature can be high enough to cause the compound to break down; in this area the so-called self-cleaning action of the arc prevails, revealing a bare metal spot. A special case is the silver-tungsten oxide at elevated temperatures. Silver oxide is stable in this form (pure silver oxide decomposes at about 180° C and does not form at an appreciable rate below this temperature) so that one can say that the silver loses its nobility in the presence of tungsten. This is sometimes a problem in circuit breaker contacts, not so much when they are subject to short circuit because then the temperature of the arc is such that the contact surface is eroded away at a rapid rate, but when the breaker is actuated at a lamp load of around 20 amps. Formation of silver-tungsten oxide can be prevented by increasing the silver content in the surface layer by infiltrating extra silver into the silver-tungsten or by a thin electroplate of fine silver over the finished part.

Contaminants produced under the influence of a discharge are not necessarily the result of chemical compound formation; they can also be generated by decomposition. Organic vapors coming from such sources as lacquers, fluxes, insulating materials and from the case of the device can be broken down by the temperature of the discharge and deposited in the form of carbonaceous material on the contact surface. This reaction does not take place in the gas-phase itself; the first step involves the adsorption of the vapor at the surface. The phenomenon is most pronounced at current levels of roughly 0.1 to 1 amp. Below this area, breakdown of organic material is not very significant; and sufficiently high currents maintain the self-cleaning action of the arc blowing away the carbonaceous material from the contact surface. The material has been found to be almost pure carbon(*29*) and affects the contact performance in two ways. First, the surety of make is impaired(*30*) and an open circuit can be caused by the particles. The small particles also drastically change the mechanism of electrical breakdown of the gap and in turn can lead to a different rate of contact erosion or transfer than the one taking place in the absence of organic vapors(*31*). This so-called activation needs only extremely small concentrations of organic vapors. The reaction is not limited to carbon-containing vapors. Silicones are also affected and are just as detrimental as carbonaceous materials or even more so because the decomposition products tend to form glass-like insulating layers on the contact(*32*).[11]

Determination of Electrical Contact Contaminants

In discussing measurements of contact resistance, Freudiger writes:

Conditions under which contact resistance is measured has to be carefully specified because they can significantly alter the results. Contact force, for instance, determines whether elastic or plastic deformation is predominant in the contact spot, and the resistance of clean contacts is a direct function of the applied force. The force can also mechanically break down a film, particularly if wiping action takes place. Contact voltage, determines whether or not contact material is softened or melted. Field strength across a film on the contact of approximately 10^6V per cm causes the film to break down electrically. Therefore, contact resistance measurements must be taken at applied voltage of 50 mv or less to eliminate contact surface effects.

Contact resistance data obey statistical laws(*33*); hence, a number of readings have to be taken to get significant average values. ASTM has set up a specification(*34*) for measuring contact resistance. Another method allows probing the contact surface in individual spots, thereby detecting variations in the contact resistance over the surface(*35*). Based on this idea an apparatus has been constructed(*36*) which allows plotting the contact resistance distribution over the whole surface. A simple apparatus for resistance determination consists of a balanced beam whose contact can be moved by a micro-manipulator. The same apparatus can detect the breakdown by applying a sawtooth voltage displayed on an oscilloscope. Figure 4-5 shows the circuit diagram. The voltage necessary for breakdown is called "fritting" voltage.[12]

Freudiger further elaborates on the subject of determination of contaminants by stating:

Once a resistance measurement has established the fact that contamination is present at the surface, it is best to look at the contaminant under a binocular microscope. Optical inspection allows a certain classification of the foreign material and often facilitates subsequent analytical methods. One can recognize if the deposit is soft (greasy), if it is hard, and whether or not it adheres strongly to the surface. The shape can indicate if the particle is a piece of fiber or a piece of mineral dust.

The electron microscope is a suitable tool(*17, 37*) for identification of very small particles. It can also be used in connection with electron diffraction, allowing the analysis of the structure of the contaminant.

Bell Laboratory(*38*) workers have developed a method by which it is possible to strip off the contamination by means of a replica method, permitting examination of the contaminant and eliminating confusion with the underlying contact material.

Before any type of microchemical test reactions are performed, it is very useful to run some solubility checks which in combination with visual observation will often lead to an almost positive identification of the substance. Here is an example:

Let us assume that a silver contact is covered with a thin, dark film of soft texture that could either be silver sulfide or some organic condensation product. Testing the solubility of this material in potassium cyanide differentiates the two possibilities. Silver sulfide will immediately dissolve in the potassium cyanide, whereas organic material is practically unaffected. This finding can further be corroborated with a test for silver and/or sulfur, or in the other case, a general test for organic materials such as the reduction of chromic acid dissolved in sulfuric acid. Pure carbon is hard to identify, but it can be reacted with potassium azide to form cyanide . . .[13]

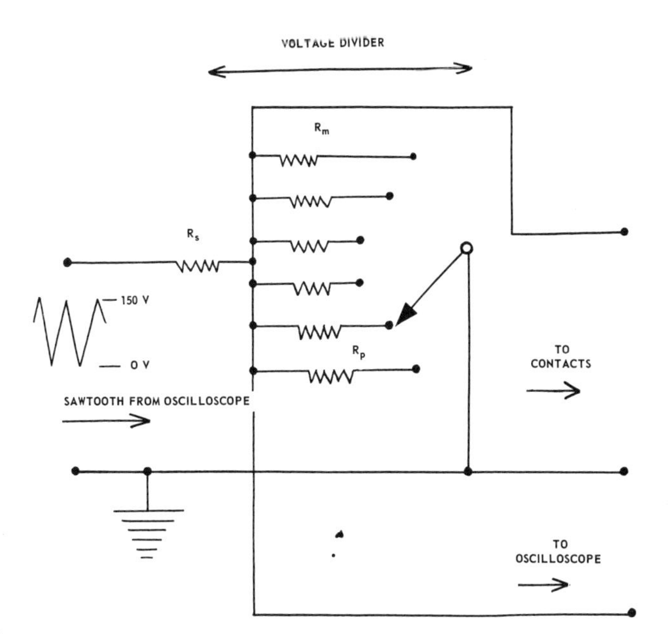

FIGURE 4-5. Circuit diagram of contact resistance apparatus with sawtooth voltage displayed on an oscilloscope for detecting breakdown(*21*).

A variety of microchemical tests are available for determining the contaminants found on contacts, but these tests have to be interpreted with caution.

[11] Reference *21*, pp. 11 and 12.

[12] *Ibid.*, p. 12.

[13] *Ibid.*, p. 13.

Many of them are so sensitive that it is of extreme importance to run a blank test along with the analysis of the sample to eliminate positive reactions which can be caused from sources other than the contaminant. Another problem is the determination of the significance of the results. Tests for metals such as iron, copper, nickel, etc., are so sensitive that one has to check whether or not the traces which can almost always be found really are responsible for the faulty performance of the contact. This can be done by running a simultaneous test on a clean piece of contact material of the same composition. Again, an example to clarify this point:

Let us assume that a fine silver contact showing a high resistance has dark deposit on its surface. It is soluble in nitric acid and shows the presence of copper. To conclude that copper would be the source of the contact problem might be erroneous, because silver always contains traces of copper which, however, never impair the contact performance. Some of this silver-containing copper will go into solution and copper, therefore, will be found regardless of whether or not the black deposit contains any copper at all. This problem does not occur if the deposit can be removed by the replica method, but not all contaminants can be stripped off by this technique. A test performed simultaneously on the sample and on an uncontaminated silver piece will, however, show distinctly whether or not the deposit is in fact a copper-containing material.[14]

No matter what the type of electrical contact or its end use, it should always be protected from particulate matter. Control of humidity is desirable not only to prevent the formation of rust on steel parts or oxidation products on nonferrous metal parts but also because moisture greatly influences the rate of formation of many corrosion products. Some oxide and sulfides will not form at all if moisture is absent, since the reaction must proceed through intermediate steps involving water. For instance, hydrogen sulfide does not attack silver, but the sulfide formation will take place if a small amount of water vapor is present. Sealing the contacts in polyethylene bags is a good method to protect them from particulate matter. It should be pointed out that both water and hydrogen sulfide will slowly diffuse through the polyethylene bags; however, the reaction at the contact surface will be greatly retarded. Plastic bags(*39*) sometimes contain enough moisture inherent in the plastic that in an environment of low humidity the moisture sometimes comes out inside the bag after sealing. A small package of a moisture absorber such as silica gel in a container is very effective in picking up all the moisture.

The contamination problem in contact unit assembling operations is essentially the same as in the parts fabrication, but, in addition, soft soldering operations are often performed. It is important that none of the solder is splattered onto the contact; otherwise, oxidation of the surface will occur. The flux used in the soft soldering operation has to be soluble in commercially available solvents even in the partly decomposed state. No general rules can be given because of the multitude of available fluxes manufactured under various trademarks. Ultrasonic cleaning is suitable for removing small particles before the assembly is hermetically sealed or enclosed.

Contacts in the Finished Assembly

Wiping action greatly increases contact reliability if contaminants are present. Reliability can also be significantly increased by using multiple contacts. In a good contact arrangement, surfaces are parallel to the direction of gravity or centrifugal forces, thus preventing the collection of particles on the contacts. All the precautions are useless if the switch itself is a generator of particles. Another problem cited by Freudiger(*21*) occurred when a switch failed in service in a critical defense application even though it was manufactured under the most carefully controlled conditions including a clean room, ultrasonic cleaning, outgassing of components, and proper choice of contact material. A plastic pin was rubbing against a sharp steel edge, and the resultant particles on the contact caused an open circuit in the switch.

Hermetic sealing and back-filling with reducing or inert atmosphere is not the answer to all contact problems(*17*). Outgassing of organic components can result in adsorption of a layer of organic material thick enough to raise the contact resistance in a sensitive relay to an unacceptable level. The tendency for outgassing can best be measured by measuring the weight loss of the organics after subjecting them to elevated temperature for several hours. The temperature level depends on the

[14] *Ibid.*, p. 13.

particular device; 160°C is the upper limit for a sealed relay.

If the possibility exists that the contact material will corrode under the given ambient conditions, a reputable contact manufacturer can make a recommendation for a contact material that will not tarnish under the circumstances.

Functional Operation of Precise Devices[15]

Generally speaking, most precise devices are predominantly mechanical in nature. They include bearings and timer assemblies, pneumatic and mechanical actuators, and power transmission and conversion systems. Contaminants cause varied problems in these devices. In electrical devices contaminants interfere mainly with adequate contact. In optical devices contaminants produce problems mainly in the area of light-path interference. The physical properties of a device can be affected differently by different contaminants.

Materials of construction are of importance in that their comparative hardness, reactivity, resistance to abrasion, etc., are part of their sensitivity to the composition of the contaminant. The physical dimensions (size and shape) of contaminants affect the materials of the device. Materials and design must be considered together. For example, contaminants hard enough to gouge or score a material may not be large enough to cause harm if the clearances in the device are larger than the contaminant particle.

Various functions of a device are sensitive to contamination. For example, the primary function of a relay is to control the passage of electric power, but the sensitive facets of this function are solenoid motion and the make-or-break operation at the contacts.

A number of operational factors regarding precise devices must be considered in light of possible contamination of the devices. The required precision of the device must be analyzed, since this involves the reproducibility of the operation. Also, requirements for precision or for accuracy of tolerance may exist independently. For example, a one-shot operation may not require precision but may require accuracy, whereas a repetitive device may require high precision but little accuracy. In either case, contaminants may affect the operation.

The contaminant environment will affect the life of a device operating in such an environment. This parameter is tied in with design in so far as packaging and contaminant tolerance are concerned. Duration, number of cycles, and obsolescence are other aspects of device life to be considered. Depending on whether continuous, intermittent, or one-shot operation is required, the tolerable contaminant environment will vary. For the same operating life, continuous operation will permit a higher level of contamination than intermittent operation. Between intermittent operations, contaminants may enter the device or migrate within it. One-shot operation may permit storage in contaminated environments but will require clean assembly.

The length of shelf life of an item depends on packaging, design, assembly, and storage contamination levels. In addition, transportation to and from storage aggravates the possibility of contaminant migration within the device.

Implementation of Device Operation[16]

Various operations, including the device parameters discussed above, can be affected by contamination. The device operations to be discussed in detail are position, motion, constraints, mechanical loading, and energy transmission.

Position and Motion

Lieberman states:

> Both linear and angular positioning of components in a device involve sliding motion and actuation. The primary effects of contamination will occur either at the beginning or the end of the movement. The contaminant effect will be mainly one of blocking. That is, the contaminant will interfere by introducing random resistances to the motion of the component. These will be of greatest importance when the actuating force either begins or stops.
>
> Essentially all precise devices that can be considered involve moving parts. Many require that a fixed clearance be maintained. In most cases of this sort, either the clearance limits a fluid flow rate or provides a fixed amount of control on a component movement. The concept of motion without finite clearance implies moving members in contact.[17]

An excellent example of this is gear teeth in a

[15] Abstracted from reference *40*, pp. 1 and 2.

[16] *Ibid.*, pp. 3-11.

[17] Reference *40*, p. 3.

power train. True direct contact does not take place, except for electrical contact deformation. Actually, the two moving surfaces are separated by a film of gas, fluid, or oxide. It should be noted that the film thickness depends on the force between the surfaces and usually will vary with time also.

In the case of motion with finite clearance, Lieberman writes:

> . . . the particles on the surface of one of the parts will usually produce a change in clearance resulting in interference with the motion. In the case of motion without finite clearance, the force is usually great enough so that a contaminant particle will either imbed itself in one of the surfaces or be crushed. In the latter case, there is no immediate concern. In the former case, the presence of the imbedded particle will sooner or later be harmful. The motion may be immediately stopped by the particle or the particle may cause sufficient surface damage to one of the parts to increase the power requirement greatly.[18]

Any of the following types of motion may exist between components.

Sliding motion with a finite clearance is a major part of the motions of importance in precise devices. Relays, switches, actuators, displacement indicators, etc., depend on this motion's taking place at a fixed rate with constant or controlled driving force. For one-shot operation, unidirectional sliding motion can include a single pass of a surface over another surface. In many cases, this type of motion will involve repeated passage of one surface over a track. In this situation the contamination problem is aggravated by the motion. Wear particles can add to the external contaminants and will be harmful.

Intermittent sliding motion may or may not involve repeated passage over the same track. The necessity for repeated start-and-stop action makes the presence of contaminants on the track more serious than for continuous motion. The effect of particles on the track will be a higher coefficient of static friction, which can be disastrous.

The considerations of unidirectional and intermittent motion discussed above apply to reciprocating motion with the additional certainty that wear particles or other material produced by repeated contact over the same surfaces will be present.

The simplest example of sliding motion with superimposed rotation is the movement of a float in a rotameter barrel. A more sophisticated application would be a ball-disk integrator. In either case, particulate contamination can result in appreciable error in readout for devices employing rotating motion.

In discussing rolling motion, which is distinct from sliding motion, Lieberman reports:

> The most frequent application for rolling motion in precise devices is probably in bearings. Because of the small clearances and low torque often accompanying this application, the presence of contaminants presents a very serious problem. The considerations applying to the first three types of sliding motion apply here as well. The possibility also exists of combinations of both sliding and rolling motion. Such combined movement will be most sensitive to contaminants because of the possibility of stress.[19]

Motion changes with time are significant. Two situations are of importance with respect to motion in precise devices. In the first, it is important only that a part be transferred from one position to another as a result of some action. In the other it is important that a part move from one position at a fixed velocity (or acceleration) and not necessarily with a specific destination. A simple two-pole switch illustrates the first situation; a repetitively driven wafer switch illustrates the second.

Both sliding motion and rolling motion at fixed velocity are sensitive to the presence of contaminants. The degree of sensitivity is a function of the clearance. Also, the inherent inertia of the system will determine whether the contaminant interferes with the operation or whether the contaminant is rejected by ejection, crushing, embedding, and other similar actions. The same considerations apply for acceleration and jerk as with velocity effects.

Constraints

The presence or acquisition of contaminants will have little, if any, effect on a fixed constraint. This situation exists because such a constraint involves a cessation of positive motion with enough force to overcome contamination. Normally, the allow-

[18] *Ibid.*, p. 4.

[19] *Ibid.*, p. 5.

able dimensional tolerance will be much larger than the contaminant particle size. A bearing action type of constraint involves sliding and/or rolling motion. The same considerations apply as for a fixed constraint.

Mechanical Loading

The presence of contaminants will cause local variations in loading which can be very harmful. Direct contact is a requirement for mechanical loading. Contaminants will interfere with contact or result in stress concentrations. Transmission of force to permit mechanical loading, whether by direct contact or through a lubricant film, should be directly through the design components. Inclusion of contaminant particles will result in pressure concentration or nonuniform loading that may be harmful. This applies primarily to actuation and is not so serious for contact. When deformation is part of the normal operation of a device, the presence of contaminants is of no consequence.

In discussing stresses due to mechanical loading, Lieberman states:

> All parts which are to be mechanically loaded in order to perform their function will be stressed. Under normal operation and with good mechanical design there will be no overstressing, or stress concentration. However, if contaminants are present, the possibility of stress concentration exists at the point where the contaminating particle contacts a loaded area. Damage can be produced at that point. In addition, the presence of stress can produce particles broken from the surface, and these will act as further contamination.[20]

Energy Transmission

Generally the presence of contaminants will not affect transmission of large amounts of energy but will be troublesome in transmission of small amounts of energy. Unfortunately, no quantitative information is available concerning the exact energy transmission level at which contamination becomes a problem. A reasonable hypothesis for the relationship between contamination effects and energy level might be a family of curves of various contamination levels, one axis being "effect" with a cutoff point at failure, and the other axis being "energy level."

In the transmission of mechanical energy, two mechanisms should be considered—positive drive and frictional drive. Depending on the scale of the drive mechanism and of the contaminant, interference can result with mechanisms of positive drive. This may range from a minor decrease in efficiency, as a result of increased friction, to complete blockage or jamming. Normal operation of frictional drive mechanisms results in production of such large amounts of particles that contaminants will add an insignificant amount of material to that already present. This is true to an unspecified energy transmission level at which point particle production will decrease and contaminant effects will become more noticeable.

> Contamination will always affect hydraulic or pneumatic energy transmission systems. The actual effect, however, is mainly one of interference with mechanical operations by contaminants transported by the fluid in the hydraulic system. Interference can occur with sliding motion, with motion changes with time, and with constraints. In addition to interference with any of the moving parts, contamination in a hydraulic system can result in changes in fluid flow because of partial blockage of a flow line. Partial blockage of a metering orifice demonstrates this problem.[21]

Few precise devices involve transmission of thermal energy directly as part of their operation, but the process is of some importance and will be included for completeness. The thermal energies considered are radiation, conduction, and convection. The presence of contamination on the surface of a radiating body will affect the rate of heat transfer, especially if the emissivity of the contaminant is different from that of the substrate. The major result is a nonuniform surface temperature distribution.

Since heat transfer of thermal energy by conduction depends on direct contact, any interference with such contact will affect the process. Contaminants will then interfere, except in the case of surface-to-gas transfer (or vice versa). In the case of convective heat transfer, the presence of contaminants will have no effect. The special case of dust-laden gas streams for increased specific heat is not considered.

The transmission of electrical or magnetic energy includes electromagnetic radiation and electrostatic

[20] *Ibid.*, p. 7.

[21] *Ibid.*, pp. 8 and 9.

force. This type of energy transfer is quite sensitive to contamination. This sensitivity exists because of the diversity of media through which the energy passes, the need for dimensional and composition control, and the effects at interfaces during energy transfer.

Transmission of radiant energy requires an emitting surface, a medium, and collecting surface. These requirements apply to transmission of electromagnetic radiation regardless of wavelength. When a well-defined beam of radiation is required, the contour of the emitting surface and the condition of the emitter–medium interface must be free of contaminants. This consideration holds both for long-distance signaling and for transfer of electrons in a vacuum tube or in a semiconductor. In addition, the high energy flux at such surfaces can be easily degraded by contamination. Energy loss by scattering or absorption from contaminant particles can be high, depending on the wavelength and the particle size. In the case of electrostatic or magnetic devices, the electric field or the magnetic flux is extremely sensitive to substrate configuration. For this reason, a contaminant particle will act as a sharp edge, intensifying the field locally and possibly causing breakdown.[22]

Conduction of electrical energy, writes Lieberman,

. . . probably is much more affected by contamination than is radiation. The problems arise in conducting electrical energy from one component of a device to another. It is necessary to obtain intimate contact over the largest possible area. The presence of contaminants on one or the other of the surfaces will cause poor contact, leading to high resistance paths and in some cases causing arcing. The severity of the contamination problem is inversely proportional to the force used in obtaining contact, and voltage applied, and the area of contact. For many precise devices the available contacting force and the system voltage are so low that normal atmospheric particles will cause contamination problems.[23]

Failure Mechanisms[24]

Contaminants cause failure and contribute to failure in various ways. Predictable or wear-out failure is the major category in which contamination can cause or accelerate failure. All precise devices have a finite operating life, expressed either in rated number or duration of operations or as mean time before failure (especially for devices with no moving parts.) Under the best conditions, the operating life will be limited only by degradation of part of the device. Under normal operation, contaminants in the device will accelerate the degradation process. The following paragraphs discuss the possible modes of degradation that may lead to failure.

Dimensional change is probably one of the most important contamination effects. Change in a dimension of a component will degrade the operation of the component in some way, thus affecting performance of the device.

Collection of particles on a component surface will increase the dimensions of the surface. When a critical clearance must be maintained, the original component dimension plus that of the particle(s) may result in an oversize part. Motion can be blocked entirely. In many cases, abrasive particles may be trapped between two moving parts. In time, abrasion will reduce a dimension to the point where operation is marginal. Generally an increase in dimensions will result in more rapid failure than a decrease.

Linear dimension changes occur most commonly when the dimensions of a component have been decreased. The scouring action of particles will result in a loss of material at a rate dependent on fractional powers of particle size, shape, hardness, and concentration. These factors will usually not change abruptly.

Attachment of contaminants to a component surface will usually take place at a random rate and with widely variable dimensional changes. The irregular change in dimension is a direct function of particle size, of "sticking" probability, of embedding ability, and of particle delivery rate. These parameters will vary as discontinuous functions of each particle that arrives at the surface.

Each individual contaminant particle will produce a local effect. During a period of time, abrasion may take place over a general or restricted area depending upon the motion involved in causing the abrasion. When a particle produces an increase in dimension, a local change occurs, even though a general effect may be noted. As an example, partial blockage of a fluid metering orifice may occur as a result of deposition of contaminants at only one point. Some typical descriptions of localized dimension variations are flaking, cracking, embedding, and gouging. General dimensional variations are wear, abrasion, and galling.

Much has been written on problems of friction and wear. The consideration of interest here is that of dimensional change insofar as it affects friction and wear. Any system with moving parts must have some friction to operate satisfactorily. Almost all the fasteners depend on friction to maintain the parts in alignment. The amount of frictional wear that takes place between two moving parts will depend on the dimen-

[22] *Ibid.*, p. 10.
[23] *Ibid.*, pp. 10 and 11.
[24] Abstracted from reference *40*, pp. 11-15.

sional tolerances which can be affected by particulate contamination.[25]

Friction and wear are usually manifested by some form of interference with motion in the device. This interference may be galling, seizing, complete blockage, or stick-slip.

Irregular wear can result from loading variations. Local overloading will result in an overstrained condition which can cause flaking, indentation, etc. The presence of discrete particles can result in local overloading, since these particles may cause a dimensional misfit in a small area.

When the stress on a component can be considered in terms of the total force per unit area, contaminant particles in the system will reduce the area to that of a particle, thus increasing the stress at the point where the particle is present. The stress may be increased sufficiently to overstrain a component. The probability of overstraining a component because of particle-caused local stress will depend on the relative hardness of the component and of the particle: i.e., either the particle is crushed or a component surface is damaged.

. . . When close tolerance components are part of a device, the temperature must be controlled sufficiently so that unequal thermal expansion does not cause any misfits. If contaminants are present, excessive frictional heating may take place. If so, local expansions may cause further excessive friction, snowballing to the point where damage can be caused. In high-speed devices structural failure can occur; in lower-speed devices welding can occur; in electrical systems arcing across heated conductive materials can occur.

Normal machined surfaces can be considered as having corrugations whose scale is specified as surface finish. Surface finish specifications are usually made for friction reasons. Changes in surface finish may cause excessive friction between sliding parts.[26]

Particle contamination will cause increased roughness in surface finish. No measurable changes in dimensions will be caused, but the scouring action of the particles on the surface will destroy the specified smoothness either grossly or in a localized position. The effect on operational performance of increased surface roughness will be higher friction between moving parts. In some cases, motion can be halted. In others, the interference may cause faulty operation, loss in sensitivity, etc. The effect of degradation of surface finish on optical components is obvious.

[25] Reference *40*, pp. 11-13.

[26] *Ibid.*, pp. 14-15.

Diffusion effects result from collection of particulate contamination on the surface of a component. The materials of the component and of the contaminant are important, since the diffusion effects depend on the contaminant diffusing into the component and reacting to form a compound or alloy whose physical properties differ from those of the base material. In general, the results of diffusion of a contaminant into a substrate are minor in comparison to the results of dimensional changes or surface finish variations. One problem cannot be neglected, however, the change in properties due to diffusion will produce particles at a much more rapid rate than would normally be expected.[27]

Unpredictable or catastrophic failure may occur at any time and is not necessarily dependent on contamination. It would be due to such causes as defective material, improper operation, or gross misuse.

Failure Consideration[28]

In Lieberman's final report (*41*) on contamination effects, he states:

An understanding of both the applicable failure modes and failure mechanisms is of prime importance in any attempt to correlate particle contamination with subsequent device failure. The first term refers to the observable pattern of device failure; that is, failure by fracture, by excessive wear, by tolerance deterioration, by pitting and corrosion, by cracks and subcritical fractures or by other recognized gross failure patterns. The latter term refers to the physical means whereby the failure occurred. Representative failure implementing concepts are, creep, fatigue corrosion, friction-wear, and other surface failure mechanisms.

There are two primary facets in the failure mode-mechanism association with device contamination. If the device . . . can be described in terms of device operational characteristics and the effects of particle contamination can be determined on the operational characteristics, . . . then, in general, the correlation between contamination and device failure can be expressed quantitatively. On the other hand, if the possible failure modes can be determined then qualitative predictions as to the effect of particle contamination can be made. If post mortem information is available on past failures of a similar type, then qualified predictions are simplified. In a logical and planned approach to the device failure-contamination problem, the latter process will normally precede the former, thus providing information upon which to develop more refined conclusion."

The study of failure mechanisms is a complex task.

[27] *Ibid.*, pp. 14-15.

[28] Abstracted from reference *41*, pp. 22-31.

Little is quantitatively known at present about certain phases of the field. However, current work should shed considerable light in this direction.[29]

A limited survey was conducted by Armour Research Foundation, and the results are contained herein. Certain aspects of the grosser predictive technique were also covered and will be discussed.

Typical Failure Modes

In the broadest sense, failure of a device part means any action resulting from service conditions and prior manufacturing history causing it to cease to function satisfactorily. The following paragraphs discuss the classifications of device part structural failure modes.

A device may fail because of deflection of an element beyond its design limits. This is an excessive elastic failure.

Elastic buckling can be described as a sudden deformation beyond the design limits. This type of failure is rapid in nature, and the symptoms preceding its occurrence are not readily discernible.

Plastic deformation of a device part remaining as a "set" after the load is removed represents failure or a significant degradation of device structural integrity.

Damage by creep, the continuing distortion of a material under steady load, is similar in character to damage by plastic deformation. The difference is that creep continues while simple plastic deformation virtually stops after a short period of loading. For the common structural metals, creep is important only at elevated temperatures.

Unlike plastic deformation or creep, which involve appreciable volumes of metal before noticeable structural damage is done, fracture may start at some point of localized stress concentrations. From the nucleus it may spread to total fracture of the piece. This process occurs in brittle materials under steady load, and in ductile materials under repeated stress. In the latter case, the crack is due to exhaustion of the ductility of the overstressed material, and once started, will spread even under relatively low stress.

Such a fatigue crack often starts under shearing stress within the crystalline grains of the plastically deformed metal. When the crack spreads in a region of tensile stress, it assumes a direction at right angles to the principal tensile stress. When it spreads in a region of compressive stress the crack usually follows a direction of maximum shearing, and proceeds more slowly than it does in a region of tensile stress.

[29] Reference *41*, pp. 22 and 23.

In addition to structural failures another type of considerable importance is functional failure. A device or mechanism is considered to have failed if it did not or cannot perform its intended function, regardless of any structural damage. This class of failures is characterized by two general types:

Failure by malfunction is defined to mean prevention of the successful performance of a device function by some external or internal agent which does not appreciably affect the structural integrity of the device. Examples of this type of failure might be sticking of component interfaces, or binding or hindering in movement of a mechanical action.[30]

Degradation failure is apparent by a change in device output characteristics, due to a slow drift or change of component operating parameters outside an allowable tolerance zone. Two examples of this type of failure are backlash (the lost motion between two elements of a mechanism) and distortion (a change in the form of a device output due to off-tolerance components).

In examining the concept of correlation of failure with contamination, practically no information is available concerning the relationship to structural failures. Some information concerning antifriction bearing raceway failures is available(*42*). Failures that are partially structural and partially degradational in nature are discussed by Ling(*43*) and by Reichenbach and Kingsbury (*44*). Some information involving contamination and both malfunction failures and degradation failures are discussed by Ling(*43, 45*), by Tabor(*46*), and by Rabinowicz *et al.*(*47*). In general, this information is concerned with electromechanical instrument-type devices, mechanical gears, and antifriction bearing.

Typical Failure Mechanisms

In discussing typical failure mechanism, Lieberman writes:

> . . . a knowledge of the failure mechanisms applicable to a particular device under particular circumstances is extremely important in a quantitative failure-contamination analysis. In addition, basic knowledge of the factors involved in the mechanisms of various failures may be used to determine the most probable modes of failure for a component or device, providing input information for the grosser predictive technique. Following are brief descriptions of the factors (failure mechanisms) involved in a number of failure modes.

[30] *Ibid.*, pp. 23 and 24.

Ductile fracture implies a flow of material prior to fracture. Failure may result from the distortion reaching an intolerable level or from the fracture itself. The distortion is governed by the stress-strain diagram of the material involved. The shape of the curve depends on the strain hardening or the ductility of the material.

A common assumption is that an increment of strain, $\triangle e$, is proportional to the deviatoric stress, S, in the component directions.

$$\triangle e = kS \qquad (4\text{-}2)$$

Final fracture depends also on the material properties, and a variety of theories are available for predicting the state at which fracture occurs.

Brittle fracture implies a rapid failure without significant prior flow of the material. The phenomenon is usually associated with an area of stress concentration such as a scratch, small pit, or crack. Most theories of brittle failure are based on the Griffith theory of crack propagation. This theory states that a crack of length $2C$ will propagate and create catastrophic failure when the value of average stress reaches the value

$$S = \frac{2ET}{\pi C} \qquad (4\text{-}3)$$

when E is Youngs Modulus and T is the surface tension of the material per unit thickness. Normally ductile materials may fail in brittle manner if the temperature is sufficiently low. The critical temperature is the so-called "transition temperature."

Instabilities may occur whenever long or thin members are under compressive axial loading, torsion, or are rotating. Such members include shafts, bars, rings, beams, plates, tubes, and shells. Failure occurs when the rate of increase of strain energy of the member due to distortion exceeds the rate at which work is being performed by the loading. A simple example is a prismatic bar with compressive end loading which buckles when the load reaches the "Euler load" of

$$P = \frac{\pi^2 EI}{l^2} \qquad (4\text{-}4)$$

where EI is the modulus of rigidity and l is the length of the bar.

Creep is the phenomenon where materials continue to flow even under uniform load. The distortion is generally at a very slow rate but is sensitive to both stress level and temperature. The region of constant creep rate may generally be described by an exponential function of the stress, S, and temperature, T. (Empirical relation by Bailey).

$$\frac{de}{dt} = aE^{bT}S^n \qquad (4\text{-}5)$$

where a, b, and n are material constants. For most engineering materials at room temperature creep is negligible below the elastic limit.

Fatigue implies failure of a material by fracture due to repeated loading. The phenomenon may be best described by a plot of stress versus cycles to failure (S-N diagram). Most engineering materials exhibit an "endurance limit," S_e, which is the value of stress below which an infinite number of cycles are required to produce failure. In general the relationship may be described by

$$S = k_1\,(S - k_2)^{-k_3} - k_4 \qquad (4\text{-}6)$$

where k_1, k_2, k_3, and k_4 are empirical constants, k_2 being the endurance limit. For sinusoidal loading, the stress may be described by

$$S = S_m + S_r \sin wt$$

where S_m is the mean stress level and S_r is a variable stress. The effect of mean stress on fatigue failure at a specified number of cycles may be stated mathematically as

$$\frac{S_r}{S_e} + \frac{S_m}{S_u} = 1 \qquad (4\text{-}7)$$

When a material is cyclicly loaded at different stress levels, Miner's criterion may be employed to estimate the cumulative damage from fatigue. This states that a material will fail when the sum of the ratios of cycles n, at each load and the cycles to failure, N, at the same load exceeds about .8 to 1.0.

$$\sum_i \frac{n_i}{N_i} \leq 0.8 \text{ or } 1.0 \qquad (4\text{-}8)$$

Wear occurs whenever materials rub over each other. The rate of wear is proportional to the product of normal contact load, N, and length of travel, of one part over the other, and inversely proportional to the hardness of the material, H.

$$\frac{dw}{dt} = k\,\frac{NL}{H} \qquad (4\text{-}9)$$

Wear rarely causes breakage of a member, but failure is caused by parts becoming out of tolerance and not performing their required functions satisfactorily.[31]

Corrosion of a material can be defined as the gradual deterioration of the surface by chemical reaction with its environment. The most likely type of corrosion to occur in electromechanical equipment is atmospheric corrosion. The metal combines with oxygen to form oxides which then usually flake, chip, or wear off relatively easily. Moisture

[31] *Ibid.*, pp. 25-28.

commonly accelerates the process. Also, metals under stress tend to corrode more rapidly than unstressed metals. Corrosion may form pits which act as stress-raisers for materials subjected to cyclic loads. This will greatly reduce the fatigue strength of the material.

Impact strength can be considered the energy-absorbing quality or "toughness" of a material. Impact strength implies a rapidly applied load. In general, increased rate of loading improves the strength properties of a material. Young's modulus, yield strength, ultimate strength, and maximum deformation are usually all higher values. If the impact is applied while the metal is below the transition temperature, however, ductility will be reduced, and failure may be brittle in nature. It has been demonstrated that a critical velocity does exist above which fracture is assured. This velocity is given for uniaxial tension by the relation

$$V = \int_0^{e_0} \frac{d_s\, d_e}{\rho}\, d_e \qquad (4\text{-}10)$$

where e_o is the strain at maximum load, $d_s\ d_e$ is the slope of the stress-strain curve, and ρ is the density of the material.

Galling occurs by the digging or gouging of the surface of one material by another. Materials in contact exert interface pressures on one another and create a stress distribution in a region. When the maximum stress exceeds the yield strength of one material, the surface becomes permanently or plasticly deformed. If relative motion is involved, the surface is "galled." This phenomenon is based on a derivation by Hertz for the maximum interface pressure between two bodies in contact. If in the region of contact the radii of curvature are R_1 and R_2, the modulii of elasticity are E_1 and E_2, and the Poisson's ratios are μ_1 and μ_2, respectively, for the two materials, the maximum stress resulting from a contract force P is shown to be

$$S_{max} = \frac{1}{\pi}\left[\frac{6P\left(\frac{1}{R_1}+\frac{1}{R_2}\right)^2}{\frac{(1-\mu_1)^2}{E_1}+\frac{(1-\mu_2)^2}{E_2}}\right]^{1/3} \qquad (4\text{-}11)$$

Galling occurs when $S_{max} \geqq S_y$, the yield strength of one material.

Lieberman states:

> Sticking occurs when parts in contact cease to have an intended relative motion. Slipping, conversely, occurs when parts in contact exhibit an unintended relative motion. Both effects are governed by the friction between the materials. If F is the tangential shear force applied at the interface and N is the normal force applied, the friction force is $f = \mu N$ where μ is the coefficient of friction for the materials. Slippage occurs if $F > f_s$, and sticking occurs if $f_d > F$ where f_s and f_d are calculated using the static and dynamic coefficients or friction, respectively. An important factor which affects the friction force is clearly the normal contact load N. This load is often a direct function of the temperature of the materials. Differential expansion or contraction of the parts increases or decreases N in a manner such that the external constraints on the two parts are satisfied.[32]

Gross Failure Considerations

As explained in the previous section there are two possible methods of attacking the problem of failure versus particle contamination. It appears that the gross approximate technique may initially yield the most fruitful results.

The listing entitled "Contaminant Effects Parameters Summary" allows a gross characterization of the device operation. It also lists those probable macroscopic factors which most likely effect device failure. The list is fairly inclusive. This listing is not intended to apply to any particular device, but any device can be characterized by the appropriate heading.

Contaminant Effects Parameters Summary[33]

I. Functional Operation of Device
  A. Device Type Examples
    1. Watch mechanisms
    2. Low torque sliding contacts (wafer switch)
    3. Miniature electric motors (bearings, shafts, and collars)
    4. Barometric linkages
    5. Relay contacts
    6. Miniature printed circuit boards and welded circuitry
    7. Gas and fluid metering orifices (0.062, 0.038 in.)

---

[32] *Ibid.*, p. 30.
[33] *Ibid.*, Appendix A.

8. Gyro mechanisms

B. Hardware Considerations
1. Materials
2. Design
a. Geometry
i. Shape
ii. Clearance
iii. Finish
(a) type
(b) class

C. Operational Considerations
1. Required precision
a. Intended usage
b. Usage environment
2. Accuracy tolerances
3. Device life required
a. Duration of operation
b. Number of operational cycles
c. Obsolescence factor
i. New models
ii. Modifications
4. Mode of operation
a. Continuous
b. Intermittent
c. One-shot
5. Shelf life
a. Storage prior to operation
b. Storage between operations

II. Implementation of Device Operation
A. Position
1. Linear
a. Accuracy of position
b. Tolerance limits
2. Angular
a. Accuracy of position
b. Tolerance limits

B. Motion (B-1) with Finite Clearance
(B-2) without Finite Clearance
1. Sliding motion
a. Unidirectional
b. Reciprocating
c. Intermittent
d. Rotating
2. Rolling motion
a. Unidirectional
b. Reciprocating
c. Intermittent
3. Motion changes with time
a. Velocity
b. Acceleration
c. Jerk (rate of onset of acceleration)

C. Constraints
1. Fixed
2. Bearing action
a. Journal or sleeve
b. Anti-friction
c. Fluid
d. Elastic constraints

D. Mechanical Loading
1. Force
a. Actuation
b. Contact
2. Deformation – strain
3. Stresses

E. Energy Transmission
1. Transmission of mechanical energy
a. Mechanisms
i. Positive drive
ii. Frictional drive
b. Fluid transmission
i. Hydraulic
(a) flow
(b) pressure
(c) sizing
2. Transmission of thermal energy
a. Radiation
b. Conduction
c. Convection
3. Transmission of electrical or magnetic energy
a. Radiation
b. Conduction

III. Device Effects – Failure Modes and Mechanisms
A. Predictable (Wear-out) Failures
1. Dimensional changes
a. Increase or decrease
i. Linear
ii. Irregular
b. Type of change
i. General
ii. Local
c. Friction and wear considerations
i. Loading variation
ii. Stress-strain consideration
iii. Materials
iv. Manifestations of friction and wear
(a) galling
(b) seizing
(c) blockage
(d) stick-slip phenomenon
d. Temperature effects
i. Gross
ii. Local
2. Surface finish variations
a. Changes in specified finish
b. Effect on operational performance
3. Diffusion effects
a. Fatigue acceleration
i. Contributory factors
ii. Correlation with design life
b. Creep rate change
i. Plastic deformation
ii. Secondary environment effects
(a) temperature
(b) previous loading history
c. Embrittlement

i. Secondary environment effects
ii. Material considerations

B. Catastrophic Failure
1. Gross design errors
2. Mis-assembly
3. Functional misapplication
4. Material malfunction

IV. Contaminant Properties
A. Delayed
1. Gaseous
2. Particles
a. Diffusing into materials to produce delayed weakness
b. Size effects, such as slow erosion
c. Migration to sensitive areas
B. Prompt
1. Hard particles (depending on substrate) to produce wear, jamming, galling, etc.
2. Soft particles
a. Dimensional changes, weight imbalance, motion interference, etc.
3. Size considerations
a. Large, direct action
b. Small, agglomeration after deposition
C. Energy Content, (Particle-Substrate)
1. Electric
2. Kinetic
3. Thermal
D. Chemical and Physical Properties
1. Nucleating
2. Sticking
3. Secondary contamination

V. Contaminant Sources
A. Manufacturing of Component
1. Casting inclusions
2. Carryover from previous machine operation
3. Chip production and/or dirty cutting oil, etc.
B. Assembly of Component
1. Flux and solder fragments
2. Adhesive particles
3. Wire-drawing
4. Grinding and other fitting operations
5. Handling or deformation by tools
C. Storage
1. Deposition from air
2. Transfer from container
3. Breathing of container
4. Corrosion-product formation
D. Cleaning
1. Dry transfer
2. Wet transfer
E. Air
1. Energy-gradient deposition-gravitational, electric, thermal
2. Impaction
3. Diffusion, coalescence, nucleation, etc.
F. Assembly environment to air
1. Through air-cleaning system
2. Reentrainment from room surfaces, jig and tool surfaces
3. Personnel, skin, from or through clothing
G. Normal Operation
1. Wear
2. Overspeed, etc.
3. Migration to critical zone

Fluid-Flow Device Characterization

As an example, a fluid-flow device might be characterized by using the contaminant effects parameters as follows:

I. Functional Operation of Device
A. Device Type Examples
1. Gas and fluid metering orifices
B. Hardware Considerations (entire listing)
C. Operational Considerations
1. Required precision
a. Intended usage
b. Usage environment
2. Accuracy tolerances
3. Device life required
a. Duration of operation
b. Number of operational cycles
4. Mode of operation
a. One-shot
5. Shelf life

II. Implementation of Device Operations
A. Position
1. Linear
B. Motion with Finite Clearance
1. Sliding motion
a. Unidirectional
2. Rolling motion
3. Motion changes with time
a. Velocity
b. Acceleration
C. Mechanical Loading
1. Force
D. Energy Transmission
1. Transmission of mechanical energy
a. Fluid transmission

III. Device Effects – Failure Modes and Mechanisms
A. Predictable (Wear-out) Failures
1. Dimensional changes
2. Surface finish

The functional characterization of a device can be logically extended to complex systems. The systems are subdivided into functional modules, each module consisting of several components whose sole function is one particular job. An example of this would be a positioning servo, in which a functional module might be those components associated with the output or positioning portion of the servo system. A gross assumption can be made that similar functional modules under similar environmental stressing will probably fail in a similar fashion, owing to somewhat the same causes. Such an assumption, although indeed gross, does permit an extension of the previously mentioned techniques to the broader or systems area.

An example cited in the literature of an application of failure prediction along lines similar to those encompassed by device functional operation is the so-called failure therblig technique. This approach[33a] was originally initiated by D. R. Earles and M. F. Eddins of the Reliability Analysis Section of AVCO Corporation, Research and Advanced Development Division. In their paper, they define a failure therblig as follows:

> A failure therblig is defined as a design feature failure function. Where therbligs were related to human functions originally, failure therbligs are related to hardware functions. Where therbligs were used in motion studies to eliminate ineffective movements, failure therbligs are used in reliability studies to simplify design concepts and eliminate ineffective complexities. The failure therblig concept can therefore be defined as the establishment of fundamental design feature function with which a rate of failure can be associated to establish the failure potential for any combination of these functions in an equipment design.

The term therblig was coined by Frank B. Gilbreath in the early days of industrial engineering to describe an elementary subdivision of a cycle of human motion. The failure therblig, as previously described, is truly a device functional operational parameter. Currently the failure therblig concept has not been carried much beyond the initial conceptual stage. The concept is an interesting one, however, and certainly bears consideration.

To conclude the discussion of gross failure considerations, an examination of the straightforward approach is in order. Certainly a fruitful approach is that of statistical evaluation of device failures. This technique involves the testing to failure under controlled environmental conditions of all those devices that characterize a particular field of interest. By noting the mean time to failure of each device, by varying the environmental factors of particle contamination, and by having previously characterized the devices by functional parameters, a statistical correlation can be drawn. The obvious drawbacks to this approach are the long testing times involved and the high cost of testing to failure of complex and expensive devices.

[33a] *Ibid.*, p. 34.

Experimental Studies

The following modes of operation define in general the sample mechanisms studied by Armour Research Foundation(*41*). They represent the input for this functional characterization.

1. Sliding Motion
   a. Unidirectional
   b. Rotating
2. Rolling Motion
   a. Unindirectional
   b. Intermittent
3. Fluid Flow
   a. Orifices
   b. Clearance

These three operational modes are extremely broad in coverage. Any individual device can be categorized much more completely in terms of the outline of contaminant effects parameters. For the purposes of this discussion, the more general classification will suffice.

Proper initial design from a functional standpoint and subsequent proper assembly from a mechanical standpoint being assumed, the contamination–failure interaction can take two forms. The reasons for failure of devices characterized by sliding and rolling motion can be traced to friction and wear phenomena. Among the failure modes involved are (1) galling and seizing, (2) deterioration of tolerances, (3) development of stress concentrations, and (4) breakdown of surface finishes.

A number of other secondary effects become noticeable as the friction and wear processes continue.

An attempt was made by Lieberman, through the use of the available literature, to define the relationships between particle contamination and various friction and wear phenomena. It was concluded that the degree to which these phenomena affect an individual device is a function of the exact operational mode or purpose of the particular device. The same device, if used for slightly different purposes, will in all probability be affected in varying degrees by frictional phenomena. This problem typifies the difficulty in formulating general contamination criteria.

The major failure mechanism of fluid flow appears to be directly related to the deleterious effect of particle contamination on tolerances. The effect of particle clogging of orifices and flow paths on device operation is relatively easy to evaluate from a qualitative standpoint. The quantitative evaluation of the same phenomenon is difficult, however. The question arises, "How much of a change in device operation constitutes a failure?" If a device employing fluid flow also employs a sliding motion, such as a piston and cylinder combination, these friction effects should also be considered. In many cases, the frictional effects are second-order effects when compared with particle clogging of the primary flow orifice.

To illustrate the functional characterization of equipments and the application of the gross techniques, Lieberman selected a typical equipment type. A gross characterization, as discussed previously, was made in terms of functional characteristics. An analytical expression was derived for the failure of this particular device in terms of its operational parameters.

To show the complex nature of what appears to be a simple failure problem, consider a timer using a pneumatic piston and cylinder with an orifice. The mode of operation of this particular device is one of modulated motion. The size of the orifice and the strength of the driving spring determine the time required for the piston to traverse its length of travel. This is used to time some other event. The most significant mode of failure here is the degradation of operational time beyond the acceptable zone of tolerance, due to particle contamination of the flow orifice or cylinder wall.

The device in question can be described as a piston and cylinder combination with a circular bleed hole in the piston to be used as a timing mechanism (see Figure 4-6). The piston is driven downward by the action of a helical spring. The time required for the piston to break and make electrical contact

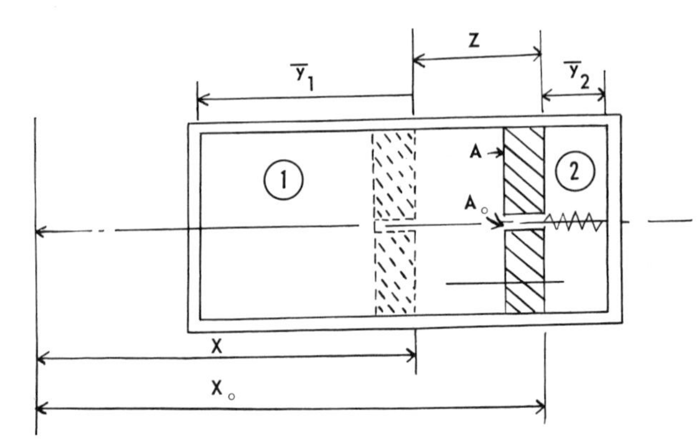

FIGURE 4-6. Piston timer(*41*). $\bar{y}_1$ = initial volume, control space ①; $\bar{y}_2$ = initial volume, control space ②; A = cross-sectional area of piston; A_0 = cross-sectional area of orifice; $\bar{m}_1$ = mass of air in initial volume $\bar{y}_1$; m_1 = mass in ① at time t; $\bar{p}_1$ = initial pressure in ①; $\bar{p}_2$ = initial pressure in ②; p_1 = pressure in ① at time t; p_2 = pressure in ② at time t; V_1 = volume in ① at time t; V_2 = volume in ② at time t; $\bar{m}_1$ = mass of air in initial volume $\bar{y}_2$; m_2 = mass in ② at time t.

(to complete one traverse of the cylinder) is specified within close tolerances. Failure of the device to operate within these tolerances shall constitute device malfunction.

With an expression for the time of operation in terms of the orifice area (A_o), one can qualitatively discuss the effects on device operation of reduction in orifice area by adherence of contaminant particles or by the erosive action of particles in the air stream. Relationships governing these specific modes of contamination are not discussed here, but their evaluation is as difficult as the correlation problem.

Some equations for this problem can be stated. Since the duration of piston travel is relatively short, assume that adiabatic flow conditions apply.

$$p_1 v_1^n = p_2 v_2^n = \text{constant} \qquad (4\text{-}12)$$

where $n = c_p/c_v = k$.
c_p = specific heat of gas at constant pressure.
c_v = specific heat of gas at constant volume.

and

$$\frac{p_1}{p_2} = \left(\frac{v_1}{v_2}\right)^k \qquad (4\text{-}13)$$

Now

$$v_i = \frac{1}{\rho_i} = \frac{V_i}{m_i} \tag{4-14}$$

At time t

$$v_2 = \frac{V_2}{m} = \frac{(\bar{y}_2 + Az)}{(\bar{m}_2 + \Delta m)} \tag{4-15}$$

where $z = x - x_0$
Δm = change in mass during time $(t - t_0) = \Delta t$.

and

$$v_1 = \frac{V_1}{m_1} = \frac{(\bar{y}_1 - Az)}{(\bar{m}_1 - \Delta m)} \tag{4-16}$$

Hence

$$\frac{p_1}{p_2} = \left[\frac{v_2}{v_1}\right]^k = \left[\frac{\bar{y}_2 + Az}{\bar{y}_1 - Az} \cdot \frac{\bar{m}_1 - \Delta m}{\bar{m}_2 + \Delta m}\right]^k \tag{4-17}$$

and

$$\Delta m = \int_{t_0}^{t} w \, dt$$

where w = mass flow rate through orifice. (4-18)

From any standard reference on thermodynamics, the mass flow through an orifice under adiabatic conditions can be expressed as

$$w = \text{Mass flow rate} = \frac{A_0}{v_1} \cdot \left\{ \frac{2g_0 J c_p T_1 \left[\left(\frac{p_2}{p_1}\right)^{2/k} - \left(\frac{p_2}{p_1}\right)^{(k+1)/k}\right]}{1 - \left[\frac{p_2}{p_1}\right]^{2/k}} \right\}^{1/2} \tag{4-19}$$

and, since $p_1 v_1^k = c$, (4-20)

$$v_1 = \frac{1}{p_1} c^{1/k} = \frac{\bar{c}}{p_1} \tag{4-21}$$

$$w = \frac{A_0 p_1}{\bar{c}} \cdot \left\{ \frac{2g_0 J c_p T_1 \left[\left(\frac{p_2}{p_1}\right)^{2/k} - \left(\frac{p_2}{p_1}\right)^{(k+1)/k}\right]}{1 - \frac{p_2}{p_1}^{2/k}} \right\}^{1/2} \tag{4-22}$$

where $g_0 = 32.17 \dfrac{\text{ft - lb}_m}{\text{lb}_f \text{ - sec}^2}$

$$J = 778 \quad \frac{\text{ft - lb}_f}{\text{BTU}}$$

Now, solving equation (4-17) for Δm, we have

$$\frac{\bar{m}_1 - \Delta m}{\bar{m}_2 + \Delta m} = \left(\frac{p_2}{p_1}\right)^{1/k} \left(\frac{\bar{y}_1 - Az}{\bar{y}_2 + Az}\right) = \underline{\bar{X}} \tag{4-23}$$

$$\bar{m}_1 - \Delta m = \underline{\bar{X}} (\bar{m}_2 + \Delta m) + \Delta m \tag{4-24}$$

$$\Delta m \left[1 + (1 + \bar{m}_2) \underline{\bar{X}}\right] = \bar{m}_1 \tag{4-25}$$

and

$$\Delta m = \frac{\bar{m}_1}{1 + (1 + \bar{m}_2) \underline{\bar{X}}} = \frac{\bar{m}_1}{\left[1 + (1 + \bar{m}_2) \left(\frac{p_1}{p_2}\right)^{1/k} \left(\frac{\bar{y}_1 - Az}{\bar{y}_2 + Az}\right)\right]} \tag{4-26}$$

The rate of change of mass is the mass flow rate, w. Thus

$$\frac{d}{dt}(\Delta m) = w = \frac{d}{dt} \cdot \left[\bar{m}_1 \left[1 + (1 + \bar{m}_2) \left(\frac{p_1}{p_2}\right)^{1/k} \left(\frac{\bar{y}_1 - Az}{\bar{y}_2 + Az}\right)\right]^{-1} \right] \tag{4-27}$$

and

$$w = -\bar{m}_1 \cdot \left[1 + (1 + \bar{m}_2) \left(\frac{p_1}{p_2}\right)^{1/k} \left(\frac{\bar{y}_1 - Az}{\bar{y}_2 + Az}\right)\right]^{-2} \cdot \frac{d}{dt}\left[1 + (1 + \bar{m}_2)\left(\frac{p_1}{p_2}\right)^{1/k} \left(\frac{\bar{y}_1 - Az}{\bar{y}_2 + Az}\right)\right] \tag{4-28}$$

Now equating (4-22) and (4-28), we have

$$w = \frac{A_0 p_1}{\bar{c}} \cdot \left\{ \frac{2g_0 J c_p T_1 \left[\left(\frac{p_2}{p_1}\right)^{2/k} - \left(\frac{p_2}{p_1}\right)^{k + 1/k}\right]^{1/2}}{1 - \left[\frac{p_2}{p_1}\right]^{2/k}} \right\}$$

$$= -\bar{m}_1 \left[1 + (1 + \bar{m}_2)\left(\frac{p_1}{p_2}\right)^{1/k} \left(\frac{\bar{y}_1 - Az}{\bar{y}_2 + Az}\right)\right]^{-2} \cdot$$

$$\cdot \frac{d}{dt}\left[1 + (1 + \bar{m}_2)\left(\frac{p_1}{p_2}\right)^{1/k}\left(\frac{\bar{y}_1 - Az}{\bar{y}_2 + Az}\right)\right] \quad (4\text{-}29)$$

where $p_1 = p_1\,(t)$.
$p_2 = p_2\,(t)$.
$z = z\,(t)$.

Theoretically this equation can be solved for the ratio of the pressures (p_2/p_1). This would enable one to express the difference $\Delta\, p$ and hence obtain an expression for the resistive force F_R.

The above expression is quite unwieldy, and difficult to solve. In addition, expressions for the time-dependent variables must be obtained. One method of solution is to make the required determinations experimentally; another is to represent the entire problem on an analog computer and solve the problem by parameter variation.

In regard to contamination on sliding contacts, Lieberman performed a study on the effect of particle contamination on electrical contacting devices. This apparatus is shown in Figure 4-7. The apparatus is based on a metal probe in sliding contact with a metal disk rotating at a constant velocity. Contact voltages were measured during the experiments. Although at the completion of these tests it was concluded that the data obtained were insufficient to provide correlation between fallout and contact voltage, this set of experiments will be discussed in detail to give an insight as to how similar experiments can be performed.

Description of Equipment

Lieberman states:

The 1 mm. diameter probe was constructed from nickel and mounted in a Shure Dynitic cartridge. The disc was aluminum, 10″ in diameter, with a ½″ wide copper strip, 8″ in diameter, fitted into it. The voltage drop was measured across the copper-nickel junction. The disc is mounted on a turntable and placed in a Sterilshield dust free hood where a controlled amount of contamination could be introduced.

The probe is electrically energized by a 400 cps signal from the oscillator. The open-circuit voltage at the probe is limited to 20 mv peak-to-peak by a voltage divider; a 2000 ohm load resistor limits the closed-circuit current to 10 microamps. A Hewlett-Packard 415B standing wave indicator is used to give the voltage amplication necessary to detect the resistance induced potential drop across the probe-disc junction with a high degree of sensitivity. The 415B responses to frequencies within a narrow band around 400 cps and has a sensitivity of 0.1 uv. The pulsating d.c. output from the amplifier is divided by a 470 : 1 voltage divider. The smaller voltage is fed into an Esterline-Angus Model AW strip chart recorder and the larger portion is connected to a capacitance-type integrator. In operation, current flows into the capacitor through a diode. The high backward-to-forward resistance prevents discharge of the capacitor during periods of low resistance. The voltage appearing across the capacitor at the end of a traverse is proportional to the product of the contact resistance and time. This voltage is measured on a microvolt-ammeter, Hewlett-Packard Model 425.

For additional observation of resistance, especially open circuits that occur too fast for the recorder, the signal from the probe was fed to an oscilloscope. The scope was externally triggered by a light sensitive germanium diode observing an illuminated pattern on the disc so that the display represents one revolution of the rotating disc. The signal from the germanium diode was fed into a one-shot multivibrator and the multivibrator output in turn was fed to a cathode follower coupled to the recorder. This arrangement provided a marking pulse for the strip chart. A York timer per-

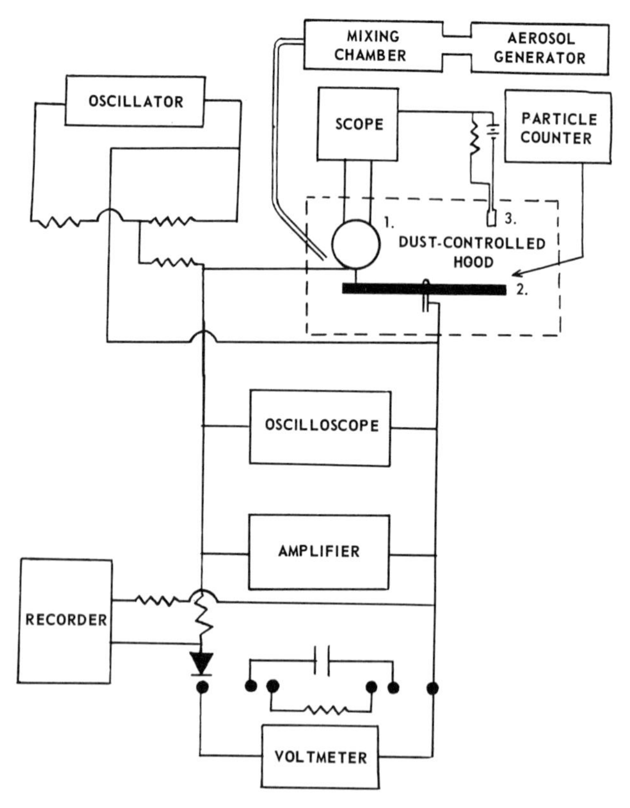

FIGURE 4-7. Measurement apparatus for particulate contamination of electrical contacts(*41*). (1) Pickup arm. (2) Turntable. (3) Photo-diode trigger.

mitted the recorder to operate two minutes every two hours.[34]

Operating Procedure

The probe and disc were polished, cleaned, and photographed under the microscope using a Zeiss Ultrapak overhead illuminator. The probe was then placed level on the disc and the load adjusted to 8 to 10 grams. The strip chart indication was adjusted to zero, the contact opened and the signal generator output set at 20 mv. The lock-in 400 cps amplifier output was adjusted to a 20 mv full scale display on the strip chart. The disc was started turning at about 45 to 50 sec per revolution and the probe set on the copper strip. Polaroid photographs were taken of the first few revolutions of the disc and the contact voltage recorded on the strip chart.

Contamination was produced by the Wright dry dust feed mechanism and sent to the plenum chamber of the Sterilshield where it was disseminated throughout the hood. By changing gear ratios the dust feed mechanism can produce aerosols of widely varying concentrations. The aerosol concentration and particle size distribution within the Sterilshield were monitored periodically with the Armour Research Foundation electronic particle counter. The fallout concentration and particle size distribution were determined from a microscope count of a microscope slide placed on the turntable and exposed to the contaminated atmosphere. At the end of each test the oscilloscope trace was photographed and the disc and probe were photographed under the microscope.[35]

Cleaning Procedures

Prior to each test the probe and disc were polished and cleaned. The probe was polished using a Buchler polishing wheel and 1 micron diamond paste. The probe was leveled on the polishing surface to insure even polishing.

The plate was mounted in a lathe for polishing and turned at 300 rpm. The first step in polishing was with carborundum waterproof paper, type 400A, using Deo Base as a polishing medium. This was used until all apparent scratches were gone. Then Deo Base was used for about 10 minutes. A final paper, 3/0 emery paper was also run about 10 minutes. When using 0 and 3/0 papers adequate polishing medium was kept on the copper surface to prevent scratching. At this stage the plate was washed with a soap solution to remove the oil. The plate was then finished with 3 micron alumina powder in distilled water using surgical grade cotton as an applicator. Other types of cotton were tried but found to contain abrasives which scratched the surface of the copper.

After polishing, the probe and the plate were cleaned using filtered solvents. The solvents were prepared by filtering them through solvent resistant Millipore filters, Type 0. It was found that unfiltered solvents left contaminants on the plate after cleaning.

In order to clean the probe and disc, they were first washed with acetone to remove polishing compound. Methyl alcohol was then used to clean films from the surface. Next, a solution of 1% HNO_3 in methyl alcohol was used to thoroughly loosen particles and provide a mild etch. Finally, a large volume of 50% methyl alcohol–acetone in a pressurized wash bottle was used to wash away other solvents and loosened particles. The parts were then dried with compressed air passed through an absolute filter. In cleaning the probe, cotton swabs were used to apply all solvents except the final wash. In cleaning the disc, lint free lens paper was used for applying all solvents except the final wash. These materials were only used as applicators, as rubbing caused scoring.

The glass microscope slides used to measure the fallout were cleaned in hot chromic acid solution, rinsed in boiling distilled water and stored in distilled water until just before use. They were then wiped dry with a single stroke of non-linting lens tissue and placed on the turntable. Cover slips were cleaned in a similar manner. A portion of slide was covered with a cover slip before exposure so a background count could be obtained. After the test run, the exposed portion of the slide was covered to prevent both further contamination and loss of fallout.[36]

Test Aerosols

During this study, four different dusts were used. They were zinc sulfide NJZ 2210 fluorescent powder, carbonyl iron spheres, and fine and coarse natural Arizona dust standardized for air cleaner testing. The size distributions of these aerosols in the Sterilshield are shown in Figures 4-8 and 4-9. Although the original dusts varied in particle size, the method of generation allowed the larger particles to settle out in a surge chamber located between the Wright dust generator and the Sterilshield. The result was that the aerosols in the hood showed similar mean diameters and particle size distributions. The size distribution of the particles that fell onto the microscope slide during this test period are shown in Figure 4-10. In all cases the average particle size of the fallout is greater than that of the aerosol from which it came. Figure 4-11 shows the relationship between the aerosol concentration and the rate of particle deposition.

---

[34] *Ibid.*, pp. 43-45.

[35] *Ibid.*, pp. 45 and 46.

[36] *Ibid.*, pp. 46 and 47.

Test Results

The data obtained from ten tests to determine the effect of particle contamination on contacts are shown in Table 4-3. The fallout rate was determined by counting the particles on a known area of the microscope slide and dividing by the test time. The contact voltage per revolution was calculated by integration of the strip chart recording. The per cent open during a revolution multiplied by 20 mv (fully open contact) provided the contact voltage per revolution. By use of Figure 4-12 the voltage can be readily converted to resistance.

Figure 4-13 shows representative test results in which fallout and contact voltage are plotted. Test No. 1 represents a case in which fallout had little or no apparent effect on contact voltage. Tests No. 5 and 7 were similar. Test No. 2 represents a continuous and rapid increase in contact voltage with particle fallout. Although all tests exhibited some cycling of contact voltage, test No. 4 is an example of pronounced cycling.

Results

In discussing the results of the Armour tests, Lieberman writes:

The test results appear to represent the several types of failure and failure mechanisms met in practice. For

TABLE 4–3

EFFECT OF CONTAMINATION ON CONTACTS**

Test Number:	*1*	*2*	*3*	*4*	*5*	*6*	*7*	*8*	*9*	*10*
Aerosol:*	*CRD*	*FRD*	*FRD*	*CRD*	*CRD*	*FRD*	*FRD*	*CI*	*CI*	*ZnS*
Aerosol concentration (particles/liter)	10,700	4,100	258,500	5,900	21,800	52,600	91,000	1,600	5.300	18,300
Fallout rate (particles/mm^2 min)	0.364	0.206	1.072	0.301	0.311	0.436	0.688	0.147†	0.256	0.280
Test duration (min)	1256	1280	1270	1320	1275	1283	1425	987	990	967
Total fallout (particles/mm^2)	460	264	1361	397	397	559	980	145	253	271
Time per revolution (sec)	44	44	47	47	46	45	55	46	53	44
Time exposed to dust (hr)	*Contact Voltage per Revolution (mv)‡*									
0	0	0.40	1.18	0	0	1.12	0.42	0	0	1.24
1	0	0.22	0	2.78	0.62	1.40	0.56	1.28	1.24	1.96
3	0.84	0.56	0.06	1.60	0.38	1.36	0.32	0.46	2.16	4.56
5	0.70	4.24	1.18	1.62	0.80	1.82	0	1.16	3.26	7.00
7	0	9.52	7.18	2.08	0.96	1.74	0.32	3.48	2.70	2.34
9	0.38	8.52	10.30	5.48	0	1.08	0.32	1.56	0	2.34
11	0	9.64	7.90	0.66	0	2.62	0.24	2.00	1.72	2.86
13	0	12.72	14.78	6.10	1.12	2.86	0.36	3.06	2.48	2.94
15	1.06	15.58	13.84	0.36	1.38	0.56	0.88	3.18	0.22	1.70
17	0.76	14.12	14.06	1.60	2.10	0.80	0.88	7.52	—	—
19	0.62	15.70	14.24	7.02	—	1.86	0.46	2.06	—	—
21	—	16.42	11.92	8.74	—	0.56	—	—	—	—
Average	0.40	8.97	8.05	3.17	0.74	1.48	0.43	2.30	1.53	2.99

* CRD, coarse road dust; FRD, fine road dust; CI, carbonyl iron; ZnS, zinc sulfide No. 2210.

† Experimentally determined value of 0.049 was corrected on basis of data in Fig. 6.

‡ Maximum is 20 mv for open circuit per revolution.

** Abstracted from reference 41, p. 53.

example, Test No. 1 represents a case where a device remains operable in spite of a contamination of its environment. Apparently a contaminating particle did not become lodged in a critical area or was so oriented that it was easily swept out or pushed aside by the sliding contact before it could cause a failure.

Test No. 2 represents a case where a device became inoperable immediately after it was put in operation. Here a wear or fallout particle or particles apparently became lodged in a critical position almost immediately and continued to affect and degrade the device operation. A particle caught in a pit or crevice could account for the results obtained in this test.

Test No. 4 represents a case where contamination was swept out of a critical area by the wiping action of a rotating contact. This would give the intermittent type failure observed during this test.[37]

As stated previously, the present data are insufficient to provide correlation between fallout and the contact voltage. Apparently a minor variable is being measured whose effect is unpredictable and unrelated to the number of fallout particles. The contamination effect is more likely related to the position of single particles rather than to mass concentration. To evaluate this effect properly would require many tests and a statistical evaluation.

[37] *Ibid.*, p. 56

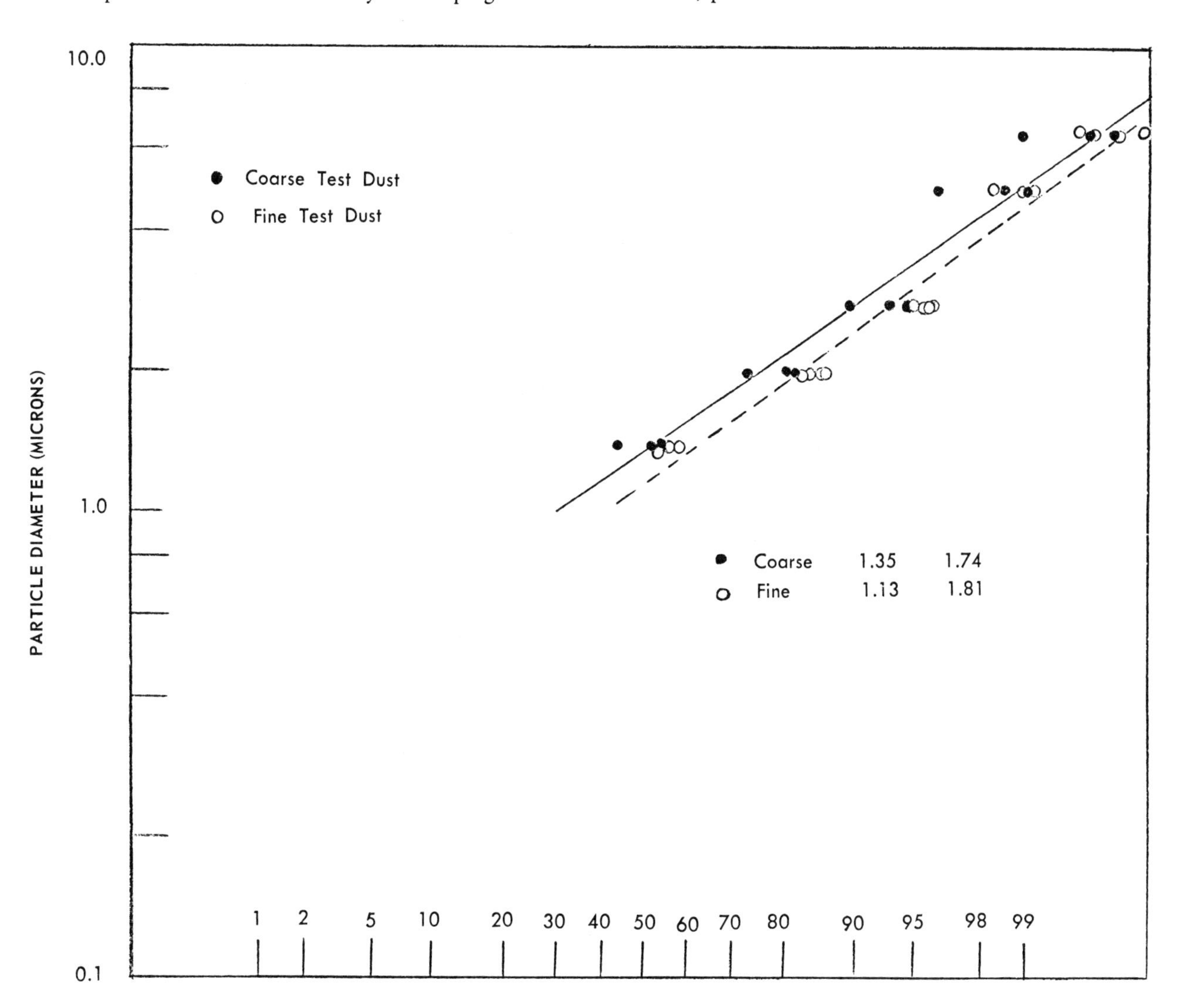

FIGURE 4-8. Size distribution of Arizona dust(*41*).

Contamination Study Recommendation[38]

The following recommendations are based on work carried out at Armour Research Foundation as well as on observations of problems, procedures, and results at other laboratories and in industry. It is believed that the parameters of importance should not be studied as individual entities. Future efforts should be directed toward obtaining quantitative correlations between selected contamination parameters.

Several methods can be employed to obtain functional module evaluation. One approach entails an initial review of the specified equipments and a complete functional characterization of each equipment type in terms of functional modules. The types or modes of failure that these functional modules could conceivably exhibit are considered, once this evaluation has been completed. For each failure mode a correlation is made between this failure and the possible effects of particle contamination. Each failure mode will have associated with it one or more probable effects relating to particle contamination.

At this point the functional modules are com-

[38] Abstracted from reference *41*, pp. 62-72.

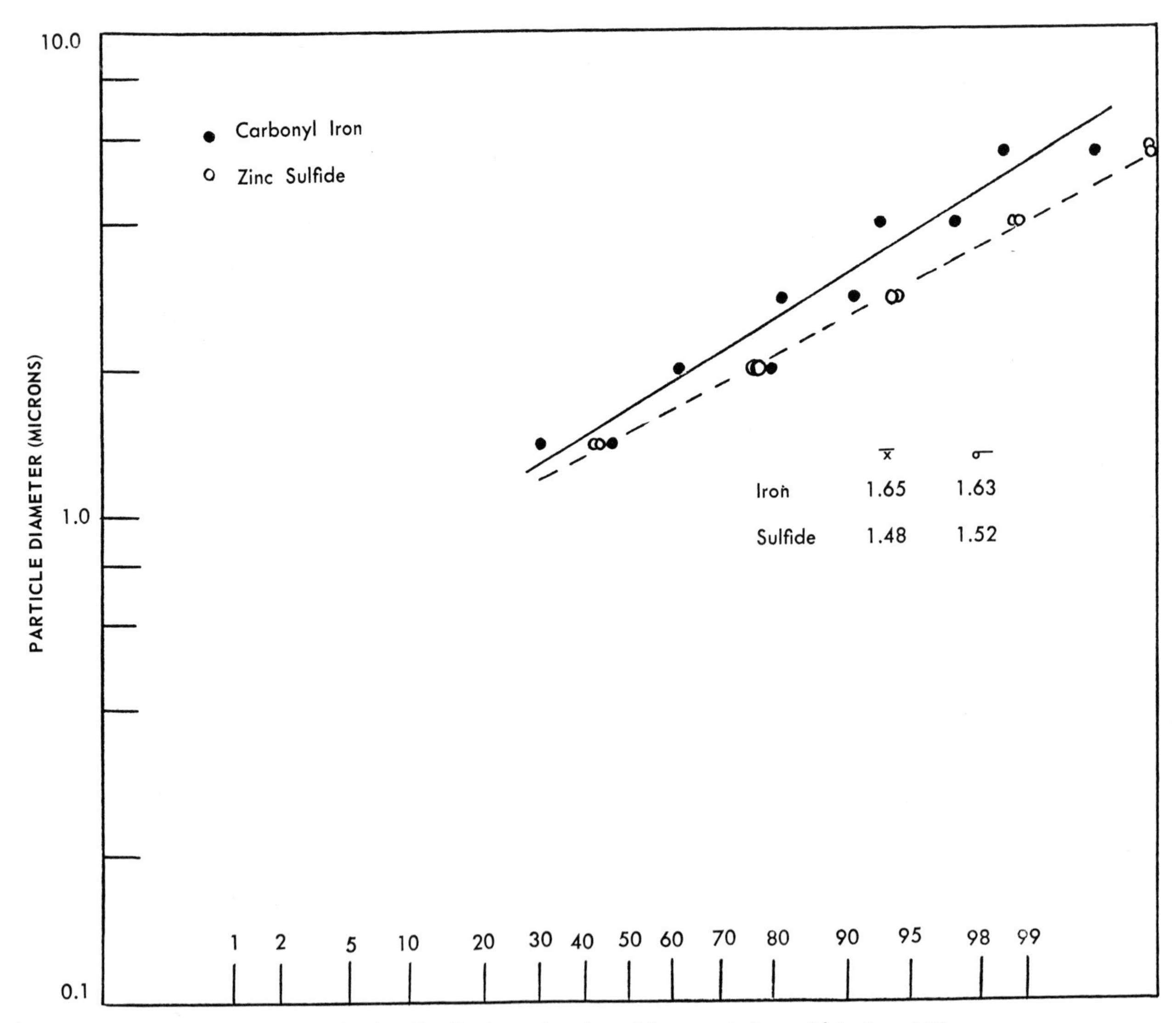

FIGURE 4-9. Size distribution of carbonyl iron and zinc sulfide dusts(*41*).

bined in series or parallel relationships to represent an entire device type. Current reliability literature contains techniques for this combination. Once this is accomplished, a means is available whereby one can qualitatively evaluate the performance of any functionally similar device in terms of particle contamination and subsequent failure. Although this is a gross relationship, it can be effectively employed to reduce the effects of particle contamination on device failures.

Lieberman states:

The second or more sophisticated and comprehensive approach to the problem, that of the employment of physics of failure techniques, is a more difficult and time consuming technique. The basic approach employed is to again characterize an equipment type in terms of functional modules. Each module is then considered to be a separate mechanism or device. The aspects of failure as a function of particle contamination are then evaluated for this module in terms of environmental stresses and various particle contamination parameters. It must be understood that in order to accomplish such an evaluation, recourse must be made to prior failure data or such data must be experimentally generated during the course of the investigation.

By employing both of the approaches to the same problem, it is possible to evaluate fairly early in the course of an investigation the relative effectiveness of the two approaches. A decision can then be made as to

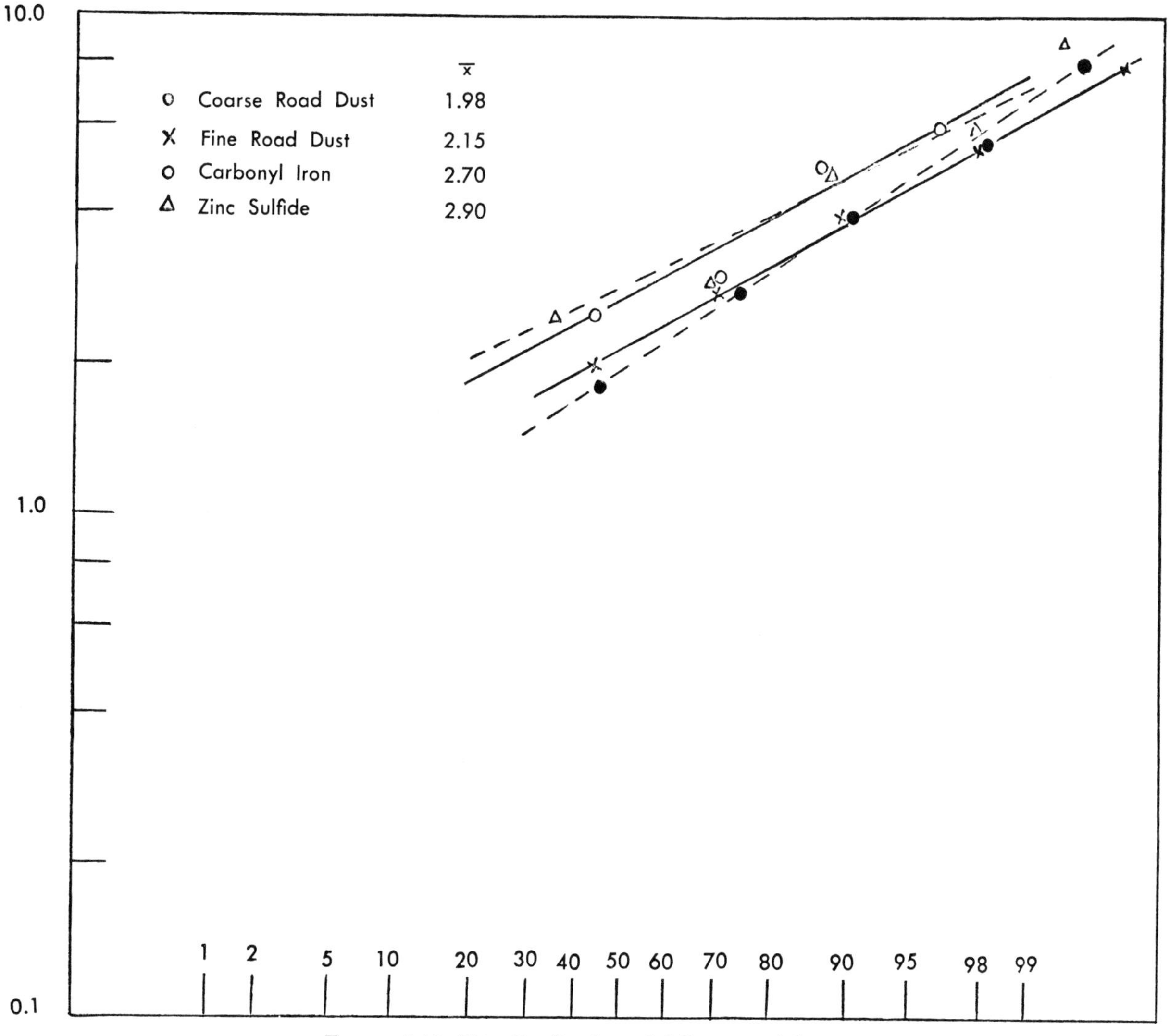

FIGURE 4-10. Size distribution of fallout particles(*41*).

the ultimate direction the investigation should take. It should be noted that this evaluation includes the mode of failure when failure occurs and the probable mechanisms by which this failure occurred. Once this information is available, then it is possible to draw quantitative correlations between the particular module's failure vs. particle contamination and the predicted failure of functionally similar modules of a totally different device. In order to make this correlation, the failure mechanisms or physics of failure must be employed as the correlating means.

An example of this correlation might be the following: Consider failure data concerned with a sample of spur gears. These gears failed in two fashions under the action of specific loads, speeds, in the presence of a specific lubrication, and being subject to particular environmental stresses. The most predominant mode of failure was the generation of excessive back-lash due to pitting and wearing away of material on the tooth flanks. The secondary mode of failure was tooth fracture at the root area due to insufficient radii and under the action of impact type loading generated by the excessive back-lash condition. Sufficient data concerning all of the parameters was available and a failure analysis was made.

Prediction of the expected life of a set of helical bevel gears is required, based upon the available information concerning the spur gears. By considering the service application of the bevel gears in relation to that of the spur gears, by noting the difference in loading, the difference in geometrical configuration, the difference in gear material, the difference in environmental stresses, and by employing the mechanisms whereby the known spur gear failures occurred, valid and significant predictions can be made concerning the predicted failure of the bevel gear. Without detailed knowledge of the failure mechanisms, however, such a correlation could not be made.

Implicit within the previous discussion is the detailed knowledge of the failure mechanisms. It has been previously stated that this is not always on hand but that much information is required in the field of failure physics. Thus, it can be seen that in the implementation of the second approach to the device failure contamination problem considerable effort must be expended in the determination of the various failure mechanisms. This problem is not as great a task as it may at first appear, because of the limited number of failure mechanisms which can be considered to be effected by particle contamination. For example, consider the . . . failure modes and failure mechanisms . . . discussed. The failure modes included excessive elastic failures, elastic buckling, plastic deformation, creep, fracture, malfunction, and device degradation. Of this list only the latter two topics, that is device malfunction and device degradation, appear to readily correlate with particle contamination. As a first approach then, only those failure mechanisms active under these two failure modes would be subject to detailed investigation.

This investigation must . . . take the form of experimental evaluation. The means whereby this experimental evaluation can be conducted, and the specific form of the experiments are not readily apparent at this stage. However, consideration should be given to the dual use of any experimental work. That is, the experiment may well provide the means for evaluating the various failure mechanisms and, at the same time,

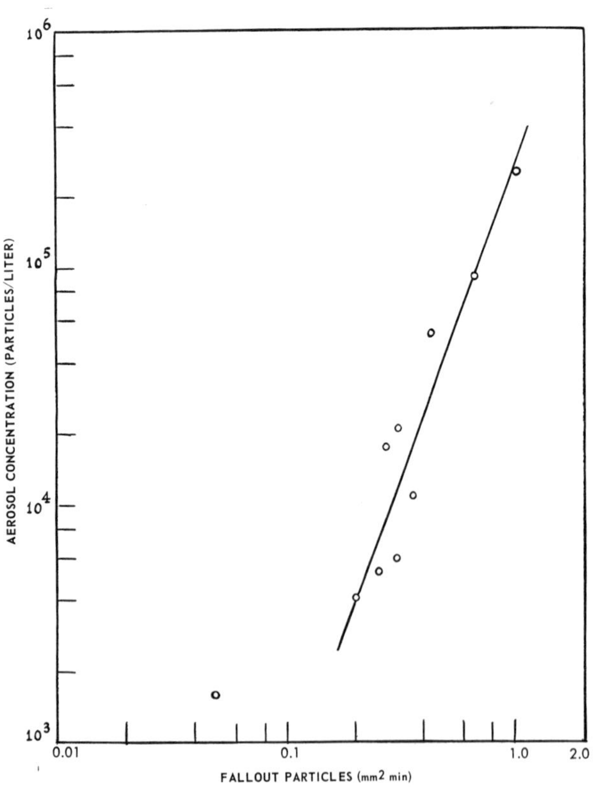

FIGURE 4-11. Relationship between aerosol concentration and rate of particle deposition(*41*).

may provide information concerning the correlation of failure mechanisms to particle contamination. A large extent of any future work, even work of an apparent analytical nature must, of necessity, be partially experimental. Experiments which should be carried out, must include friction and wear experiments on typical bearing and slider mechanisms, corrosion and fatigue studies on flexural components, and flow and motion evaluations of piston cylinder combinations. This list is by no means comprehensive but merely is indicative of the area in which experimentation must ultimately be conducted.

A recent promising approach to the subject of device failure particle contamination, predictive techniques, is the application of response surface techniques. Perhaps a better term for this entire technique would be "synthesis of contaminant de-rated services (systems)."

The general problem might be described as an attempt to minimize some characteristics of equipment (device) design, subject to certain constraints on the design. For example, what should be the device design parameters for a particular functional operation, to maximize the life expectancy of the device, subject to its operation within an environment containing specific particle contaminants? Alternately, what is the effect of specific contamination environments on the life of a device with a particular set of design characteristics? This is a most ambitious undertaking, but one which offers great recompense in successful device operation, and meaningful predictions.

Two general approaches to the problem are apparent. The more general (and more difficult) one would be to consider methods whereby the optimum device characteristics could be deduced from information concerning the desired device performance levels. The second approach would be to specify a more or less general functional form for the device characteristics and then seek to establish the specific equipment parameters which optimize the device performance in

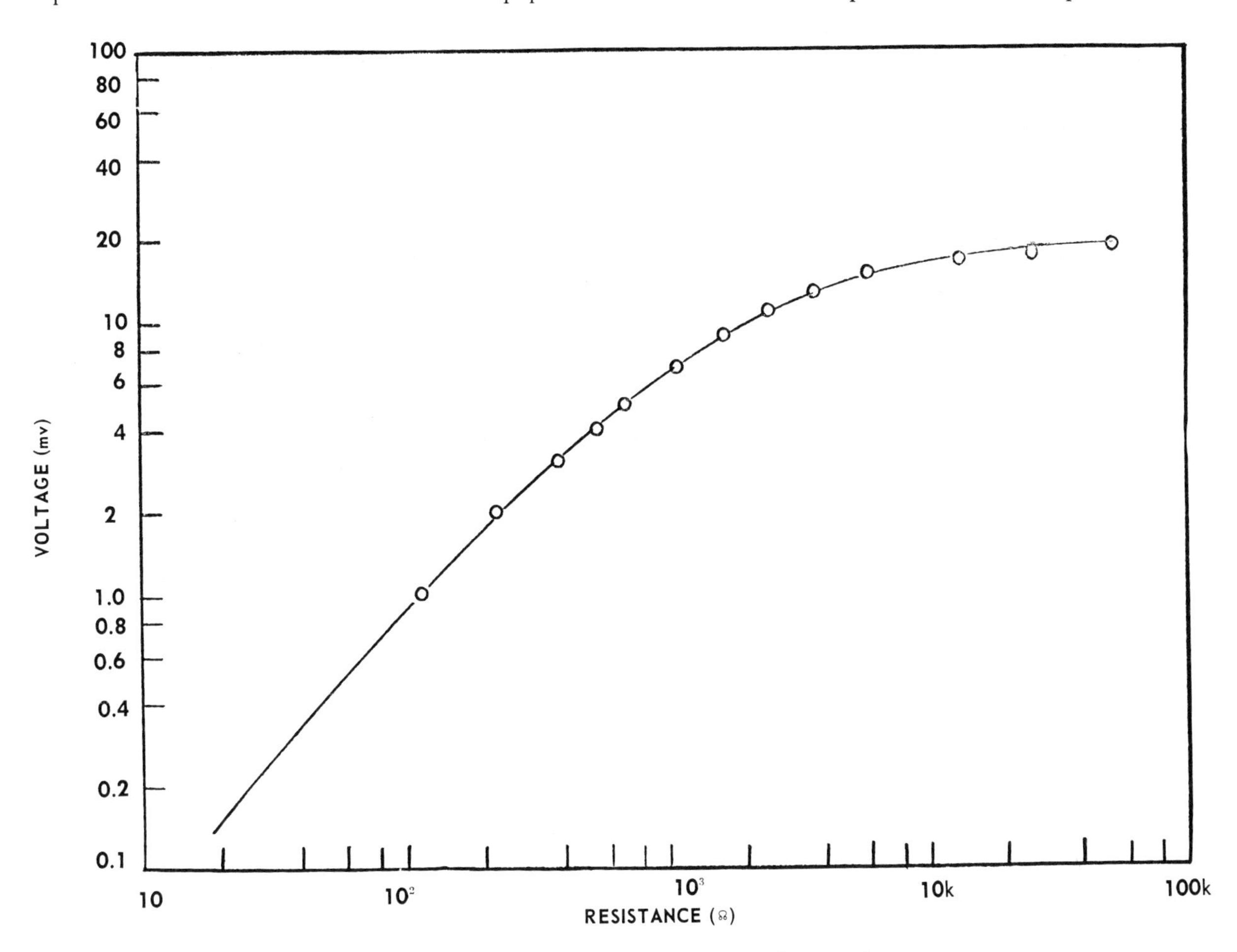

FIGURE 4-12. Relation between contact voltage and resistance(*41*).

some specified manner. It is the second approach that appears to be the most judicious selection for maximum return on invested effort.

. . . Consider the second mentioned approach, wherein the system is defined in terms of a family of parameters from among which we wish to select a set for which the system response is optimum. Clearly, this is representative of a wide class of problems reducible to that of minimizing (or maximizing) a function of many variables (defined in a closed region) subject to certain constraints. Where application of the formal methods of the calculus is not clear, as is most often the case, the method of solution becomes that of searching the parameter space in some manner. . . . The brute force approach to the "search" in a multi-dimensional parameter space (i.e., based on a multi-dimensional mesh) rapidly becomes impractical with increasing order of the space, even when employing the largest computers. Various selective methods of search ranging from gradient techniques to random sampling techniques have been proposed and have found application to a host of varied problems.[39]

[39] Reference *41*, pp. 63-67.

One particular method of search appears interesting because of its conceptual basis and the novel framework within which deterministic problems may be expressed simply. The framework is that of the statistical design of experiments, and the searching technique is the so-called method of ridge analysis, an extension of steepest ascent techniques introduced by Hoerl *(48)*. Methods of statistical design of experiments are essentially empirical in nature and are applied to situations wherein either a functional relationship between the system parameters and system output is unknown, or the "yield" of an "experiment" involves a burdensome degree of effort (that is, time and/or cost). The functional relationship between system parameters and desired response is known implicitly in the present application, being given by the expressions for the various failure mechanisms which are applicable. The "experiment" consists merely in evaluating these relationships for the desired character-

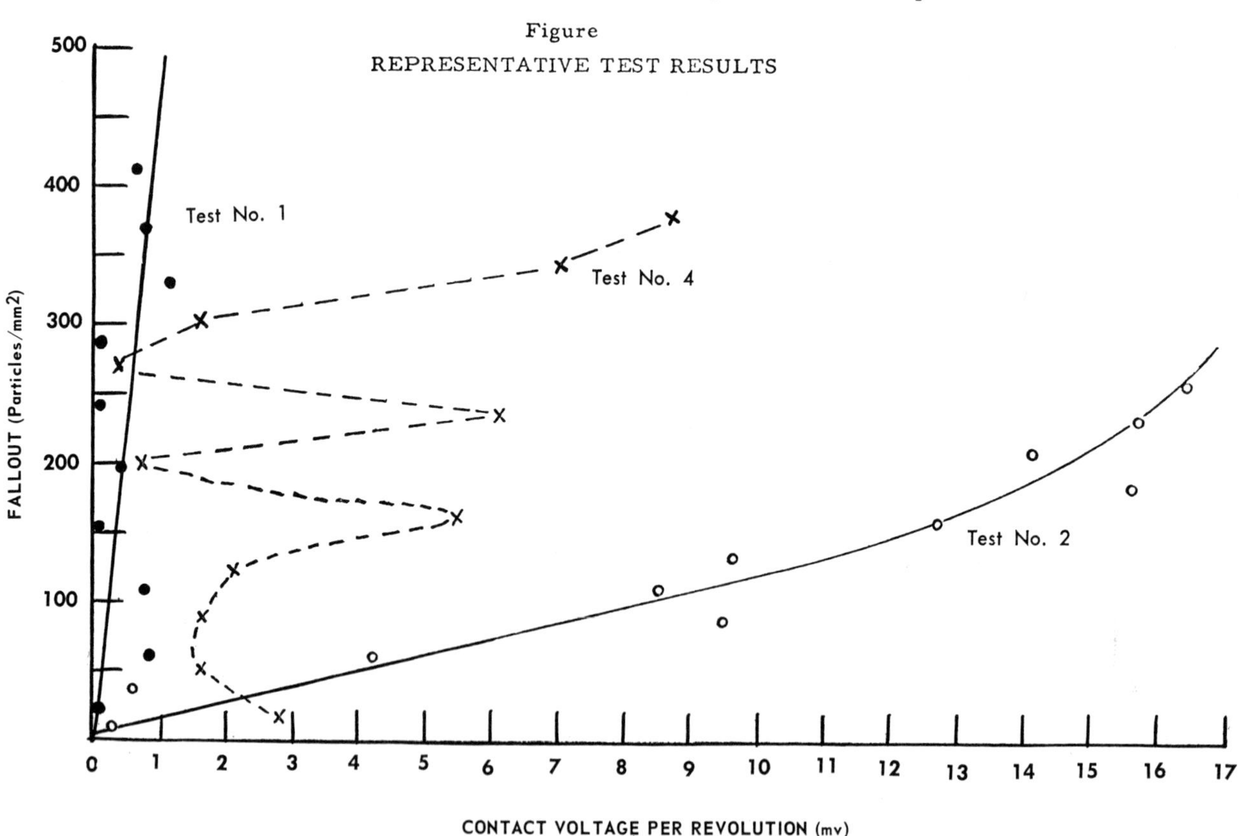

FIGURE 4-13. Representative tests results(*41*).

istics of the device. In general, if it will be prohibitive to perform this evaluation for each possible combination of system parameters, the possibility of establishing an explicit functional relationship between the desired response characteristic and the system parameters based on a very limited number of "experiments" becomes attractive. This functional relationship or response surface provides a basis for selecting the optimum system parameter values according to the desired response characteristics. Geometrically speaking, the searching technique becomes the means whereby the topology of the response surface is investigated to establish local "hills," "valleys," and "ridges."

It should be noted that the "design of experiments" offers methods to sample the space of system parameters statistically and to construct the response surface. The method of ridge analysis offers the means of systematically exploring the topology of the response surface.

As an example, consider a system depending on n parameters, and the response surface to be a hypersurface in an $(n + 1)$-dimensional space. From a geometrical point of view, the method of ridge analysis consists in establishing the intersection of an n-dimensional sphere with the response surface, and identifying the points on the surface of "intersection" for which the relative slopes are zero. A succession of these points defines ridge lines of the surface which point to the high peaks and low valleys. In terms of a two-parameter system, the response surface is a three-dimensional $(n + 2 = 3)$ mountain range where altitude is the desired response characteristic to be extremized. The n-dimensional sphere reduces to a circular cylindrical surface.

It should be pointed out that considerations of feasibility and practicability of ridge analysis appear to be wholly computational in nature. Hoerl's original paper presents a simple computational scheme for a quadratic response surface in which the radius of the intersecting sphere is implied from the calculations.

The technique described above has great value in its application to mechanical reliability predictive techniques. In fact, several reliability organizations employ this technique at the present time, although in a slightly different form. The extension of the technique to the problem of device or system synthesis appears to be reasonably straightforward, if somewhat involved.

The following general conclusions concerning the problem of interplay of device failure and particle contamination can be made.

1. The state of the art is such that no broad quantitative relations can be made between . . . parameters.
2. Qualitative relations can be made, subject to the constraint that each device in question must be treated as a separate entity. Each entity is governed by its own operational parameters and its particular environmental stresses.
3. Any attempt to predict the reliability or useful life of one device, based upon information obtained from another dissimilar device, will yield results with a low associated confidence level.
4. Analytical evaluation and investigation of a single part of the problem, by itself, is not the answer. Any significant results must include an extensive and comprehensive program.
5. By employing the techniques discussed . . . in a planned program of research, significant progress can be made.[40]

Armour Research Foundation, in a report to Sandia Corporation, states that development of improved air-cleaning and air-handling techniques[41] has made it possible to provide air of sufficient cleanliness so that airborne particles are of no significance in comparison to those from other sources. In combination with this development, the conclusions drawn from the experimental work on fallout efficiency show that no further work is necessary to develop control methods for airborne contaminants. Some applications studies are needed, however, to permit maximum utilization of these air-cleaning and air-handling techniques.

This conclusion is based on present-day contamination sensitivity of precise devices and on present-day state of the art in air-handling and air-cleaning apparatus. If the requirements of the first should some day exceed the capabilities of the second, then research will be required to improve the situation.

It is recommended that work be done on parts cleanliness requirements. The work should first provide information on the degree of cleanliness required for a specific component surface in order

[40] *Ibid.*, pp. 70 and 71.

[41] See Chapters 12 and 13 on clean work stations.

for the device to perform its job satisfactorily. Next, the kind of contaminant that will affect a specific device operation should be specified. The end results should provide information on the concentration and size distribution of contaminant particles collected on the surface of a component which will degrade the device performance by a specific amount. Variation of such degradation as a result of variation in physical or chemical properties of the contaminant should be determined.

Contaminant sources can be described broadly as manufacturing, assembly, and operation sources. A study of the type of contaminant produced during these processes will provide data that can, after analysis of cleanliness requirements, permit description of trouble spots. Analysis of problem areas may result in recommendations for changes in materials, procedures, or design. Along with research in the problem areas, practical knowledge of requirements leading to such problem areas must be developed.

A study of a contaminant manipulation process would concern itself with definition of contaminant transfer processes. Such a study would be based on an implicit assumption that complete control of contaminant sources is impossible. That is, some contamination will always be produced and/or collected by a component. It may be possible, however, to manipulate the contaminant either by adequate cleaning processes or by component shape design so that it is removed from trouble areas. An appreciable research study can well be directed toward definition of adequate cleaning for specific needs.

It is well known that the greatest problems in contamination control arise from the presence of personnel. Their natural exudations act as a source of contamination; in addition, human error in handling, assembling, and operating precise devices can cause contamination generation. Research should be carried out on the need to develop techniques to protect the components from personnel-produced contaminants.

REFERENCES

1. KODEL, I. M. "The Role of the Manufacturing Development Engineer in Dust Monitoring at Sandia's Suppliers Plants." *Dust Monitoring in Clean Rooms.* SCTM-131-61(25), pp. 7, 8. Office of Technical Services, Department of Commerce, Washington, D.C., April 1961.
2. SLOANE, EUGENE A. "A New Departure in White Rooms!" *Air Engineering,* Vol. 4, pp. 7, 8 (August 1962).
3. GEHRKE-MANNING, J. E. "Dust in Tubes." *Journal of the American Association for Contamination Control,* Vol. II, No. 3, p. 25 (March 1963).
4. PAULY, J. *The Dust Environment and Its Effect on Dust Penetration.* AD 110472. Southwest Research Institute, September 1956.
5. MCKEE, H. C. "Deleterious Actions Due to Combined Effects of Humidity, and Atmosphere Pollutants Phase 1." *Study of Existing Problems Involving Ordnance Materiel.* AD 236212. Southwest Research Institute, January 1960.
6. CARTER, T. *A Study of Some Factors Affecting Rolling-Contact Fatigue Life.* NASA R60. Cleveland, Ohio: Lewis Research Center, 1960.
7. RILLINGS, K. W., and WILLIAMSEN, C. T. *Micro Particle Contamination of Aero Fluid Control Systems.* Project AD-13-08-60-0. Bethpage, N.Y.: Grumman Aircraft Engineering Corp., 1960.
8. MEAGHER, G. F. *Hydraulics and Pneumatics,* Vol. 15, No. 2, p. 49 (1962).
9. WHEELER, H. L., and SHERRILL, E. A. *Hydraulics and Pneumatics,* Vol. 15, No. 2, p. 54 (1962)
10. OSGOOD, R. E. *Hydraulics and Pneumatics,* Vol. 15, No. 2, p. 51 (1962).
11. HUGGETT, H. L. *Effects of Servo Valve Contamination: Hydraulic and Valve Forces.* Los Angeles Symposium on Hydraulic Fluid Contamination. Philadelphia, Pa.: American Society for Testing and Materials, October 1962.
12. PARKER, J. W. *A Summary of Contamination in Hydraulic Fluid Systems on USAF and Support Systems.* AD 273788. January 1962.
13. MADDOCK, A. J., *et al.* "The Effects of Dust and Force upon Certain Very Light Electrical Contacts." *British Journal of Applied Physics,* Vol. 8, p. 471 (1957).
14. KEEFER, H. J., and GUMLEY, R. H. *Bell Systems Technical Journal,* Vol. 36, p. 777 (1958).
15. BERRY, L. M., *et al. Contact Resistance and the Effect of Materials and Process Variables on Contact Resistance and Contact Reliability in Switching Devices.* SCTM 73A-60(16). Albuquerque, N. Mex.: Sandia Corp., February 1960.
16. HERMANSE, H. W., and EGAN, T. F. *Bell System Technical Journal,* Vol. 37, p. 377 (1958).
17. CHAIKIN, S. W. "Mechanics of Electrical Contact Failure Caused by Surface Contamination." *Electro-Technology,* Vol. 67, pp. 70-75 (1961).

18. ANON. *Contact Resistance Symposium.* SCR-18. Albuquerque, N. Mex.: Sandia Corp., June, 1957.
19. WILLIAMSON, J. B. P., *et al. Proceedings of the Royal Society,* Series A, Vol. 237, p. 560 (1956).
20. GEBAUER, R. *Prerequisites to Relay Reliability.* 8th National Conference on Electromagnetic Relays. Stillwater, Okla.: Oklahoma State University, May 1960.
21. FREUDIGER, EDGAR. "Manufacturing Components with Clean Electrical Contracts." *E/E Production.* Vol. 3, pp. 10-16 (January-February, 1963).
22. FREUDIGER, EDGAR. "Investigation of Surface Contamination on Fine Silver Contacts." *Electrical Contacts Seminar Proceedings.* Pennsylvania State University, College Park, Pa. 1960.
23. FISCHMEISTER, H., and DROTT, J. "Reaction Rate and Growth Forms of Reaction Product in the System Ag-H_2S." *Acta Metallurgica* Vol. 7, pp. 777-781 (1959).
24. EGAN, T. F., and MENDIZZA, A. "Creeping Silver Sulfide." *Journal of the Electrochemical Society,* No. 4, p. 107 (1960).
25. GERBER, Th. "Kontakte und Relaiskontakte–Eigenschaften und Vergleichende Untersuchungen." (Contacts and Relay Contacts–Characteristics and Comparative Investigations.) *Technische Mitteilungen PTT.* (Switzerland), No. 3, pp. 89-114 (1955).
26. HERMANCE, H. W., and EGAN, T. F., "Organic Deposits of Precious Metal Contacts." *Bell System Technical Journal,* Vol. 37, pp. 739-776 (1958).
27. STEPHAN, K. "Lubrication of Rotary Switch Contacts." "*Electrical Contacts Seminar Proceedings,* pp. 84-94. Pennsylvania State University, College Park, Pa. 1961.
28. CAMPBELL, W. E. "Factors Affecting Reliability of Electrical Contacts Lubrication of Sliding Contracts." *Electrical Contacts Seminar Proceedings.* Orono, Maine, University of Maine, 1962.
29. "Zur Bildung Widerstanderhoehendes Belaege organischen Ursprungs aut electrischen Kontakten." (Deposits of Organic Origin on Electrical Contacts). *Zeitschrift fuer angewandte Physik,* Vol. 11, pp. 399-403 (1959).
30. GUMLEY, R. H. "Contact Phenomena in Sealed Containers." *Bell Laboratories Record,* (June 1954.)
31. GERMER, L. H., and SMITH, J. L. "Activation of Electrical Contacts by Organic Vapors." *Bell System Technical Journal,* Vol. 36, p. 769 (1957).
32. MOBERLY, L. E. "Performance of Silver Contacts in Atmosphere Containing Silicone Vapors." *Insulation,* Vol. 6, pp. 19-24 (1961).
33. CAMPBELL, W. E. "Use of Statistical Control in Corrosion and Contact Resistance Studies." *Bell Systems Technical Publications,* Monograph B-1350, 1942.
34. "Surety of Make of Electrical Contact Materials." *ASTM Standards,* Part 3, p. 601. Philadelphia, Pa.: American Society for Testing and Materials, 1961.
35. FLOM, D. G., and SAVAGE, R. H. "Detection of Thin Insulating Films on Metals." *General Electric Report,* RL-1188. 1954.
36. CHAIKIN, S. W., ANDERSON, J. R. and SANTOS, G. J. "Improved Probe Apparatus for Measuring Contact Resistance." *Review of Scientific Instruments,* Vol. 32, pp. 1294-1296 (1961).
37. PFISTERER, H., and FUCHS, E., "Identifizierung von Kontaktverunreinigungen mit elektronen-optischen Verfahren." (Identification of Contact Contaminants with Electron-Optical Means.) *Siemens-Zeitschrift,* pp. 484-488 (1960).
38. HERMANCE, H. W., and EGAN, T. F. "Examination of Electrical Contacts by the Replica Method." *Transactions of the American Institute of Electrical Engineers,* Part 1, Vol. 34, pp. 756-762 (1958).
39. TAYLOR, M. R. *The Application of Contamination Control in Critical Component Assembly Areas in TCA Facilities.* Trans-Canada Air Lines, December 1958.
40. LIEBERMAN, ALVIN. *Contamination Effects Study.* ARF 3216-4. Chicago, Ill.: Armour Research Foundation, October, 1962. Prepared for Sandia Corp. Albuquerque, N. Mex.
41. LIEBERMAN, ALVIN. *Contamination Effects Study.* ARF 3216-5. Chicago, Ill.: Armour Research Foundation, November 1962. Prepared for Sandia Corp., Albuquerque, N. Mex.
42. FENG, M. "The Influence of Surface Activity on Friction and Surface Damage." *Wear,* Vol. 4, p. 269 (1961).
43. LING, F. F. "Thermal Aspects of Galling on Dry Metallic Surfaces in Sliding Contact." *Wear,* Vol. 1, p. 80 (1957).
44. REICHENBACH, G., and KINGSBURY, E. *A Fundamental Study of Rolling Contact Fatigue.* Cambridge, Mass.: The Alloyd Corp., August 1961.
45. LING, F. F. *Investigation of Sliding Friction and Interface Temperature between Two Metallic Surfaces.* Pittsburgh, Pa.: Carnegie Institute of Technology. Ph. D. Thesis, 1954.
46. TABOR, D. "The Mechanism of Free Rolling Friction." *Lubrication Engineering,* Vol. 12, pp. 379-386 (November-December 1956).
47. RABINOWICZ, E., DUNN, L. A., and RUSSELL, P. G. "A Study of Abrasive Wear under Three-Body Conditions." *Wear,* Vol. 4, p. 345 (1961).
48. LEAKE, C. E. *Understanding Reliability.* Pasadena, Calif.: Pasadena Lithographers, Inc., 1963.

Chapter 5. *Conventional Clean Room Design*

Introduction

The conventionally designed clean room will be defined as any room with an air-handling system that does not produce laminar air flow. All clean room construction was conventionally designed up to the early 1960's, when the laminar-flow theory for clean room construction was introduced.

The design of clean rooms was considered similar in nature to the design of air-conditioned rooms. This was not a valid assumption. The conditioned air normally is distributed throughout the room not only by the direct emission from the diffuser but by secondary effects. Ceiling diffusers in an air-conditioned room are designed to take advantage of the sweep of the cool air as it is turned upward from the floor and then curled inward. This secondary effect is utilized to spread the conditioned air throughout the room. For normal air conditioning, this effect is beneficial and can be used. It is also very effective, however, in reintroducing settled dust and spreading it throughout the room.

The following mathematical model of a clean room will further enforce the statement made in the preceding paragraph. The factors that most affect the cleanliness of the room are the filter efficiency *(a)* and the volume of air flow *(k)*. By maximizing a and k in equation *(5-15)*, the lowest ambient room contamination level is achieved. Thus filters of *highest efficiency* and the *shortest air-flow path* through the room should be selected.

Mathematical Model of Clean Room

Let N = number of particles per cubic foot present at time t in minutes.
V = volume of clean room, in cubic feet.
K = number of complete changes of clean room volume per hour.
G = total number of particles per minute entering clean room air because of particulate generation operations.
a = efficiency of the filter.

Then

$$\frac{NVK}{V60}(1 - a)\,\Delta t =$$

Total number of particles per cubic foot entering clean room air during the interval Δt because of the inefficiency of the filters. (5-1)

$$\frac{1}{V}\,G\,\Delta t =$$

Total number of particles per cubic foot entering clean room air during interval Δt because of particulate generation operations. (5-2)

$$\frac{1}{V}\;\frac{NVK}{60}\;\Delta t =$$

Total number of particles per cubic foot leaving clean room air during interval Δt. (5-3)

$$\Delta N =$$

(Total number of particles per cubic foot entering) − (total number of particles per cubic foot leaving). (5-4)

Substituting equations (5-1), (5-2), and (5-3) into equation (5-4), we obtain equation (5-5).

$$\Delta N = \frac{NK}{60}(1 - a)\,\Delta t + \frac{G}{V}\,\Delta t - \frac{NK}{60}\,\Delta t \quad (5\text{-}5)$$

Equation (5-6) produces the value $\Delta N/\Delta t$ by combining and rearranging of terms.

$$\frac{\Delta N}{\Delta t} = \frac{G}{V} - \frac{NKa}{60} \quad (5\text{-}6)$$

Since the differential for dN/dt can be substituted for $\Delta N/\Delta t$, equation (5-6) becomes

$$\frac{dN}{dt} = \frac{G}{V} - \frac{NKa}{60} = \frac{G}{V}\left(1 - \frac{aKVN}{60G}\right) \quad (5\text{-}7)$$

By collecting like variables N and t on opposite sides of the equation, the following equality is formed:

$$\frac{dN}{1 - (aKVN/60G)} = \frac{G}{V}\,dt \quad (5\text{-}8)$$

Multiplying the left side of equation (5-7) by $(-60G/\,aKV) \times (aKV/-60G)$ and establishing the integrals results in equation (5-9).

$$\frac{-60G}{aKV}\int \frac{-\dfrac{aKV\,dN}{60G}}{1 - \dfrac{aKVN}{60G}} = \int \frac{G\,dt}{V} \quad (5\text{-}9)$$

Equation (5-9) becomes equation (5-10) on integration.

$$\frac{-60G}{aKV}\ln\left(1 - \frac{aKVN}{60G}\right) = \frac{G}{V}t + C \quad (5\text{-}10)$$

where C = the constant of integration. By substituting the boundary condition, if $t = 0$ and $N = 0$, then $C = 0$.

$$\frac{-60G}{aKV}\ln\left(1 - \frac{aKVN}{60G}\right) = \frac{G}{V}t \quad (5\text{-}11)$$

By reducing terms, equation (5-12) is obtained.

$$\frac{-60}{aK}\ln\left(1 - \frac{aKVN}{60G}\right) = t \quad (5\text{-}12)$$

By rearranging terms, equation (5-12) becomes

$$\ln\left(1 - \frac{aKVN}{60G}\right) = -\frac{aKt}{60} \quad (5\text{-}13)$$

Changing the form of this equation from a natural log function ($\ln = \log_e = \log_{exp}$) to a power-form equation gives equation (5-14).

$$\left(1 - \frac{aKVN}{60G}\right) = \exp\left(-\frac{aKt}{60}\right) \quad (5\text{-}14)$$

The final form of the equation after rearranging and combining of terms becomes

$$N = \frac{60G}{aKV}\left[1 - \exp\left(-\frac{aKt}{60}\right)\right] \quad (5\text{-}15)$$

Although the primary purpose of the clean room was to limit airborne contamination, it was not unlikely to see final design specifications for such construction with no reference to dust count or filtration. In many cases the clean room designer was not faced with the problem of designing an operationally clean room. The contamination level of a conventionally designed room is in part dependent on the activity in the room. Therefore, almost any clean room design will yield a low level of contamination if no activity takes place within the room and if the room is given sufficient time to "clean up." Since design and operating criteria were not separated, in most cases the clean room design did meet the requirements when the room was "at rest" (no activity taking place). When operating personnel tried to use many of these rooms, however, they were no longer clean. The designer had given them a clean room, and it was now up to the operators to keep it clean. (This particular problem will be discussed in detail in Chapter 6.)

Despite these problems, some of which have just recently been solved, many conventionally designed clean rooms do maintain operationally satisfactory contamination levels. Some of these facilities will be discussed in the last section of this chapter.

A conventional clean room is a room in which a high degree of cleanliness is achieved and maintained by controlling the generation of particulate matter inside the room. In laminar-flow rooms it is not necessary to control contaminant generation to the degree it is with conventional rooms, since contamination is removed as soon as it is generated. Studies performed by MAMES, Olmsted Air Force Base, Pennsylvania, in September 1963, show that laminar-flow clean rooms can maintain an operational contamination level of approximately 1000 particles per cubic foot, greater than 0.5 micron in size. This contamination level is about one-tenth that of the best conventionally designed clean rooms. Laminar-flow rooms are second-generation clean rooms. They are also in their infancy, since the majority of clean rooms in use today are of the conventional type and were designed and built prior to the introduction of the laminar-flow principle. These conventional clean rooms represent a substantial investment. They have been accomplishing their purpose of providing a clean work space. It is up to the operator of such clean rooms to determine the efficiency and adequacy of his room. This chapter on conventional clean room design and Chapter 6, on their operation, are presented to assist the operators in analyzing their rooms and getting the most out of them.

Air-Handling Systems

The cleanliness achieved by a clean room is dependent on the air-handling system's ability to purge the room of contaminants. This includes not only effectiveness of the filters and the number of air changes per hour but also the distribution of the air within the room. Consider a room with but one air defuser in the center of the ceiling and one exit a short distance away, near the side of the room. With this arrangement, many areas within the room never get "washed" with clean air. Increasing the number of air changes will help up to a point, beyond which a further increase will ag-

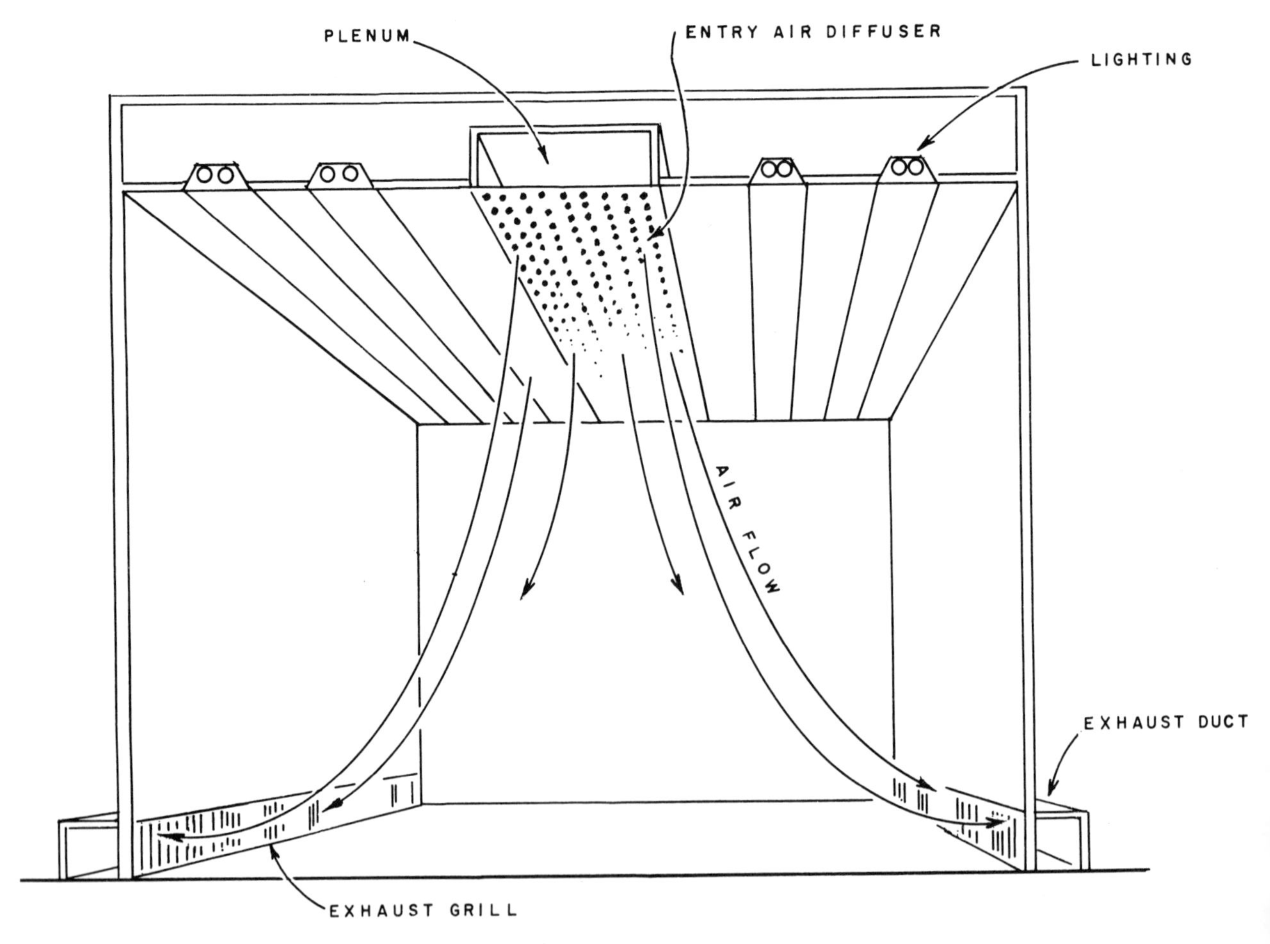

FIGURE 5-1. Conventional clean room air-flow pattern.
U. S. Air Force Technical Order 00-25-203

gravate the situation, as the higher velocity stirs up more dust and reintroduces it into the room.

The key to an effective air-handling system is low velocities of air entering through large areas. The exits should be dispersed in such a manner that the entire room is "swept" by clean air. The ideal design would be to have the entire ceiling a diffuser and the entire floor the exit. This would produce a steady down-flow of air which would sweep contaminants out as soon as they were formed. A departure from this ideal design for the sake of economics consists of a wide center plenum with a perforated defuser, and wall exhausts, at the floor, parallel to the plenum. (See Figure 5-1). Multiple rows of defusers may be used in larger rooms; however, multiple rows of exhaust grilles should also be used. This will require an exhaust duct in a trench to handle the middle of a set of diffusers. With proper room layout, these exits should be placed beneath workbenches. The floor (particularly the floor area in the proximity of the employee as he stands, sits, or manipulates during his work operations) is generally the most contaminated section of the room(*1*). If the floor exits are located here, much of the contamination generated can be removed. The air-handling system in Figure 5-1 allows predictable air-flow patterns and will, in fact, follow essentially parallel paths (for short distances) during the transition from defuser to exit grille.

The air-handling system should be designed to change the room air approximately twenty times per hour. This figure is no magic number; however, it seems to be accepted in the field as a standard. The room's ability to rid itself of contaminants is a function of air changes; however, at some point the increased velocities (mentioned previously) stir up more dust than they purge. Generally, this value would have to be arrived at by experimentation in each individual room. Since this is not possible, and since it is felt that twenty changes can be designed into a workable system, the use of this value has been widespread.

The conventional clean room should be limited in size. Conventionally designed rooms larger than 24,000 cubic feet (a room 40 by 75 feet with an 8-foot ceiling) present difficulties in environmental control. It has been proved that extremely large clean rooms have problems in "cleaning up" and exhibit varying contaminant levels within the room. The air-handling equipment for large rooms tends to be inefficient in gathering and purging of particulates. Long distances to exits and traffic in large rooms are big contributing factors to increased dust levels. If a large amount of clean room floor space is desired, it should be divided into several rooms(*1*).

Room pressure is another factor which must be considered. The function of increased pressure is to force clean air out of any cracks or leaks, thus preventing contaminated outside air from forcing its way into the room. The increased pressure also creates an outward flow of air when entry doors are open, preventing the entry of outside air. It is possible to maintain room pressure by discharging excess room air through a pressure-sensing regulated barometric damper. Since make-up air must be added to clean room atmospheres for the physiological needs of the employees, some air will have to be expelled from the system. Twenty-five per cent has been the generally accepted figure for the amount of make-up air. In many areas, state and local regulation will govern the per cent of make-up air used. A positive pressure of 0.10 inch (water gauge) will be adequate for most applications between clean room and uncontrolled areas. If more than one room is involved, it may be necessary to raise this value so that the rooms may be "staged" from the most closely controlled room to the least-controlled room. Where rooms are "staged," 0.05 inch of differential pressure (water gauge) between rooms is sufficient.

The selection of filters for the system is not difficult. Theoretically, filters may be selected on an individual basis. Since they are percentage devices, it is possible to calculate the amount of contaminants that they will pass when the contamination level of the ambient air is known. Therefore, a filter that will yield the level desired may be selected. It has been the experience of the Air Force(*2*) that rooms that do not use HEPA filters contain a large amount of small particles (smaller than 1 micron). This is due to the fact that these particles have a very long life in the air, and, once they are generated, they never settle out or are never intercepted by the filtering system. These smaller particles continue to build up and are in fact trapped in the room. On a particle-count basis, rooms without HEPA filters have a very high total count, owing to the large quantities of small particles. Large quantities of small particles are potentially dangerous to the operations in the clean room regardless of which particular size of particles is known to be detrimental to these operations. This is because small particles will coalesce and form larger particles, both in the room and inside the critical assembly. For this reason, filters for clean rooms should be nothing less than the best. In addition, the filter installation should be thoroughly checked for leaks. Sealing of HEPA filters is critical, and a small leak can pass large quantities of contamination. (Refer to Chapters 6 and 13 for methods of checking filters for proper seal.)

When filters are ordered, the filter manufacturers should be notified that they are for clean room installation, since HEPA filters will receive special handling if they are for this type of service. Air should never be discharged into or drawn through the supply duct without the HEPA filter in place.

For clean room applications, it is essential that the high-efficiency filter be located on the discharge[0] rather than on the suction side of the fan. On the suction side, inward leakage of atmospheric dust through faulty ductwork or improper gasketing of the filter will contaminate the filtered air supply. When the filter is on the discharge side of the fan, such leakage will be outward. To avoid duct corrosion products from being discharged into the clean room, the high-efficiency filter should be located as near as possible to the clean room discharge.

Ductwork should be nonflaking and corrosion-resistant to prevent the introduction of contaminants from the duct. Stainless-steel ducting is best, but aluminum has been found to be satisfactory. Galvanized ducting may be used upstream from the filter system if economics so dictate.

Round ducts are preferred over rectangular and should be used whenever space permits. Care must be taken to prevent air leakage into or out of supply ducts. Ducts should be tested for leaks and sealed before insulation is applied. Insulation should be vapor-proofed, and all joints taped.

[0] See Reference *3* this chapter.

Many clean room operators wish to maintain the air changes per hour within rather close limits. Accordingly, filters are replaced when the accumulated dust load prevents the desired air flow. In practice, the usual basis for filter change is a predetermined rise in resistance. To use this method effectively, (1) the performance curve of the fan must be known, and (2) the filter must constitute the major source of resistance in the system.

The flow delivered by the fan is represented by the intersection of the fan volume-pressure curve and the system resistance curve. This volume, common to both curves, is the only flow that the fan can develop at this point on its performance curve. Therefore, if the filter is the major resistance, Δp measurements across it can be used to estimate flow during dust loading. Obviously, if fan volume-pressure data are not known, these measurements are meaningless.

HEPA filters may be used with resistance differentials up to 10 inches (water gauge) *(4)* with allowable rise in filter resistance determined by fan capacity. Therefore a fan must be selected that is capable of delivering the desired air flow against the total resistance, that of the ductwork plus that of the dust-loaded filter. Using a filter resistance increase of 100% as a basis for replacement indicates that filters will last on an average about 18 months. Annual operating costs for a 10,000-cfm system generally run between $55 and $65 per 1000 cfm*(5)*.

Frequently, users may note little or no resistance rise above that of the clean filter, but at the same time observe that air flow is gradually decreasing. On investigation, it usually is seen that the fan being used has a flat, broad pressure-volume curve developing barely enough pressure to deliver the desired air flow through the clean filter. With rise in filter resistance taken as a criterion, this fan will provide an infinitely long filter life, but the clean room will be starved for air in the process.

The fan should preferably be characterized by a steeply rising pressure-volume curve to provide reasonably constant flow during dust loading. As an example, Figure 5-2 shows a hypothetical case in which the predetermined allowable rise in filter resistance is assumed to be 100% of that of the clean filter operated at 1000 cfm. This flow is assumed to

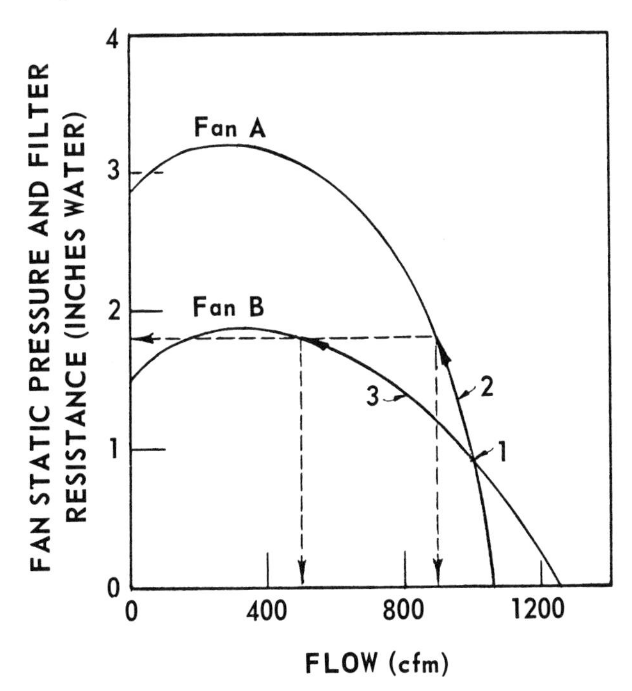

FIGURE 5-2. Effect of fan performance on air flow through dust-loaded filter. (1) Initial filter flow with either fan. (2) Dust load versus flow with fan A. (3) Dust load versus flow with fan B. *Courtesy Air Engineering*

be the design air-flow requirement of the clean room. Fans A and B both have sufficient capacity to deliver 1000 cfm against a clean filter resistance of 0.9 inch (water gauge). From the curves, it is seen that doubling the resistance to 1.8 inch across the filter produces only a 10% flow reduction when the steeply rising pressure characteristic of fan A is used, whereas with the lower, broader characteristic of fan B it results in a 50% reduction in flow.

A fan with the same performance curve as fan B, but developing a higher static pressure and capable of greater maximum flow, may be used to give reasonably constant flow during filter loading if a damper is installed in the system. Acting as a second variable resistance, the damper is partially closed when the clean filter is installed and then gradually opened during filter loading to maintain the desired flow rate. Because a relatively constant system resistance is maintained, reasonably constant flow is achieved. Now that the system contains two major sources of variable resistance, however, Δp measurements across the filter can no longer be related to flow rate. In this case, flow should be measured by means of a Pitot tube or similar technique. When the desired flow rate cannot be maintained with the damper wide open, the filter should be changed, regardless of the pressure drop. Best constant-flow conditions will, of course, be obtained by using a damper with a fan having a steeply rising pressure curve.

Since it is desirable to locate the high-efficiency filter on the supply air system as close as possible to the clean room, multiple filtered air outlets may be located in or near the ceiling of the clean room. Each outlet may have its own filter connected in parallel to one fan through a central manifold supply air duct. Here, individual dampers and provisions for Pitot tube flow measurements for each filter are always necessary, since filter resistance measurements are not a reliable indication of the flow rate. When one fan serves two or more filters in parallel by means of branched ducts, flow through a clean filter and a dust-loaded filter adjusts itself until the Δp across each filter system is the same.

Figure 5-3 shows a typical layout of mechanical equipment for a single-duct central system. Reheat coils are shown after the spray coil section. In certain cases, the reheat coils may be located at the branches to the different areas to compensate for variations in cooling and heating load.

The most important item to emphasize is the location*(6)* of the super-interception, or HEPA, filter. This filter should be located so that it is the last item of mechanical equipment downstream before the duct work. High-efficiency precleaners may be put in their conventional location before the spray coil units, but the HEPA filter must be the very last element in the mechanical line-up. This assures that all air to the clean room is filtered and that there is no possibility of contamination with unfiltered air.

It is equally important that the HEPA filters be installed in such a way as to prevent any possibility of leakage around them. Figure 5-4 shows an installation that demonstrates the fundamentals in design which must be followed. If the filter bank is going to be high, it should be backed by suitable angle supports as shown in the first section on the left.

The forming of an absolute seal between the filter

case and the filter holder has always been a problem. One unique method of filter mounting prevents any contaminated air that passes around a poor filter seal from entering the uncontaminated air stream. This method uses a primary seal on the rear (in the direction of air flow) of the filter and a secondary seal, which is not as critical, at the front of the filter. The mechanics of the filter installation can be simply arranged so that tightening of a hold-down device at the rear of the filter pushes the rear holder frame against the rear seal and at the same time forces the entire filter forward, thus compressing the front gasket against the front holder frame. The design trick is to vent the area between the two seals to ambient air. Since the pressure differential across the front seal is very low, the seal is more efficient, and contaminated air passing through the rear seal is vented and does not enter the uncontaminated air being emitted from the filter.

Outside intake ducts supplying make-up air should face downwind from the direction of the prevailing wind. They should also be located away from localized particle generation operations such as trash storage areas and packing and unpacking areas. Intake ducts turned face down are good for preventing ingestion of windborne contaminants only if they do not tend to collect all the sweepings off the roof when the wind blows in their direction across the roof. There are several vivid examples of this problem. One clean room had a make-up air intake duct downwind from a nearby

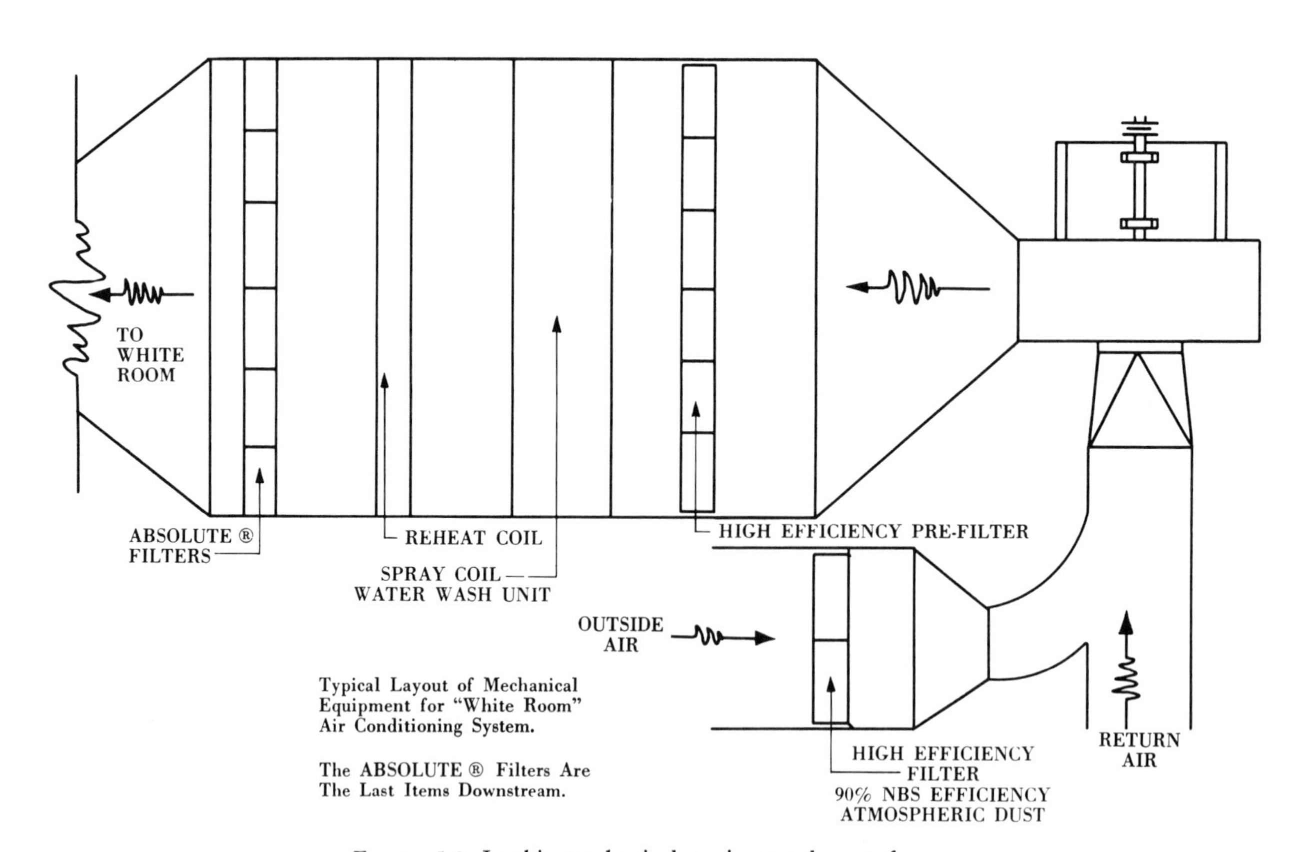

FIGURE 5-3. In this mechanical equipment layout for a single-duct central system, note the position of the HEPA or super-interception filter. The filter must be the last item of mechanical equipment downstream before the ductwork. *Courtesy Air Engineering*

FIGURE 5-4. This bank of HEPA or super-interception filters illustrates progressive stages of illustration and construction details such as backing angle, filter installation without frame, bolted assembly to secure tight gasketed seal, and filter shipped in plastic bag. *Courtesy Air Engineering*

incinerator. The particle count in the clean room was found to be related to incinerating operations, wind direction, and wind velocity. In some other clean rooms, the contamination levels were found to be related to wind direction and velocity; however, in these cases the cause was not an incinerator and an air intake duct but poor sealing of the clean room. Another installation had difficulty in the winter months, when wind-blown snow and ice carried roof gravel to the water tower; when the snow and ice melted, the dirt was deposited in the system. The result was clogged circulating pump filter screens and subsequent malfunctioning of the air conditioning. Many small but annoying and time-consuming maintenance tasks can be avoided with adequate attention to details during the planning stages.

Materials of Construction[1]

The selection of materials of construction can be influenced by consideration of a great variety of characteristics, with their relative importance dependent on the usage of the facility and on the sensitivity of the end product to particular degrees and types of contamination. Several basic requirements are usually common to most types of conventional clean rooms, however, in that surfaces must:

1. Be free of crevices, pits, openings, porosity, etc., by which contaminating material can be retained or enter.
2. Be resistant to abrasion or other damage in the normally expected usage.
3. Resist deterioration leading to particle formation in sizes potentially harmful, either through exposure to the normal environment, or through exposure to decontamination procedures and materials.
4. Possess dielectric properties, suitable for either retention or dissipation of electrostatic charges, as desired.
5. Provide or permit needed acoustic treatment.
6. Provide needed light-reflectance qualities, including color.
7. Provide needed control of vapor transmission.
8. Be joinable to other materials, and compatible therewith.
9. Be producible in usable shapes and sizes.
10. Be reparable, or replaceable, as may be necessary in the life of the facility.
11. Be dimensionally stable, on aging or thermal cycling, so that surface fissures or distortions detrimental to effectiveness of cleaning procedures will not develop.
12. Be capable of absorbing, without damage, movements imposed by building strains, including vibratory movements.
13. Permit, or provide, needed control of heat transmission.

Some of these desired qualities are not attainable in the surface material alone but rather are the result of proper combinations of surface and substrate

[1] Abstracted from reference 7.

FIGURE 5-5. Installation of bench supports in clean room at Hill Air Force Base. *Courtesy Hill AFB, Utah*

or supporting materials. This is particularly true in matters of acoustic properties, heat transmission, dimensional stability, and possibly even vapor transmission. This need to properly support or supplement the surface material forces us to consider the characteristics of all the structural materials having a bearing, as installed, on the performance of the clean facility. These supporting materials generally are not within the controlled environment and may be subject to wide variations in stress, temperature, humidity, or position, due to exterior influences, with potentially seriously damaging effect on the performance of an otherwise well-designed facility. Control of vibration, whether induced internally or externally, is also a function of supporting structure, of extreme importance in some installations.

Noise and Vibration Problems[2]

Location of a clean room should be seriously considered before construction is begun. Localized ground vibrations as experienced at most industrial areas should not be overlooked. Transmitted energies from ground vibrations and/or air-carried vibrations in the range of 0 to 200 cps can disrupt fine precision measurements.

Careful consideration should be given to isolating the noise and vibration generated by equipment, machinery, and support and administrative areas from clean rooms where precision work with delicate instruments is being carried on; however, duct liners should not be used in air ducts for any reason.

Conventional vibration isolation pads should prove satisfactory for high-frequency vibration. Care should be exercised, however, to ensure that the isolators do not become dust generators or collectors. Low-frequency isolation pads should be specially designed blocks. Above-floor isolating devices for low frequencies should be avoided in order not to generate requirements for excessive headroom. The design should give special attention to the framing system of the superstructure in order to prevent vibration transmission through ceilings, walls, and floors into the structure.

Cleaning Requirements during Construction

Specific provisions for constant, thorough cleanup throughout the construction of a clean facility must be a part of the design. Constant, thorough cleaning and vacuuming of furred wall spaces and other potential sources of dust should be carried on until the spaces are closed off. All dust-producing construction activities such as sawing, planing, and sanding should be accomplished as far as possible from clean areas. Construction planners should consider the sequence of operations in order to schedule dirty work such as cutting or plastering, breaking up concrete, and excavating ahead of other operations.

All air-handling ducts intended for use downstream of HEPA filters should be thoroughly cleaned and sealed at the factory prior to shipment. After erection, the ducts should be vacuumed clean with an industrial-type vacuum cleaner and sealed until used. All openings in the duct system must remain sealed during construction. Air must never be permitted to flow into or out of the ducts unless the HEPA filters are in place.

[2] Abstracted from reference *1*.

All equipment, furniture, utilities, and material installed under the construction contract should be thoroughly cleaned by the general contractor prior to his turning the facility over to the user. When equipment is placed in the room prior to acceptance, provision should be made to clean such items.

The above precautionary measures should be clearly outlined in the specifications and made a part of the facility design. Figure 5-5 shows the construction of a clean room at Hill Air Force Base, Utah. Note the cleaning equipment and trash receptacle available during construction. It is of interest to point out that the bench support is about to be fastened to the floor with epoxy glue. Each circular floor cutout was saved for the future repair of the floor should these bench supports be removed and other equipment installed.

Floors

Floors are a particular problem in clean rooms. They are subjected to shear forces when people walk across them. This action generates particles in relation to the inability of the flooring to resist breakdown. It is possible for 150 million particles, each 1 micron in size, to be generated by wearing away of thickness of 1 micron from an area the size of a postage stamp. For this reason it is important to obtain a flooring with long life and high resistance to breakdown. Vinyl is particularly

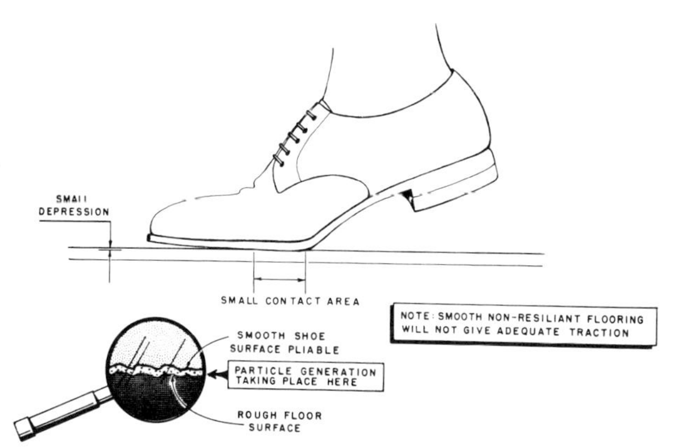

FIGURE 5-6. Particle generation by shoe materials or coverings on nonresilient flooring. *Courtesy MAMES, Olmsted AFB, Pa.*

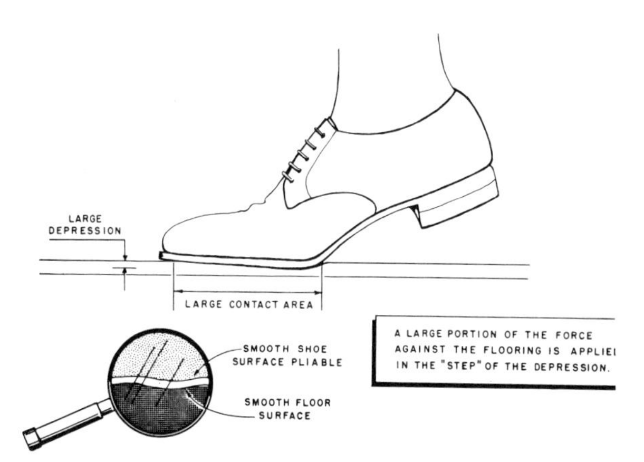

FIGURE 5-7. Larger contact area of shoe and depression of resilient flooring greatly assist in reducing contaminant produced by normal walking movements. *Courtesy MAMES, Olmsted AFB, Pa.*

adapted for this use for a number of reasons. Since it is tough and somewhat elastic, the shear force is lessened by the deflection of the flooring under load which then presents an edge to bear against. (See Figures 5-6 and 5-7).

The problem presented by the floor has been discussed previously. The fallout of airborne particulate matter continually contaminates horizontal surfaces and particularly the floor, since it is at the lowest level. This contamination is reintroduced by walking and by other actions that stir up the settled matter. It is, therefore, desirable to have a smooth surface which will be easy to clean and will not collect dust. Coved corners where the floor meets the walls will simplify the cleaning operation. The joints should be tight and sealed if possible. There are two methods of sealing joints in vinyl sheeting. One method uses a solvent to dissolve the adjoining sheets and run them together. Some installations using this method have experienced difficulty in the seam area because of permanent softening, which allows contaminants to collect. If this procedure is used, it is necessary that the seam area be returned to the original flooring hardness if satisfactory results are to be obtained. The other method uses heat to seal the vinyl. This operation requires some experience for satisfactory results. To accomplish the sealing, the flooring must be asbestos-backed. The backing retains the heat and allows the seam to seal completely. A household iron with the adjustable dial set on the "linen" setting has been found to be satisfactory. The iron is moved on top of a piece of aluminum foil which has to be laid over the seam.

When long lengths of coiled floor material such as vinyl are to be used for floor surfacing of clean rooms, it is suggested that this material be first laid out on the site and allowed to flatten out for several days before being bonded to the floor. Experience with this type of material has shown that considerable shrinkage occurs between the time of unwinding from the coil until bonding to the floor.

In missile clean rooms, floors may be subjected to heavy loads, and vinyl would not be suitable. Because of chemical attack and heavy loadings, epoxy and polyester topping is usually recommended. West Coast aerospace corporations have had remarkable success with epoxy floorings. The secret to a successful covering is preparation of the surface. Manufacturers' recommendations must be followed. Care must be taken at expansion joints so that the action of the joint will not be impaired by the topping.

Walls

Because some clean room operators found their rooms lacking in desired cleanliness, an effort was made by designers to eliminate all possible sources of contaminants from future rooms. The walls were no exception. The flaking of wall-covering materials was one of the contributing sources. As a result, "nonflaking" wall materials were used in some of the more sophisticated clean rooms. Stainless steel, vinyl coating, and formica-type sheeting were some of the more popular selections. In addition, coving was installed in all corners in a further effort to prevent the gathering of dust. These measures together with additional room refinements and increased worker control proved successful in yielding lower contamination levels in a number of cases.

Measures taken to eliminate contamination deriving from the walls have been expensive. In addition, the amount of contaminants contributed by walls has been overestimated. Before present knowledge was available, the tendency was to use whatever material would produce the fewest particles, with almost no regard to cost.

A smooth, durable surface subject to little or no chipping and flaking will be satisfactory. Gypsum board with a good-quality paint is satisfactory where impact strength is not essential. When the application of a wainscot is required for impact resistance, the following materials are recommended: hardboard, job-painted factory prefabricated hardboard; metal, prefinished or job-painted; an epoxy or similar durable paint. It is recommended that no horizontal dividing strip be installed between the two wall materials, a flush joint being preferred.

Hollow concrete masonry has become popular for construction, owing to its fire resistance and low cost. This type of construction may be used in clean rooms, but every effort should be made to get the finished surface as smooth and hard as possible if no covering material is used. Epoxy paints have proved very satisfactory.

The use of wood in structural elements is discouraged because of its unstable action in areas where there is a change in humidity; motion caused by expansion and contraction of the wood due to changes in its moisture content will result in the breaking of dust seals. The use of masonry walls, metal studs and bar joists, and/or metal furring is preferred for this reason.

Coved corners are not necessary unless they can be justified by the time saved during cleaning of the walls, which may be necessary because of a peculiar operation. The sealing of the walls should be adequate to prevent any large losses of pressure.

Window and door frames and the doors themselves should be constructed of metal and set into the clean room so that they come close to being flush with the interior walls. Window frames may be constructed of aluminum, steel, plastic, or other highly durable material.

The introduction of large volumes of console-type equipment adds an additional heat load and provides possible collectors and sources of contaminants. In many cases the room is unable to accept this load and still meet the standards required. As a result, many clean rooms have built this type of equipment into the wall. This places the heat load, etc., outside the room. It also allows maintenance on the unit without the necessity of entering the clean room. When equipment is built into the wall, it should be gasketed to prevent excess loss of room air. This is sometimes difficult, since the equipment itself, unless especially designed, will offer many openings for the air to escape.

Ceilings

Since ceilings are not subjected to potential impact, they may be surfaced with any material that does not produce or collect dust and is easily cleaned. Many clean room ceilings are of the suspended type. Ceiling panels and lights are set in channels suspended from the existing ceiling. This type of support has decided disadvantages if not properly constructed. Since the lay-in panels are held in place by the channel edge and gravity, there is ample space for pressure loss and contamination entry unless proper panel sealing is provided. The area above the clean room is usually highly contaminated, fallout dust lays on the ceiling panels and slight movement permits enormous (on a particle-count basis) quantities of dust to enter. Proper construction will provide a seal and clamp for the panels and lights to prevent these problems. When lay-in panels are installed and clamped in place, they cannot be removed from below. This is a decided disadvantage when work must be done above the ceiling. If work is to be accomplished in the area above the ceiling, a catwalk must be installed. Figure 5-8 shows hardboard lay-in panels being installed in a suspended ceiling. Note the light fixtures and insulation blankets which are installed as the ceiling is put up. These particular lay-in panels are gasketed and clamped.

Lighting

Lighting fixtures of the fluorescent type should be used. Fluorescent and other discharge-type lamps are by their nature a potential source of radio (RF) interference. RF interference will adversely affect sensitive electronic equipment, resulting in erroneous and erratic readings or disturbing static. Corning Glass Works #70 Low Brightness Lens Panels or an equal substitute should be provided on all fluorescent fixtures where RF interference is a potential problem.

Strangely enough, lighting is a controversial subject. At one clean room conference*(8)*, attended by some of the most knowledgeable people in the field, one of the most heated discussions concerned lighting. The Air Force Technical Order 00-25-203 specifies 100 foot-candles *minimum*. For extremely intricate work, this will not be enough and auxiliary bench lights will be required. In one clean room

FIGURE 5-8. Hardboard lay-in panels are installed in suspended ceiling of Bldg. 28 clean room at Olmsted Air Force Base. *Courtesy MAMES, Olmsted AFB, Pa.*

FIGURE 5-9. Maintenance man servicing clean room lights from above the clean room. *Courtesy Grumman Aircraft Engineering Co.*

the architect-engineer made a mistake in calculating the requirements, and the room was constructed with approximately 400 foot-candles at bench level. This particular room was operated with the lights at that level—there were no complaints; however for intricate operations individual bench lights were provided in this facility. Observations of many clean room throughout the United States indicate that a base level illumination for the room supplemented by high intensity light sources at those work stations requiring it, is the most economical design.

In an effort to reduce the amount of contaminant-producing activities taking place in a clean room, many clean rooms have installed flush ceiling lights which can be serviced from above. Figure 5-9 shows a maintenance man servicing this type of lighting. Note the ceiling glass panel in front of the worker's foot. This makes for expensive construction, not only because of the cost of fixtures but also because of the cost of additional construction requirements for overhead servicing and a load-bearing ceiling.

In some cases the maintenance man working on the lights above the ceiling produced as much contamination as he would if he changed them from below. This contamination was generated through inducing movement in the ceiling and light fixtures with resultant deposition of dust in the clean room.

Recessed lights with flush face plates which can be serviced from below are preferable; however, flush-mounted lights may be used if they offer no horizontal surfaces to collect dust. When lights are

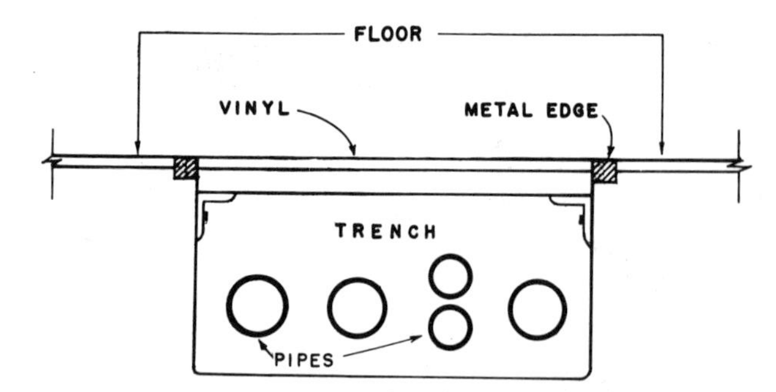

FIGURE 5-10. Cross-section of utility trench showing narrow metal edge at trench joint to protect the flooring material when the trench cover is removed. *Courtesy MAMES, Olmsted AFB, Pa.*

FIGURE 5-11. Utility distribution panels are shown on top of workbenches. *Courtesy Hill AFB, Utah.*

to be serviced from inside the clean room, they should be changed all at one time on a scheduled basis. Data on optimum lamp replacement time are available from the manufacturer. This maintenance should be performed when the room is shut down. Sufficient time can then be allowed after replacement to permit the room contamination level to return to normal.

Utilities

The distribution of service lines (water, electric power, vacuum, compressed gas, etc.) presents a major problem to the clean room user who must build flexibility into his room. For rooms with a fairly stable workload, this may not be as much of a problem. Lines must be brought to equipment in various room locations, and these lines should not present a dust-collecting surface or interfere with air or work flow. In some cases trenching has been provided throughout the room so that a connection is not far from any location.

In one clean room designed with trenches and vinyl flooring, the personnel had great difficulty in removing the trench covers without also tearing up the vinyl flooring. This was the result of butting the flooring at the joint with a tight fit. (A loose fit would be a dirt collector.) This problem could have been avoided by providing a narrow metal edge

FIGURE 5-12. Utility distribution panels are shown behind workbenches. *Courtesy Robins AFB, Ga.*

at the trench joint which would be flush with the flooring on each side. (See Figure 5-10).

Lines are also brought in through wall connections by means of specially built utility panels in rows of work benches. Figures 5-11 through 5-13 show such utility distribution panels. However these utilities are provided, their entrance into the clean room should be sealed (Figure 5-14) to prevent pressure loss and contamination entry. Figure

FIGURE 5-13. Utility distribution panels are shown flush with bench top. Panel cover is suspended below table. *Courtesy Litton Systems, Inc.*

FIGURE 5-14. Sealed utility pipes entering Litton clean room. These utilities will be mated with benches shown in Figure 5-13. *Courtesy Litton Systems, Inc.*

5-15 shows a unique sealed entry point for multiple utility lines. If it is necessary to run horizontal exposed lines into a room, they should be covered and coved into the wall surface. One guidance manufacturer using epoxy coatings on the wall placed the piping against the wall and then blended them in with several coatings of epoxy compound. This

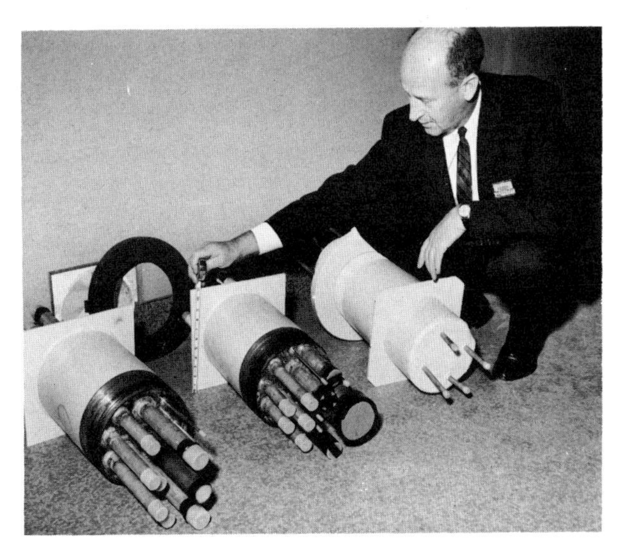

FIGURE 5-15. Unique sealed entry point for multiple utility lines. *Courtesy AiResearch Division, Garrett Corp.*

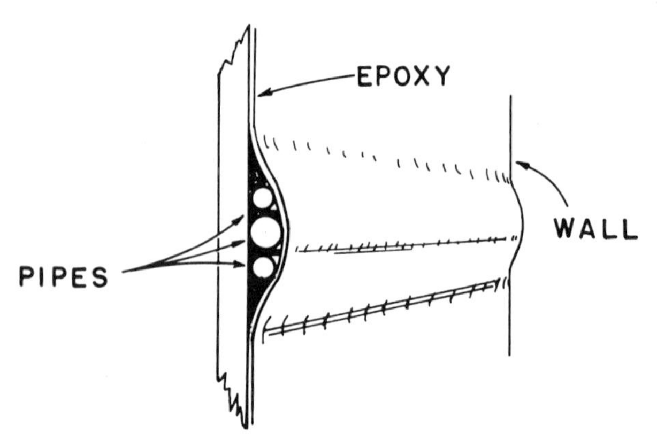

FIGURE 5-16. Unique installation of utility lines, coving into epoxy-coated wall with epoxy coating.

worked out quite satisfactorily. (See Figure 5-16.)

Technical power systems of different frequencies should be run separately. Higher-frequency systems must be shielded to prevent interference with test equipment.

Pass Boxes

The use of pass boxes can be traced back to the early days of clean rooms. Whether the designers were trying to limit personnel movement in the clean rooms or were just trying to separate the dirty operations is not known; actually they did both. The means to prevent personnel from walking into the room with an item was the pass box. A wall was used to separate dirty operations, and a pass box was provided to get the items through the wall.

Pass boxes are subjected to a large amount of wear and should be constructed of a material that will resist abrasion and rough use. Stainless steel is best; however, formica-type material will be satisfactory for light loads. The box edges should be reinforced. A double door with an interlock which will permit only one door to be opened at a time will prevent direct contact through the opening. (See Figure 5-17.) Another method provides a turntable arrangement with but one opening which must be turned to your side for access. (See Figure 5-18.) Pass-box framing should be metal to ensure rigid support. Since pass boxes are designed to prevent a direct opening between rooms, a means of communication must be provided alongside the box. This can be an intercommunication system, a voice diaphragm, or a speaking tube. An air vent may also be provided in the box to help purge it of contaminants.

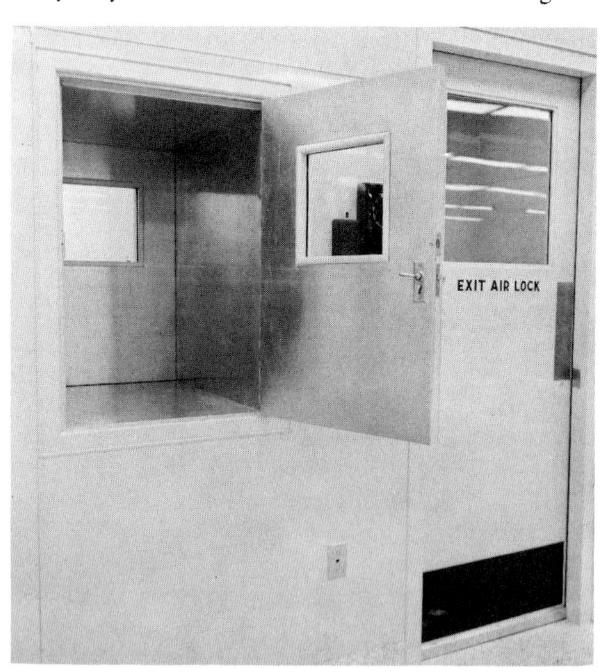

FIGURE 5-17. Pass box with interlock door system, Bldg. 95, Olmsted Air Force Base. *Courtesy Olmsted AFB, Pa.*

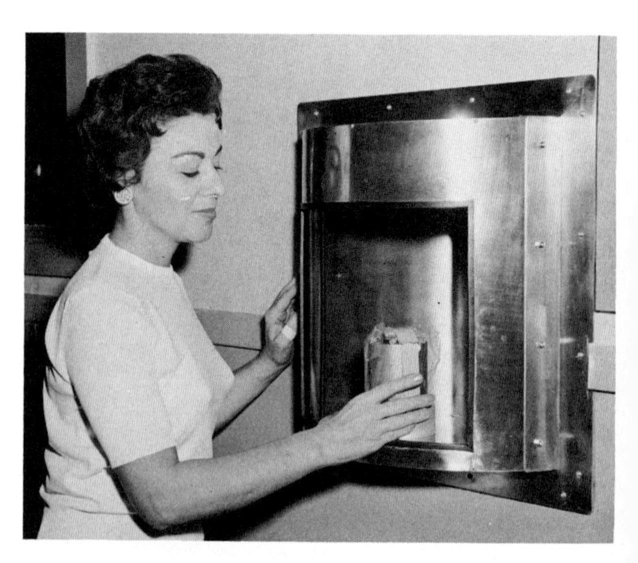

FIGURE 5-18. Circular pass box. Item is placed in box and is then rotated 180 degrees. *Courtesy Kearfott Division, General Precision Inc.*

Air Locks

Pressurization of clean rooms is essential; therefore, it is necessary that pressure be maintained during entry to and exit from the room. This is accomplished by means of an air lock, a small (relative to the clean room) chamber with interlocked doors. The size of the air lock depends on its use. A personnel air lock may be only large enough for one man, or it may be large enough for a group of people, depending on the number of people that must enter the clean room in a given length of time. Pass boxes for tools and equipment should be designed as air locks unless their size is so small that the pressure loss would be insignificant.

Equipment should not be moved into or out of the clean room during normal operation. Replacement or new equipment should be installed when the room is not in operation. Ample time should also be allowed after completion of the task to permit the room to "clean up." If it is anticipated that equipment will have to be moved during room operation, an equipment air lock should be provided.

Air Showers

Air showers were developed to de-dust personnel prior to their entry into the clean room. Since there is a very delicate balance between the contamination level and the number of personnel (activity) in the clean room, it was necessary to clean the contamination clinging to an individual's garments prior to his entry into the clean room. In theory this was an excellent idea, but in practice it often did not work. One of the difficulties with this theory was that clean room operators overestimated the amount of contamination that could be prevented from entering their clean room through the use of air showers. The other primary difficulty was the design of the air showers. Many of them were ineffective. Air velocities on the individual were not high enough to produce efficient contaminant removal. The air shower exhaust was also inefficient and resulted in subsequent re-entrainment of particulate matter that had been removed. All these factors helped to give the air shower a bad reputation.

At Robins Air Force Base a number of clean rooms are equipped with two air showers (one prior to entering the change room, and one prior to entering the clean room). In a series of tests, the air showers were turned off singly and in unison (*9*). The results of these tests proved that air showers can appreciably reduce the amount of contamination brought into the clean room. The instantaneous level of contamination caused by personnel entering the clean room with both showers operating was half of what it was with no air shower operating. When only one air shower was used, no difference was found whether it was operated before the change room or before the clean room. Test runs to determine this resulted in approximately the same contamination level in both cases.

It should be pointed out that the employees at Robins are well disciplined in the use of the air shower. This indicates another difficulty which can be encountered—the improper use of a good air shower.

The development of air shower theory has been primarily by trial and error, since the mechanics of removing contaminants from street clothes and clean room garments are not well understood. More research in this area is needed. The purpose of an air shower is to remove the gross particulate matter from personnel clothing. This particulate matter is

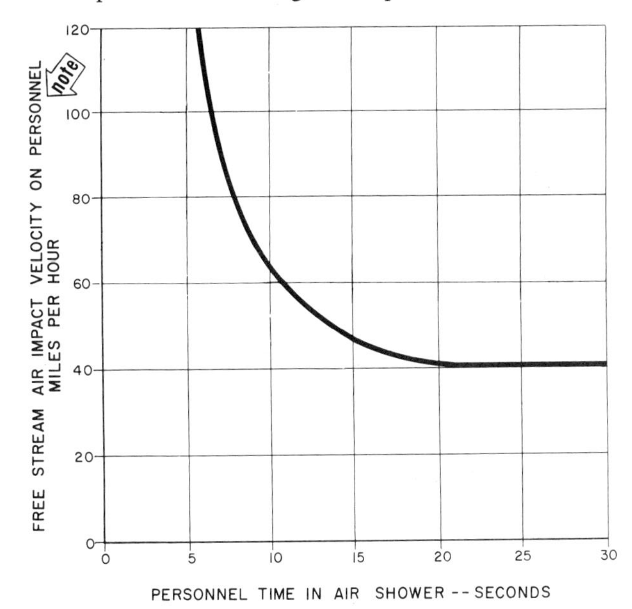

FIGURE 5-19. Air shower velocity-time curve. *Air Force Technical Order 00-25-203.*

that which would be expelled into the clean room by personnel under normal work conditions.

Figure 5-19 is an air Shower velocity-time curve. Its purpose is to relate time in an air shower to air velocity of the shower. This curve was developed by using limiting condition techniques. The following assumptions were made:

1. An individual in an air shower wearing clean room clothing simulates a circular cylinder having an infinite aspect ratio.

2. Turbulent air-flow conditions, sufficient to remove particulate matter from the individual, will be generated when the transition Reynolds number is exceeded.

3. The average individual's maximum transverse torso dimension is 16 inches. For a circular cylinder, a turbulent boundary-layer condition exists at a Reynolds number of 500,000.

The Reynolds number can be expressed as:

$$R_N = \frac{\rho VD}{\mu d} \tag{5-16}$$

where D is the transverse dimension for the cylinder. The value ρ is density of air equal to 0.002378 lb-sec²/ft⁴ for standard condition; V is the velocity of air; and μ_d is the dynamic viscosity equal to 0.0383×10^{-5} slug/ft-sec for standard conditions.

The following calculations are made for the minimum velocity for turbulent boundary-layer conditions.

$$R_N = \frac{\rho VD}{\mu d}$$

$$500{,}000 = \frac{(0.002378 \text{ lb-sec}^2/\text{ft}^4)\ (V)\ (1.33 \text{ ft})}{0.0373 \times 10^{-5} \text{ lb-sec}^2/\text{ft}/\text{ft-sec}}$$

$$V = \frac{500{,}000 \times 0.0373 \times 10^{-5}}{0.002378 \times 1.33}$$

$$V = 58.8 \text{ fps}$$

$$V = 40.0 \text{ mph}$$

In establishing the first limit, it is known that for velocities less than 40 mph a very long period of time will be needed to remove particulate matter. Thus, a point can be established on the curve at 40 mph and time equal to a large value or infinity.

The second limiting condition is that at least a short period of time must be spent in the shower. Therefore, the curve must be asymptotic to the vertical axis. Also, there is an air velocity that is unsafe for air loading of personnel.

Since the equation for drag on the individual in the air shower is $D = C_D K V^2$, where C_D and K are constants, this is a second-order equation. But D is a function of the boundary layer and the type of flow in the boundary layer. Therefore, the curve of Figure 5-19 is a function of a second-order equation and is shown as plotted.

It should be pointed out that the velocity is the *impact* velocity on the individual in the shower. It is the *free stream* velocity of a streamline which is perpendicular to the surface area of the individual as measured in the position that he will occupy during shower operation. It is not the velocity issuing from the nozzles. The curve shows that velocities should be from 50 to 90 mph for effective cleaning. Nozzle velocities will depend on the nozzle opening and the distance to the individual. Since the air is directed from opposite sides, little imbalance will occur on the individual. In addition, these velocities are not dangerous, since the mass of air is not adequate to overbalance the individual even if directed asymmetrically. The most significant air shower deficiency has been low velocities on the individual. The clothes must be "flapped" if proper

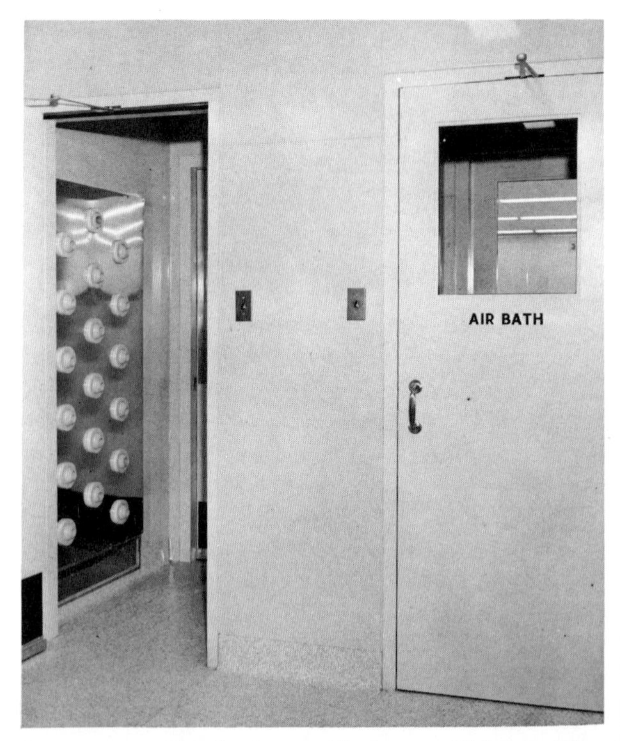

FIGURE 5-20. Circular louver air shower, Bldg. 95, Olmsted Air Force Base. *Courtesy Olmsted AFB, Pa.*

FIGURE 5-21. Vertical slotted air shower, Bldg. 28, Olmsted Air Force Base, *Courtesy Olmsted AFB, Pa.*

cleaning action is to take place. Velocities higher than those shown are potentially dangerous and should be tested prior to use.

Air showers are usually built into air locks. The interlocked doors are timed so that an employee cannot get out of the shower until adequate cleaning has taken place. The interlock system is provided with a manual override for emergency use.

One arrangement of an air shower is shown in Figure 5-20. In this arrangement, the employee enters the air lock, closes the door, has his clothing air-blasted, and then enters the critical area after the air shower has stopped. Adjustable louvers supplying air at high velocity are set in the walls of the air lock. By the use of suitable interlocks it is possible to prevent a worker from passing through while the air shower is in operation. Where safety regulations prevent the installation of automatic door locks, workers can be reminded of their responsibilities by interlocking a klaxon or other alarm so that violations of rules are made obvious to the offender and his fellow workers.

Figures 5-21 and 5-22 show vertical slotted air showers that process employees on the move. The exit door will not unlock until enough time has elapsed for the employee to go through the appropriate cleaning motions.

Figure 5-23 is an unusual air shower with very high-speed nozzles drilled in the overhead rectangular pipe. A similar air shower at Norton Air Force Base, California, uses four vertical poles rather than the overhead pipe for distribution. In this arrangement 1/16-inch-diameter Mach 1 nozzles are spaced 12 inches apart from floor to ceiling on four vertical pipes. These pipes form the corners of a 36-inch square. Air velocities on the person are sufficient to produce garment flutter and good cleaning. An air shower at Olmsted AFB, Pa., makes excellent use of this design for processing 300 persons into a 30,000 square foot clean room. Fourteen pipes are arranged in a "U" shaped shower. Each pipe has 8 nozzles spaced 9 inches apart in a vertical configuration. The high pressure air system is used to supply air to the nozzles after it passes through an inline filter. The central vacuum system is used to exhaust the air from the shower confines. Nega-

FIGURE 5-22. Vertical slotted air shower in action at Litton Systems, Inc. *Courtesy Litton Systems, Inc.*

FIGURE 5-23. Overhead high pressure, small-nozzle air shower. *Courtesy Kearfott Division, General Precision, Inc.*

tive pressure with respect to the clean room is maintained in the air shower.

The General Electric Space Technology Facility has three air showers, one between the street-clothes area and the main locker room, and two between the work areas and the wash area. (See Figure 5-24.) All operate in the same manner. Each air shower is served by a separate supply blower and an exhaust blower. The design air volume supplied is 1100 cfm, from a 5-horsepower pressure blower through an HEPA filter and ducted into special nozzles built into the wall of the air shower enclosure. The blower intake is from the factory air outside the white room. The exhaust blower for each air shower is designed for 1500 cfm at ¼ inch of water static pressure, which is sufficient to maintain a slight negative pressure in the air shower enclosure when operating. Exhaust blowers discharge into the factory.

The entrance and exit doors of the air shower are interlocked so that only one of them can be opened at any given time. The closing of the entrance door starts the blowers. Until the cleaning cycle is completed, the exit door remains locked. The duration of the air blast is 18 seconds for the air shower that separates the two locker rooms. A 10-second cycle is used in the final shower. If an emergency develops, the air shower cycle can be interrupted by a "panic" button. This safety feature was provided to prevent injuries that might occur from claustrophobia, dizziness, etc. So far, however, no occasion for its use has arisen(*10*).

It is important to stress the fact that many de-

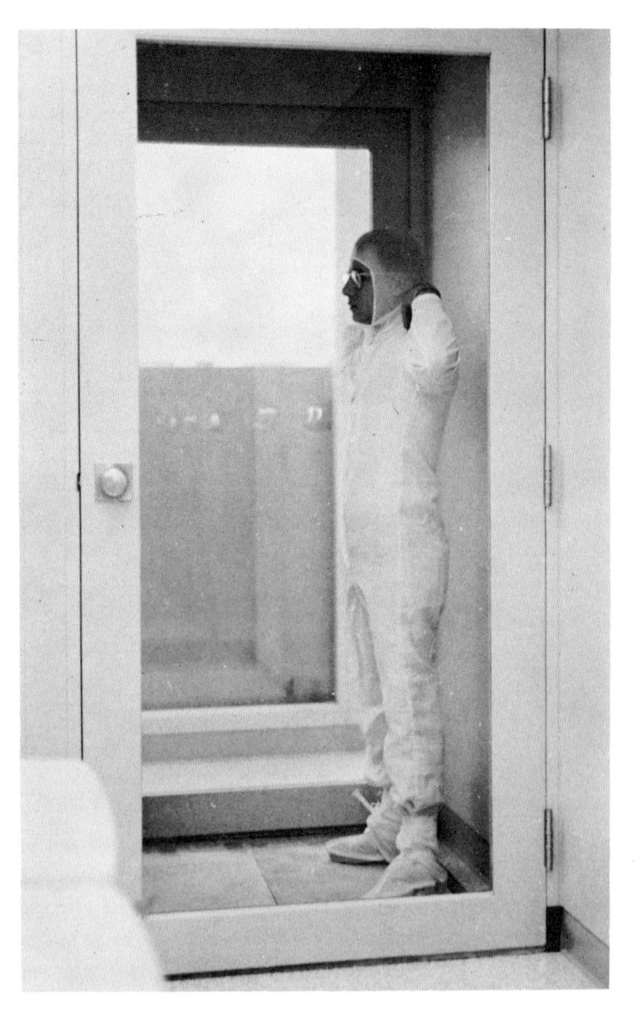

FIGURE 5-24. General Electric clean room employee demonstrates proper air shower cleaning technique when dressed in clean room clothing. *Courtesy General Electric Technology Center.*

signers of air showers have not considered the build-up of heat load in the shower as it is used. This results in the shower operating at 10 to 20 degrees above ambient temperatures. It is both discomforting and disturbing to those passing through the shower. Further, little or no provision for filtration of the air used in the shower is made. This results in impingment of particles on the garment.

Support Rooms

Since the conventional clean room operator must control the contamination entering his room, the accepted practice has been to include support rooms inside clean or semiclean areas, the theory being that the individual would not have to go "outside" where he could be contaminated. This practice has increased the cost of installing a clean room. Support rooms can include locker rooms, wash and rest rooms, change rooms, and offices. These rooms are usually constructed of the same materials as the clean room. The air-handling system, for the sake of economics, is usually not so elaborate as that in the clean room.

Change rooms are provided as an area for employees to change into their clean room garments.

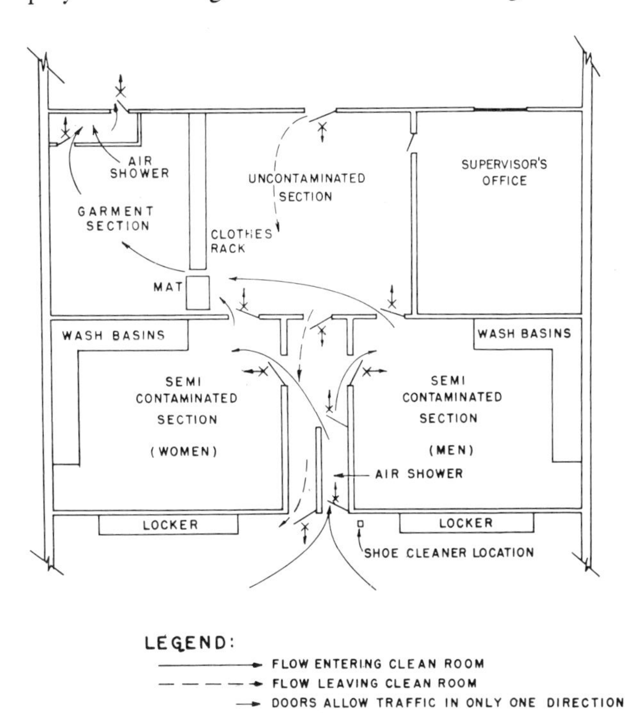

FIGURE 5-25. Sample change-room layout.

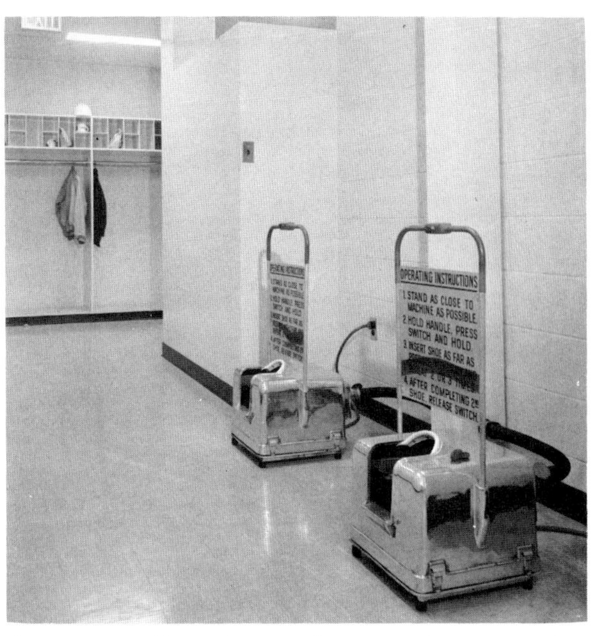

FIGURE 5-26. Shoe cleaners for use prior to entering change area. *Courtesy Olmsted AFB, Pa.*

The purpose of a change room is to provide a transition for the employee from a contaminated object to a decontaminated object without introducing the removed contamination into the clean room. This is accomplished through the use of personnel cleaners, limited-linting garments, and proper control of personnel. The control of personnel is in part discipline; however, the design of the change-room area can prevent the employee from making mistakes. This can be shown by referring to a

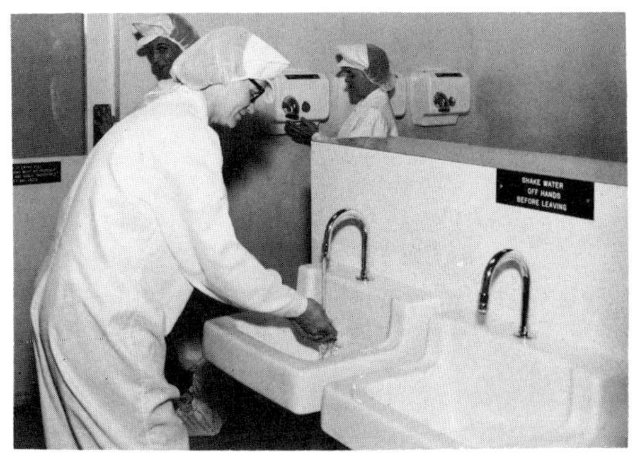

FIGURE 5-27. Foot-operated washstands. *Courtesy Lear-Seigler, Inc.*

FIGURE 5-28. Tacky mat installed in Grumman clean room entrance. *Courtesy Grumman Aircraft Engineering Corp.*

sample layout. (See Figure 5-25.) The "key" is the path that the employee is forced to follow, not the placement of the rooms, doors, etc. Many layouts which might look unlike the example will also establish this path. (See discussion of employee discipline in Chapter 6.)

The change room should be divided into three distinct areas—an uncontrolled area, a semicontaminated area, and an uncontaminated area. Lockers are placed in the uncontrolled area for housing the inclement weather garments, overcoats, etc. When proceeding from the uncontrolled area to the semicontaminated area, the employee must utilize a shoe cleaner (see Figure 5-26) and an air shower. (The location of air showers was discussed previously.) The employee is now semicontaminated. Washing and toilet facilities are located in the semicontaminated area. These facilities consist of foot-controlled washstands, liquid soap dispensers, and an air hand-drier. (See Figure 5-27.) The entrance to the uncontaminated section is guarded with a shoe-sole cleaner—a tacky or sticky mat. (See Figure 5-28.) This section is provided with covered clothes racks or lockers for clean room garments, and with benches or foot rails if shoe covers are to be donned. The entrance to the clean room is made through an air shower. Separate entrances should be provided for traffic moving toward the clean room and traffic moving out of the clean room. This prevents the transfer of contamination into the clean room. The details on entry and exit procedures may be found in Chapter 6.

Many existing change rooms have high dust counts which tend to grossly contaminate garments not in use but stored on open racks. This is due to the activity taking place and the lack of adequate air handling. Clothing change by its very nature produces a large amount of particulate matter. It should be realized that this activity is also critical, and change rooms should receive more attention, both in design and in maintenance.

Supervisor areas are often located adjacent to the

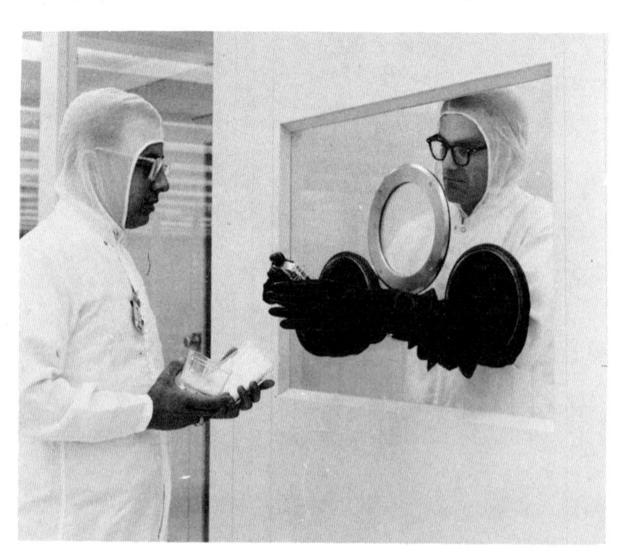

FIGURE 5-29. Glove ports in General Electric Space Technology Center clean room. *Courtesy General Electric Space Technology Center.*

uncontaminated section. Since paper work is not permitted in the clean room, this location permits easy access. Personnel leaving the supervisor area must go through the room entry procedures prior to entering the clean room. To facilitate communication between the supervisor and the clean room personnel, a window and intercommunication system or voice diaphragm should be installed between the two areas. Figure 5-29 shows a supervisor inspecting a part through glove ports. Communication is possible through a voice diaphragm. Pass boxes, glove ports, and similar devices may be installed if necessary.

Lunch areas, if required, may be located adjacent to the locker area.

Clean Room Equipment[3]

Furniture and fixtures for clean room use should be selected with care. Materials should be chosen to resist the generation of particles by chipping, flaking, oxidizing, or other deterioration. Normal paint should not be used in areas subject to repeated contact with personnel or other objects in the clean room (such as workbench legs). Should such surfaces require painting, an epoxy, polyester, or similar surface coating should be used. (*Note:* Instructions for the preparation and application of these coatings must be followed exactly in order to obtain desired results. Surfaces must be prepared properly.) Contemplated usage should dictate the choice of materials for clean room furniture and

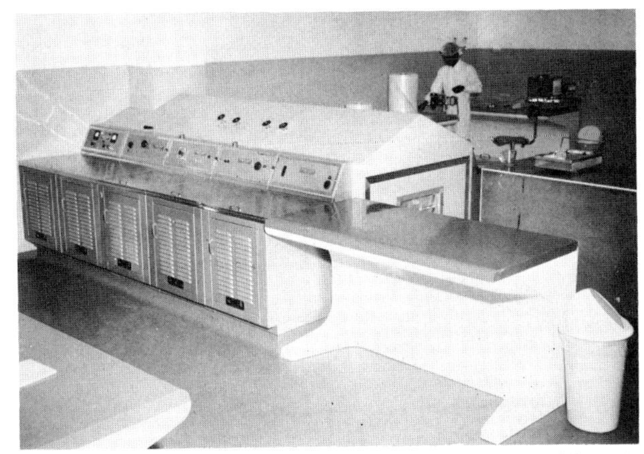

FIGURE 5-30. Formica-topper, epoxy-coated workbench and ultrasonic cleaner. *Courtesy Hill AFB, Utah*

[3] Abstracted from reference *1*.

FIGURE 5-31. Plastic "tote box" in pass box. *Courtesy General Electric Space Technology Center.*

fixtures. Items that can expect to be bumped, knocked, abraded, etc., by personnel should possess a tough, resilient, low-particle-generating surface such as stainless steel, a formica-type material, or material of equivalent surface qualities. If not subject to such treatment, the items may be of conventional design. Principles of sound engineering economy should prevail. Figure 5-30 shows a formica-topped epoxy-coated workbench and an ultrasonic cleaner designed for clean-room operation.

Material handling equipment has a very definite place in a clean room. A well cleaned wire mesh shopping cart works well as a piece of such equipment. Mechanized or automated handling equipment should be so designed that it will not contribute significantly to the contamination level of the room. Mechanical equipment, including carbon brush wear, which could cause exhaust fumes and thus contaminate the room should be shielded or avoided. Particular care must be exercised in choosing bearing surfaces and other conveyor materials. Contamination-producing parts used in mechanized or automated handling equipment necessary to clean room operation should be shielded to prevent room contamination.

Normal handling equipment should be of the "tote box" or "plastic bag" type. (See Figure 5-31). The surfaces of the containers should be smooth to prevent the generation of particulate matter. Cleanliness is of utmost importance. The care exercised in cleaning the container must be as good as, or better than, the cleanliness of the part to be carried. If plastic bags are used, special attention should be given to ensure that they are clean. Plastic bags are generally not clean enough for clean room use when they come from the supplier. Some suppliers do manufacture and package plastic bags in controlled-environment areas. If the plastic bags are not purchased from a supplier who is using a clean environment for the manufacturing or packaging of his containers, the plastic bags should be cleaned before use.

The product will seldom be cleaner than the container that holds it. Therefore, the choice of, and the cleaning of, material handling equipment is of the utmost importance.

A shoe cleaner should be designed for effective removal of particulate matter from the entire shoe. It should not permit high-speed particles to escape into the atmosphere; dirt removed should be collected by a vacuum system. This unit should be designed to allow rapid processing of personnel. A cleaned shoe should not be recontaminated on removal from the unit.

A sole cleaner should be designed so that particulate matter is removed from the undersurface or walking surfaces of the shoe.

A hand cleaning area should contain washing facilities with foot-controlled washstands, liquid soap dispensers, and filtered air hand-driers.

A central vacuum-cleaning system may be included in the design for shoe cleaners, janitorial vacuuming of clean and service areas, etc. Outlets should be flush-mounted in the walls approximately 4 feet above the floor. Normally they should be spaced so that hose length does not exceed 50 feet and so that every spot within the area can be reached by the hose intake fitting. The design should provide for four outlets in operation simultaneously, with 1¼-inch hoses and fittings. Vacuum suction at the end of the hose should be not less than 25 inches of water.

If a central vacuum cleaning system is not used, a portable clean room vacuum, equipped with a HEPA final exhaust filter, should be employed.

Examples of Conventionally Designed Clean Rooms

So far, the design and construction of conventional clean rooms have been discussed. Some examples of operating clean rooms will now be considered.

New Departure Miniature & Instrument Ball Bearing Plant, Sandusky, Ohio

An example of the contamination control deemed necessary for miniature and instrument ball-bearing assembly and test is shown by the New Departure clean room. (See Figure 5-32). This room has 1300 square feet of clean room space. Extreme precautions were taken in the design of this room to eliminate dust-collecting ledges and contaminant-producing materials of construction. Doors are frameless plate glass without any protruding hardware. All other surfaces are designed of stainless steel, No. 4B finish. Ceilings are as devoid as possible of any projections and are finished with butt-jointed plastic sheet material. The most novel feature in New Departure's clean room is the slanted walls which lean at about 3 degrees off plum into the room. This was planned to aid gravity in the precipitation of any particles that might adhere to a vertical wall surface.

This room is constructed with no perpendicular or right-angle intersections of architectural surfaces, except at door jambs and headers. Ceiling and floor surfaces are coved into walls and partitions on sweeping radii. All vertical surfaces are broken on 45-degree or "flatter" angles. Vertical interstices at panel window junctions are closed with stainless-

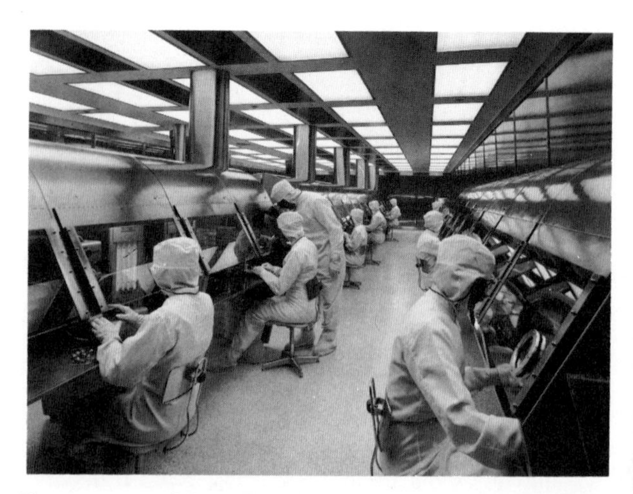

FIGURE 5-32. New Departure clean room. *Courtesy New Departure Division, General Motors Corp.*

steel battens. These battens have streamlined edges to avoid sharp corners for collecting dust.

All vertical walls and partitions are stainless steel or plate glass. Trim is also stainless steel. All steel is copper wire, grounded to discourage static. Copper grounding is concealed behind streamlined stainless moldings that cover the junction of the floor coves to the partitions.

Partitions are of single thickness, without studding or other framing. Stainless-steel-clad plywood and plate glass are self-supporting from structural-steel floor curbs to structural-steel ceiling members. No thermal insulation is required in partitions, since adjoining rooms are at the same temperature.

Frameless tempered plate-glass doors, with pivots and closing mechanisms flush with casing headers and floor, eliminate the usual moldings and ledges that present even minor dirt-accumulating ledges.

Ceiling height is 8 feet, minimizing the volume of air to be conditioned. A vinyl sheet covers ceiling surfaces with nearly invisible butt joints. Floors are covered with a vinyl sheet material, not static-conductive.

Even screwheads, potential resting places for dust, are covered with stainless-steel buttons that streamline them into flat surfaces. No crevice that could collect dust has been overlooked. Plastic metal, hard enough to require filing or grinding to get smooth, is flowed into all open joints that could not be butted tightly.

To remove any temptation to use dirt-producing local lighting fixtures, a general illumination of better than 200 foot-candles at work level is provided. This is accomplished by four-tube fixtures with plastic prismatic diffusing lenses, flush-mounted and sealed into the ceiling surface, using 8¼ watts per square foot. Well-diffused shadowless lighting is the result.

Maintenance of lighting fixtures is accomplished from above, outside the clean room, so that lights can be changed at any time without the necessity of maintenance personnel entering the facility itself.

Close attention was given to design of the air-conditioning system, based on 95°F with a maximum of 90% relative humidity outdoors. Make-up air is 25% outside air, with modulating dampers which spill excess return air above that which exfiltrates and which is required to maintain positive pressure in the room.

Air movement in the room was figured for twenty changes per hour, yet velocity is held down to less than 360 fpm at the perforations in the ceiling diffusing plates. Room temperatures are held to ±1°F from the selected level.

Air is introduced at the ceiling, with return grilles as close as possible to the floor, assuring that any motion of airborne contaminants will be downward. Three refrigeration compressors with a 100-ton peak design load supply the air-conditioning requirements.

For reasons of physical space, New Departure's fan room had to be located at a considerable distance from the clean room. In previous installations, the reheat coil was installed in the fan rooms, immediately after the condensing coils. Room-condition response to the controls, which were actuated by sensing elements in the room, lagged considerably. In the latest room, the refrigerated air is ducted to the reheat coils, which are separated from the ceiling diffusers only by the HEPA filters and the humidifying devices.

Humidification at New Departure warrants some mention. With winter temperatures in Sandusky, Ohio, sometimes approaching the zero mark, the dew point is frequently below that which would result in 40% relative humidity when air is reheated to room temperature. Experience has indicated that undesirable static has been generated by employees in nylon uniforms at 30% relative humidity or below. Thus, New Departure's relative humidity design has been established at between 30% and 40%. Control instrumentation causes introduction of steam in the ductwork immediately after reheat, and upsteam of the filters.

A word of caution here. As originally installed, the steam-injecting device was too near the filters, and a costly array of filter elements was saturated with moisture the first time steam was required. Moving the humidifier back to a point upstream of a splitting-vane duct elbow caused entrainment of the moisture in vapor phase instead of droplets, and the problem was solved.

Super-interception filters are installed immediately ahead of the first diffuser, with all downstream ductwork of stainless steel. Each diffuser constitutes a miniature plenum chamber, with three adjustable valves above a perforated stainless-steel ceiling plate. There are sufficient perforations to realize a very low exit velocity to minimize the "secondary" air currents within the room.

To decontaminate clean room personnel, New Departure uses a vacuum-connected motorized shoe cleaner, a narrow de-dust chamber with 40-mph slot blasts of 0.3-micron filtered air and floor grille exit, and another shoe-sole brushing device prior to entering the garment changing room. After donning nylon protective garb which covers all but a small portion of their faces, the employees must sit on a bench, swing around, and put on nylon

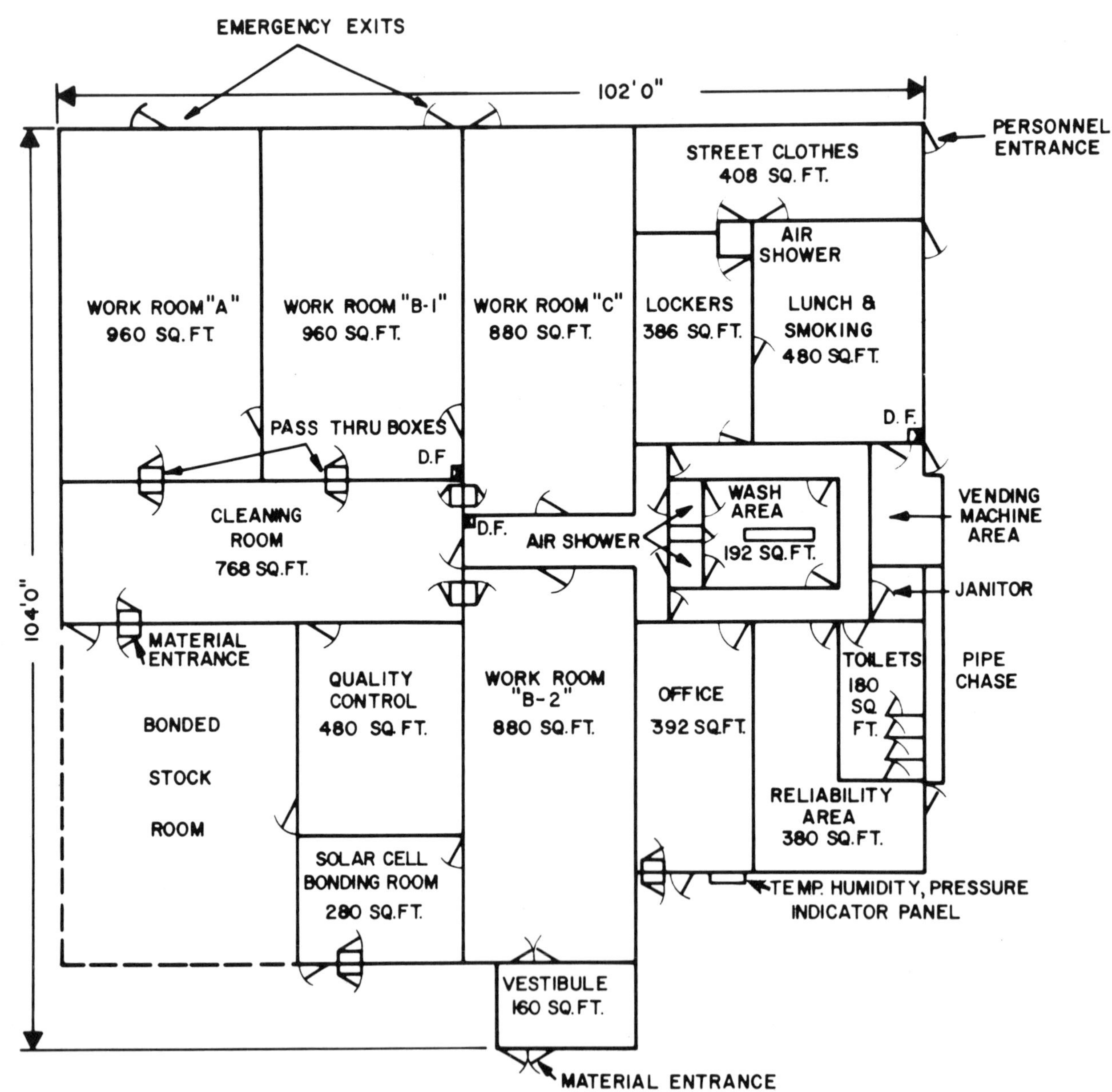

FIGURE 5-33. Floor plan of clean room facilities at General Electric Space Technology Center. *Courtesy General Electric Space Technology Center.*

bootees before stepping on the "clean" portion of the dressing-room floor. Then they must pass through another de-duster before entering the clean room.

No attempt is made to seal doors or to provide air locks. Exfiltration is invited through elevated pressure at 0.25 inch (water gauge) over adjacent rooms, with pressure decreasing in counterflow to that of the product. Thus an outward flow of air from the clean room facility to slightly less clean areas is always maintained, preventing any possibility of airborne dust's entering through doors, pass-throughs, etc.

General Electric Space Technology Center, Valley Forge, Pennsylvania[4]

The Valley Forge Controlled-Environment Facility of the General Electric Company was designed to be a Class IV Clean Room by Air Force Technical Order 00-25-203, March 1961. This installation was completed in February 1962. It was built to provide contamination, temperature, and humidity controls that meet the most rigid requirements of the space industry, now and for the foreseeable future. Construction of the facility was accomplished by Shielding, Inc., and was built to General Electric specifications. The immediate reason for building a clean room of this high degree of control was the need to maintain dust-free conditions during the assembly of solar cell devices, pneumatic systems, sun sensors, electromechanical devices, and critical electronic assemblies. As an example of a General Electric Company specification to be met in this facility, the pneumatic systems equipment was to have no particles larger than 12 microns and was to be 98% free of particles over 5 microns. This complex of clean rooms was built for these and other requirements.

The General Electric clean room facility occupies 11,000 square feet on the main floor of the Space Technology Center. (See Figure 5-33.) This space encompasses corridors and a bonded storage area and has temperature and humidity controls, as well as the clean room enclosure itself. The clean room has 8364 square feet distributed among eight distinct and separate areas. Of these, 5980 square feet are used for cleaning and assembly purposes. The remaining floor space is utilized in locker rooms, a lunch area, air showers, a washroom, an office, toilet facilities, a development room, and an inspection center. Each of these rooms, with the exception of the men's room, is separated from adjacent areas by partitions, which in some cases are of glass extending from floor to ceiling. When wall space is required for equipment, glass is used in the upper half of the panel. The solid portions of the partitions are pastel in color, with yellow, blue, and beige shades predominant. This variety serves to identify the separate areas and adds interest to the work environment. (See Figure 5-34).

The entire clean room area is zoned to provide for both pressure and temperature gradations. Pressure zoning is accomplished by the maintenance of a differential that ranges from 0.6 inch (water gauge) to a minimum of 0.004 inch. The area of highest pressure exists in the room farthest from the entry to the clean room. Changes in the levels of positive pressure are made by manually adjusting the dampers in the supply air ducts to each room. Transducers located above each room actuate a battery of pins on two pressure recorders located in the special equipment room just outside the clean room office. The recorder panel charts are positioned directly against the glass wall of the office within sight of every supervisor's desk.

Temperature zoning depends on an individual thermostatic control in each room. The desired level is maintained by means of reheat coils in the cooled air supplied to the individual areas. The

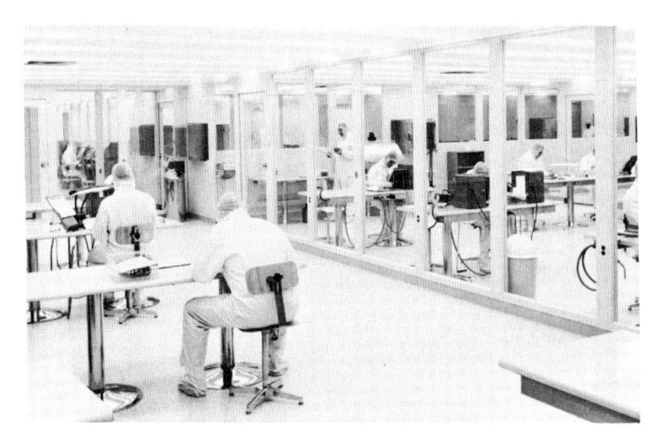

FIGURE 5-34. General view of critical assembly area "A." *Courtesy General Electric Space Technology Center.*

[4] Abstracted from reference *10*.

capability for producing temperature variations exists, but a uniform condition is maintained throughout the entire enclosure.

Partitions are of glass or metal or, in some cases, a combination of both. The metal is covered with a baked-on acrylic finish. All partitions, including the outside walls, are movable and are designed according to the modular principle. Sections are interchangeable, so that doorways, pass-through cabinets, and windows can be readily shifted.

The ceiling panels are hollow rectangular box sections designed to span distances of 38 feet between bearing walls. Made of 18-gauge steel, these panels are rigid enough to carry 10 pounds of dead load per square foot, and 20 pounds of live load. Long and narrow, they form strips that alternate with translucent plastic sheet diffusers above which are high-output fluorescent troffers. Thus, the clean room ceiling presents a pattern of illuminated strips alternating with solid structures that serve as a catwalk and a support for overhead equipment, such as the air conditioners, ductwork, and cooling units. (See Figure 5-35.)

The windows and interior glass wall panels are seated in slots in metal partition frames. Urethan glazing compound is used as a seal around the edges. Removal or replacement of glass is accomplished by lifting the pane with suction cups against the downward force provided by a spring-loaded rail in the top of the frame. Sufficient side clearances permit a simultaneous shifting of the glass in either sidewise direction so that the pane can be made to clear two edges of the window opening. With these two motions, the removal becomes a simple, two-man operation.

The seal between the clean room interior and the fluorescent light troffer proved to be more troublesome because of the flexibility of the diffusers. The four edges of the diffusers were at first fastened to the rim of the troffer with adhesive. Since the troffers themselves are sealed on the top with a lid resting on a gasket, little difficulty in excluding dirt was anticipated. But some buckling of the plastic sheet diffusers occurred, resulting in opened seams that allowed an excess of air to escape from the room. This problem was solved by the addition of spring-loaded metal strips placed on the inner edges of the diffusers. These provided a firm, mechanical clamp to reinforce the adhesive sealer.

Where wall construction is concerned, dust ac-

TABLE 5–1

Room	*Area (sq ft)*	*Occupancy*	*Equipment Load (kw)*	*Design Air Supply (cfm)*	*Exhaust Air (cfm)*
C	960	20	4	2850	—
B–1	960	15	4	2600	—
A	880	15	4	2500	—
B–2	880	10	4	2400	—
Quality control	480	6	4	1800	—
Reliability	380	8	2	1300	—
Cleaning	768	6	4	2500	3000
Office	392	6	—	1050	—
Locker	386	0–4	—	800	300
Lunch	480	0–15	—	1250	400
Street clothes	408	0–5	—	1000	—
Washroom	192	—	—	260	100
Vestibule	160	—	—	150	—
Corridors	440	—	—	1200	—
Toilet	180	—	—	—	400
Closet	36	—	—	—	50
Bonding	280	—	—	—	—

cumulation is minimized by chamfered window ledges and by flush surfaces on all panels and doors. Electrical outlets are flush-mounted, as are the central vacuum system outlets. The base of each wall panel is set back approximately 0.5 inch from the face to provide space for the conventional vinyl core base strip. The floor itself is covered with vinyl. Where the walls meet the ceiling, a plastic sealer is used to fill the slight but invisible gap.

No sprinkler system is incorporated in the design of the Valley Forge clean room, but an ample number of emergency exit doors are provided for safeguarding personnel. For this operation these doors require only a slight force in excess of that provided by the positive air pressure maintained at all times in the area.

All tables, benches, chairs, cabinets, and work shields are made so as not to flake, chip, or in other ways produce dust particles and contaminants. Nothing is of wood. Instead, these items are constructed of materials such as stainless steel, chrome-plated steel, sheet metal with a baked-on acrylic finish, and glass. Each item is contoured to minimize dust-collecting surfaces. In the case of tables, for example, the work surface is supported on two large pedestals whose vertical, cylindrical surfaces flow smoothly into a large circular base that rests directly on the floor.

In the parts-cleaning area, stainless-steel hoods

FIGURE 5-35. View of ducts and general construction of upper portion of clean room facility. *Courtesy General Electric Space Technology Center.*

FIGURE 5-36. Fan section of air-handling unit with capacity of 22,500 cfm. *Courtesy General Electric Space Technology Center.*

collect and remove noxious fumes. Where critical operations require an environment with a lower dust count than that of the room level, the work is carried out in enclosed work cabinets.

Six work areas are kept at a temperature of 72° ±1°F and a relative humidity of 40 ±5%. In the service areas, such as the locker and lunch rooms, temperature variations are wider, ranging from 72° to 75°F. The design air quantities needed to establish and hold these conditions are given in Table 5-1. A certain occupancy is assumed for each separate area of the clean room. Other heat inputs include ventilation supply air, ovens, other operating equipment, and lights. Heat input from lights amounts to 7 watts per square foot in the production areas and 4 watts in the service facilities.

Suspended above the roof duct, the medium-pressure air-handling unit (see Figure 5-36) supplies approximately 22,500 cfm of air from its fan section, driven by a 40-horsepower motor. Since the required temperature and humidity conditions in the work areas correspond to a dew-point temperature of 46.3°F, its task is to cool this number of cubic feet to 44°F. Two individual cooling coils of four rows each are used for this purpose.

Approximately 14,500 cfm of air passes through the cooling system; the remaining 8000 cfm is bypassed. In passing through the first four rows of coils, the air cools from 76°F dry bulb and 61.7°F wet bulb to 52.4°F dry bulb and 51.2°F wet bulb. This is equivalent to 36 tons of refrigeration. This water is drawn from the main plant's chilled-water circulating system. Approximately 140 gallons per minute is required. Entering the bank of coils at 45°F, the water leaves at 51°F.

The second stage of cooling (see Figure 5-37) requires roughly 23 tons of refrigeration to establish a dry-bulb temperature of 43.9°F and a wet-bulb temperature of 43.6°F. The 35°F cooling system installed to accomplish this has a capacity of 31 tons and is sufficient to handle future expansion of the clean room. The equipment consists of a 3-horsepower pump and a cooler capable of chilling a mixture of water and 20% ethylene glycol from 43°F to 35°F at a rate of 100 gallons per minute. Actually, the cooler can be operated at half, two-thirds, or full load, depending on the time of year. At Valley Forge, humidity is low in the winter, so that the factory make-up air requires no dehumidification. At such times, the chilled-water coils are interconnected and valved off so that the 45°F chilled water circulates through both coils. Thus, during four to five months of the year, the pump with its supply of water and ethylene glycol is inoperative.

Since the air leaving the chilled-water cooling system at 44°F is at a much lower temperature than is needed to handle the heat loads and to maintain

FIGURE 5-37. Second of two cooling units, used primarily for dehumidification. *Courtesy General Electric Space Technology Center.*

72°F, approximately 8000 cfm of return air bypasses the cooling coils through a duct installed above the air-handling unit. This uncooled air at 72°F and 40% relative humidity then mixes with the cooled and dehumidified air at 44°F just ahead of the fan section. The mixed air at 55°F in passing through the fan is heated several degrees and emerges for distribution through the ductwork at 58°F. If the rooms are unoccupied and the lighting is turned off, 58°F is below the temperature required to maintain 72°F. For this reason, an auxiliary damper in the bypass duct is interlocked with the main light switch so that less than 14,500 cfm of air passes through the cooler.

A return air thermostat in the return air duct from each room maintains the individual room temperature by actuating a three-way water valve which controls the flow of hot water to a reheat coil. These reheat coils are located in the branch air supply ducts to the rooms shown in Figure 5-33 as C, B, A, B-2, cleaning, quality control, and reliability. Water at 140°F enables each unit to raise the supply air from 58°F to 72°F, should the individual room load decrease to a minimum.

As a general rule, the reheat water flow and the supply air temperature are adjusted so that no more than 2°F of reheat will be required when the rooms operate at maximum cooling load. This means, of course, that the quantity of air bypassed around the cooling coils is at an optimum level from the standpoint of operating economy.

In the Valley Forge area during winter, the humidity occasionally falls below 40%. For this reason, the bypass duct was equipped with a humidifier that operates on 25 psi of steam.

Two stages of filtering on the intake side of the air-handling unit and one stage on the supply side make up the air filtration system. The first stage consists of eighteen throwaway units, 20 by 25 by 2 inches, used to prefilter the mixture of make-up and return air. Made of glass fibers, these filters are inexpensive and increase the operating life of the second and third stages. They are inspected once a month and are replaced if they appear to be heavily loaded with dust particles.

Also, on the inlet side of the fan section are thirteen high-velocity filters, each with a rated capacity of 1800 cfm at an initial pressure drop of

0.35 inch (water gauge). Pressure tops on each side of this filter bank permit the use of a draft gauge to determine when the unit should be replaced. Presently, new filters are installed when the pressure drop across the bank reaches 0.6 inch. The box is so designed that two more filters can be added if an extra room or an expanded operation requires an increased air supply.

The final, or third, stage of filtering makes use of HEPA filters which are 99.97% efficient on 0.3-micron particles and which are installed directly above each ceiling air outlet. Because of the two stages of prefiltering, the HEPA filters have a life expectancy of up to two years. Here again, a pressure drop is used to establish the need for replacement. On installation of the filter, the pressure drop across it depends on the air flow. When this initial reading doubles in value, the operating rules call for replacement. Because of a tight-fitting shutoff damper located in each branch supply duct, the change of filters for any given room can be accomplished without disturbing the air supply to the other rooms. These same dampers, incidentally, are usually set in an intermediate position to meter the approximate quantity of air required in each room. More-accurate metering depends on the adjustment of a second damper located just above the ceiling diffusers. For convenience, this balancing damper can be manipulated from within the room without disturbing the diffusers.

Relative to the factory space surrounding the clean room, a positive pressure is maintained within the facility. This varies from 0.2 to 0.4 inch (water gauge) in the working areas and from 0.05 to 0.2 inch in the service areas. The level in any given room is established by adjusting the return air

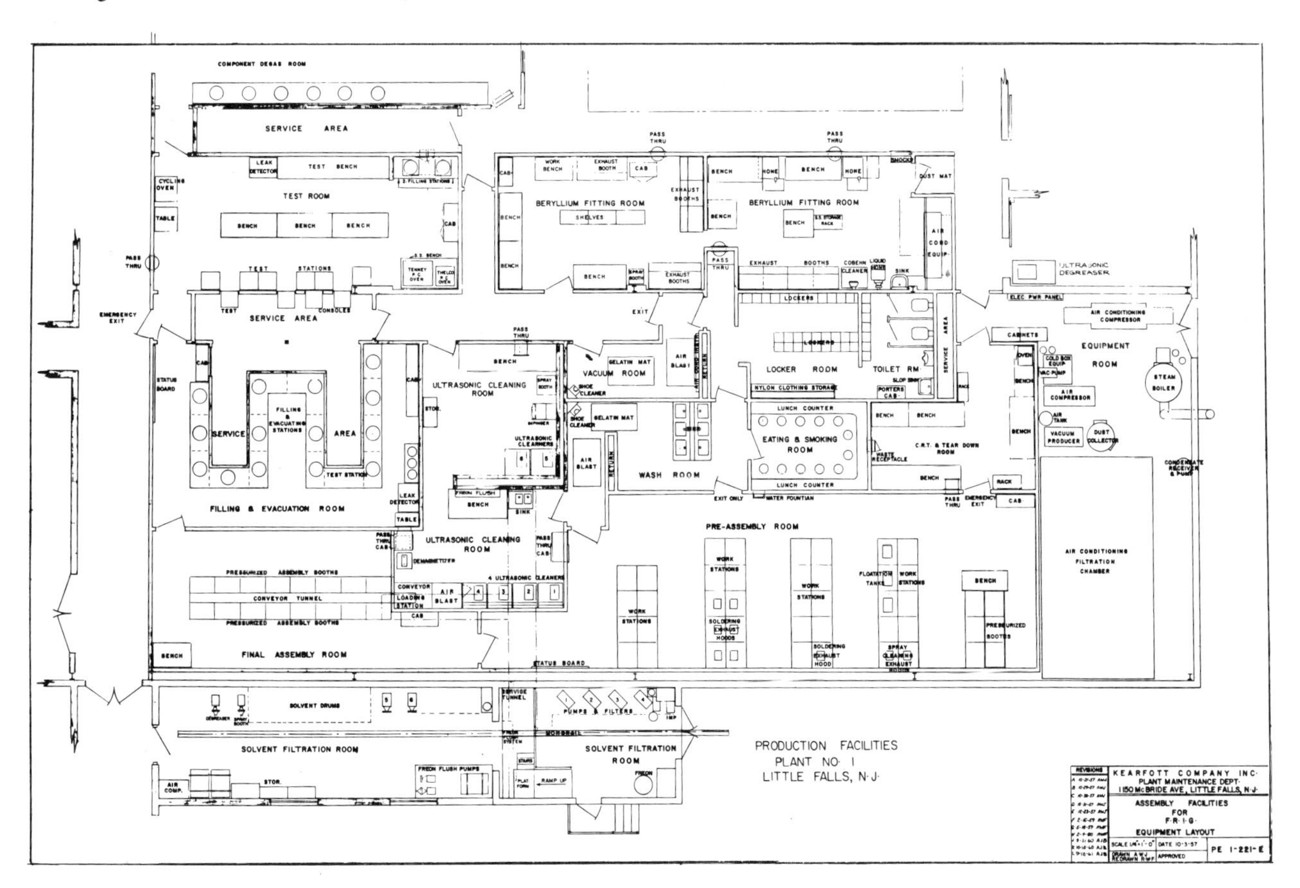

FIGURE 5-38. Floor plan of Kearfott Division clean room at Little Falls, New Jersey. *Courtesy of Kearfott Division, General Precision, Inc.*

damper located immediately behind the return air grille. Relevant to this operation, of course, is the balance between exhaust air and make-up air. Some 1250 cfm is discharged from the locker room, lunch room, toilet area, and janitor's closet. An additional 3000 cfm vents from the cleaning room. To offset this discharge, as well as to maintain room pressure and compensate for leakage, the make-up air intake damper is adjusted to admit 6000 cfm of air from the surrounding factory areas.

Since the clean room is equipped with a number of emergency doors so that each room has at least one means for quick exit, special provision has to be made for the maintenance of a minimum positive pressure, relative to the factory space, of 0.05 inch. This is done by means of a static pressure regulator inslotted in the main return air truck duct. If several emergency doors are opened, this regulator will throttle the return air damper. As a result, more than the normal quantity of 6000 cfm of factory make-up air will flow through the filtering system and will compensate for the abnormal air leakage.

The cleaning room exhaust presents a special problem. The 3000 cfm of air required is considerably more than is needed for cooling and temperature control. Accordingly, a return air relief grille allows 1000 cfm of air to bleed from room C (see Figure 5-33) into the cleaning room. This means that the pressure in the cleaning room has to be held at a low level, approximately 0.1 inch (water gauge) below that of room C.

The area on Figure 5-33 marked solar cell bonding room is not cooled directly. This room is cooled, when in use, by return air from B-2. When the door connecting B-2 and the solar cell bonding

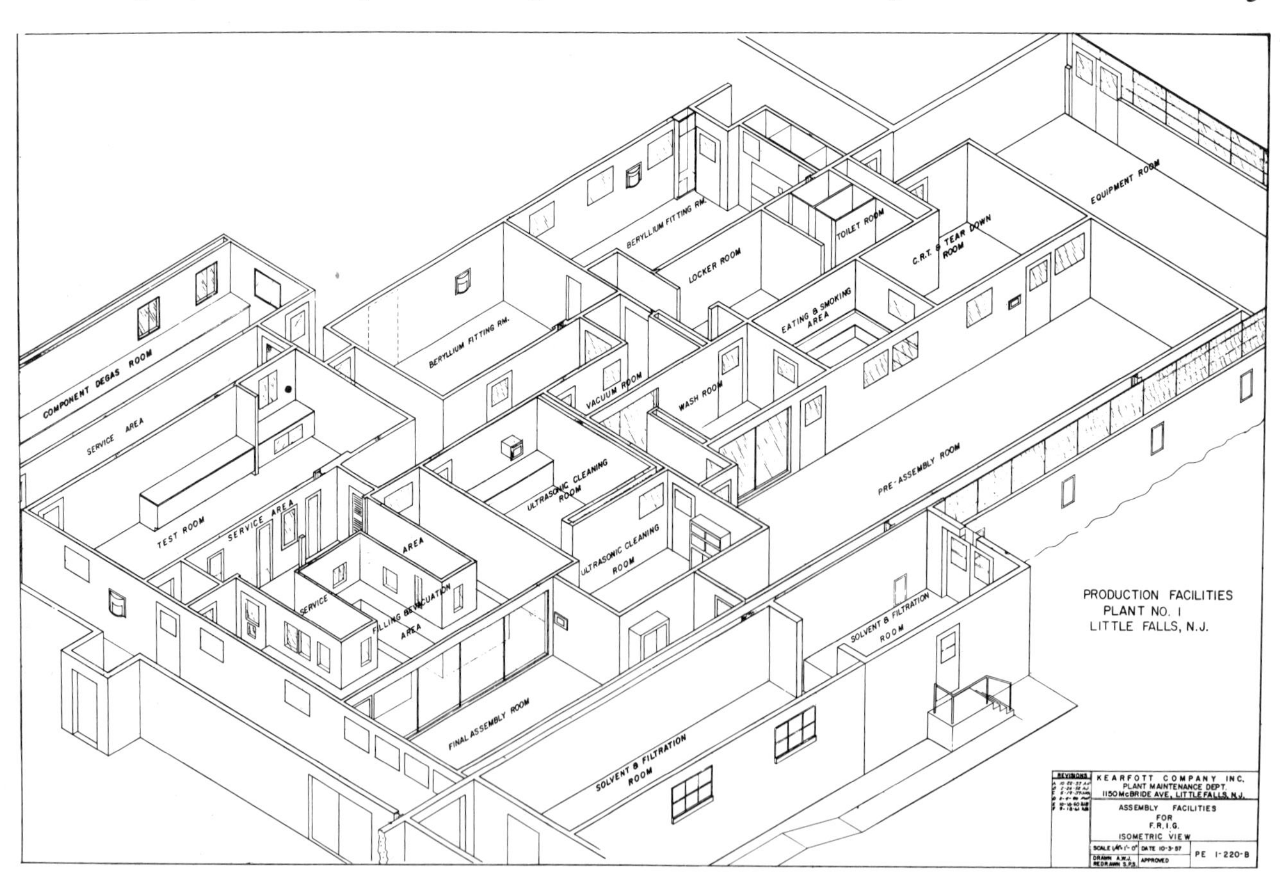

FIGURE 5-39. Three-dimensional view of Kearfott clean rooms at Little Falls, New Jersey. *Courtesy of Kearfott Division, General Precision, Inc.*

room opens, the damper behind the solar cell return air grille also opens, and the return air damper in G-2 closes. These two dampers are interlocked, and the motor that actuates them is controlled by a switch on the door between the two rooms.

Kearfott Division, General Precision, Inc., Little Falls, New Jersey

In the clean room facility of Kearfott Division, the need for painted surfaces has been eliminated by covering the walls and ceilings with smooth vinyl plastic. In the ultrasonic cleaning room, stainless steel covers the walls. Door and window frames are fabricated either of stainless steel or of chrome-plated steel and are so constructed that ledges are eliminated. The doors themselves are covered on both sides and all edges with formica and are hung from special ball-bearing hinges.

Floors are covered with continuous strips of black vinyl sheeting, thus eliminating edge joints normally associated with the use of tile flooring. Black vinyl was selected so that any dust present would be easily detected.

The major areas of this facility are the soldering area, the ultrasonic cleaning area, the preassembly area, and the final assembly area. (See Figures 5-38 and 5-39.) The soldering area covers 209 square feet. This area contains five hooded, vented, stainless-steel soldering benches, two ovens, one cold-box, plus additional stainless-steel workbenches. Leak test equipment, although used in this area, is located outside the pressure wall.

FIGURE 5-40. Final assembly booths with stainless-steel conveyor inside. *Courtesy Kearfott Division, General Precision, Inc.*

The ultrasonic cleaning area covers 224 square feet. This area contains four ultrasonic cleaning machines, benches, and other wash tanks. Cleaning fluid is constantly circulated and filtered at a rate of 4 gallons per minute. Vapors generated during cleaning are vented directly outdoors.

The preassembly area covers 948 square feet. This area has nine stainless-steel-hooded work stations and thirty-one regular work stations. All work stations are fabricated of seamless steel or are covered at top, edges, and bottom with black bakelite formica.

The final assembly area covers 380 square feet. This area encloses a sixteen-station stainless-steel booth 21 feet long with eight stations per side. (See Figure 5-40.) Fixtures for illuminating each station in the booth are mounted externally over a sealed plate glass to facilitate replacement of fluorescent tubes without contaminating the booths. By means of slots and louvers, a continuous, 140-fpm discharge of filtered air is obtained. Cutouts are provided in each booth for the operator's hands, and each operator wears protective coverings over his fingers. Test equipment used for interim checking at the final assembly stations is mounted externally at operator eye level to eliminate any contamination within the booth. The booth assembly encloses a conveyor belt leading to the ultrasonic cleaning room.

Extreme care is taken in processing materials into and out of the clean room facility. All material delivered to the stock room is received through a pass-through tunnel, entered on stock-room records, and placed on stainless-steel shelving for eventual use. Material leaving the stock room is sent to the ultrasonic cleaning room through a pass-through tunnel and packaged carefully in lint-free non-shedding containers.

All assembly tools used in this facility are specially designed and supplied to each employee in a covered glass dish after ultrasonic cleaning and inspection. At the end of each shift, each employee returns his tool kit for inspection and cleaning prior to reissue the next day.

Subassemblies that have been processed through the ultrasonic cleaning equipment and filtered air blast are loaded on stainless-steel trays under a pressurized hood prior to being placed on a conveyor leading from the ultrasonic room into and through the sixteen-station pressurized final assembly booth shown in Figure 5-40.

Personnel who enter the clean rooms must follow a set decontamination procedure. Overcoats, overshoes, and hats are stored outside the area, and entry into the anteroom is controlled by an attendant. After entering the initial decontamination anteroom, the employee first cleans his shoes by means of a vacuum brush, walks on a tacky gelatin mat to remove dirt from shoe soles, then steps on an electric floor treadle mat actuating an overhead multidirectional high-velocity air shower for 15 seconds. Lint and dirt thus dislodged are removed by an air exhaust at floor level. A door leading to the locker room automatically unlocks when the air shower has been completed. In the locker room, the employee undresses to his underwear and stores his clothing in an assigned locker. He then dons a white nylon cap, white nylon boots, and a tan orlon coverall. After dressing, he scrubs up in the washroom containing surgical sinks with knee-operated controls for temperature-controlled water, liquid soap dispensers, and hot-air hand and face driers. (See Figure 5-41). Leaving the washroom, he cleans his boots once more by means of the vacuum brush, walks across a tacky gelatin mat, and steps on an electric treadle which activates a second high-velocity air shower. This air shower lasts 10 seconds. At the end of this time, a door automatically unlocks, providing access into the preassembly area.

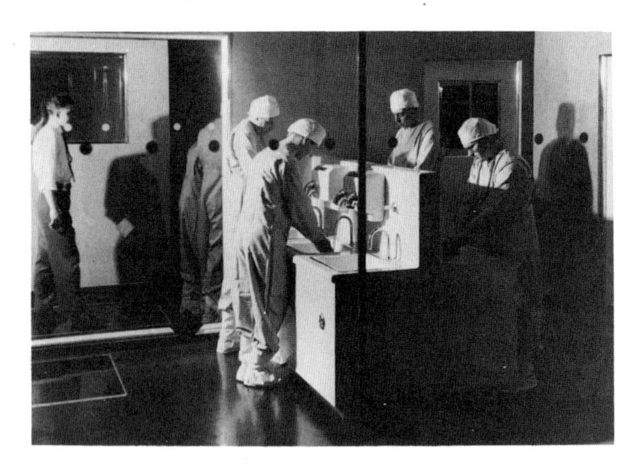

FIGURE 5-41. Surgical type washroom; note tacky mats in floor. *Courtesy Kearfott Division, General Precision, Inc.*

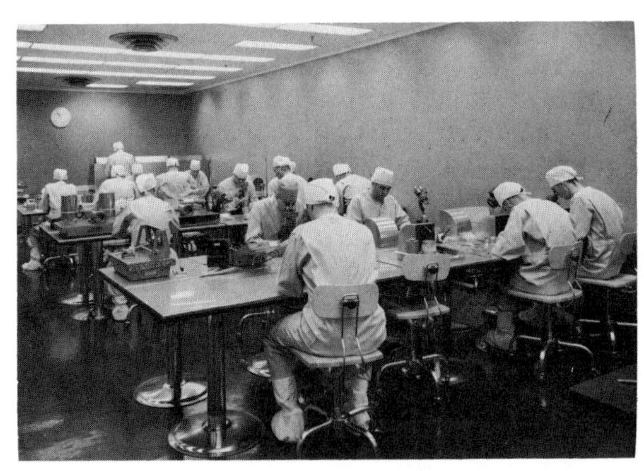

FIGURE 5-43. Preassembly area; note small soldering exhaust hoods on bench. *Courtesy Kearfott Division, General Precision, Inc.*

FIGURE 5-42. Gyro evacuation and filling at Kearfort. *Courtesy Kearfott Division, General Precision, Inc.*

Figure 5-42 shows gyro evacuation and filling work stations. The glass bell jars are protected by implosion shields. These shields are raised and lowered with ease, since they are cable-supported and counterweighted. The counterweights are incased in sealed tubes in a maintenance service corridor to preclude the possibility of contamination's being brought into the room when the cables are raised and lowered. Vacuum pumps are located under the counter and are serviced from the maintenance corridor in a noncritical area. Note the flush-mounted test panels which are also serviced from the maintenance corridor.

Figure 5-43 shows the preassembly area. The assembly benches have black formica on the sides and undersurface, and stainless steel on the working, or top, surface. These benches also contain small exhaust hoods which are used for light soldering operations. The air from these hoods is exhausted outside the clean room. The stainless-steel hood in the rear of the room contains two HEPA-filtered pressurized work stations and one exhaust station. The pressurized stations are used for assembly of critical units and the exhaust station for soldering of same.

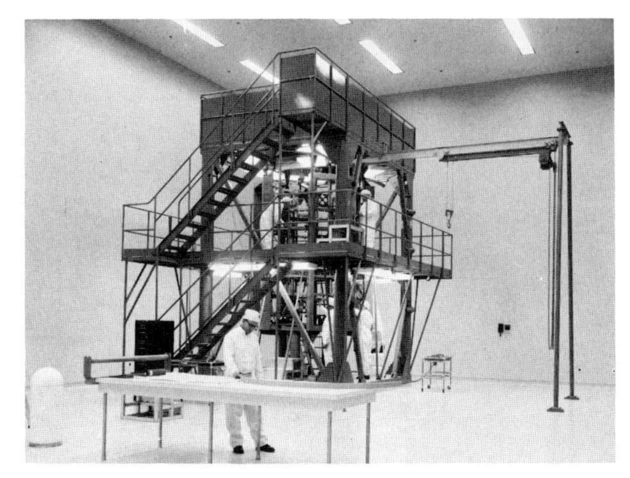

FIGURE 5-44. Grumman's high-bay clean room used for assembly of Orbiting Astronomical Observatory. *Courtesy Grumman Aircraft Engineering Corp.*

Grumman Aircraft Engineering Corporation, Bethpage, New York

Grumman's clean room is a high-bay facility which provides the environment essential for assembly, alignment, and demonstration testing of aerospace vehicles and components. Currently the Orbiting Astronomical Observatory (OAO) is being built in the room. The OAO is shown being assembled in Figure 5-44. With a floor space greater than 8500 square feet, the facility contains provisions for electronic, weight and balance, and solar cell testing. Several support clean rooms adjoin the high-bay clean room and are used for cleaning and inspecting of parts to be used in the OAO.

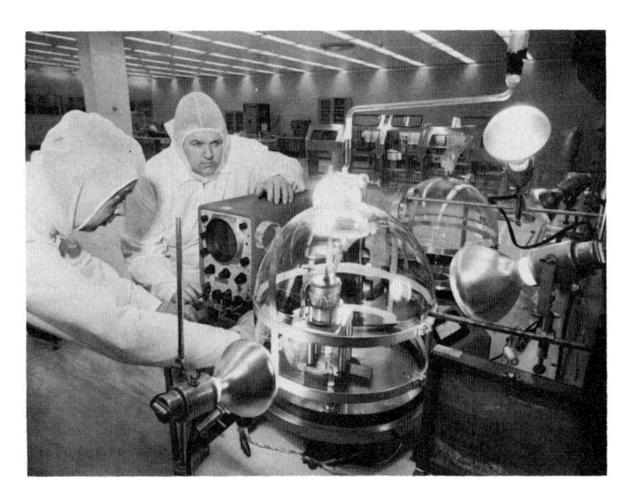

FIGURE 5-45. Large clean room at Norden shortly after pilot production of integrated electronic circuits was begun. *Courtesy Norden Division, United Aircraft Corp.*

Norden Division of United Aircraft Corporation, Norwalk, Connecticut

Another example of a well-planned clean room facility is the Norden complex at Norwalk, Con-

FIGURE 5-46. Wet chemistry clean room. *Courtesy Norden Division, United Aircraft Corp.*

FIGURE 5-47. Vacuum evaporation operation. *Courtesy Norden Division, United Aircraft Corp.*

FIGURE 5-49. View of general inspection room shows shadowless light diffuser panels in ceiling. Door in rear of picture leads to air shower which is common to the rough cleaning, final cleaning, and ready rooms. *Courtesy General Electric Co.*

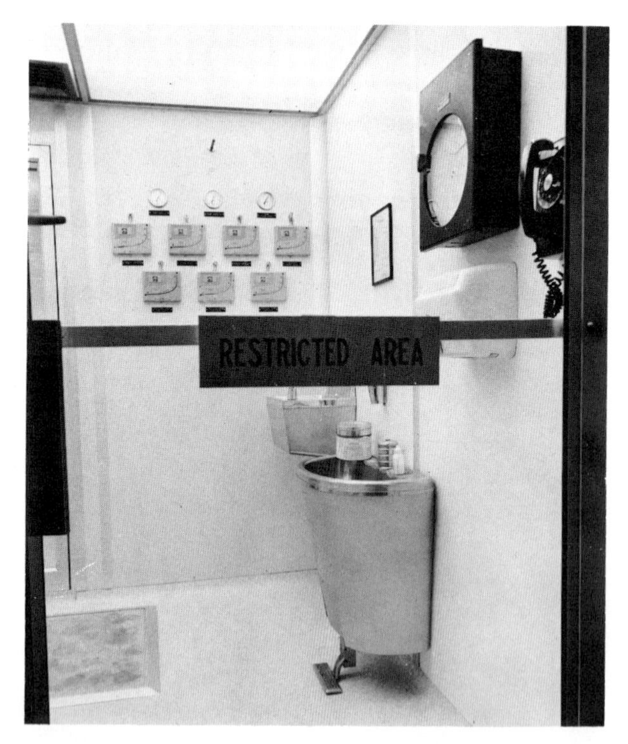

FIGURE 5-48. Ready room of General Electric clean room is used to prepare for entry into the clean room complex. *Courtesy General Electric Co.*

necticut. These rooms were put into use during the winter of 1963–64. This new facility will have a capability of 50,000 integrated electronic circuits per month and will serve as an internal supplier of circuits for Norden systems as well as for customers. The rooms in this facility are designed to meet the old Class IV standards of the Air Force. Figure 5-45 shows pilot line operations being performed in clean rooms shortly after construction. Notice the complete garmenting of the individuals even to rubber gloves. These clean room suits are one piece, having hood and boots attached.

Norden has good reason for its precautions. Cleanliness is critical in the handling of the silicon wafers, which are not much thicker than a human hair and are an inch in diameter. As many as 150 circuits are imposed on the wafers. Transistors, diodes, resistors, and capacitors, which are driven into the silicon base, are linked with aluminum wiring through vacuum-evaporation and photoengraving processes. A contaminant can mar the building of the matrix and destroy the effectiveness of the circuit.

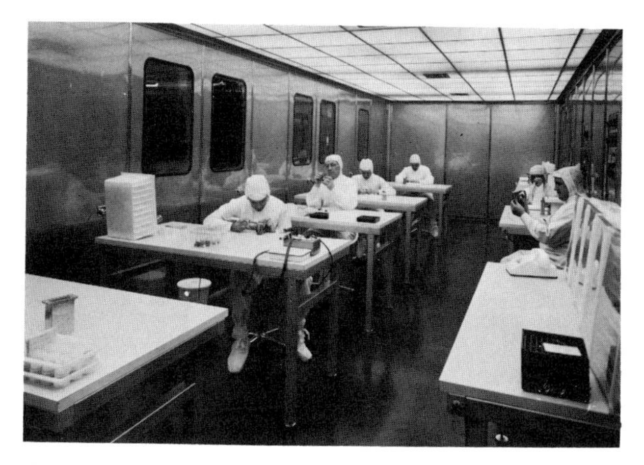

FIGURE 5-50. Inside view of Baker Company prefabricated clean room installed at Weston Instruments. *Courtesy Weston Instruments and Electronics Division, Daystrom, Inc.*

Figure 5-46 shows the wet chemistry clean room in which solvent sprays are prepared. Figure 5-47 shows a room in which vacuum evaporation operations are performed.

General Electric Company, Lynn, Massachusetts

The General Electric Company bearing clean room facility at Lynn, Massachusetts, has about 960 square feet and was built during the summer of 1963 to meet the old Air Force Class III clean room criteria. Figure 5-48 shows the ready room which is the main entrance to the clean room. Notice the log scale pressure manometer and disk recorder on the walls. Figure 5-49 shows the general inspection room. In this room all failure analyses, analytical analyses and design studies on bearings are performed. The room is designed to make twenty to twenty-five air changes per hour. Although General Electric requested 200 foot-candles of shadowless illumination at bench level, the diffuser ceiling panels provide 350 foot candles at bench level.

Weston Instruments and Electronics Division of Daystrom, Inc., Newark, New Jersey

An example of a prefabricated clean room built by the Baker Company can be seen in Figure 5-50. This facility is Area A of Weston Instruments Advanced Products Area and is designed to meet the old Air Force Class IV requirements. The wall panels are stainless steel. The room has approximately nine work stations and has an area about 500 square feet. All electronic consoles are built into the wall.

Inflatable Clean Rooms

A portable balloon-like "tent," which requires only a few hours to erect, may fill an immediate need of a clean room operator. It appears to be the easiest and fastest means of establishing a separately controlled environment. At the Astro-Electronics Division of RCA, Princeton, New Jersey, such a portable clean room provides a clean environment for installing and testing spacecraft television camera systems and other components. This air-supported structure, 12 feet long by 10 feet wide by 11 feet high, is made of white vinyl-coated nylon (16-ounce type) by Space White Industries, Rahway, New Jersey. High-efficiency particulate air filters are used in the air-handling system which is

FIGURE 5-51. Stable platform area in high-bay clean room at Newark Air Force Station. *Courtesy Newark AFS, Ohio.*

equipped with a 100-cfm direct-drive centrifugal blower. The structure undergoes about fifty air changes per hour. The tent is anchored to the plant's tile-covered cement deck with explosive-fired bolts and structural aluminum angles. Three clear vinyl windows provide outside visibility, with the roof of the tent being clear vinyl to enable overhead existing fluorescent lamps to light the interior. It is recommended that, when this type of clean room is purchased, the "at-rest" cleanliness levels of the erected room be guaranteed by the manufacturer.

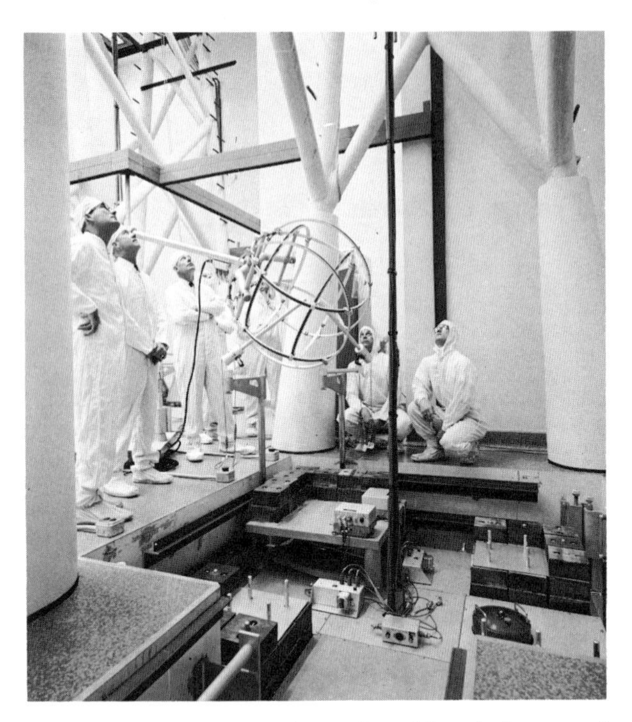

FIGURE 5-52. Close-up view of stable platform and Helmholtz coil. *Courtesy Newark AFS, Ohio*

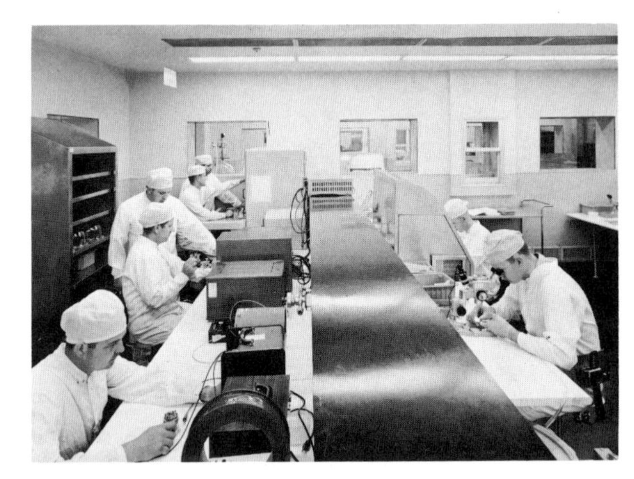

FIGURE 5-54. Air Force clean room formerly designated as Class IV. *Courtesy Newark AFS, Ohio.*

FIGURE 5-53. Underside of stable platform. *Courtesy Newark AFS, Ohio.*

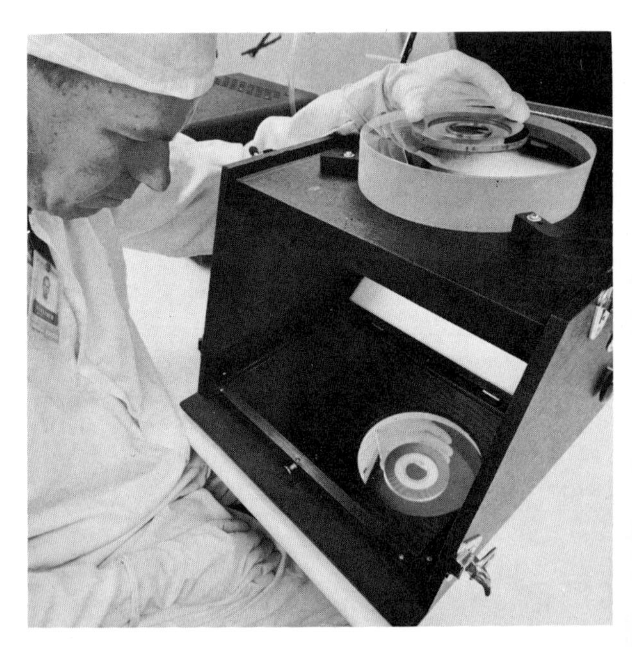

FIGURE 5-55. Flatness check with monochromatic light. *Courtesy Newark AFS, Ohio.*

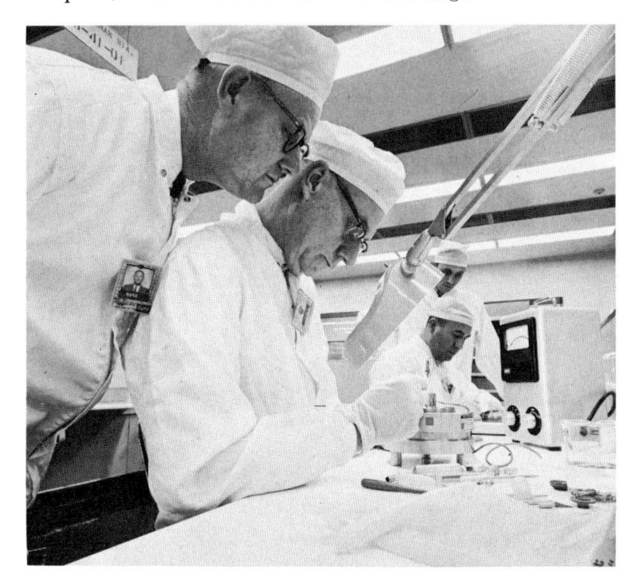

FIGURE 5-56. Precision assembly operation on Minuteman component being performed in Air Force clean room. *Courtesy Newark AFS, Ohio.*

Stable Platforms

An example of a unique Air Force conventional clean room is the table platform area of the Newark Air Force Station Calibration Laboratory, Ohio. Figure 5-51 shows the high-bay clean room with

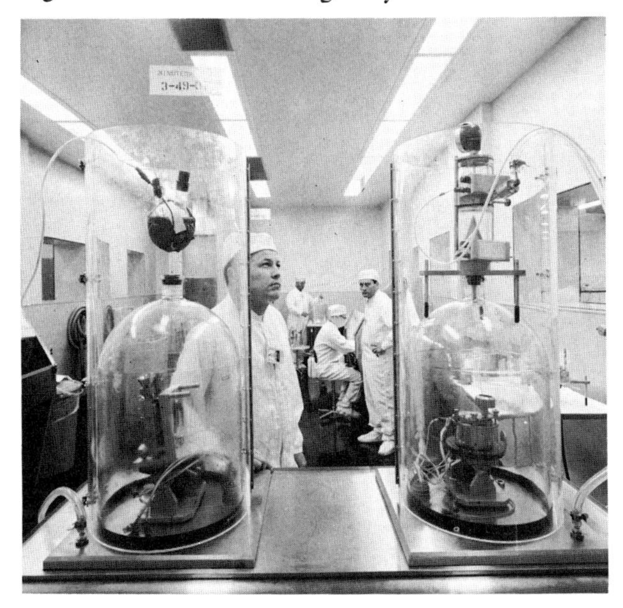

FIGURE 5-57. Evacuation and filling operation. *Courtesy Newark AFS, Ohio.*

several A-frames mounted over the stable platforms. Noticc the rod running through the center of the A-frame which acts as the arm of the pendulum supporting the stable platform. Figure 5-52 shows a close-up view of the stable platform including a Helmholtz coil used to shield a device under calibration from any electromagnetic influences. This pendulum has a 20-ton platform and is claimed to be the most vibration-free spot in the world. Figure 5-53 shows the underside of the stable platform.

Air Force Conventionally Designed Rooms

An example of a conventionally designed clean room at Newark Air Force Station which was built as a Class IV clean room under the former Air Force Technical Order 00-25-203 is shown in Figure 5-54. In this room are overhauled Minuteman gyro assemblies and components. Strict discipline

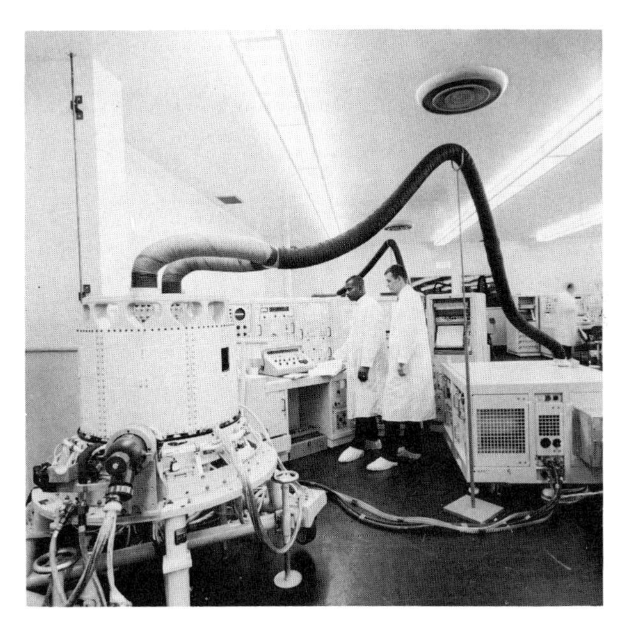

FIGURE 5-58. Functional test on Minuteman missile guidance system. *Courtesy Newark AFS, Ohio.*

is required of employees to ensure the highest product reliability. Notice that items stored in the shelves to the left of this figure are covered with plastic protective covers.

Figure 5-55 shows an item being checked for flatness with monochromatic light and optical flat in the same room shown in the previous figure.

Figure 5-56 shows a precision assembly operation in this same room. Notice that a base light level is maintained within the room and that only every other row of lights is operating. Pinpoint light is provided by auxiliary light sources, as shown in this figure. Magnification lenses are incorporated into this light source. Sufficient work space is provided the employee to allow him to maintain an orderly work station.

Figure 5-57 shows Minuteman evacuation and filling stations at the Newark Air Force Standard clean room undergoing functional tests. Figure 5-58 shows conditioned air being supplied directly to the Minuteman guidance unit. The black square on the right side of the unit is an optical aligning port.

REFERENCES

1. *U. S. Air Force Technical Order 00-25-203, Standards and Guidelines for the Design and Operation of Clean Rooms and Clean Work Stations.* Office of Technical Services, Department of Commerce, Washington, D.C., July 1963.
2. Austin, 1/Lt. P. R. *Size Distribution Relationships for Airborne Particulate Matter.* Report 17.0002.04.01. Olmsted AFB, Pa: MAMES, April 1963.
3. Lindeken, C. L. "Selection, Installation, and Maintenance of White Room Filters." *Air Engineering,* Vol. 5, No. 2, p. 20 (February 1963).
4. "Recommended Minimal Specifications Revised for the High Efficiency Filter Unit." *Health and Safety,* Issue 120. U. S. Atomic Energy Commission, Washington, D.C., January 1961.
5. Northrup, D. H. "The AEC or CWS Air Filter." *Chemical Engineering Progress,* Vol. 49, No. 10, pp. 513-517 (October 1963).
6. Avery, R. H. "The Meaning of Clean Air, Part II." *Air Engineering,* Vol. 1, No. 2. pp. 29-32 (May 1959).
7. Giffels, C. A. *Materials of Construction.* The American Association for Contamination Control, April 1962.
8. Flinn, F. L., and Gosma, J. "Laminar Air Cross-Flow Room." *Conference on Clean Room Specifications.* SCR-652. Office of Technical Services, Department of Commerce, Washington, D.C., May 1963.
9. Timmerman, S. W., Austin, 1/Lt. P. R., and Frith, 1/Lt. C. F. *Reduction of Contamination Levels in Clean Rooms by Application of Air Showers.* Report 17.0005.14.01. Olmsted AFB, Pa.: MAMES, September 1963.
10. Russell, J. A., Waite, R. E., and Kindig, E. V. *The Controlled Environmental Facility at the Valley Forge Space Technology Center.* Valley Forge, Pa.: General Electric Space Technology Center, August 1962.

Chapter 6. *Conventional Clean Room Operation*

Introduction

The introduction to the discussion on conventional clean room design emphasized one fact that is true of all conventional clean rooms—the cleanliness level. Plots of relative contaminant levels taken with the room. Therefore, operating techniques that tend to control particle generation and dispersement are of paramount importance.

The Air Force, in a survey of their clean rooms, found that the operational cleanliness level averaged three times that of the "at-rest" level and that peak activity periods averaged five times the "at-rest" level. Plots of relative contaminant levels taken with automatic particle counters for a 24-hour period were very enlightening. (See Figure 6-1.) With some knowledge of room activity it is possible to determine exactly what takes place in the room and when, by studying the contamination level plots. With reference to Figure 6-1, starting at midnight, the count is very low; the room is, in fact, in "at-rest" condition, since no activity has taken place for approximately 8 hours. At 7:30 A.M., when the working day starts, the contaminant level shoots up considerably. Actually, the early arrivals start the count on its way up before 7:30 A.M. After the people get settled, the room begins to "clean up," until break time, when the contaminant level starts up again as the employees leave the room. During the break the room begins to "clean up" again. The twin peaks at break and lunch are attributed to a flurry of activity in anticipation of break and lunch, respectively, and the activity of leaving for break and lunch. After the rise from the activity of returning from lunch, the personnel "settle down," and the room "cleans up" quite well. The act of leaving at the end of work starts the cycle all over again. The next peak is caused by the maintenance people cleaning in the room. This activity could more aptly be called "dirtying" the room, as can be seen on the graph as the line went off the scale to a value of 30. If the previous discussion of the graph did not cause much anxiety, this should. The act of cleaning a clean room creates an extremely (off-the-chart) dirty atmosphere which may, depending on the room, take a good deal of time to "clean up." Obviously, cleaning operations should not be conducted during working hours. The effect of activity can also be seen quite vividly by the "anticipation," the "break," and other rises in the contamination level caused by activity. Since activity causes contamination, it would be logical to assume that there should be some correlation between the number of people in a clean room and the contamination level of the room. Figure 6-2 demonstrates this correlation. The room-generated contamination arises from several sources. Walking produces transient turbulent air currents that encourage re-entrainment of settled particulate matter from floor surfaces; dust is pumped from inside shoes, and material is transported through the clean uniform interstices. Body surfaces shed particles of skin and hair continuously. Skin flakes depend on the amount of abrasion to which the skin is exposed and on the condition of the skin itself. Perspiration and other body exudations contribute to the problem. Extensive training is necessary to minimize the effects of the contaminants which are inevitably produced by personnel(*1*).

Employee Training and Disciplines

The contamination control potential of a properly informed, trained, and motivated employee should not be underestimated. As has been shown, people in the clean room can cause appreciable contamination to become airborne. Perhaps the first step in any plan to limit or control this problem should be employee awareness. The employee should be aware of the problems involved and how he as an individual can help to minimize them. Every new employee should receive an indoctrination course, and old employees should receive refresher courses periodically.

The contamination level in the clean room is kept at an acceptable level by two primary methods (excluding the air-handling system): (1) limiting the contamination entering the room; (2) limiting the contamination generated in the room. It is obvious that both factors are controlled to a large degree by personnel. The contamination entering is limited by proper suiting up, air showering, parts and equipment cleaning, etc. The contamination generated is limited by restricting unnecessary movement, proper work techniques, etc.

The disciplines discussed in Technical Order 00-25-203 are basic and are further enumerated in this chapter.

Personal Hygiene (2)

Personnel with skin and/or upper respiratory diseases should not be allowed to work in clean room operations. Some examples of physiological

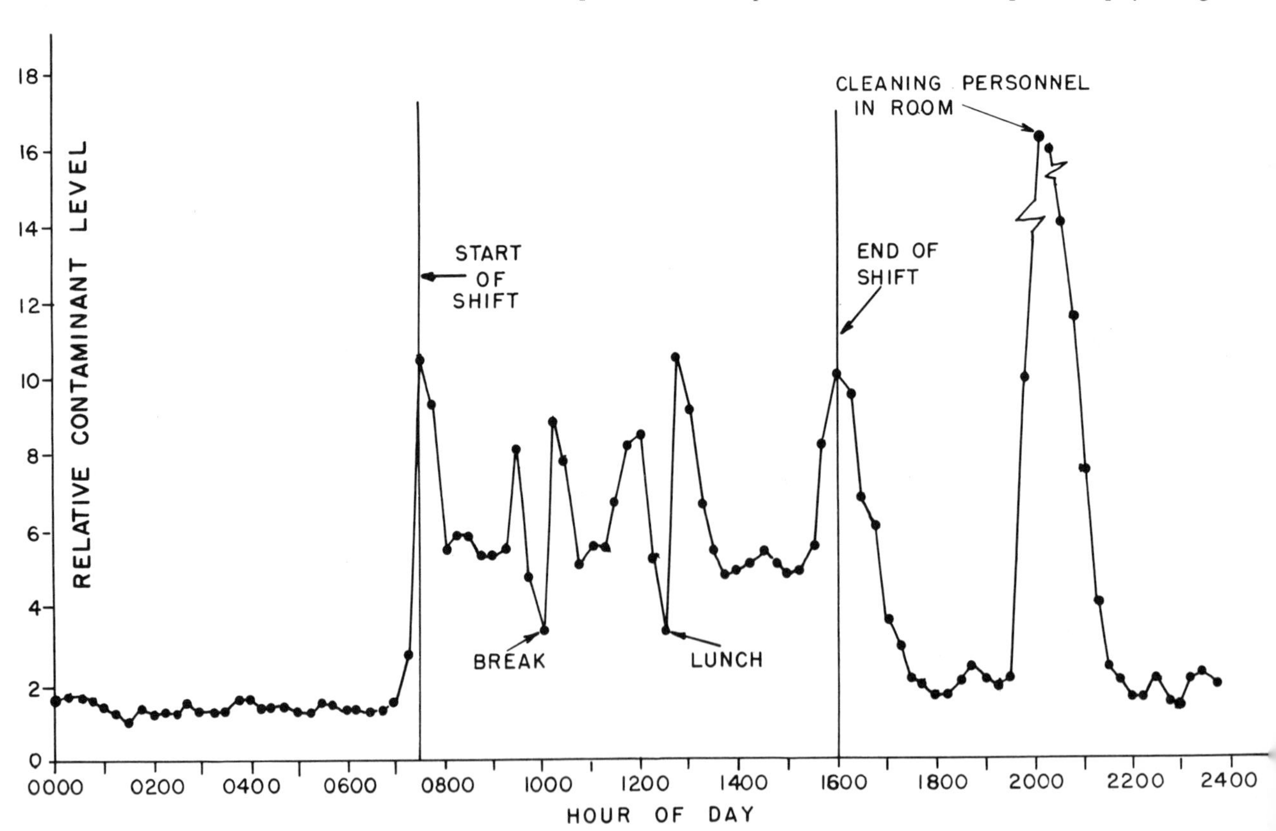

FIGURE 6-1. Typical clean room contaminant levels. The relation between activity and cleanliness is clearly shown by this plot. Increased activity increases contamination. *U. S. Air Force Technical Order 00-25-203.*

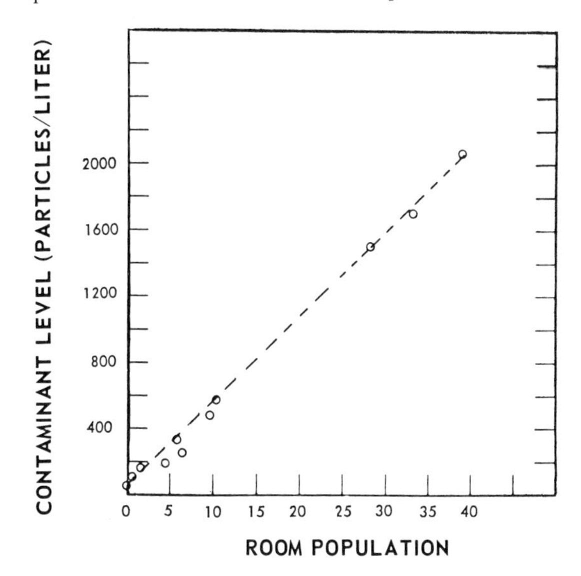

FIGURE 6-2. Contamination level versus room population. This plot shows increased contamination with an increase in personnel. *Courtesy Sandia Corp.*

problems that are detrimental to clean room operations are: (1) allergies to synthetic fabric; (2) allergies to solvents being used in various clean rooms; (3) perfuse nasal discharge; (4) skin conditions that result in above-normal skin shedding, dandruff, or skin flaking; (5) high amounts of acid found in the moisture of hands; (6) severe nervous conditions, itching, scratching, or claustrophobia.

All personnel should receive periodic indoctrination on the importance of personal hygiene in clean room operations.

All clean room personnel should practice clean room habits and observe clean room regulations to maintain a healthy environment. Personnel with colds, temporary coughing and sneezing, or severe sunburn should be assigned to temporary jobs outside the clean room until they are sufficiently recovered. Clean room personnel should take all necessary precautions against receiving severe cases of sunburn. This precaution is necessary in order to prevent peeling skin from contaminating a part or the surrounding area. The high degree of cleanliness required necessitates the indoctrination of all clean room personnel in the development of the following habits: (1) bathe frequently; (2) shampoo hair weekly and take action against heavy dandruff; (3) wear clean under and outer garments to ensure maximum cleanliness; (4) avoid scratching or rubbing exposed areas of the body; (5) wear gloves if hands are severely chapped; (6) male personnel are to shave daily or cover with masks such hair as would be shaved. The wearing of such masks will be determined by the clean room monitor. (7) keep hair confined under caps and hoods.

Clean Room Employee Disciplines[1]

Clean rooms are restricted areas, and access to them must be limited to authorized individuals. Protective clothing is to be used at all times by individuals entering the clean room. This clothing must always be worn in the room and is not to be worn outside the clean room or in the uncontaminated section of the change room. Smoking and eating are forbidden in the clean room. De-dusting procedures, when provided, must always be followed each time the employee enters the clean room. Personal effects are to be stored outside the clean room. Paper materials[2] are not allowed in the clean room unless the paper is plastic-coated,[3] plastic-covered, or sprayed to prevent linting, or is a special limited-linting paper. Pencils and erasers are not allowed in the clean room. Cosmetics are not to be worn. Tools brought into the clean room must be cleaned as well as, or better than, the work material itself.

Employee attitudes are of prime importance. Employees must be prepared to meet the challenges of clean room work before they are allowed to work in the room. They should be instructed to consider everything but their immediate work area as being contaminated and should be taught to recognize the common types of contamination (lint, paint chips, etc.). They should report any con-

[1] Abstracted from reference 2.

[2] One technique used by the General Electric Company to permit writing in the clean room is shown in Figure 6-3, which shows a writing station. The air is drawn into the front opening and then through a filter at the top of the hood. The air is exhausted into the clean room.

[3] Defined by U. S. Air Force Specification MIL-P-4703, October 22, 1953, "Paper, Printing, Plastic Coated." This specification was rescinded December 18, 1962. Paper as defined by this specification, or a similar commercial product, is acceptable for clean room use. A lighter-weight paper than stated in Specification MIL-P-4703 is recommended for the sake of economics.

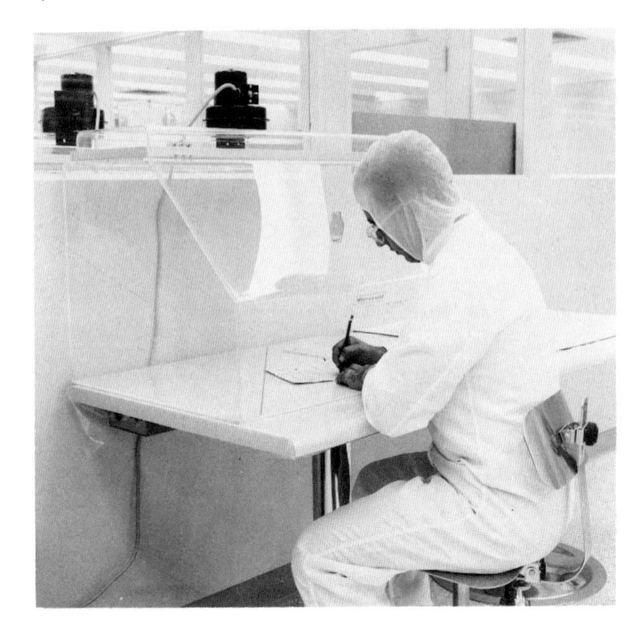

FIGURE 6-3. A writing station which pulls air through the front opening and out a filter at the top. *Courtesy General Electric Space Technology Center.*

tamination of this type to their supervisor, and should consider any work or tools dropped on the floor as being contaminated. Any work (or tools) which they consider to be contaminated, or about which they are in doubt, should be reported to their supervisors. Movement of clean room personnel should be restricted as much as possible to prevent stirring up of settled particulate matter on the clean room floor.

Supervisor disciplines determine the quality of a clean room product. Supervisors must enforce good housekeeping practices.

Visitors to the clean room must observe all the rules observed by the clean room employees. This includes top management as well as supervisors.

The following rules should be enforced to assist in the successful operation of the clean room:

1. Wash hands often.
2. Wear finger cots or gloves if required.
3. Keep fingernails clean.
4. Never comb hair in the clean room.
5. Do not wear fingernail polish.
6. Always wear the specified clothing in the specified manner.
7. Never wear or apply cosmetics in the clean room (lipstick may be worn).
8. Personal items such as keys, coins, cigarettes, matches, pencils, handkerchiefs, watches, tissues, and combs should not be carried into the clean room.
9. Valuable items such as wallets may be carried into the clean room in street clothes pockets, provided that they are not removed inside the clean room.
10. Avoid wearing jewelry (large rings, necklaces, earrings, lockets, watches, bracelets, etc.).
11. Keep parts and tools at the work station as clean and orderly as possible.
12. Keep surplus parts in appropriate containers.
13. Never leave exposed parts on the work bench.
14. Make certain that parts are clean before assembling.
15. Work on a clean surface—never on cloth or paper towels which can transfer contaminants to the work piece.
16. Watch for any particulate matter.
17. Do not walk around unnecessarily.
18. Do not eat food, chew gum or tobacco, or smoke in the clean room.
19. Avoid nervous mannerisms such as scratching the head, rubbing hands or parts of the body, or similar actions.[4]
20. When in doubt, contact your supervisor.

Change-Room Employee Disciplines[5]

Decontamination Procedure

On entering the locker room from an environmentally uncontrolled area, the employee should immediately remove his weatherprotective clothing such as raincoat, overcoat, boots, and rubbers and put them into his locker or place provided for their storage. (See Figure 5-25.) No employee should be permitted to enter into the semicontaminated section from the locker room if visible contamination such as mud, dirt, sand, salt, or cement is

[4] Actions by which hands come in contact with face skin, oil, or whiskers (see Figure 6-4) are to be avoided. Transfer of face contaminants to the product can cause product reliability problems.

[5] Abstracted from reference 2.

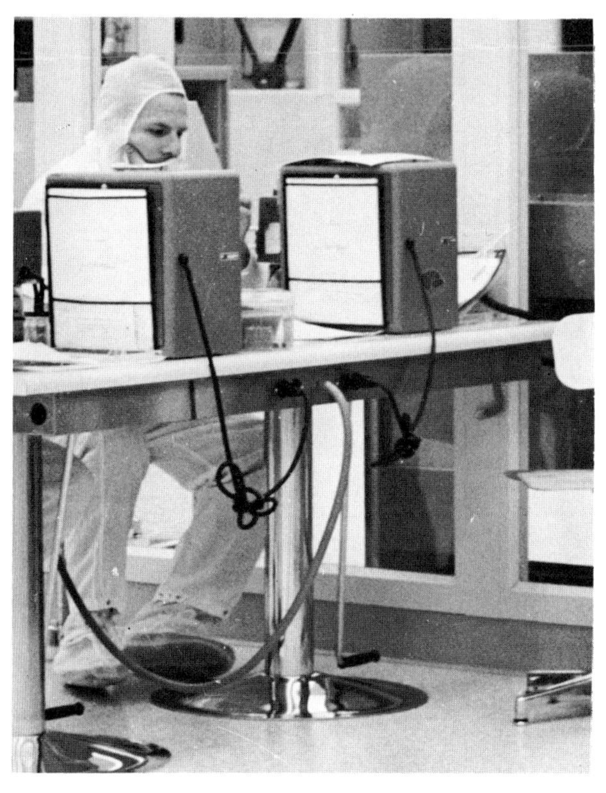

Figure 6-4. An example of head support actions which should be avoided. Contamination is being transferred to the hands where it can be retransferred to the work piece.

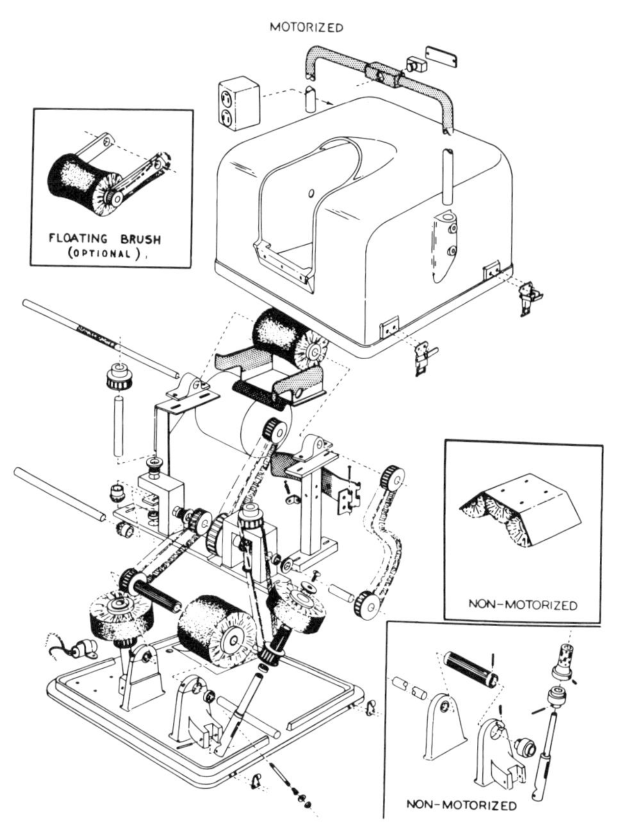

Figure 6-5. An exploded view of an automatic shoe brush machine. *Courtesy Liberty Machine Co.*

present on his shoes, clothes, or person. The employee should make a visual check of the bottom of his shoes to ensure that caked contaminants are removed prior to his entry into the semicontaminated section. He should then clean his shoes with a shoe cleaner, following the procedure prescribed by the shoe cleaner manufacturer. The cleaning procedure should prevent the cleaned shoe from becoming recontaminated on removal from the unit. This cleaner should effectively clean the sole of the shoe, including the indented area in front of the heel.

Figure 6-5 shows an exploded view of an efficient shoe cleaner. The success of a shoe cleaner depends not only on the positive removal of contaminants from the shoes by the action of brushes but also on sufficient vacuum to draw dislodged and airborne contaminants from the proximity of the shoe. It must also prevent both trajectory and airborne contaminants brushed from the shoe from escaping into the area. Further, no shoe cleaner will remain effective unless caked mud, which begins to build up on the inside of these cleaners, is periodically removed. Such mud build-up is accelerated during damp or wet days.

After cleaning his shoes, the employee continues with the decontamination procedure. In the semicontaminated section of the change room he should wash his face and hands, using the foot-controlled washstands, liquid detergent, and air drier. He is now prepared to enter the uncontaminated area through the air shower and air locks. In the air shower, the employee should manipulate his body so that all his body areas are air-scrubbed. This can be achieved by making at least two complete turns in the air blast and keeping his arms at least 3 inches away from the trunk of his body. Other body manipulations can be substituted, depending on the design of the air shower, to ensure adequate air-scrubbing of the employee. He should remain in the air shower for a sufficient length of time to accomplish air-scrubbing. (See Figure 5-19 for recommended times and air velocities.)

If special clean room shoes are to be worn by the employee, these shoes are put on just after the employee enters the semicontaminated section of the change room and prior to wash-up. In such a case, benches will be located in the semicontaminated section of the change room along with shoe racks or shoe lockers. In entering the uncontaminated section of the change room, the employee should walk over a sole cleaner, a gelatin, sticky, or tacky mat. He should then don his clean room smock or coveralls and head covering. The garment should not be allowed to come in contact with the floor during the changing procedure. If special shoes are not to be worn, benches or boot rails will be located in the uncontaminated section to assist in donning shoe covers. He then enters the air shower and air lock, using the same procedure described in the preceding paragraph.

Studies have shown that the most effective decontamination is achieved by using two air showers, one immediately prior to entering the semicontaminated section (see Chapter 5) and one prior to entering the clean room. When, for the sake of economy, only one shower is installed, its best location depends on a number of local factors. For example, if garments are to be worn for a number of work days between cleanings, or if above-average traffic is expected into and out of the clean room, then the best location would be at the entry to the clean room. If the clean room is installed in an area where the outer garments are subject to appreciable contamination, then it would be best to put the air shower at the entry to the semicontaminated section.

Exiting Procedure

On leaving the clean room, the employee should remove his shoe covers in the uncontaminated section of the change room and then place the covers in the storage area provided. Next, the employee should remove his clean room clothes, placing them in the clothes rack or locker provided. He may now enter the semicontaminated section of the change room and subsequently the locker room and uncontrolled areas. If special clean room shoes are to be used, they must be removed in the semicontaminated area before the employee enters the factory area.

Room Maintenance[6]

Good housekeeping practices are of prime importance in clean rooms. When a room is being cleaned, it should be kept in mind that the mere addition of cleaning personnel to the environment will increase the contamination level in the room. Therefore, the times the rooms are cleaned should be chosen with care. The room should preferably be cleaned when no work is being performed in the room. An important point to remember is that it will take some period of time for the increased contamination level caused by the cleaning operation to decrease. This length of time is dependent on the number of air changes per hour. As the number of air changes increases, the length of time for the contamination level to reach operational standards decreases. This fact should be kept in mind, and cleaning should be scheduled immediately after the shift ends and should be performed daily. Minor dry floor and bench vacuuming can be performed, if necessary, during room operation if the equipment and procedures used will ensure a minimum of disturbance to settled particulate matter.

Cellulose mops and sponges can be used with water that can meet a particle-count requirement of not more than 100,000 particles per cubic foot of water greater than 0.5 micron in size. High-grade plastic buckets which are not subject to flaking should be used, and anodized aluminum ladders are recommended if required. If it is necessary to use a detergent, a careful investigation should be made to determine the "residue-producing" properties of the detergent.[7]

For vacuum cleaning, a central vacuum cleaning system or a specially designed portable vacuum should be employed. Portable vacuum cleaners can be used only if the vacuum cleaner exhaust is filtered at least as well as the filtration in the room air-handling system (HEPA filters) and if the ex-

---

[6] Abstracted from reference 2.

[7] Since no standard test for this is available, detergents will have to be evaluated on a relative basis.

haust is located so that it will not cause re-entrainment of settled particulate matter and will not direct exhaust blasts at the work stations in the clean room.

An example of a portable clean room vacuum that can perform both dry and wet pickup is the Microstat vacuum produced by the Kent Company. This machine is shown in Figure 6-6. A section view and an exploded view are also included in this figure. The unit's non-bypass motor design allows the same air stream used to lift dust from the floor to cool the motor. HEPA final filters are installed above the motor.

Housekeeping equipment, utensils, and similar equipment are particularly prevalent sources of contamination. Movement of these items in and out of the clean room should be carefully scheduled. Whenever these items are to be taken into the clean room, they should be thoroughly cleaned and vacuumed prior to their entry.

Each worker should be responsible for cleaning his assigned work station at periodic intervals during the work shift. This prevents improper handling of the work piece by room maintenance personnel. Cleaning material for this purpose should be positioned at various points throughout the room.

Parts, Tools, Equipment, and Material Cleaning

Prior to entry into the clean room, all parts, tools, equipment, and material must be cleaned. The selection of cleaning methods depends on the type of contaminant, the materials of construction of the items to be cleaned, and the degree of cleanliness required.

Large items of equipment being moved into the clean room should be thoroughly vacuumed prior to entry. Rough cleaning may be accomplished in an uncontrolled area; however, the final cleaning operation should be done in an air lock. This equipment should be moved into the clean room when operations in the room are shut down.

Small hand tools used in the clean room are cleaned (ultrasonically when possible) prior to entry and at scheduled intervals. The exact schedule should be determined on an individual basis.

General cleaning of parts should occur outside the clean room. Pass boxes are used to transfer clean parts into the clean room. Where cleaning operations must be conducted inside the clean room, adequate ventilation for the cleaning equipment must be provided. An odor of solvent in the room indicates a deficiency in the design of the air-handling equipment.

In handling parts and components, the assembler's hands can be utilized yet not actually touch the part. This can be accomplished by employing tweezers, assembling and handling tools, special screw-holding screwdrivers, miniature torque wrenches, etc. This equipment is now available or rapidly appearing for super-critical jobs, to hold or handle parts and thus avoid the corrosion often started by perspiration or body acids *(3)*.

Operational Controls

The following discussion of employee selection and control at the General Electric Space Technology Center is an example of the details to be covered when operating a clean room that is manufacturing sophisticated components *(4)*.

Personnel Selection

The shop management, medical office, manufacturing engineering group, a microbiologist, and an applied psychologist deal with the problems of selection, indoctrination, and control of clean room personnel. Their studies involve consideration of both physical and human factors, including such items as manual dexterity, visual acuity, patience, concern for detail, attitude toward repetitive operations, skin condition, and reaction to the rigid disciplines that accompany confinement in a controlled-environment facility. Typical of these investigations is the research conducted by the staff doctors to develop a simple, fast technique for identifying "rusters" (those who contaminate metallic surfaces because of skin excretions). In another instance, the applied psychologist will make a survey of employee attitudes for the purpose of establishing improved standards for the selection and recognition of operator skills.

Employee Controls

Control begins before the employee enters the clean room area. Items of clothing such as raincoats, overcoats, rubbers, and galoshes are stored

FIGURE 6-6. A portable clean room vacuum cleaner which uses a HEPA final filter. *Courtesy The Kent Co.*

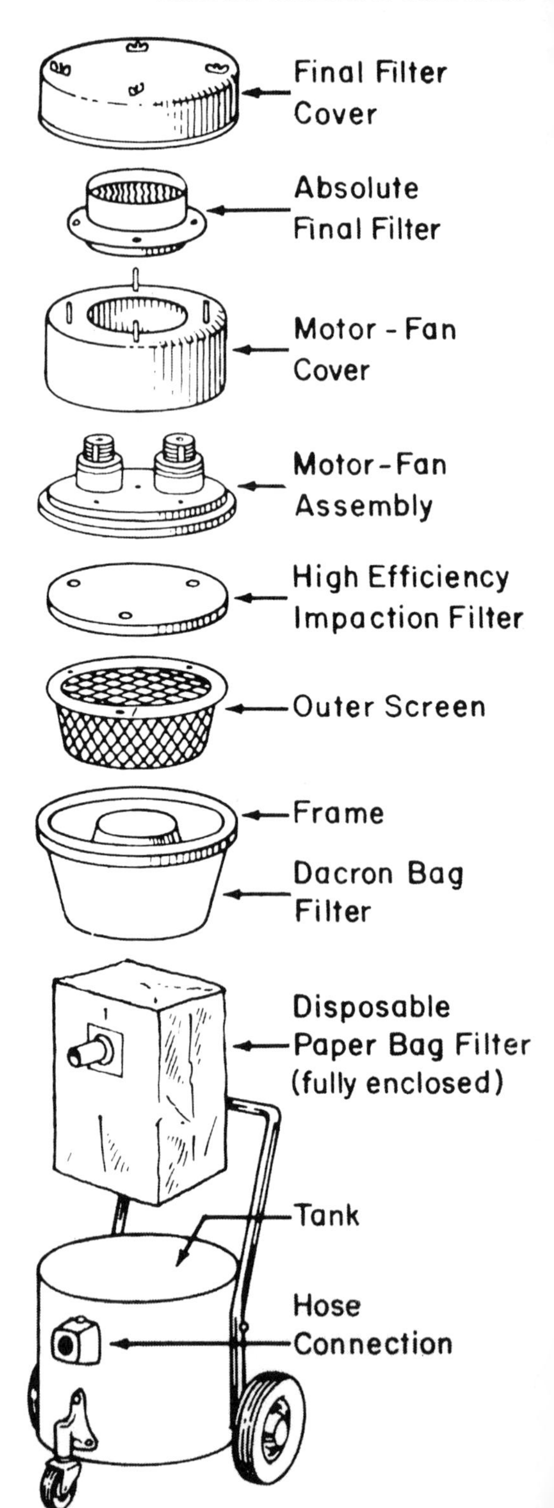

in a room completely isolated from the clean room proper. After disposing of these belongings the employee enters the corridor that leads to the clean room entrance. At this point the operator uses one of two mechanical shoe cleaners (Figure 6-7) and treads on a sticky mat before entering the outer locker room. Once inside, he again walks across a sticky mat before reaching his personal locker. Here he leaves his suit coat and personal belongings. Cigarettes, paper, books, food and similar items are left in the outside locker room. The operator then steps into the air shower that separates the storage area for personal effects from the inner locker room and remains there for 18 seconds, holding his arm aloft and rotating his body through 360°. When

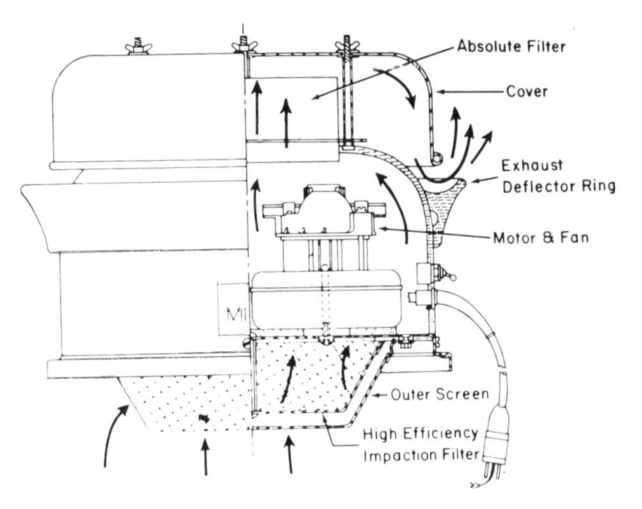

the air blast ceases, he opens the exit door from the shower and steps into the locker area where the clean room garments are kept in individual lockers. These uniforms are changed twice weekly and are fitted to each individual. Dressing is accomplished in a standing position. Once clothed in hood, jumper, and boots, the employee proceeds to the wash room (Figure 6-8). There, hands and nails are scoured with a brush and dried with a blast of warm air (Figure 6-9). Having washed, the employee proceeds through the second air shower (Figure 6-10) into the work areas. The duration of this cleaning can be altered by the shop manager. Presently, the shower operates on a 10-second cycle.

Employee disciplines are enumerated and documented so that a firm procedure is established. The following instructions are taken from General Electric's "Standing Instructions," which are pro-

FIGURE 6-7. Shoe cleaners in use at entrance to clean room. Note the tacky mat to prevent cleaned shoes from being recontaminated. *Courtesy General Electric Space Technology Center*

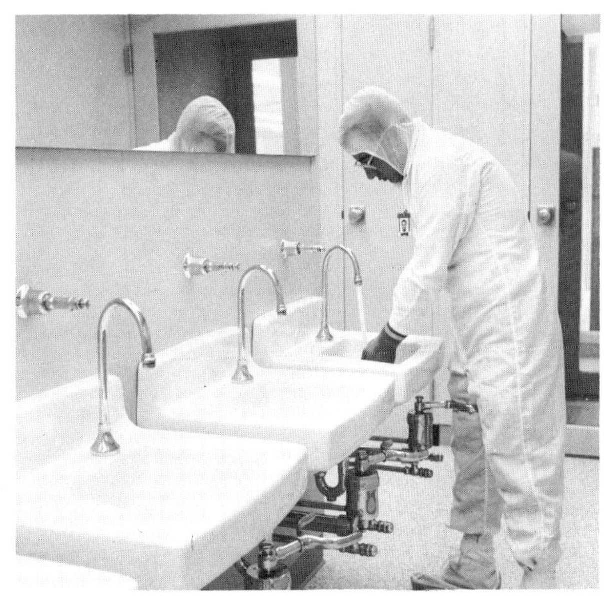

FIGURE 6-8. Washing hands prior to entry into clean room. *Courtesy General Electric Space Technology Center.*

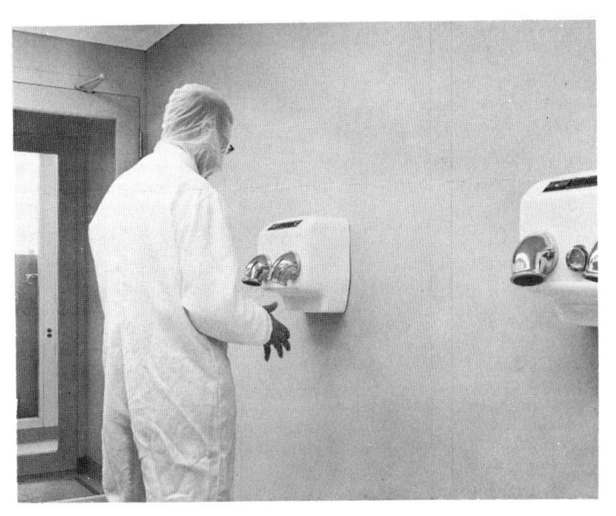

FIGURE 6-9. Drying hands with warm air to prevent contamination from toweling. *Courtesy General Electric Space Technology Center*

cedural regulations. This type of document is extremely useful in clean room operations.

4. GENERAL:

4.1 The CEF[8] will be a restricted area. Entry will be allowed only to personnel assigned to the area. A list defining all assigned personnel will be posted outside the vestibule door.

4.2 Specified protective clothing will be worn at all times within the clean room in such a manner that only the face and hands are uncovered. Such clothing will not be worn out of the clean room.

4.3 Routine cleaning of work stations will be performed by assigned operating and QC personnel on a scheduled basis according to 6.1.

4.4 Personnel assigned to the area will go through the complete personnel entry procedure each time they enter the area.

4.5 Normal floor and wall cleaning will be performed by grounds and buildings personnel specifically assigned to this task. These people will observe the personnel entry procedure for entering the area.

4.6 Visitors or maintenance personnel will enter the area only with written approval of the area manager.

4.7 Visitors and maintenance personnel, if allowed access, will follow the personnel entry procedure when entering the area.

4.8 No smoking or eating will be allowed in the area.

4.9 No personal effects will be carried into the production areas.

4.10 All paper must be laminated in plastic or sealed in a reversible plastic bag prior to entry. Under no conditions will paper be exposed in open areas within the CEF.

4.11 Personal tools will not be brought into the area.

4.12 No materials will be left on open work benches at the end of the shift with the exception of cleaning fluids. These will be covered.

4.13 Protective clothing will be changed twice weekly.

4.14 All tools will be cleaned with sonic energy in the cleaning room prior to entering production areas.

4.15 All hand tools will be scheduled for return to the cleaning room for periodic cleaning.

4.16 All writing will be performed with ball point pens.

4.17 Work benches, cabinets, and other furniture will not be moved except under instructions from the area manager. Should such items require moving, they should be lifted and carried clear of the floor. Scraping of walls and other painted surfaces will be avoided.

4.18 All blow-off or purging operations should be avoided. Where such activity is unavoidable, dry nitrogen gas should be used, GE Spec. 118A1517. This operation will be performed only in the cleaning area.

4.19 Internal communications will be accomplished through the inter-com system where possible to minimize traffic through the production areas.

4.20 Communications from outside the area will be accomplished by using the voice diaphragm.

4.21 No open waste baskets will be allowed in the area.

4.22 Central air handling unit (air-conditioning and filtering) will operate 24 hours per day, seven days a week. Filter changes and similar maintenance will be performed when the room is empty of personnel.

4.23 Central vacuum system will operate during normal work hours, but can be shut down over weekends.

4.24 When cleaning or dressing welding electrodes, the bench vacuum service should be used to carry away contaminates produced. When such activity is complete the immediate area around the welding head should be vacuumed.

4.25 Special work stations using steril-shield cabinets with exhausters will operate with a minimum of two exhaust ports, open at all times.

4.26 No routine grinding, chipping, sanding or drilling operations will be performed in the area. In specific cases drilling operations can be mandatory where precise assembly and fitting is required. In such cases Manufacturing Reliability Engineering and Applications and Processes Engineering will be responsible for setting up specific equipment, facilities, and procedures for such cases. In no case will such operations be performed without prior approval from the assigned Manufacturing Reliability Engineer.

5. PROCEDURES: [See Figure 6-10]

5.1 Personnel Entry

5.1.1 Only persons assigned to the area in writing may enter the clean room. An up-to-date list of assigned personnel will be maintained outside the vestibule entrance.

5.1.2 Only approved apparel will be worn. Complete uniform will be worn at all times within the area.

5.1.3 De-Dusting and Entry

5.1.3.1 Before entering the vestibule (the area immediately outside the clean room lunch room) leave hat, overcoat, umbrella and overshoes in locker provided for that purpose. Before entering the clean room locker area, clean shoes in the vestibule mechanical shoe cleaner.

5.1.3.2 Tread on tacky mat; proceed to assigned personal locker.

5.1.3.3 Place all personal effects in locker and lock.

5.1.3.4 Usual shirt, trousers, etc., may be worn under the clean room uniform. Outer garments such as suit jacket, sweater, etc., must be removed.

5.1.3.5 Enter air shower, close door. When

[8] Controlled-environment facility.

air blast starts, place tips of fingers on hips and rotate full 360°. When air shower stops (18 seconds) enter dressing room.

5.1.3.6 Take uniform from assigned locker and dress out complete. Exit to wash area.

5.1.3.7 Scrub hands thoroughly and clean finger nails. Shake hands thoroughly dry with warm forced air dryers. Exit to air shower.

5.1.3.8 Upon closing air shower door, place fingers on hips and rotate 360°. When air blast cuts off (10 seconds) exit to assigned work area.

5.1.3.9 A copy of the personnel entry procedure will be posted by the vestibule door.

5.2 Break and Lunch Periods:

5.2.1 Break and lunch periods will be staggered by rooms to minimize traffic.

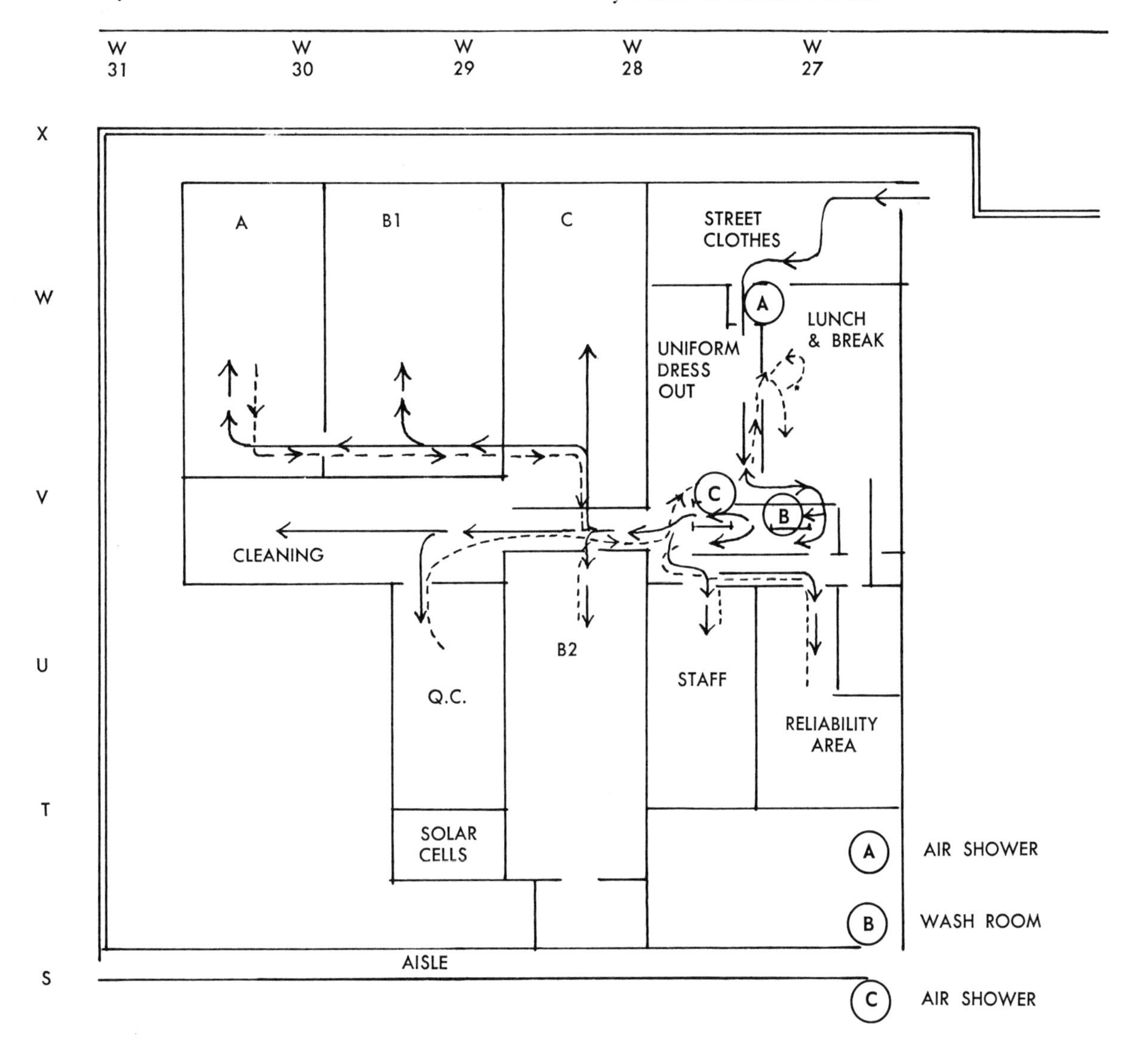

FIGURE 6-10. Personnel flow diagram for General Electric clean room. *Courtesy General Electric Space Technology Center*

5.2.2 Smocks will be worn for lunch and break periods by *all* persons in the lunch room.

5.2.3 Exit from work place to break area requires no specific instruction.

5.2.4 Exit from break area; do same as noted in 5.1.3.7 through 5.1.3.9.

5.3 Writing Stations:

5.3.1 All pens, paper, forms, etc., will be kept in reusable plastic bags within the cabinets.

5.3.2 When writing is to be performed, the exhauster will be started prior to opening the plastic bag and withdrawing the desired form.

5.3.3 Exhauster will operate while any writing is being performed.

5.3.4 When recording of data is complete, the document will be placed in a reusable plastic bag and sealed. Exhaust motor should then be shut off and the document placed with the job or routed to its final destination.

5.3.5 Stamping or initialing of planning, etc., can be done at the work station when the paper has been laminated in plastic. Note: The drawings and planning should not be subjected to excessive shuffling, handling, rolling or bending as materials used for laminating can generate excessive amounts of small particles under these conditions.

5.4 Material and Equipment Entry:

5.4.1 Entry through Cleaning Room:

5.4.1.1 All material or equipment will enter the CEF through the pass-through window in the cleaning area except when size and configuration dictates the use of the airlock entrance to area B-2.

FIGURE 6-11. Ultrasonic cleaning in General Electric clean room. *Courtesy General Electric Space Technology Center*

5.4.1.2 Where excessive dirt, oils or other contamination are present, material or equipment will be pre-cleaned prior to entry into the cleaning area.

5.4.1.3 Only complete accumulations will be sent into the cleaning area. *Note:* A complete accumulation is defined as a complete package, complete with planning, approved parts, drawings and fixtures, ready for manufacturing activity.

5.4.1.4 Any accumulations found to have a shortage, etc., will be turned into dispatch immediately upon the discovery of the shortage. *No materials* will be stored in the area other than a minimum work bank of "ready to work" jobs.

5.4.1.5 Materials or equipment removed from the CEF will re-enter through the cleaning area.

5.4.1.6 All production materials entering the cleaning area will be cleaned as called out by Manufacturing Planning. Tools, fixtures and equipment will be cleaned with sonic energy or as the area foreman prescribes subject to the approval of Manufacturing Reliability Engineering. [See Figure 6-11]

5.4.1.7 All tools, fixtures and materials will be sealed in plastic bags prior to admission to production areas.

5.4.2 Entry through Airlock to Area B-2:

5.4.2.1 Large parts such as vehicle structures and special equipment will enter Area B-2 through the adjacent airlock. An interval of 30 minutes will be allowed before entry into the B-2 area to allow the airlock to purge.

5.4.2.2 All production materials entering the B-2 area through the airlock will be cleaned as instructed by Manufacturing Planning. Material will be thoroughly pre-cleaned prior to entry into airlock and vacuumed within the airlock prior to entry into the B-2.

5.4.2.3 Functional equipment such as test racks will be blown down, if necessary spray cleaned prior to entering the airlock. The equipment will be thoroughly vacuumed prior to entering the B-2 area. Where practical, the equipment will be disassembled, cleaned and reassembled in the QC test area.

5.4.2.4 In no case will equipment be stored after cleaning. Materials and equipment should be cleaned, covered with plastic, and moved into the airlock immediately. The airlock will not be used for *storage*, but for final cleaning (vacuuming) before entry into B-2.

5.4.2.5 All assigned personnel will be counselled by Manufacturing Reliability Engineering prior to initial entry into the CEF.

5.4.2.6 All assigned personnel will be made fully cognizant of fire extinguisher locations and emergency evacuation doors.

5.4.2.7 The CEF will not be left unattended. One foreman will be in attendance during normal working hours.

6. SPECIAL INSTRUCTIONS AND DEFINITIONS:

6.1 Scheduled Cleaning of Work Stations:

6.1.1 Bench tops will be damp cleaned daily with a cellulose sponge (photo-type).

6.1.2 Welding heads and power supplies will be vacuumed daily using vacuum supply at work station. Manufacturing Reliability Engineering will check this equipment periodically and indicate to the responsible foreman when complete.

A number of practical suggestions will assist in the efficient operation of a clean room. First, whatever controls are set up for an operation should be documented in a manner similar to the standing instructions given above. Everyone working in the room should be thoroughly familiar with every rule and re-instructed at regular intervals. Even though a full written procedure is established and used, supplementary training aids are extremely helpful. Cartoon booklets work very well. Signs in the dressing room, taking the employees through the entry procedure step-by-step, are good reminders; they are even better if they are made eye-catching, are illustrated, and show a little sense of humor.

Norden requires a signed affidavit from each employee or visitor to its clean room, attesting to the fact that he has read and is familiar with the rules and procedures. This may sound a bit stringent, but employees cannot be expected to conform if they do not know what is required of them *(5)*.

Assigned group responsibilities can be a problem if not stated clearly. Engineering design should be responsible for deciding what environmental control is necessary. Production should be responsible for operation of the clean rooms and observance of all the rules and regulations. Plant engineering should be responsible for custodial services and for all the mechanical factors controlling the clean room environment. Quality control should see that the procedures and rules are meticulously carried out and that the environmental conditions remain within specification.

It is essential that monitoring of personnel procedures be almost continuous. Most of the rules are inconvenient, and some are actually a burden. If control is relaxed for a week or two, there will probably be quite a slippage in obeying the "law." Wash-up gets skimpier, perhaps winding up as a 2-second cold-water rinse of the hands. In fact, if laxity is permitted to continue, the clean-up procedure may deteriorate to the point where personnel will pass by without washing at all.

People are creatures of habit, and they thrive on bad ones. A little heckling and constant spot-checks will keep them on their toes. In addition, a formal survey every week or so, with a preprinted check sheet followed by a written report, keeps the production supervisors from letting the employees stray too far.

Psychological Benefits

The psychological benefits derived from clean room operation are considered significant by many manufacturers. A Space Technology Laboratory spokesman has stated that an important factor in instrument assembly under controlled-environment conditions is the psychological effect of the precautions on personnel. They believe that people working in a clean room environment are much more conscious of good working habits and are apt to produce more reliable products as a result*(6)*.

Throughout the clean room industry, there has been much discussion relative to the merits of wearing clean room smocks, coveralls, hats, shoe coverings, gloves, and other specialized pieces of protective clean room apparel. Many of these discussions have concerned the use of clean room garments by employees who are performing their tasks in an environment that has a relatively high level of contamination. If this high degree of contamination does exist, why should these people wear clean room garments? When considering only the high level of contamination, it is extremely difficult to judge the worth of these garments, and it would be logical to assume that there is no good reason for their use. One other consideration must not be overlooked, however—the returns to be obtained from psychological impact of garmenting on the clean room personnel.

This impact on the personnel can be seen in better work techniques, higher quality of work, better housekeeping practices, and an increased awareness that they are performing a special task which needs a special environment and special controls.

This psychological value is hard to evaluate, since cost savings that can specifically be attributed to it are hard to determine. But experience has shown that there is a difference in the quality of the work produced by those persons who are constantly made aware of the importance of their job. Such awareness has been accomplished by providing special garmenting and special tables, and by enforcing established work techniques, etc., as opposed to working on products in everyday work attire and factory environment. Special garments in the clean room tend to provide a continual stimulus to make employees constantly aware of the job they are performing.

It has been shown repeatedly in the armed services that personnel who are constantly reminded of the task before them will perform this task in a more predictable and reliable manner, such that there is little variation in the technique they use. Good work habits are paramount to clean room operation. Some good habits can be acquired by requiring clean room personnel to be orderly and neat. By such habits, contamination generation will be kept to the minimum, and such contaminants as particles of dirt, filings, and other types of foreign material will be quickly discernible in an area.

Contaminants that can be picked up from one surface and deposited on another are commonly called transfer contaminants and can markedly affect the operation and reliability of the product. Areas that are kept clean and orderly will reveal possible sources of contamination much more quickly than areas that are sloppily controlled and maintained. Thus, it is important in clean room operation that the people be made constantly aware of the job they are performing, are maintained in as strict a discipline as possible, and are constantly reminded of the nature of the work they are accomplishing. How and at what cost this degree of awareness is achieved is of the utmost importance in producing an acceptable, reliable product at minimum cost.

The worth of discipline has long been recognized as the heart of military organization. Some methods by which discipline is achieved are by controlling the tasks, by constant repetition of actions which are predictable, and by establishing a group identity for those involved. So, too, in all work performed by human beings, discipline of action can be achieved by employing these principles. Discipline will enable the managers to predict and compare the skills of the employees, thus allowing them to increase the reliability of the product. If an employee continues to do a task in the same manner, with the same precise logical discipline of actions, a very predictable product will result. It is obvious that less control will result in less efficient production techniques. When the original cost of clean rooms is considered, plus the upkeep, overhead, and maintenance, it is very important that the employees within these facilities be utilized to the utmost. This does not mean that the supervisor must be a type of Simon Legree. It means that the work to be performed by the employee should be adequately defined, and his actions and tool positions should be adequately specified, so that an operation may be performed smoothly with the least possibility of contamination by airborne and transfer contaminants.

Determining the Source of Contaminants[9]

The microscope is one of the most versatile instruments in modern technology. It finds its place in practically every scientific field. Its use in the operation of a clean room can be invaluable.

The chemical or polarizing microscope is of particular interest to anyone concerned with identifying particulates. This microscope is designed differently from the usual biological microscope in that it has a rotating stage and polarizing filters. The rotating stage permits the observer to orient a given particle in the microscopic field, and the polarizing filters are used to determine useful optical properties of transparent particles. The following examples illustrate the value of the chemical microscope in contamination control as experienced by the Walter C. McCrone Associates laboratory.

The first example concerns a supplier to the government who was having a contamination problem with a hydraulic device used in the missile program. Before this device is shipped from the factory, the components are thoroughly cleaned with a petroleum solvent in accordance with MIL-P-116C. After the components are cleaned and the

[9] Abstracted from reference 7.

device is assembled, it is again flushed with the same hydraulic fluid used in actual field operation. After bench flushing, the device is shop-cycled twenty-five times before being shipped to the job site. Use of the device in the field revealed considerable difficulty due to scoring of the hydraulic pistons, causing leakage. Scoring of the cylinders also occurred and become progressively worse with additional cycling. Spectographic analyses of the contaminants were of little assistance in tracing the scource of the problem. As a result, the Walter C. McCrone Associates were approached by the government parties concerned to investigate the contamination and determine the source of trouble.

McCrone and Salzenstein reported:

> Samples of the hydraulic fluid, wipings from the metal parts and rubber gaskets were available for study. Filtration of the hydraulic fluid yielded a small quantity, less than a microgram, of particulate matter. Microscopic examination of this residue showed cotton fibers, quartz and other minerals, plus a few unidentified microcrystalline aggregates. The mineral particles were large enough to have caused the observed abrasion. At this point, there was no obvious source of the abrasive mineral particles; however, the cotton fibers were observed to have a number of adhering black particles, very small and almost overlooked. This indicated that the fibers had come from a fiber reinforced rubber and suggested a look at the gaskets to see if they were reinforced with cotton fibers. On slicing one of the gaskets with a razor blade, it was noted that the clean, smooth rubber surface showed shiny, glassy particles at low magnification. Microscopic examination of a number of these particles showed them to be quartz. Cotton fibers with adhering black particles could also be stripped from the gaskets showing that the gaskets were wearing away and indicating that any other materials dispersed in the rubber were also being released and suspended in the oil where they could cause abrasion of the cylinder walls and pistons.
>
> Although this information was sufficient to name the gaskets as culprits, a further triumph of microscopic analysis was also obtained. A small one hundred milligram sample of the gasket was ashed at low temperature and the residue was examined microscopically. Although the components such as quartz and anhydrite were identified, the appearance, as a whole, was also observed to be characteristic of a known article of commerce, calcium silicate, as formulated by a particular manufacturer. This conclusion was based on the previously unidentified microcrystalline aggregate filtered from the oil. The quartz and other minerals were also characteristic of the diatomaceous earth source that this manufacturer uses in the synthesis of calcium silicate. Substitution of a different rubber gasket solved the problem.[10]

The most obvious application of the microscope in identifying particulates is its use in allowing an observer to see the morphology o: the particle. The size, the shape, the surface markings, the transparency, the occulsions, the color, and some other easily determined optical properties can, for the experienced observer, identify the particle. In May 1962, McCrone Associates was preparing, under a grant from the U. S. Public Health Service, an Atlas of Photomicrographs of Particulates found as air pollutants. Such an Atlas extends beyond the area of air pollution control and finds equal application in contamination control. Under this grant, over one thousand different samples of common airborne particulates are being catalogued and studied. Stereoscopic photomicrographs, in color, are being taken, and the text accompanying each photograph will describe optical properties and simple tests to aid further in the identification of the dust.

Discussing another problem, McCrone and Salzenstein write:

> In another contamination problem, a manufacturer found that a polyester film which was to be later formulated into magnetic tape was coming off the production line with defects and irregularities which could not be tolerated for the final product. The defects were examined by a number of microscopic techniques, the most successful being with the chemical microscope, for the examination of particle morphology, the location of particles by detecting strain patterns induced in the film surrounding the particles, and the measurement of the particle's optical properties. A hot stage attached to the microscope was used to observe the behavior of the film and the inclusions at elevated temperatures.
>
> Two separate and distinct inclusions were observed in the film. The first were particles which were not completely contained within the film, but protruded slightly above the surface. These particles were identified morphologically as simply glass beads and confirmed by refractive index measurements. A number of observations indicated that this type of inclusion resulted from airborne particles falling onto the film following extrusion but preceding stretching. In this way, the manufacturer could locate approximately where along the production line the glass beads were contaminating the film.[11]

---

[10] Reference 7, pp. 1-2.

[11] *Ibid.*, p. 4.

It was determined that the glass beads came from a neighboring plant, and corrective action on the air filtration was taken.

The second type of inclusion was internally imbedded in the film and, as a result, a bump was formed at the surface of the film. The most commonly observed inclusions were solid particles encapsulated within a hollow cavity in the film. This cavity probably formed because the imbedded particles did not wet or strongly adhere to the film and during stretching the film pulled away from the particles. The formation of the cavity and the strain in the film surrounding it, indicate that the particles were introduced into the film prior to stretching and the complete inclusion of the particles in the film indicates its introduction prior to extrusion.

Several of the inclusions were examined by opening the cavity with a needle and removing the solid particles. These particles were found to be soft and gel-like and were easily deformed by slight pressure of a needle. The particles were isotropic and had a refractive index near 1.58. The client was advised that these internal particles were a gel or a polymer. With this information, and before additional microanalytical data had been determined the client was able to determine that a slow leak of a silicone lubricating oil in the production equipment was contaminating the film. When the film was heated in subsequent steps, the silicone oil polymerized and produced the hardened (gel-like) inclusions.

. . . An example is the study done on electrical relays which were contaminated by a sticky deposit on the clapper and pole of the relay. Faulty relays were submitted to the laboratory for examination.

Samples of the deposits were collected and examined microscopically. It was determined that the deposit was organic in nature and would undergo decomposition when heated. Using the microscope, microchemical tests and refractive index measurements were made to characterize the deposit.

Searching for a possible source of this material, an orange pressure sensitive tape was found which was used inside a fiber glass covering of the coil. The adhesive on this tape was found to match the characteristics measured earlier of the deposits. A sample of the adhesive was heated while observing under the microscope and it was found to soften at about 40°C. and evolve some volatile components.

On the basis of these observations, it was surmised that the contaminant on the clapper and pole piece was composed of components of the tape adhesive and was deposited from the vapor phase, probably during the heating step of the assembly process. and continuing while the relays are energized and hot. It was also suggested that a trichlorethylene wash given the relays may have partially dissolved the adhesive and transferred it to the contacts. Suitable steps were taken by the client to eliminate the source of trouble.[12]

These examples typify the use of the microscope in contamination control. When the cleaning systems are operating well and the particle counts, either in a clean room or in the finished product, are below tolerances, then there is little concern for the particles themselves; but as soon as contaminant levels are reached that are no longer acceptable, then the problem of identifying the source becomes extremely urgent.

The microscope as an analytical tool for the identification of extremely small amounts of material is particularly advantageous in comparison to other means of sample identification. It is relatively inexpensive, and it can be applied to a large variety of materials.

The microscope has proved to be an extremely valuable tool in contamination control. With tolerances becoming smaller with respect to particle sizes, the limit of the light microscope is being reached, and the morphological identification tech-

[12] *Ibid.*, pp. 4 and 5.

FIGURE 6-12. Microscopic inspection of part which was also assembled with the aid of a microscope. *Courtesy General Electric Space Technology Center*

niques developed for the light microscope can be applied to the electron microscope. With the electron microscope it is also possible to identify many submicron particles by morphology alone.

Of course the microscope has many other uses in the operation of clean rooms. In Figure 6-12, a part held in a small holding jig is examined. Many times parts must be assembled under a microscope. Figure 6-13 shows the final assembly operation on a gyro unit at Litton Systems.

Space Flight Reliability and Clean Room Operation

Reliability is an inherent quality in a product. It must be built in, not through careful workmanship alone, but as a result of total reliability planning. In this effort, the quality control department plays its usual role of inspection and failure analysis. It assures that the goal of reliability has been realized. But reliability itself cannot be inspected into hardware. For this reason, a manufacturing reliability organization may be needed to prepare processes, procedures, and people in advance for the manufacture of space flight equipment. The function of such a group is to recognize critical reliability areas and to point out reliability needs to both engineering and manufacturing groups. This responsibility begins in the very earliest stages of project proposal and design. The reason for this suggested approach is that space flight hardware will need to meet the most stringent of long-life requirements; and, since few units are normally made, the sampling and statistical tools available to the inspector in mass production industries will not provide the proper kind of safeguard and assurance. Because of the high cost of space components and the pressure of schedules, production must be as nearly perfect as possible. This means no or minimal defects. To rely on quality control personnel for quality assurance may mean a waiting period longer than is allowable.

Because reliability is the prime concern in space hardware with long life requirements, the manufacturing reliability organization should have the responsibility for determining the cleanliness and handling requirements that must be observed in the processing of hardware. This includes responsibility for the standards maintained in the clean room and for the continual study of the facility's potentialities and limitations. Management should recognize that the clean room is a prime tool of reliability and not just another production facility.[13]

Room Population

As has been mentioned previously, the type of operation and the number of personnel in the clean room have a very direct effect on the operational contamination level of the room. The accompanying pictures show clean rooms that have acceptable

[13] Abstracted from reference *4*.

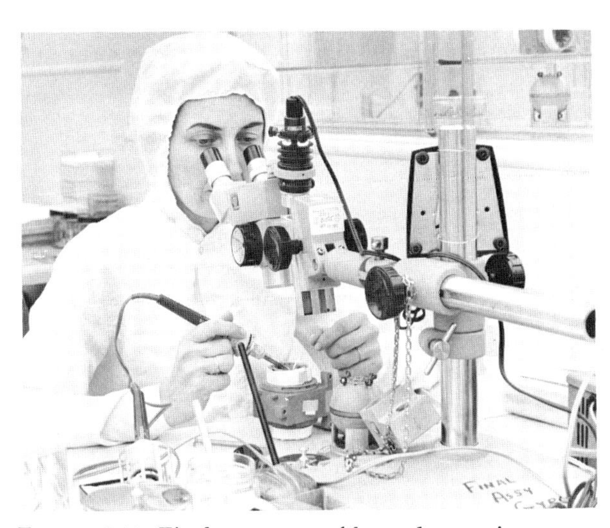

FIGURE 6-13. Final gyro assembly under a microscope. *Courtesy Litton Systems*

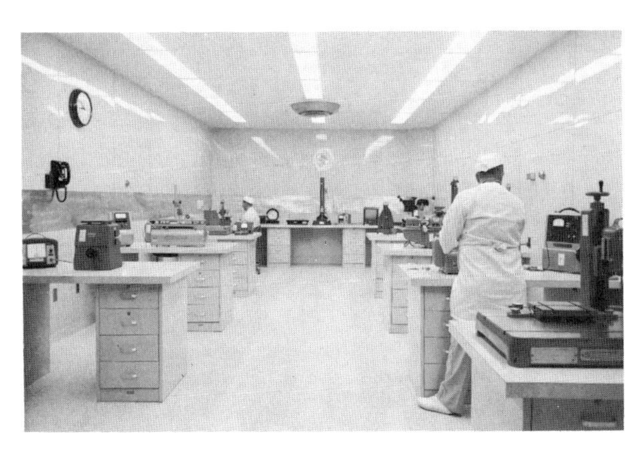

FIGURE 6-14. This standards laboratory at Olmsted Air Force Base, is limited to occupancy by no more than two people at any one time. This is due to temperature-sensitive operations. *Courtesy Olmsted AFB, Pa.*

contamination levels for the work being processed in the room. Notice also that the personnel density varies from facility to facility. Figure 6-14 shows a

FIGURE 6-15. A clean room with medium population density. *Courtesy General Electric Space Technology Center.*

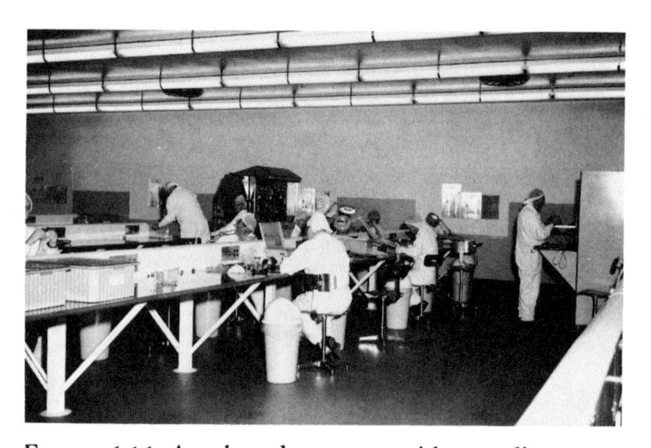

FIGURE 6-16. Another clean room with a medium population density. *Courtesy Hill AFB, Utah*

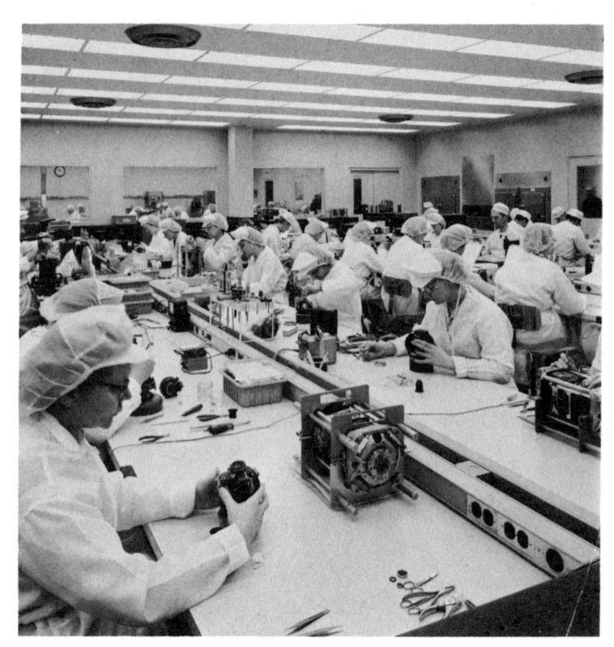

FIGURE 6-17. Two-platform gyro clean room with a high population density. *Courtesy Lear-Siegler, Inc.*

very low-density room with only two persons permitted in this room at any one time. This room is the Air Force Standards Laboratory at Olmsted Air Force Base, Pennsylvania, and is very sensitive to temperature change. Figure 6-15, the General Electric Space Technology Center clean rooms, and Figure 6-16, the clean room at Hill Air Force Base, Utah, show medium population densities. Figure 6-17, clean room at the Lear Inc., Grand Rapids, Michigan, shows a high population density. The workload for this facility is the Lear two-platform gyro. It should be pointed out that orderly, clean work places are essential to efficient clean room operation.

REFERENCES

1. LIEBERMAN, A. "Cleanliness versus Need." *Conference on Clean Room Specifications.* SCR 652. Office of Technical Services, Department of Commerce, Washington, D.C., April 1963.

2. *U. S. Air Force Technical Order 00-25-203, Standards and Guidelines for the Design and Operation of Clean Rooms and Clean Work Stations.* Office of Technical Services, Department of Commerce, Washington, D.C., July 1963.

3. TAYLOR, M. R. *The Application of Contamination Control in Critical Component Assembly Areas in TCA Facilities.* Trans-Canada Air Lines. Doval, P. Q., Canada, December 1958.

4. RUSSELL, J. A., WAITE, R. E., and KINDIG, E. V. *The Controlled Environmental Facility at the Valley Forge Space Technology Center.* Valley Forge, Pa.: General Electric Space Technology Center, August 1962.

5. LEVENSON, H. "Clean Room Rules at Norden Div., United Aircraft Co." *Journal of the American Association for Contamination Control,* Vol. II, No. 8, p. 14 (August 1963).

6. Anon. "The Cover." *Journal of the American Association for Contamination Control,* Vol. II, No. 6, p. 6 (June 1963).

7. MCCRONE, W. C. and SALZENSTEIN, M. A. *The Microscopic Study of Fine Particles.* American Association for Contamination Control Convention, San Francisco, Calif., May 1962.

Chapter 7. *Laminar-Flow Clean Room Design*

Introduction

The increased need for very clean environments pushed conventional clean room design to its limits. Further room sophistication such as stainless-steel walls, coved corners, and expensive appointments failed to provide the lower contamination levels desired. One of the first companies to look into the problem of room facility costs and the results obtained by the use of clean room facilities was the Sandia Corporation.[1] This was made necessary by the extreme miniaturization and close tolerances required to meet the specifications set by nuclear weapons designers. The Sandia people, on detailed examination of the cleanliness levels in existing clean rooms, found that these rooms were not really clean. The Air Force Clean Room Technical Order group, in a similar investigation(*1*), found that the contamination levels in existing rooms did not vary greatly from room to room. Rooms with similar "populations" and activities but with different types of sophistication had generally the same contaminant level. The only rooms achieving very low levels of contamination were those with a small population and very little activity. These observations made it clear that the key to cleaner rooms was an increase in the ability of the room to control and remove particulate matter generated within the room. Rooms with well-designed air-handling systems that were able to purge the room efficiently had the lowest contamination levels.

[1] The Sandia Corporation is a government-owned nonprofit organization set up to develop nuclear weapons.

Conventional clean rooms satisfactorily limited excessive dirt found in general laboratory and factory areas until much cleaner rooms were needed. It was at this time that the Sandia Corporation made an investigation to determine if clean rooms could be designed to achieve extremely low levels of contamination. One common characteristic was found in almost all conventional clean rooms—*the cleanliness level was dependent on the operation.* In other words, conventional clean rooms had little or no self-cleanup capability. The conventional clean room is essentially a sealed area, and contamination brought into or generated in the room and attached to surfaces has to be carried out manually by janitorial means or by dilution. Dilution, which consists in adding clean air to the room through relatively small (when compared to room size) area and removing contaminated air through an equally small area, can be a very slow process.

It is not uncommon to find conventional clean rooms that are dust traps—these rooms are dirtier than areas just outside the clean room. This is particularly true when the rooms are not using high-efficiency filters in their air-handling system. The small particles that pass through these filters continue to be manufactured within the room; and, since they are not trapped, they increase within the room and build up to fantastic proportions. Clean room personnel normally create the greatest problem by carrying in large quantities of dirt in their clothing and by shedding skin and hair particles. Air showers have been installed in an effort to clean up personnel before they enter the clean rooms. This has helped to lower the contamination level of these rooms. Since people are continually producing contaminants, however, and since air showers are only partially effective, low levels of contamination are still not achieved. Special clothing has also been provided which produces less lint and which surrounds the contaminant-producing worker and prevents these contaminants from entering the atmosphere. This clothing has not proved to be adequate for the lower levels of contamination desired.

As was stated previously, it is possible to achieve a low contamination level in a room with a small population. Thus the technique of providing a larger clean room area per clean room worker may be successfully utilized to achieve a clean room with a superior cleanliness level. This is accomplished by distributing over a larger area the contamination brought into and generated within the clean room. The obvious disadvantage of this method is that the cost of the facilities increases considerably.

The problems of conventional clean rooms may be summed up as three primary deficiencies:

1. Almost all conventional clean rooms do not have self-cleanup capabilities to offset contamination brought into the room by personnel and equipment. Most contamination has a tendency to settle to the floor or other horizontal surfaces and may be reintroduced into the air by changes in air currents or by activity in the room. Such contamination must be removed from the room by manual cleaning.

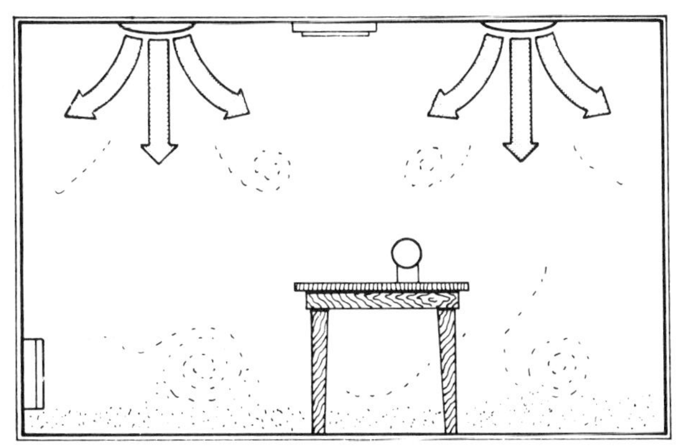

FIGURE 7-1. Air-flow patterns in conventional clean rooms. *Courtesy Sandia Corp.*

2. Air-flow patterns in conventional clean rooms are generally not uniform, nor are they directed in a manner that carries particulate matter away from critical work areas. In addition, they do not remove airborne contamination from the room as quickly as it is brought in. (See Figure 7-1).

3. Since all personnel in a conventional clean room contribute heavily to room contamination, rigid personnel controls are required.

Because of these three basic limitations, the Sandia Advanced Manufacturing Development Division reached the conclusion that, in order to satisfy current demands, another approach to the problem was needed, and a new type of clean room had to be developed. The need was great, for it was obvious that, unless a real advancement could be made, some critical work of Sandia Corporation would soon have to be done in vacuum hoods.

Four objectives were set which the new room had to satisfy:

1. It must have the best ambient air filtration system economically feasible.
2. It must have a self-cleanup capability which would offset both contamination brought into the room and contamination generated within the room.
3. Its air-flow patterns must carry airborne contamination away from the work area.
4. It must reduce personnel restrictions.

In essence, the desired room would produce airborne contamination control without inhibiting room activity.

Laminar-Flow Theory

It was apparent that a radical design—by comparison with the conventional clean room—was required. The most important initial design consideration was to provide for a much greater self-cleanup capability. It appeared that greater air flow would be a partial solution. It was known, however, that when air flow is increased in a conventional clean room the dust level rises. This is partly due to agitation of settled dust, and partly to the fact that dust is blown off personnel and equipment into the air. With these factors under consideration, work was begun on development of a method to direct large quantities of super-clean air in such a way that this problem was avoided.

An obvious solution to the air-blast problem was to bring air into the room through a very large area of diffusers. It appeared that this would not be too difficult to achieve, since the whole ceiling of the room could be made into a diffuser. The problem then, however, was to provide outlets for these large quantities of air so that particles could be carried from the room. Originally it was thought that wall outlets of sufficient size and number could be placed near the floor to prevent very high velocities. Even with this arrangement, however, the problem of larger particles settling on the floor still existed. And since these particles would have to be removed by manual cleaning methods, it was evident that this design would not provide the required levels of cleanliness.

A perforated floor was then considered as a means of moving particles from the room. It was felt that with a perforated floor the downward air flow would assist the natural gravitational fall of the particles. Investigations revealed, however, that it was not feasible to construct a perforated floor in a clean room. The most practical flooring appeared to be a close-spaced grating. But there were problems associated with this, too. It was discovered that, even though grating floors had been used successfully in air showers, a practical design had never been developed for grating floors in clean rooms. Another problem associated with grated floors was that particles that had passed through the grating floor could be swept back into the room if some provision were not made to trap them. This problem was solved by placing a rough filter material just below the grating floor. This filter served two purposes. First, it trapped particles as they were being removed from the room, and second, it served as a prefilter for the final HEPA filters.

Thus, the idea of a laminar-flow room was born. Consider the following facts:

1. HEPA filters are the most efficient filters presently available; therefore, the area in front of these filters will be the cleanest work area possible.

2. HEPA filters will produce a uniform distribution of air when a pressure differential is applied across them.

3. Essentially, laminar flow is produced when air is introduced uniformly at low velocities into a space confined on four sides and through an opening equal to the cross-sectional area of the confined space.

4. Laminar flow stratifies the air so that minimum cross-stream contamination occurs. There is little or no transfer of energy from one streamline to another. Suspended particulate matter in one streamline will tend to stay in that streamline until captured. (See Figure 7-2.)

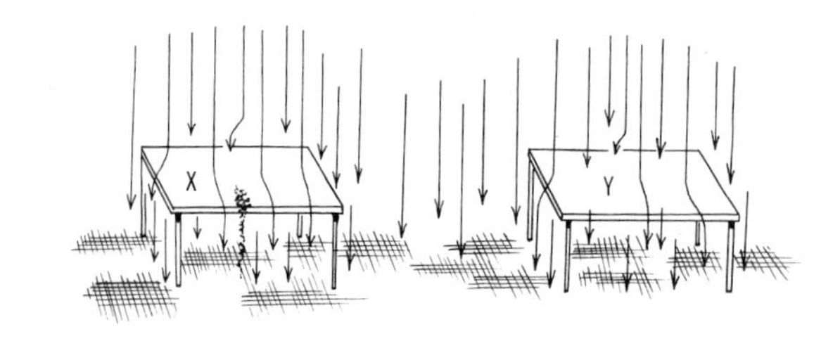

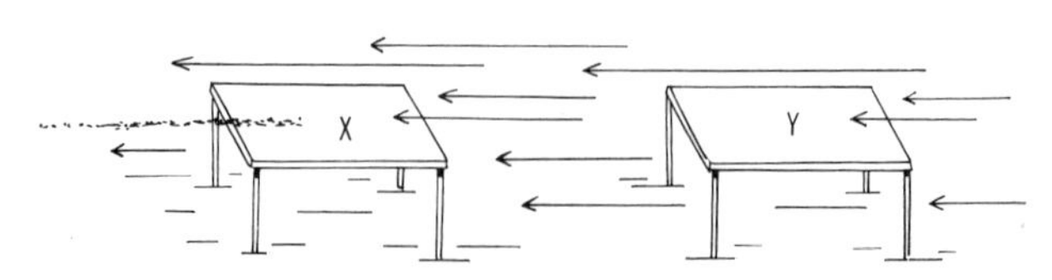

FIGURE 7-2. Particle behavior in clean rooms: *Top:* Conventional. Air currents are not forced to follow a predictable path. Particle generation at *X* can migrate to *Y*. Particles that have "fallen out" of the air can be re-entrained by movement of the foot on the floor. With laminar flow in a down-flow or cross-flow room, the air flow through the room follows a predictable path. The increased flow will dilute and carry away any generation of particles as soon as it is formed. *Middle:* Down-flow. Particle generation at *X* is completely isolated from *Y* or any other spot by a "curtain" of air. *Bottom:* Cross-flow. Particle generation at X moves downstream within streamlines where the generation took place. Downstream areas will have higher contamination levels than upstream areas. *Courtesy MAMES, Olmsted AFB, Pa.*

From these facts it can be logically deduced that a room with HEPA filters at one end or in the ceiling and an exit equal in area directly opposite will have very desirable characteristics. It will have a very low contamination level, with laminar flow proceeding from entrance to exit. Actual studies performed by MAMES, Olmsted Air Force Base, Pennsylvania, in laminar cross-flow clean rooms validated these statements(*2*).

Since critics of laminar flow cannot refute the ability of the filter to clean the air, they have argued that laminar flow will not exist as soon as people and equipment are placed in the room. This is in part true; however, the breakdown of laminar flow does not degrade room cleanliness. Unless there is particle generation in the area, only superclean air will be present in the turbulence. Smoke tests show that an object in the streamline will break up the streamline; however, the streamline re-forms some distance behind the object. If contamination is introduced within such a streamline, it will be carried off within the disturbed streamline.

The ability of the room to handle local contamination without adversely affecting the entire room is due to stratification of the air flow. If some of the streamlines are broken up, the others that are not contain the contamination as it is carried out of the room. The velocity of the air and the predictable path (straight out of the room) accomplish this very quickly. One fact should be remembered. No matter what the condition, particle generation, and turbulence, a laminar-flow room is generally better than a conventional clean room. (See Figure 7-3.)

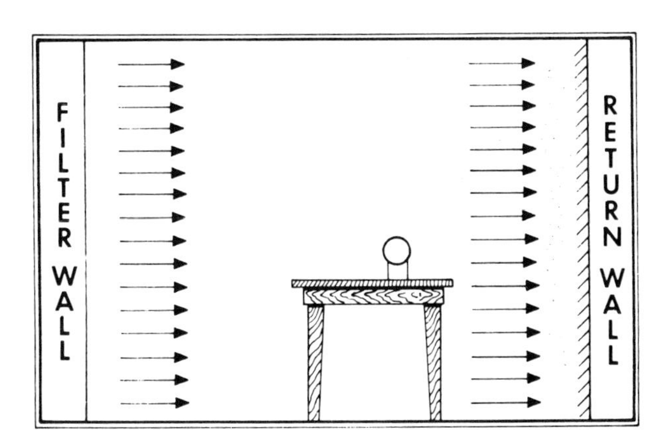

FIGURE 7-3. Air-flow patterns in a laminar-flow clean room. *Courtesy Sandia Corp.*

Prototype Rooms (*3*)

To provide a uniform air flow over a large area, and at the same time move the contamination generated by the worker away from the work area, the final HEPA filters were located by Sandia Corporation in the wall behind the workbench. The basic principles of this design are shown in Figure 7-4.

Since this design appeared to offer possibilities for providing a better clean work area than conventional designs, the decision was made to construct an evaluation model 6 feet wide and 10 feet long, with a ceiling height of 7 feet. Because it appeared that it might be possible to operate the room without an air shower, a detachable combination air shower and air lock was specified.

Early in the design phase it was obvious that this same principle could also be used in a portable clean room. The original design was then changed to limit the over-all width to 8 feet and to provide structural strength for handling and shipping by truck or rail.

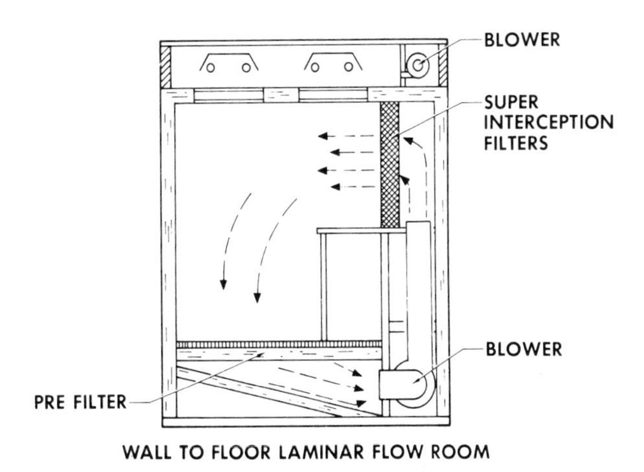

FIGURE 7-4. Plan view of a wall-to-floor laminar-flow room. *Courtesy Sandia Corp.*

The first portable model was designed for use inside other structures. No requirement was made for disassembly, and the unit was to be moved intact. Invitations for bids on this general design were sent out by Sandia's Purchasing Department. One company made a proposal to construct a knockdown, lightweight model that could be moved in sections through any standard 3-foot door. They proposed stainless-steel interior and exterior walls because of their low maintenance and minimum particle-shedding characteristics. These features are, of course, very important if the room is to be used as an ultraclean area inside a conventional clean room. They will also be important when the room is used in uncontrolled dust areas as a temporary or permanent clean room, and even more when the room is knocked down and moved.

Since it also appeared feasible to use this same design in a portable, all-weather unit which could be operated in areas without additional outside weather protection, a second model was ordered. This model is a rigid, unitized enclosure with a detachable combination air shower and air lock. The interior and exterior walls are painted galvanized steel. This room has a rigid base to allow the room to be handled with a forklift or crane, so that it can be transported as a unit by rail or truck. The room is 8 feet wide, which allows truck transportation without special highway permits.

By constructing both portable models, it was possible to evaluate this design against extreme clean room requirements. The rigid all-weather room provides a dust-controlled area for field or interior work and is portable as a single unit. This unit was built with galvanized steel interior walls so that a lower-priced material than stainless steel could be evaluated. Interior walls of this model are not subjected to the same abrasion and damage as the walls in the knockdown model. For this reason, it appears that painted galvanized steel walls will be adequate. The construction of both models provided information concerning the best type of portable room needed for a given requirement.

The Knockdown Model

The knockdown model of the clean room was installed in a general laboratory as shown in Figure 7-5. The exterior size of the knockdown model is 8 feet wide by 10 feet 9 inches long without the air shower. With the air shower, the room is 17 feet 2 inches long and 8 feet 8 inches high. The room is constructed in sections, and these sections are held in place by heavy-duty fasteners. These sections were designed to pass through a standard 3-foot door.

The base of the room is divided into two sections. One section is the main plenum chamber, and the other section contains the main blowers and the air-conditioning unit. The roof is also divided into two sections.

The knockdown room is designed to operate either with or without the air shower. The air shower can be separated from the main room by loosening the fasteners and removing one electrical plug. Leveling "feet" are mounted on both sections of this room. Figure 7-6 shows a close-up of the floor grating and the washable foam prefilter.

The Rigid All-Weather Unit

The rigid all-weather unit was set up outside on a concrete base for evaluation. The size of this unit is approximately the same as for the knockdown model, 8 feet wide by 17 feet 2 inches long and 9 feet high. It has three basic units: the entry way, the main clean room, and the roof cover.

The interior of this model is the same as that of the knockdown model except for the walls, which

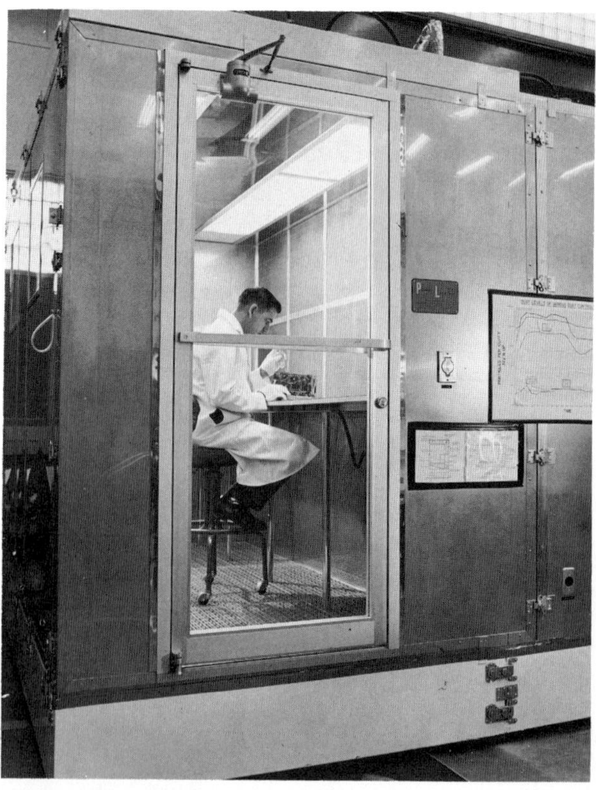

FIGURE 7-5. Portable wall-to-floor laminar-flow clean room which can be moved through a 3-foot door after disassembly. *Courtesy Sandia Corp.*

are of galvanized steel primed and painted with a flat latex paint.

The entry way is equipped with an air shower which has been converted to a make-up air unit, since evaluation of the knockdown unit indicated that an air shower was not needed.

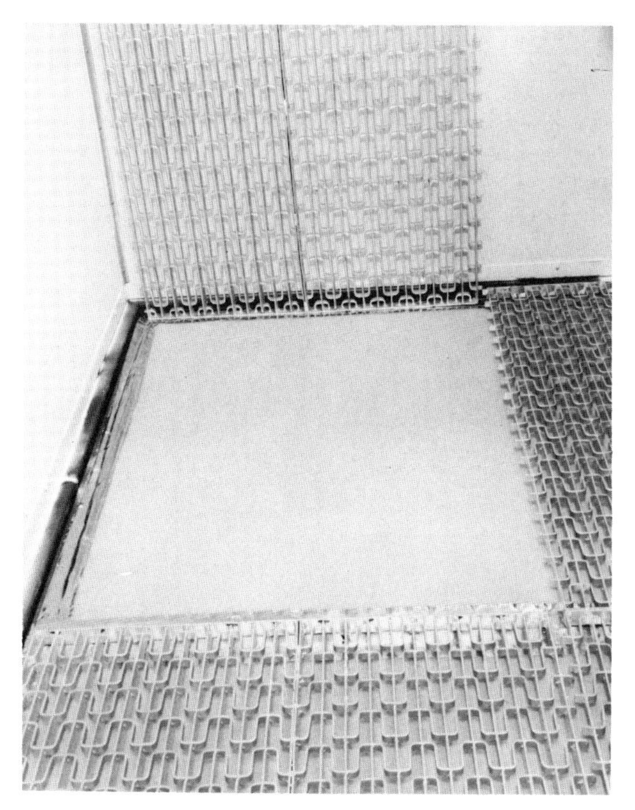

FIGURE 7-6. Close-up of the floor grating and washable foam prefilter in a wall-to-floor laminar-flow clean room. *Courtesy Sandia Corp.*

Evaluation Testing

Equipment

Airborne particle concentrations were monitored with a Sinclair-Phoenix photometer and a Royco particle counter, PC-200-A. Air-flow measurements were made with an Alnor Velometer air-flow meter. Figure 7-7 shows the inside of the laminar-flow room during testing.

Conditions of Tests

The particle samples were taken at the workbench edge nearest the center of the room, except for the tests made to determine that this location was representative of the entire workbench area. The Sinclair-Phoenix photometer and the Royco counter were run simultaneously for comparison data.

Airborne particle monitoring tests were run for 24 hours, except for the time required for room cleanup tests and tests involving induced particulate contamination. Careful calibration checks were made on both of the particle monitors before starting the tests, and periodic calibration checks were made during the tests.

No effort was made during these tests to exclude personnel from the room, once it was discovered that the personnel in the room did not cause the particle counts to change. No attempt was made to record or closely control the room temperature and humidity. Spot checks of temperature and humidity indicated that the temperature varied approximately $\pm 2°F$ from an average of 75°F. Humidity

FIGURE 7-7. Interior of wall-to-floor laminar-flow clean room undergoing testing. *Courtesy Sandia Corp.*

averaged about 20%, with a low of about 5% and a high of about 30%.

Airborne Particle Concentration Test

The Royco particle counter was used exclusively for this test, since other equipment and methods were found to be inadequate for monitoring the low levels of airborne particles found in the room (Figure 7-8). Further, data taken on five different days showed no significant change in contamination level even though personnel entered an average of

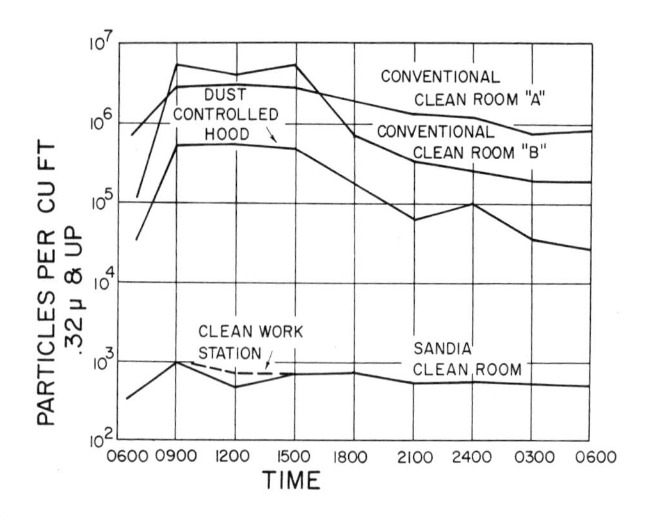

FIGURE 7-8. Dust-level chart showing comparison between the Sandia clean room and other clean rooms. *Courtesy Sandia Corp.*

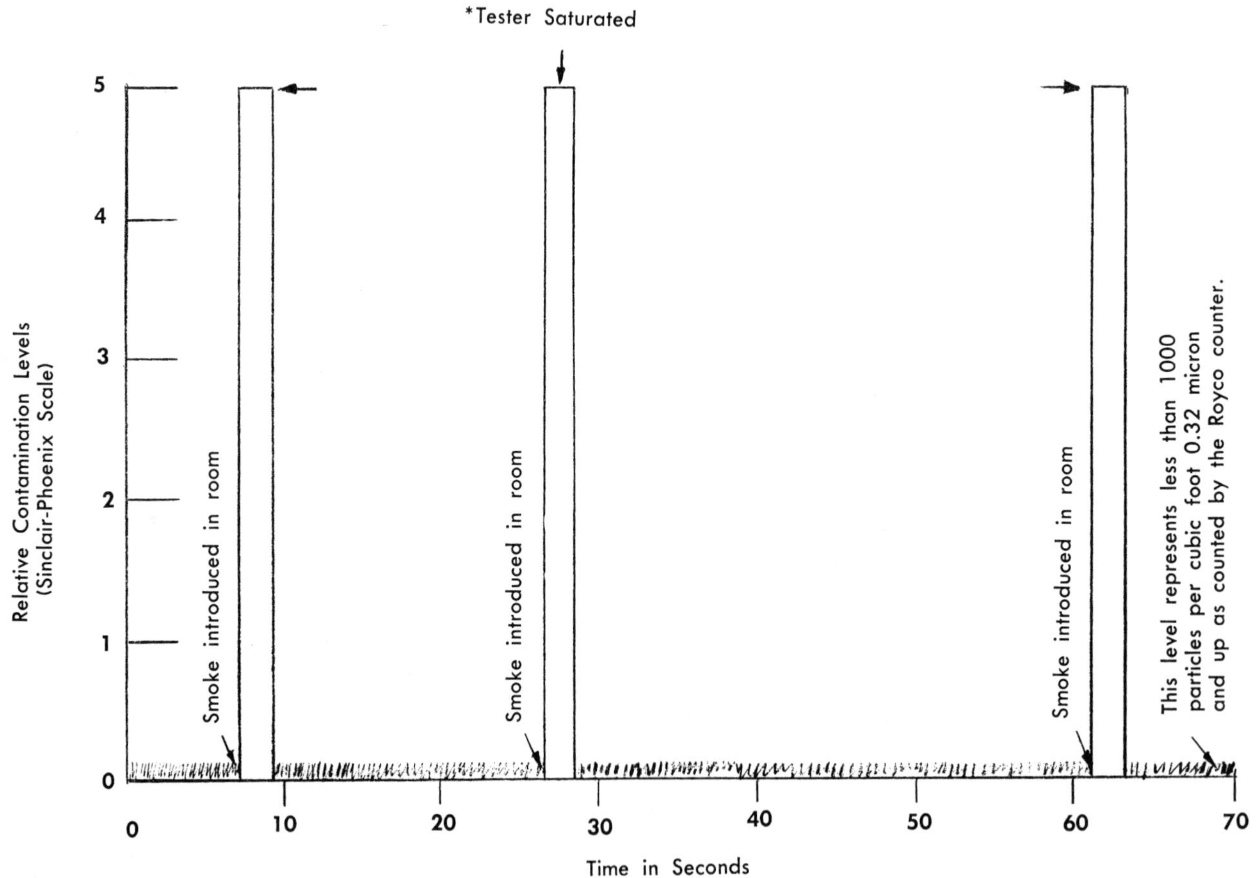

FIGURE 7-9. This plot of time versus contamination level demonstrates the room self-cleanup ability when a heavy concentration of smoke is introduced in the room. *Courtesy Sandia Corp.*

fifteen times per day without special clothing and without entry cleanup procedures.

This test was repeated in the rigid all-weather units for approximately 3 hours during a period of moderately high winds. The wind was blowing 30 to 35 mph and stirred up considerable dust in the air. No special room entry precautions were taken during this period, however. Although approximately fifteen entries into the clean room were made by several personnel during the 3-hour period, no increase in dust count occurred as a result of the dust condition outside the clean room.

Room Cleanup Tests

Cleanup tests were used (1) to test the ability of the room to remove contamination brought into or generated in the room, and (2) to test the ability of the room to clean itself after a shutdown.

The contamination removal test was conducted both visually and through the use of the Sinclair-Phoenix photometer. In the visual method, smoke was released in the vicinity of the work area. This smoke moved from the work area through the grating floor in less than 5 seconds. The Sinclair-Phoenix photometer was used for the instrumented portion of the contamination removal test. The Royco was not used for this test, since its response was much too slow to sense the rapid change of contamination. Smoke was the contaminant in this test also; results are shown in Figure 7-9.

Air-Flow Tests

The Alnor flowmeter was used to test air-flow uniformity. Room static air pressure was adjusted for 0.05 inch (water gauge) above ambient pressure (this setting was used for all tests). The air-velocity data were taken in various locations in the room; the average was 95 fpm.

Advantages of Laminar Flow *(4)*

1. Laminar-flow devices utilizing HEPA filters will achieve the lowest contamination level presently possible (two orders of magnitude lower than that obtainable in conventional clean rooms).

2. The cleanliness of the atmosphere created is almost independent of the operation or activity within the room.

3. The cost of achieving and maintaining extremely low levels of contamination by laminar-flow principles will be cheaper than by conventional means.

4. The level of contamination achieved by laminar-flow devices is considerably below that required by any device presently in production or contemplated.

Figures 7-10 and 7-11 are diagrammatic representations of two types of laminar-flow rooms—one in which the air flow is vertical (down-flow), and one in which air flow is horizontal (cross-flow). Laminar-flow rooms can be constructed at a reasonable cost. Sophisticated construction materials normally required in some of the latest conventional clean rooms are not necessary in laminar-flow rooms. A dollar saving is achieved by the elimination of support rooms and equipment and by more

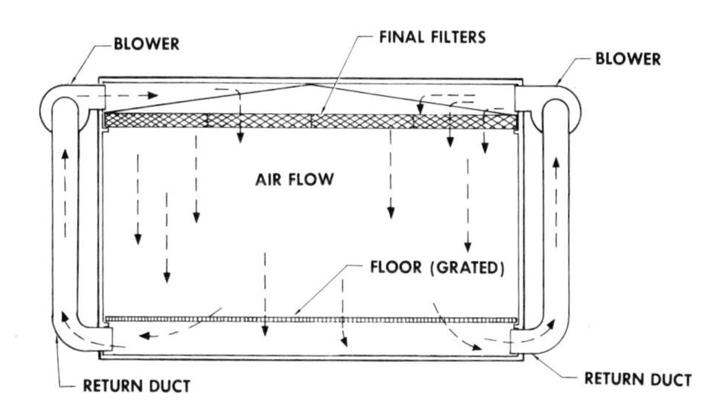

FIGURE 7-10. Ceiling-to-floor down-flow room. *Courtesy Sandia Corp.*

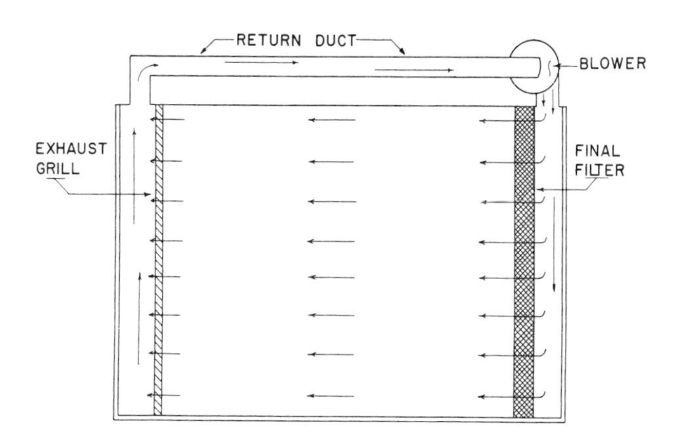

FIGURE 7-11. Wall-to-wall cross-flow room. *Courtesy Sandia Corp.*

effective utilization of floor area. (See Figure 7-12.) Additional savings are derived from operating the room only during working hours, or 24% of the time conventional rooms are in operation. (With a standard 40-hour work week, the room can be shut down a total of 128 hours per week, or 76% of the time.) Less special clothing is required, and savings are obtained by elimination of time-consuming entry and exit procedures. In addition, less janitorial service is required.

Figures 7-13 and 7-14 are artists' conceptions of the type of equipment installed in typical laminar-flow clean rooms. The aisles are shown larger than normal for the sake of picture clarity only. Aisles need be no wider than 5 feet, unless larger aisles are

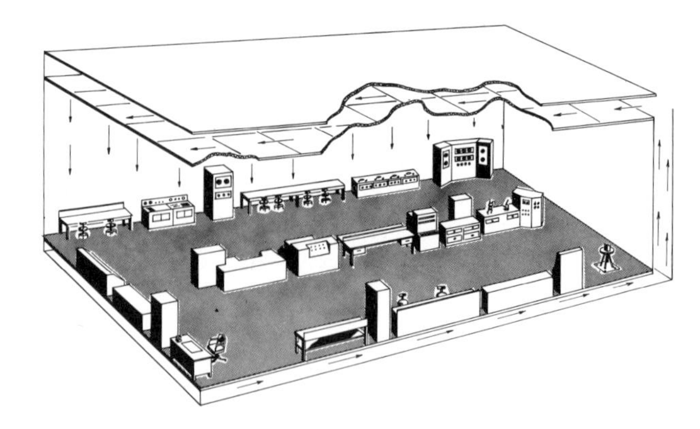

FIGURE 7-13. Equipment layout in down-flow clean room. *Courtesy MAMES, Olmsted AFB, Pa.*

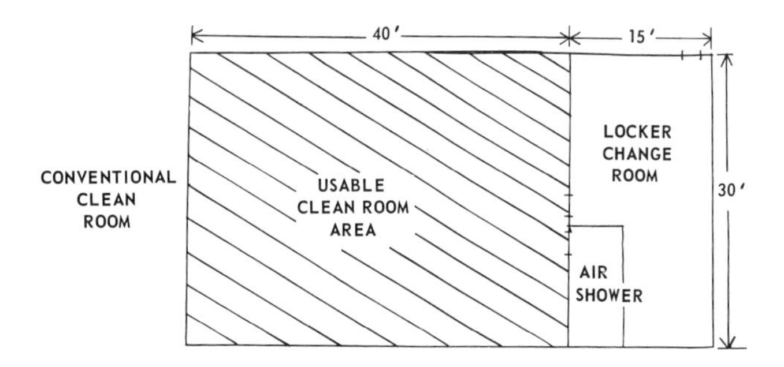

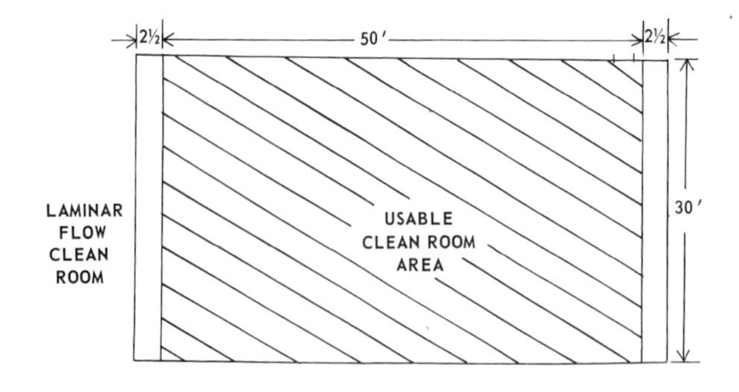

FIGURE 7-12. Savings due to increased utilization of space (cost of construction is assumed to be $40 per square foot). The conventional room yields 1200 square feet of usable clean-room space. The actual construction cost, with support room, is 55 x 30 x $40, or $60,000. The cost per square foot of usable clean-room space is then $66,000/1200, or $55 per square foot. In a laminar-flow room the cost of usable clean room space is $66,000/1500, or $44 per square foot. Thus, for the same price it is possible to obtain 300 square feet more of clean room space. *Courtesy MAMES, Olmsted AFB, Pa.*

needed for access to equipment. Figure 7-13 represents a typical equipment layout for a down-flow clean room. In such a clean room, little regard need be given to the height of the equipment or its position relative to other room equipment. It is important, however, that at least 4 to 6 inches of space separate items of equipment such as a console and workbench. It is also of prime importance that the area above the work be open from the ceiling to the work. This allows the contaminant-free air to flow from the ceiling down over the work station and then to the floor. In this type of facility, contaminant-producing operations such as soldering, sealing, cleaning, paper work, and other particle-generating operations may be performed anywhere in the room without fear of contaminating the product. This is because there is no transfer of contamination by random air flow between work stations. All air flowing over an individual work station passes directly from the work station to the floor and then is refiltered. Each work station can be considered as totally isolated from every other work station by the essentially laminar air-flow pattern of the room.

Figure 7-14 represents a departure from the down-flow clean room for the sake of economics. This figure shows a typical layout in a cross-flow facility. Notice that the cleanest operations are performed closest to the intake wall or filter wall. The dirtiest operations are performed at the air-flow exit wall of the room. In such a facility, larger and bulkier units should be placed in the down-

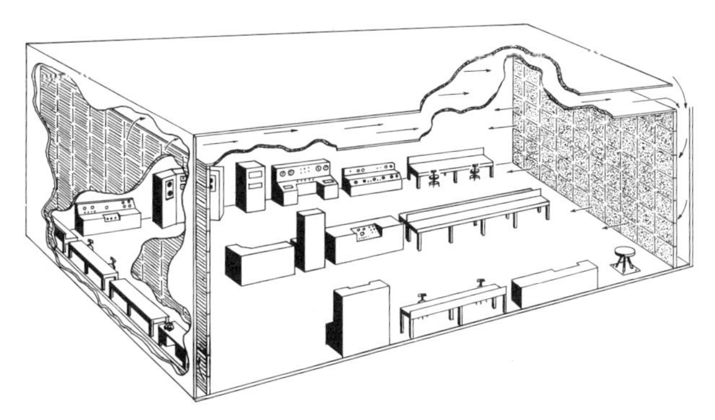

FIGURE 7-14. Equipment layout in cross-flow clean room. *Courtesy MAMES, Olmsted AFB, Pa.*

stream portion of the room. Cleaning operations and paper work may be performed at the air-flow exit of the room. Tables at this end should not restrict the air flowing out of the room, however. Shelves and consoles may be placed parallel and along each wall. The lowest contamination level of this room is in the upstream area and is similar to the contamination level of a down-flow room. It progressively becomes slightly more contaminated as it approaches the exit of the room. The over-all contamination level in the dirtiest section of the room is several orders of magnitude lower, however, than in a standard or conventional clean room. Even if the worst possible configuration, such as that portrayed in Figure 7-13, were used in a cross-flow facility, the contamination level would be lower than that presently achievable by conventional clean rooms. Contaminant-producing operations such as soldering, sealing, cleaning, paper work, and other particle-generating operations should be performed toward the exit end of the room.

Figure 7-15 represents the twin cross-flow room, which is essentially two cross-flow rooms in which the air exit of one feeds the air entrance of the other. The return duct has been put to work and is serving as a clean room. Or, to express this in another way, the clean room is its own return duct. The total clean room area needed is divided in half by a wall with flow in one direction on one side of the wall and flow in the opposite direction on the other. The obvious advantage of this design is that no false ceiling or return ducting is necessary. A twin cross-flow room can be installed in an existing (8 foot, for example) low level space. This type of design is the cheapest laminar-flow room available.

The mathematical model of a clean room presented in Chapter 5 shows that for any given room the factors that most affect the cleanliness of the room are the filter efficiency and volume of air flow. By maximizing a and K in equation (5-15) for a given room, the lowest ambient room contamination level is achieved. Thus the highest efficiency filters and shortest air-flow path through the room should be selected for the clean room. The down-flow room provides the maximum filtration for the minimum flow path, whereas the cross-flow room provides the maximum filtration for the minimum cost.

Down-Flow Room Design

Filter Arrangement

The ceiling of a down-flow room must be entirely covered with HEPA filters. Since there is a pressure differential of approximately 1 inch (water gauge) across these filters, the filter holder must be designed to withstand the loading caused by the force produced. In addition, the filters now occupy

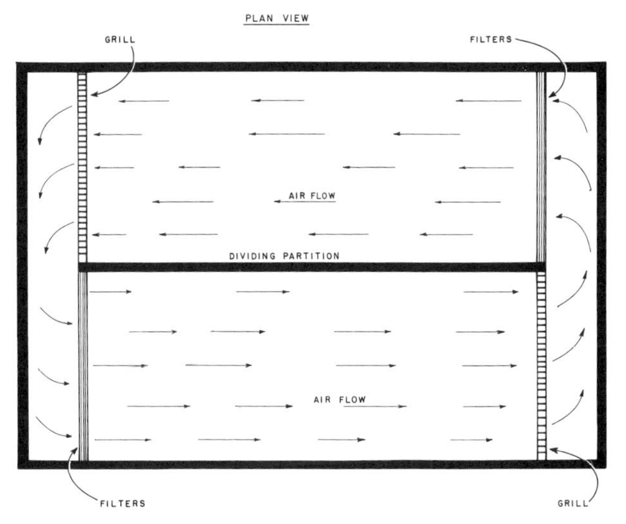

FIGURE 7-15. Plan view of a twin cross-flow clean room. This type of construction eliminates the need for return ducting. It is actually two cross-flow clean rooms side by side. *Courtesy MAMES, Olmsted AFB, Pa.*

the space normally reserved for lights. One solution to this problem is to use a series of single-row high-intensity fluorescent tubes mounted along the filter frame. Laminar-flow streamlines will separate around the tubes and re-form several inches below them. Thus the lights will not be detrimental to the room air flow.

Air-Handling System

Since gravitation is aiding in removal of the particles, the velocity of the air can be considerably lower than would be required for a cross-flow facility. It is important to remember, however, that at some velocity there will be a loss of the "isolation effect." This is due to the fact that some of the contamination particles are traveling at velocities approaching the velocity of the air flow. It is felt that the down-flow room can be operated effectively at a velocity of 50 fpm. Make-up and air-conditioning air can be added to the system by placing diffusers in the "up" ducting. This air should be introduced so that it will be evenly distributed in the main air stream and thus in the room. The air-conditioning unit should have a blower with sufficient capacity to "hold" the room humidity and temperature during nonworking hours with the main blowers shut down. Since all heat-generating operations will be shut down during this period, a rather small capacity will be adequate. Special cases (heat or moisture loading) may require a portion of the main blowers to operate in order to "hold" the temperature and humidity. Because of the large volume of air flowing through the room, the difference in temperature (Δt) and humidity (Δh) between the air-conditioning air and the room air will be very small in the long run. This is fortunate, for the air flow through the room will feel cooler than it actually is, owing to the cooling effect of velocity on personnel. Fortunately the velocity is low, so the effect is likewise low. It has been estimated that a Δt of up to 3°F will not be perceived or considered annoying by the average individual. In a normal room during normal operations the demand for Δt due to heat generation within the room should not exceed this value; if it does, it should be for a nominal period. The effect is mentioned here to acquaint the reader with this potential source of annoyance.

Blower and plenum arrangements vary from room to room, depending on the size. It is preferred that the blower motors be mounted outside the air stream. If mounted in the air stream, they will contribute a heat load and particulate matter. Motor contaminants will not reach the room but will add to the loading of the HEPA filters. Even air distribution is essential, and directional vanes may be needed in the exhaust grille and plenum to assist in changing the direction of air flow. For large rooms the plenum may be split up among individual or groups of blowers.

The grilled floor, at first thought to be a major construction problem, can be designed to advantage. Any number of commercially available grilles are suitable. The advantage lies in the fact that the under-the-floor plenum will also serve as a utility distribution channel with unlimited flexibility. The supports for the grille should be so designed that sections of the grille may be removed for ease of access to the prefilter material. Prefilter material made of a washable foam has been found to be extremely satisfactory. This material may be supported by laying it on a wire mesh which in turn is supported by the floor grille supports.

Physical Construction

The down-flow room may be constructed of any conventional building materials desired. It should be coated with a good-quality surface coating or paint. An epoxy coating can be used if superior wearing qualities are desired.

Advantages and Disadvantages

The chief advantage of the down-flow room is complete isolation of every operation by streamlines of laminar-flow air. It also produces the shortest distance from contaminant generation to contaminant removal from the room. Thus it yields the lowest contamination level of all the room designs. This room will also furnish exceptional heat transfer, since the distance the air must travel is at the minimum. No heat build-up will occur from unit to unit.

The chief disadvantage of the down-flow room is its cost. As experience is gained in building rooms of this type, short-cuts and savings will be realized which may bring the cost down. It should be remembered that the savings in operation can justify the increased initial outlay. The low over-all room contamination level is also an offsetting factor.

Application

This type of room may be used as a universal clean room and specifically for items requiring extremely close control.

Cross-Flow Room Design

Filter Arrangement

The smallest wall of a cross-flow room is completely covered with HEPA filters. The pressure differential and subsequent loading of the filter bank must be considered with this design also. In addition, a protective screen must be installed in front of the filter bank to prevent the filters from being damaged by accidental contact with the wall.

Air-Handling System

This system requires treatment similar to that of the down-flow design. The air-conditioning air in this case may be dumped into the "overhead" ducting. The further from the room entrance this air is introduced, the less sophisticated will be the mixing operation necessary to ensure even distribution. The effect of changes in temperature due to Δt within this room may be more significant as personnel approach the inlet wall. This is due to the longer distance from inlet to exit. Rooms now in operation have not presented this difficulty, and it is felt that they are still working below the threshold of awareness. The over-the-ceiling return may consist of a complete plenum, or it may be constructed of ductwork as in Figure 7-16.

Everyone concerned with the construction of a new clean room aims to make the nonproductive (support) areas as small as possible. Therefore, the air-handling system should be designed to be as compact as possible. Since the movement of air can produce noise and vibration, changes in direction and pressure are usually accompanied by gradual bends and large transition ducts. Motors and fan units are placed a considerable distance from diffusers to muffle the noise generated. In designing compact units this is not possible, and the effect of such designs on the noise level must be con-

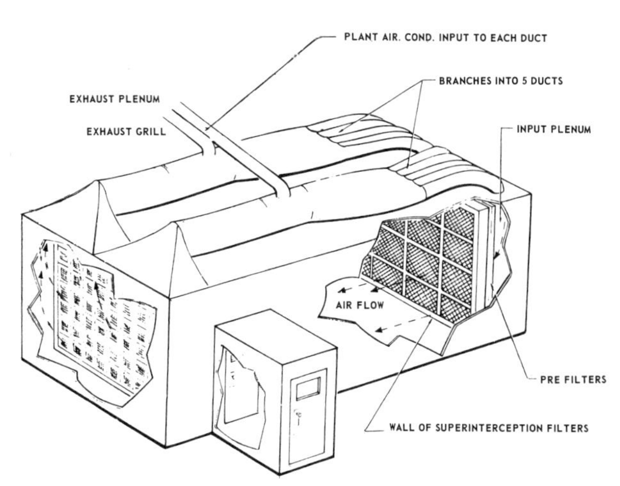

FIGURE 7-16. A cross-flow room using ductwork for returning the air from the exhaust wall. The feeder ducts are used to add make-up and conditioned air to the system. *Courtesy Sandia Corp.*

sidered. Careful design is necessary to prevent what could be a serious problem.

It is wise to include fixed louvers in the exhaust grille. These louvers may be adjusted on installation testing to even out the room air flow which may vary somewhat owing to inherent air-handling characteristics. This adjustment may be made by inducing smoke into the room and studying the patterns formed. Children's balloons filled with helium and balanced to the weight of air they displace can also be used for studying flow characteristics.

Physical Construction

The same general construction materials may be used for the walls and ceilings as for the down-flow room. It is not necessary to service lights from above. Recessed lights provide unrestricted flow but are not essential. Lights may protrude down from the ceiling. Lights streamlined in the direction of air flow would be best. Since the floor is a primary source of contaminants, it is recommended that a highly wear-resistive floor such as vinyl be used. (See Chapter 5.) Sheet vinyl which can be sealed at the joints is preferred, since joints collect dirt.

Advantages and Disadvantages

The cross-flow room will achieve superior cleanliness levels approximately two orders of magnitude higher than in conventional clean rooms for approximately the same cost. It may be used for heavy floor loadings or for other situations where a grated flooring would be unsatisfactory.

The cross-flow room will not isolate operations from each other. Operations "downstream" will be in a dirtier atmosphere than those "upstream." This is compensated for by "staging" the room (placing the most critical operations closest to the filters, and so on, until the least-critical operations are being accomplished at the return grille). It should be pointed out again that the dirty end of a cross-flow room is still considerably cleaner than the best conventional room.

During the past several years sophisticated consoles have been developed for the check-out of various flight and navigational instruments. These consoles contain numerous power-supply and check-out units and are excellent sources or generators of heat. In certain applications, it may be necessary to use many of these consoles in a confined area for a particular series of check-out operations. If these consoles must be used in clean rooms, the heat load dumped into the clean room (whether it be a conventional or laminar-flow room) can become a serious problem. The case to be considered is the lining up of a number of these high-heat-generating consoles in the direction of air flow. With such positioning, if the heat is not vented to the outside of the room, it will be carried downstream to the next unit in line, increasing the temperature at that position. The result will be a high temperature gradient throughout the room. Take the example of four consoles rated at 6000 watts (20,490 BTU/hr) each, lined up in a row. The heat load produced will be approximately 81,960 BTU/hr, or an amount equal to the output of a furnace of a normal-size home. The temperature increase at the exit of the room will be substantial if the heat load is not adequately handled.

It is possible, therefore, to create heat-loading problems with cross-flow rooms. Such problems are created when a number of heat-generating devices are placed in line with the air flow. Since the laminar flow stratifies the air, the heat from such equipment will be picked up by the adjacent air and carried downstream where more heat will be encountered. Normally the increased (compared to that in a conventional room) air flow in a laminar-flow room will be enough to compensate for this problem. Only in extreme cases, with a large amount of heat-generating equipment in a line parallel to the air flow, will it be necessary to take any action to rid the room of this heat directly.

The value of the temperature rise (Δt) due to heat load may be calculated from the following formula:

$$\Delta t = \frac{\text{Heat load (BTU/hr)}}{1.08\ (\text{BTU/hr/cfm}) \times \text{air flow (cfm)}} \qquad (7\text{-}1)$$

In cases where the entire output of the console will not be utilized at one time, the appropriate factor (80% of full load, for example) should be applied. If the entire row of consoles will not be operating at one time, a factor for this should be applied also.

The "air flow" should be the affected air flow or the flow around the equipment in question. Laminar flow will, because of stratification, tend to limit heat transfer from one layer of air to the next. Because of this, it has arbitrarily been assumed that the active area will extend 2 feet from the surface of the heat-emitting unit. For example, a console 2 feet wide by 4 feet high will transfer heat to an area 6 feet wide by 6 feet high, which at an air flow of 100 fpm represents 3600 cfm. The heat load (BTU/hr) for a piece of equipment may be calculated by multiplying its wattage by 3.415. The heat load of equipment in a row parallel to the air flow should be added to determine the total temperature gain at the room exit. This gain should be compensated for by the Δt applied to the room by the air-conditioning unit. If this gain is unacceptable and cannot be compensated for, the heat will have to be either collected and removed or compensated for by additional localized cooling.

The suggested solution to this problem is shown in Figure 7-17. Each console has been equipped with an exhaust stack which carries off the hot air created inside the unit. The exhaust stacks can be connected to a manifold which is in turn connected to an exhaust fan. Most consoles are equipped with an internal fan which will be sufficient to move the air inside the unit. In most cases this unit fan will not be powerful enough to force the hot air out of the exhaust stack, and therefore an exhaust fan will be required. The stacks, manifold, and exhaust

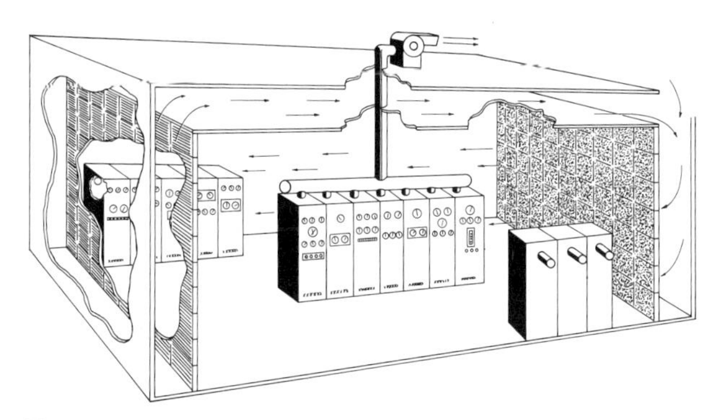

FIGURE 7-17. Venting an abnormal amount of heat generation in a cross-flow room. *Courtesy MAMES, Olmsted AFB, Pa.*

piping can be insulated to minimize heat transfer to the room. When exhaust stacks are utilized, the loss of room air will have to be compensated for by additional make-up air.

It should be pointed out that Figure 7-17 represents the worst possible case, where, for some reason, the consoles must be physically located in the clean room. It is strongly recommended that, when possible, consoles be located *outside* the clean room, with only the control face inside the room. By such a technique, air-conditioning costs can be reduced, maintenance of consoles can be simplified, and costly clean room space can be better utilized*(5)*.

This type of room may be used for general clean room work and is specifically adaptable to operations involving large objects which must be hauled around on dollies, such as missiles and rocket engines.

Twin Cross-Flow Room *(6)*

Filter Arrangement

The filter arrangement is similar to that used in the cross-flow room. The twin cross-flow room is, in effect, two cross-flow rooms placed side by side and turned "head to toe" with the filter plenum of one connected to the exit of the other at each end. The air flow is as shown in Figure 7-15.

Air-Handling System

In general, the air-handling system is also similar to that of the cross-flow room. The twin cross-flow room eliminates the need for return ducting from the exit end of a cross-flow room to the filter plenum at the other end. This is accomplished by using the room itself for its own return duct. Over head areas which would normally house the return duct are also no longer necessary. A small change in temperature across both halves of the room is achieved by applying air conditioning to both ends of the room. Since most rooms will require multiple air-conditioning and blower units, this represents no additional expense.

Physical Construction Features

The suggested construction features are shown in Figure 7-18. The dividing wall can be of simple stud and plasterboard construction; a glass partition will suffice if this is desired. The door connecting the two rooms is located in the middle of the wall where the contamination levels should be approximately equal. The door location is not considered significantly detrimental to the contamination level, however, doors and pass-through windows may be located where they are needed. The door should be a sliding door which will not open into, and disrupt, the air flow.

Immediately behind the return grille is the prefilter section. The prefilters should be readily accessible from the room for periodic cleaning. Any dirt released during cleaning will be caught by the HEPA filters. Behind the prefilters is the make-up air entry which will have its own prefilter. The air-conditioning, reheating, and heating coils are next downstream. The ducting then leads to the center of the fan "squirrel cage" from where it is forced into the filter plenum of the "other" room. Note that the blower motors are not placed in the air stream where they would contribute a heat load and produce various contaminants. The room exit may be divided up into any number of blower units, depending on room size. The air-conditioning control for one room controls the unit located in the other room's air exit. This system provides an even distribution of conditioned air.

Advantages and Disadvantages

This type of room can be constructed in a low-ceiling area where it would be difficult or impossible to place a ducting system overhead. It will filter the air flowing past a specific location in the room twice, whereas a single cross-flow room would filter the air past this point only once. This is accomplished with no additional filters or expense. It should be pointed out, however, that this air has also become contaminated between filtrations. In spite of this, and everything else being equal, the double filtering will result in a lower contamination level.

Another advantage of using a twin cross-flow room in place of a single cross-flow room is that the heat-loading problems will be less significant. In addition, in the single cross-flow room the overhead area where the ducting is placed is usually considerably hotter in the summer and possibly colder in the winter than the clean room. The result is that there is heat gain or loss in the duct work which must be allowed for in the air-conditioning and heating system. The twin cross-flow design considerably reduces this problem, with a resultant gain in operating economy.

The principal disadvantage lies in the fact that the clean room area must be divided in half by a partition.

Application

The twin cross-flow room is adaptable to the same workload as a single cross-flow room.

Support Rooms

Support rooms for laminar-flow clean rooms offer no special problems. They may be designed in any manner that is desired. The only consideration that must be followed is that entrance to a cross-flow room should be at the dirty end. Since air showers are not needed, no provision is made for this item. A "protected" entrance is necessary. Such "protection" should not allow stray wind currents, weather, high-velocity industrial dusts, etc., from entering when the door is open. A normal hallway is sufficient. If entrance is made directly from outside a highly contaminated area, a small air lock will be sufficient. (See Figure 7-16.) When garments are to be used inside the room, provision will have to be made for storage in a support room. Locker rooms will not be necessary, as full suiting-up will not be required except in unusual cases.

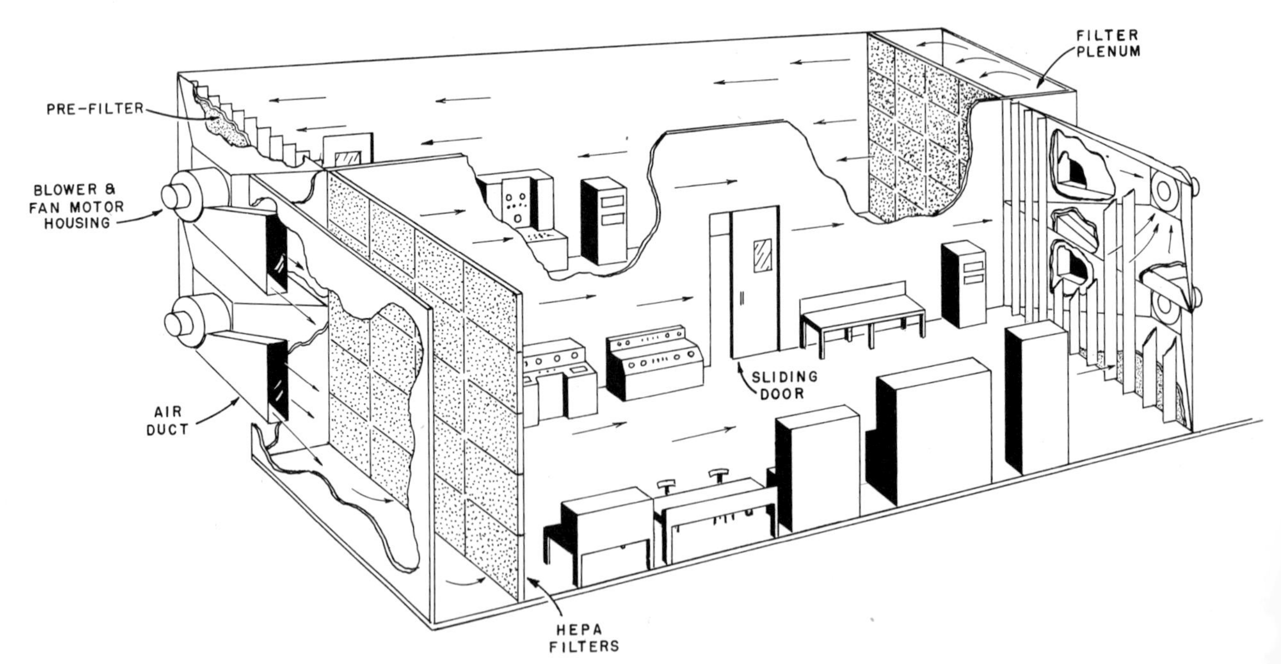

FIGURE 7-18. Equipment layout in a twin cross-flow clean room. *Courtesy MAMES, Olmsted AFB, Pa.*

Other Applications of Laminar-Flow

Mobile Clean Room (7)

Often a temporary clean environment is needed at a remote location, as in field repair of sensitive components or equipment, final assembly at on-site locations, or emergency medical operating facilities. Also, since a clean facility is often needed only temporarily at a given plant location, a permanent installation may not be justified.

A mobile clean room to fit this type of need has been developed by Sandia Corporation. The proposed design is shown in Figure 7-19. The trailer-mounted room will be coupled to an auxiliary air supply and power source unit. The air supply feeds through an overhead plenum and a bank of HEPA filters in the ceiling. The air flows vertically through the room and grating floor and back to the air supply unit. This design is for a central highly controlled section with laminar flow and two lesser controlled sections on each end. The advantages of a mobile clean room are (1) a high level of cleanliness possible independent of the field conditions, (2) the immediate cleanup capability of the design, and (3) the utility of such a unit.

Hood and Curtain Devices

These devices have found wide usage and are discussed in Chapter 13.

Examples of Cross-Flow Rooms

General Dynamics, Pomona, California

General Dynamics was interested in obtaining a super-clean area for the assembly of a miniature gyro. This gyro is unique in that it does not have a housing until it is mated with another assembly. It is, therefore, necessary that it be exposed during most of the setting-up and testing. These operations are very critical and must be protected from contamination. After some deliberation, management decided to build a cross-flow facility in order that the cleanliness levels would be assured. It was also decided to build a new room within an existing building and to air-condition the area independently of any other plant air-conditioning system. The layout of this facility is shown in Figure 7-20. The most critical work was placed at the cleanest or filter end of the room (the right side of the drawing).

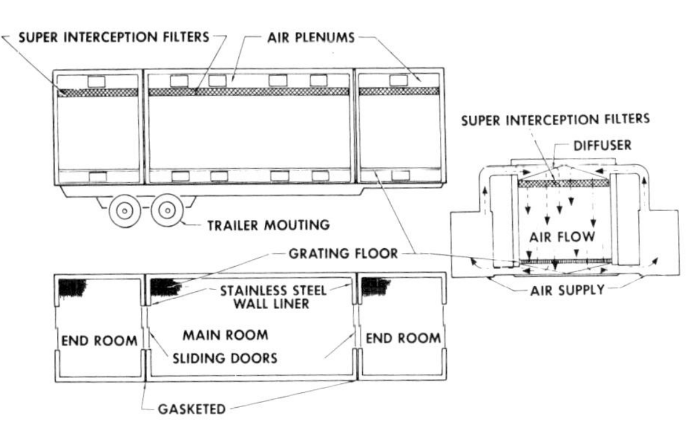

FIGURE 7-19. Portable (trailer-mounted) down-flow clean room. *Courtesy Sandia Corp.*

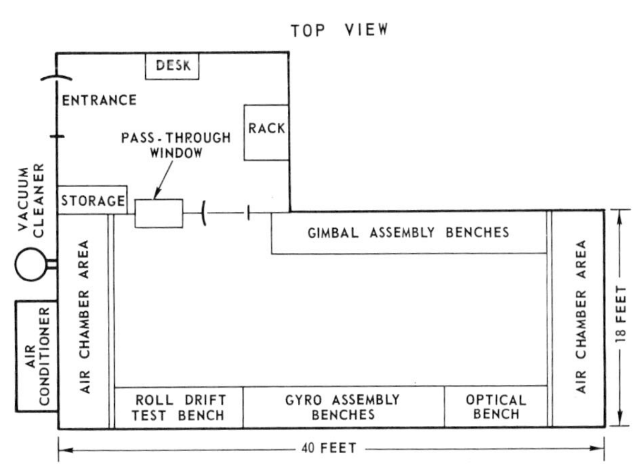

FIGURE 7-20. Cross-flow clean-room layout at General Dynamics, Pomona, Calif. *Courtesy General Dynamics Corp.*

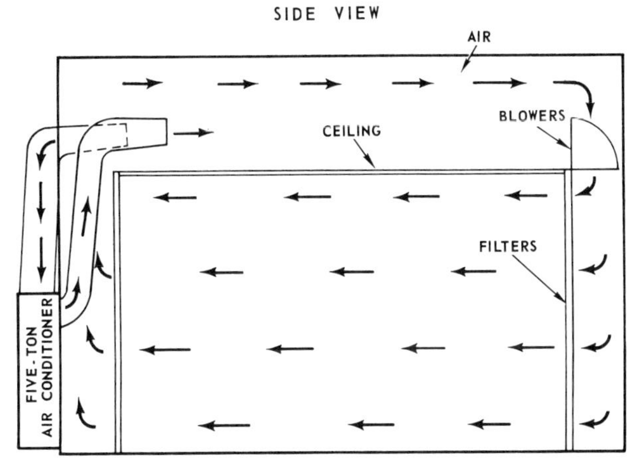

FIGURE 7-21. Schematic side view of air-flow pattern of General Dynamic's cross-flow clean room. *Courtesy General Dynamics Corp.*

Figure 7-21 shows the air flow as established by the air-handling system. The air-conditioning unit conditions only a small portion of the air which is returned to the "over-the-ceiling" plenum. Positive mixing is accomplished by the blowers.

Figure 7-22 shows a structural cutaway of the room. The area between the new structurally supported ceiling and the suspended ceiling serves as the air return passage.

Figures 7-23 through 7-26 show the progress of construction. The first steel erection is shown in Figure 7-23. The welding of the roof supporting members is shown in Figure 7-24. Installation of the main sprinkler piping, further roof supports, and nailable stringers are shown in Figure 7-25. Figure 7-26 shows the application of plaster board to the walls and outer ceiling. Note the inner ceiling supporting wires hanging from between plaster board seams, and the sprinkler piping extending down to below the inner ceiling level. (This was required by fire regulations.) The doorway shown will open into an air chamber area.

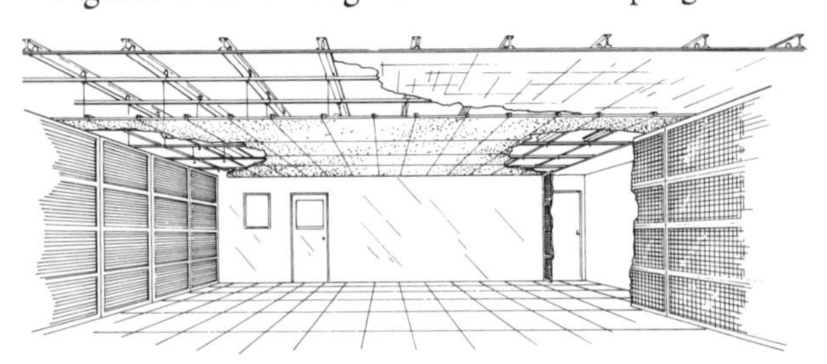

FIGURE 7-22. Structural cutaway of room showing hung ceiling and other construction features. *Courtesy General Dynamics Corp.*

FIGURE 7-23. First steel erection for structural support. *Courtesy General Dynamics Corp.*

FIGURE 7-24. Welding of roof supports. *Courtesy General Dynamics Corp.*

Figure 7-27 shows the suspended ceiling nearing completion and the air-conditioning intake and exhaust diagramed in Figure 7-20.

Figure 7-28 shows a filter bank supply module used to construct the filter bank in this clean room.

Figure 7-29 shows the completed room in operation. Note that the employees are fully garmented. General Dynamics maintains this garmenting even after achieving extremely low levels of contamina-

FIGURE 7-25. Installation of sprinkler piping and other supporting steel work. *Courtesy General Dynamics Corp.*

tion in this room. It is felt that it is an added measure of protection for the gyro, and it constantly reminds those working of the necessity for cleanliness. Additional benches, work stations, and equipment were added to the middle portion of the room soon after the photograph was taken.

Lockheed Missiles and Space Co., Van Nuys, California

Lockheed's cross-flow clean room was adapted to an existing facility rather than built in its entirety. The room is approximately 34 feet by 43 feet (1462 square feet). A minimum of construction was required. The existing asphalt tile flooring, lighting (additional units were added), and three existing walls were utilized. The added wall was constructed of grade A plywood, taped and sanded. The other walls and ceiling were of similar construction.

Figure 7-30 shows the filter bank of this room. Note that the bank of filters does not go to the top of the room. The lights protrude down into the room, with the bank of filters below this level. (A better light arrangement would be to have the lights parallel to the air flow.) The small wall area not in filters, located between the top of the filter bank and the ceiling, does not affect the laminar-flow characteristics of the room to any great extent. Particle counts show that the upper streamlines carry off the void area contamination (if and when produced) and protect the lower levels.

It should be pointed out that a large amount of blank area in the wall containing the filter bank can pose serious problems. This is because of an open-nozzle effect whereby contaminants are aspirated into the filtered air stream at the filter face. This can be explained by the fact that a lower pressure exists at the filter face than would exist downstream, since stream velocity lost because of nozzle expansion becomes increased static pressure (Bernoulli's equation). A technique employing a

FIGURE 7-26. Application of plaster board. *Courtesy General Dynamics Corp.*

FIGURE 7-27. Suspended ceiling nearing completion. Note the air-conditioning intake and exhaust. *Courtesy General Dynamics Corp.*

checkerboard pattern of HEPA filters and bell-mouth nozzles for the intake wall has not been tried as yet. Such a technique is indicated, however, if economics prevent the erection of a complete wall of HEPA filters. It is the authors' opinion that fewer operational problems will be encountered by using a complete wall of filters. Furthermore, in the long run the same total amount of filters will be needed for either type of installation (it being assumed that a given amount of contaminants is filtered out per unit time).

Figure 7-31 shows the pass-through entrance doors and window. Note that all appointments shown are standard equipment, not clean room equipment. This is true right down to the standard room baseboard.

Figure 7-32 is a view of the return grille. Since the room was not rectangular in shape, the return grilles are staggered. The entrance doors and stainless-steel tracks in the floor are for moving in large, heavy equipment.

Figures 7-33 and 7-34 are two other views of the large product entrance doors and room return grille. When these doors are open there is a slight increase in room contamination. When the doors are closed, the room almost immediately returns to normal.

Figure 7-35 is a view of the ductwork installed in the "overhead" area to return the air from one end of the room to the other. This system is similar to that shown in the drawing in Figure 7-16. The air-conditioned air is fed into the system by the rectangular duct in the center of the picture. This system adds existing plant air-conditioned air to the return air. The filter plenum is at the rear of the photographic scene. The three large ducts supply a rectangular manifold which in turn supplies five individual ducts. Each of these ducts serves a blower which pressurizes a vertical bank of filters, five high. The existing hung ceiling and high overhead area permit the use of large round ducts.

This room is used for the assembly and test of

FIGURE 7-28. Filter bank supply module used in construction of filter wall. *Courtesy Agnew-Higgins, Inc.*

rocket fuel transfer consoles. Benches, equipment, a large ultrasonic cleaner, and a vapor degreaser have been installed since the photographs were taken. The cleaning equipment is installed at the

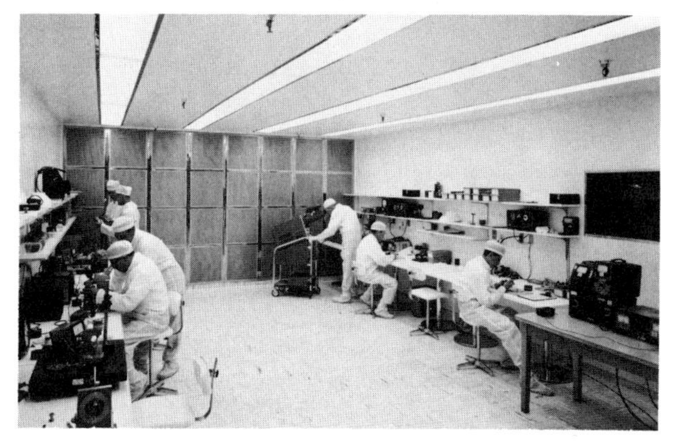

FIGURE 7-29. Completed cross-flow room in operation. *Courtesy General Dynamics Corp.*

FIGURE 7-30. View of the filter bank at Lockheed Missiles & Space Co., Van Nuys, Calif. *Courtesy Lockheed Missiles and Space Co.*

FIGURE 7-31. Side view from inside clean room. *Courtesy Lockheed Missiles and Space Co.*

FIGURE 7-32. Staggered return grilles made necessary by existing room shape do not affect room cleanliness. *Courtesy Lockheed Missiles and Space Co.*

FIGURE 7-33. Large product entrance doors (closed) do not affect room contamination. *Courtesy Lockheed Missiles and Space Co.*

FIGURE 7-34. Large product entrance doors (open to admit work) affect the contamination only slightly. Almost immediate cleanup results when the doors are closed. *Courtesy Lockheed Missiles and Space Co.*

Figure 7-35. Air ducts over ceiling of cross-flow clean room. The filter modules are fed by the manifold system shown. *Courtesy Lockeed Missiles and Space Co.*

Figure 7-36. View of filter bank prior to installation of HEPA filters in AiResearch cross-flow clean room. *Courtesy AiResearch, Garrett Corp.*

Figure 7-37. View of return grilles which can be adjusted to balance air flow. *Courtesy AiResearch, Garrett Corp.*

"return" end of the room. Assembly work is performed in front of the filter wall.

AiResearch Manufacturing Division, The Garrett Corporation, Los Angeles, California

This cross-flow clean-room facility was built to house the assembly operations of the environmental systems for Project Apollo. The clean room is 40 by 80 by 8 feet (3200 square feet). The decontamination room (shown later) is 20 by 30 by 8 feet (600 square feet).

Figure 7-36 is a view of the filter bank prior to filter installation. It consists of seventy-two HEPA filters and is divided into nine plenum chambers. (The doors to these chambers can be seen in the photograph.) This unit supplies 36,000 cfm of

Figure 7-38. View of exhaust grille and double entry doors from filter bank. *Courtesy AiResearch, Garrett Corp.*

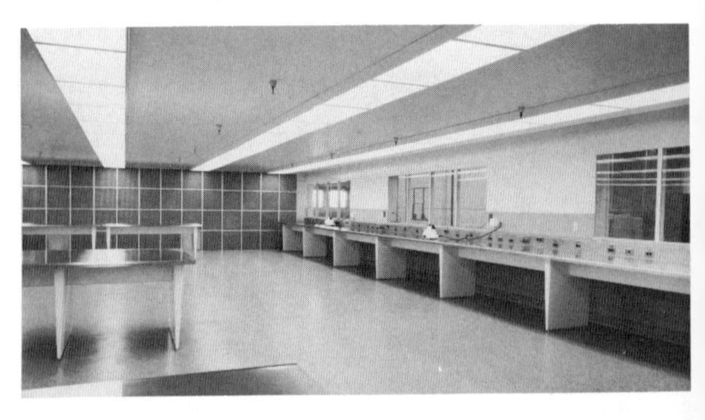

Figure 7-39. Installation of benches. Note incorrect placement of legs on wall-mounted benches; this was later corrected. *Courtesy AiResearch, Garrett Corp.*

filtered air. The air supply to the individual plenums is automatically balanced and controlled by pneumatically actuated dampers to maintain 0.4 inch (water gauge) of differential pressure across the filter elements.

FIGURE 7-40. Blower room located above the filter bank plenum. *Courtesy AiResearch, Garrett Corp.*

FIGURE 7-41. Filter bank for decontamination room. *Courtesy AiResearch, Garrett Corp.*

FIGURE 7-42. Return grilles and open pits for degreasing equipment in decontamination room. *Courtesy AiResearch, Garrett Corp.*

Figure 7-37 shows the exit grille. The exit grille does not fill the complete wall, since entrance to the room is made through double doors at the exhaust end. The flow in the room was balanced by adjusting the louvers. The void in the return wall caused by the entrance doors necessitated careful adjusting to balance the air flow at this point. A unique visual test was employed to check the room air flow. Balloons were filled with helium and balanced to the weight of the air they displaced; when the balloons were balanced to neutral buoyancy, they followed the air-stream lines without rising or falling. When the balloons were released, the exact flow of air could be traced.

Figure 7-38 shows the exhaust grille and double

FIGURE 7-43. Installation of degreasing equipment. *Courtesy AiResearch, Garrett Corp.*

FIGURE 7-44. Owing to voids in the return wall, some filters had to be blocked off in order to balance the room air flow. *Courtesy AiResearch, Garrett Corp.*

doors as viewed from the filter bank of the room. Note the utilities entrance under the raised platform. A high-pressure (5000-psi) test stand was mounted on the floor at this position. A cryogenic test stand was mounted downstream of the high-pressure stand, followed by a low-pressure test stand. The electrical supply channel can be seen on the opposite wall. A bench mounted flush with this channel is shown in Figure 7-39. The streamline bench support correctly mounted in line with the air flow on the bench in the center of the picture was removed from the wall-mounted benches and replaced with a leg that did not restrict the air flow.

Figure 7-40 shows a view in the blower room which is located at the end of the "between-the-ceiling" duct. Eight of the nine blowers can be seen. The blowers shown on the left supply air to the decontamination room. This air is exhausted to the outside, owing to toxic fume generation. In operation, air comes from the left of the picture across the clean room ceiling and into the room in the foreground. The walls of this room house pre-filters which are installed in the rectangular mounts shown. The air then passes into the larger room and into the in-line blower openings (covered with plastic during installation) and then by ducts to the plenums below. The blowers are driven by a belt from a 5-horsepower motor (under the "house-shaped" box on the blower). The controls for the dampers can be seen forward of the blower motors.

Figure 7-41 shows the filter plenum for the decontamination room. It consists of thirty filter elements divided between three plenum chambers and supplies 14,100 cfm of air.

Figure 7-45. Completed decontamination room. *Courtesy AiResearch, Garrett Corp.*

Figure 7-42 shows the return grille openings and the pits for the installation of degreasing equipment. Note the double entry doors in the middle of the exit wall.

Figure 7-43 shows the installation of the degreasing equipment, and Figures 7-44 and 7-45 show the completed room. Note in Figure 7-44 that some of the filters have been blocked off. This was necessary in order to balance the air flow in the room and was due to the location of the return grilles and the void caused by the center entry doors. The monorail hoist in the picture is equipped with nylon wheels to reduce particle generation.

Additional Facts

Air Velocity: The average air velocity in the laminar-flow work area of the cross-flow clean room is 112 fpm, and in the decontamination room it is 117 fpm.

Air Conditioning: Twelve thousand cubic feet per minute of conditioned make-up air is supplied to a plenum chamber above the ceiling of the facility. Twelve recirculation blowers draw air from this plenum through a bank of roughing filters and deliver it to the HEPA filters.

Humidity: Humidity is controlled and recorded to 40 to 50% relative humidity in the work areas.

Temperature: Temperature is controlled and recorded to 72° ± 1°F. Required temperature and humidity conditions are maintained by conditioning the make-up air.

Vent System: The decontamination room is equipped with a supplementary vent system to minimize the release of vapors from the cleaning process tanks.

Pressure Differential: The 12,000 cfm of make-up air maintains a minimum positive differential pressure in the facility of 0.05 inch of water.

Lighting: The facility is lighted with 400-cycle continuous-strip lights which give a light intensity of 150 foot-candles in the work area.

Floor: The floor is covered with dust-resistant vinyl, welded and smooth at all joints.

Walls and Ceilings: Walls and ceilings are treated with hard epoxy paint over cloth.

Furnishings: All work surfaces are stainless steel.

Ward-Leonard Electric Company, Hagerstown, Maryland

This company manufactures thin film resistors. The cross-flow installation is used for vaporizing metallic compounds onto ceramic housings. Cleanliness is important, since small particles of dust or moisture can change the resistor characteristics or cause premature failure.

The cross-flow facility was constructed by Ward-Leonard personnel at a minimum cost of approximately $13 per square foot. Construction is wood stud with plasterboard covering and epoxy paint. Flooring is vinyl sheet.

Figure 7-46 shows the room air exit which is built around a stainless-steel conveyor. This conveyor brings ceramic platforms containing the ceramic resistor parts into the room from a baking oven.

Figure 7-47 shows some of the room support equipment (vacuum pumps) located outside the room. The stud construction can be seen in the foreground.

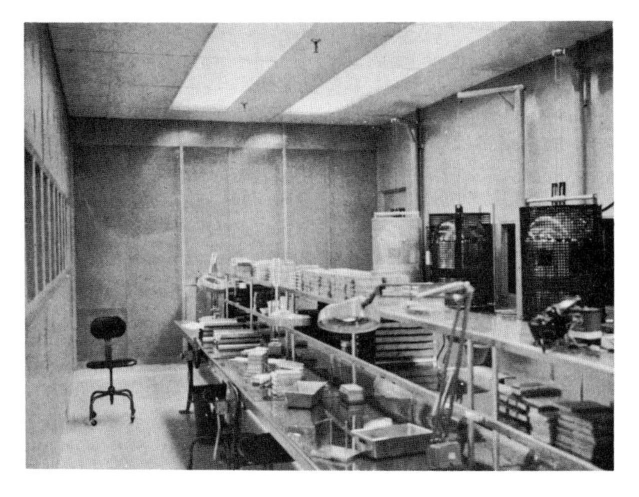

FIGURE 7-46. View of Ward-Leonard cross-flow clean room from the filter end. *Courtesy Ward-Leonard Electric Co.*

FIGURE 7-47. Construction features and support equipment for the Ward-Leonard room. *Courtesy Ward-Leonard Electric Co.*

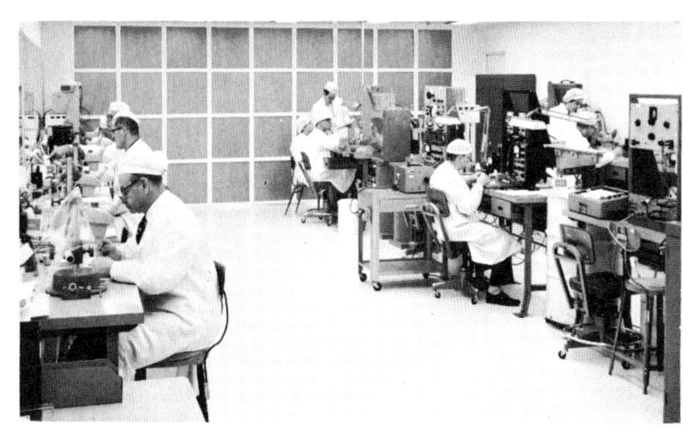

FIGURE 7-48. View of filter bank of United Control laminar-flow clean room. The assembly line is located to the left of the picture, the test and checkout equipment on the right. The end wall is composed of Agnew-Higgins filter modules. *Courtesy United Control Corp.*

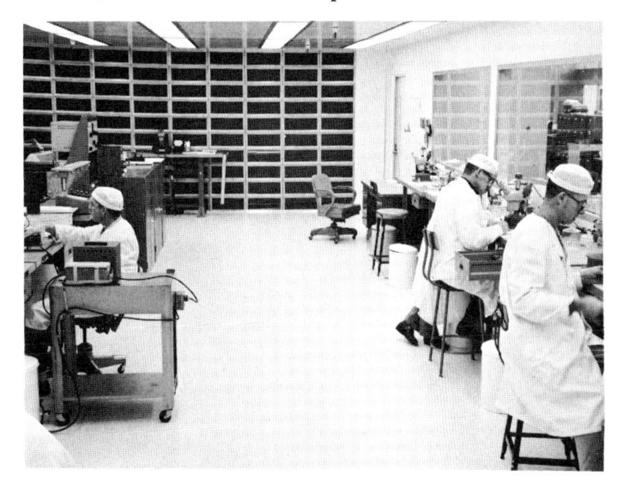

FIGURE 7-49. The end wall of the United Control clean room consists of adjustable return grilles for laminar-flow control. This room incorporates flush lighting and ceiling sprinklers. *Courtesy United Control Corp.*

United Control Corporation, Redmond, Washington

Palomar Scientific Corporation, a United Control Corporation subsidiary, manufactures small accelerometers and cryogenic liquid sensors in this facility. In November 1963, United Control Corporation built a laminar-flow clean room for its subsidiary in Redmond, Washington, at the Overlake Industrial Park Plant. Figure 7-48 shows the interior of this laminar-flow clean room. This room is approximately 50 feet long by 20 feet wide and has a Worthington Model SCY-80 7½-ton packaged air-conditioning unit. Approximately 15 to 20 people work in this facility. The cost of construction was approximately $35 per square foot. Figure 7-49 shows the exhaust end of the room.

Entry to the clean room is through an air lock approximately 9 feet by 6 feet. The entire clean room facility is wood frame with plaster board on all walls and the ceiling. Sheet vinyl with coved corners is used on the floor. The design specifications call for the temperature to be maintained at 75° ± 1°F and 40 ± 5% relative humidity.

ITT Federal Laboratories, Fort Wayne, Indiana

This company has constructed a horizontal cross-flow clean room with essentially laminar-flow characteristics. Its dimensions are 70 feet long by 40 feet wide by 10 feet high, and it was built for less than $20 per square foot. Farr 200 HP filters have been installed in a checkerboard pattern in the filter bank. HEPA filters will be used for upgrading this room. A flattened "V" perforated metal baffle (150°) with 50% free area is installed on the downstream side of each filter. A plastic grille with approximately 80% free area is installed downstream of the filters. In Figure 7-50, the filter pattern is shown with the plastic screen being supported by the light-colored vertical members.

FIGURE 7-50. Horizontal cross-flow clean room incorporating checkboard filter pattern. *Courtesy ITT Federal Laboratories*

Thirty tons of air conditioning are provided with an additional 30 tons available when an additional coil is installed. Three Trane 13,000-cfm climate changers are used to move the air. The anticipated operating air-conditioning tonnage is 6.5. The maximum air-conditioning tonnage generated is 17.

A work force of about 30 assemble and test electronic equipment in this clean room.

Typical Specification Format for Construction of Cross-Flow Clean Rooms[2]

The following format can be used in writing a specification to be put out for bid to general contractors for the construction of cross-flow clean rooms.

The laminar-flow clean room described in this specification is one in which a bank of HEPA filters[3] forms one end wall of the room and a bank of return air dampers[4] occupies the other.

This specification can also be used as a guide for designing controlled areas in which clean work stations will be used. The floor-to-ceiling modules, return damper wall, and return air plenums can be

[2] This format is abstracted and modified from that given in Chapter IV of reference *8*.

[3] HEPA filter/blower modules used to form the filter bank have shown excellent particle-removal characteristics. They offer additional advantages. Room construction is simplified and faster. The modules are guaranteed by the manufacturer to be properly sealed, to produce contamination levels similar to the filter characteristics, and to produce a stated air flow. These modules are designed for ease of removal and change of prefilters and HEPA filters. It should be noted that proper construction of large HEPA filter banks is not an easy task. The HEPA filter and its filter medium are easily damaged. A small pinhole or small puncture can void the use of a filter. A general contractor not familiar with HEPA filters or their installation can build in problems for the room operator which will be noticeable after the room is in operation for a short period of time. Agnew-Higgins, Garden Grove, California, has built a number of rooms using the filter bank module techniques with excellent results.

[4] Room air damper modules may be used. The use of such modules will decrease room construction time.

omitted, and the room-air-conditioned by conventional methods. The room is then equipped with sufficient laminar-flow clean work stations to recycle its atmosphere one hundred times per hour. This cleans the aisle atmosphere to Air Force standard clean room levels (Class 100,000 of Federal Standard 209) or better, and in addition it provides a "first air" work chamber for every critical task. Any building contractor who is qualified from the standpoint of proximity to the job site, financial resources, and willingness to bid the job can be considered able to build a first-rate laminar-flow clean room.

Construction Specification Laminar-Flow Clean Room

1.0 *Scope*

This specification covers the furnishing of materials and labor for the construction of a laminar-flow clean room. The clean room shall be complete and suitable for its intended purpose in all respects and shall include the enclosure, consisting of a main clean room and an anteroom,[5] the laminar-flow air-handling system, an air-conditioning system, an electrical system including lighting and convenience outlets, a central vacuum cleaning system,[6] and accessories as specified below. The clean room shall pass requirements of the U.S. Air Force standard clean room as stated in USAF TO 00-25-203 (1 July 1963) and in first-air areas of Class 100 of Federal Standard 209.

2.0 *Applicable Specifications*

The following military and government agency specifications are referenced to this specification and made a part hereof:

2.1 USAF Technical Order 00-25-203 (July 1, 1963): "Standards and Guidelines for Design and Operation of Clean Rooms and Clean Work Stations."

2.2 NASA MSFC-STD-246 (July 29, 1963): "Design and Operational Criteria of Controlled Environment Areas, Standard for."

2.3 Federal Standard No. 209 (December 15, 1963): "Federal Standard—Clean Room and Work Station Requirements, Controlled Environment."

3.0 *Drawings*

The following drawings show the major features of this clean room. Bidders should make arrangements with the procuring activity to visit the construction site to familiarize themselves with actual construction conditions.

3.1 Architectual Drawing No. ____________.
This drawing shows plan and elevation of the proposed clean room, together with cross-section details.

3.2 Mechanical Drawing No. ____________.
This drawing shows the arrangement of air-conditioning ducts, air-conditioning units, laminar-flow air-handling system, and piping and drain lines.

3.3 Electrical Drawing No. ____________.
This drawing shows layout of electrical services, together with diagram showing distribution panels and their design.

4.0 *Information to Be Submitted by Bidders*

4.1 Bids that are in strict accordance with these specifications shall bear a statement to that effect. If exceptions are deemed necessary by the bidder, a list of the proposed exceptions entitled "Exceptions to Specifications" with suggested substitutions and reasons therefore shall be included with the bid.

4.2 Bidders shall furnish preliminary design drawings, showing major design features and major materials of construction with a general dimensioned layout. These design drawings shall show the major design features and major materials and construction of the structure of the enclosure, the air-conditioning system, lighting system, electrical system other than lighting, and the accessory units, if any, proposed to be furnished.

4.3 A working schedule showing the estimated time which the contractor will require to carry out the different phases such as design, fabrication, and installation and acceptance tests shall

[5] This anteroom may be omitted, depending on the location of the room. Some laminar-flow clean rooms are being planned for part of existing large conventional clean rooms. In such cases, personnel entering from the conventional clean room into the laminar-flow clean room will be sufficiently prepared. In other cases, the anteroom may consist of only an air lock at the return air end of the room.

[6] A portable clean room vacuum cleaner may be substituted if cost and usage dictates.

be submitted by the bidder at the time of submitting his proposal.

5.0 *Enclosure*

The clean room enclosure consists of a main clean room having inside dimensions of_____ feet wide by_____ feet long and an anteroom having inside dimensions of_____ feet wide by_____ feet long. Height to inner ceiling of main enclosure is _____ feet_____ inches. Reference is made to Drawing No._____ showing architectural details of the enclosure. The room can be built of conventional materials and, unless a particular material is called out on the drawings, standard materials should be chosen that will be suitable for the purpose so as to keep cost to a minimum.[7]

The clean room enclosure is made up of the walls, ceilings, doors, windows, floor covering, painting, and change room or entryway.[8]

5.1 Walls. Wall construction shall be:

________Wood stud and dry wall.

________Steel stud and dry wall.

________Steel framework with __________panels. (Specify type.)

________Movable panels. (Specify type.)

________Other.[9]

5.2 Ceiling. In the single laminar-flow clean room, a double ceiling may serve as a return air plenum. In the twin laminar-flow clean room, each half of the room returns the air for the other. These two types will be dealt with in turn.[10]

5.2.1 Double-ceiling construction (single laminar-flow clean rooms).

5.2.1.1. Upper ceiling.

________Suspended from the existing building roof (as wood joist and dry wall). (Specify type.)

________Supported by trusses. (Specify type.)

________Existing. (Describe.)[11]

5.2.2 Single-ceiling construction (twin laminar-flow clean rooms). This shall be of steel joist and dry-wall construction. (Specify here whether clean room is to be free-standing or whether clean room ceiling may be suspended from existing building roof.)

5.3 Doors

Door schedule is shown on architectural drawing No.__________. Doors shall be:

________Flush steel panel type with upper panel glazed.

________Plate glass in aluminum frame.

________Other. (Describe.)

Surface-mounted Neoprene weatherstripping shall be applied to door stops on jambs and header. Neoprene wiper shall be installed on the

---

[7] Unlike conventional clean rooms, the enclosure is not a functional part of the clean room beyond furnishing the physical boundary for the movement through it of ultraclean air. It should be designed to inspire clean work habits, with adequate lighting, light-colored walls, and an uncluttered appearance. It should be weatherstripped to prevent the possible entrance of drafts and to contain a slight positive pressure. It should be finished with washable materials and coved for ease of housecleaning. It need not, however, be constructed of special materials chosen for their nonshedding characteristics which may not be widely used in the building trade. Any slight particulate matter occurring from the inner surfaces of the clean room will be carried out along the walls or ceilings and will not have an opportunity to reach the work in progress.

[8] It serves the vital function, however, of being the place to put on clean room smocks and serves a further psychological purpose as a staging area for workers to adjust their attitudes to the clean room rules which will apply to their conduct inside the clean room.

[9] The main consideration for the choice of a wall construction is appearance, followed by movability. A good appearance can be had by any of the above types of wall construction. Movability may have a value if the clean room is to be classed as a movable structure for leasehold or tax purposes. A clean room, because of its substantial investment in electrical systems, piping, ductwork, and floor covering, can usually be replaced at a cost approaching the cost of moving it because of the low percentage of recoverable items and the labor of disassembly, moving, and re-erection. It should be emphasized that any one of the suggested materials listed above will do its job equally well in so far as any measurable difference in dust count between one and the other is concerned. At any rate, the type of wall construction preferred should be indicated, since this is a major determinant in the cost of the enclosure and hence will serve to place bidders on an equal level.

[10] If a double floor already exists or is required for extensive runs of electrical cable, it may serve as a return air plenum. Down-flow clean rooms in which return air ducts are located outside the walls are not treated in this specification.

[11] An existing attic space may be used as a return air plenum, and the existing ceiling used as the ceiling of the clean room.

bottom of the door, and a smooth threshold member shall be installed across the door opening. Doors shall be held against this weatherstripping by an automatic door-mounted door closer. A cylinder deadlock shall be provided on the outer door to the clean room provided with thumbturn on the inside of the door. Push/pull plates shall be provided on the entrance door (push/pull bars in the case of glass doors).

5.3.1 Panic exits. Panic exits as shown on architectural drawing No.________ shall be flush steel doors with panic hardware on the inside and no means of opening on the outside. Weatherstrip as above for entrance doors. *Note:* Panic exit in double-door arrangement, with one leaf inactive, will serve additional purpose of providing a means of getting bulky objects into the clean room.

5.4 Windows. Windows shall be fixed and located as shown on architectural drawing No.________.[12]

5.5 Floor covering. Floor covering in main enclosure and in anteroom shall be:

________Vinyl asbestos tile.

________Vinyl tile.[13]

5.6 Painting. Washable enamel having a satin finish shall be applied to inner and outer surfaces of the clean room. Interior finish shall be off-white or ________ in color. Outer finish shall be________ color. (Specify.)[14]

6.0 *Laminar-Flow Air-Handling System*

The laminar-flow air-handling system consists of modules creating a bank of HEPA filters (high-efficiency, particulate, air) at one end of the room and a bank of return air members at the opposite end of the room. The filters and the dampers, with allowance for trim members, shall fill the entire area of the walls.[15] Laminar-flow supply and return air modules shall be as manufactured by________.[16]

6.1 Supply air modules. Supply air modular wall shall be made up of properly designed plenum chambers, blower and motor units, and prefilter and final filter units.

6.1.1 Plenum chamber. Plenum chamber shall be designed so that flow of air outward from face of filter bank shall be uniform from top to bottom and from side to side of the module. The plenum chamber shall be of fireproof construction so as to qualify for the handling of conditioned air under prevailing building codes. Plenum chamber shall have acoustical properties such that sound level of the filter wall while in operation as measured from any point 6 feet from the face of the filters inside the clean room shall be________ db on the "A" scale when the ambient noise level is________db.

6.1.2 Prefilters. Prefilters shall be a minimum of 63% effective on atmospheric dust as measured by the National Bureau of Standards Dust Spot Test. They shall be capable of being vacuumed off in place for ease of maintenance. They shall be easily replaced or removed for servicing without the use of special tools and without disturbing the final filters or breaking the seal between the final filters and their frames. Servicing methods shall be such that they may be accomplished by owner's maintenance personnel without special

---

[12] Sill-less windows are sometimes preferred for clean rooms. These can be made up by setting the glass flush with the inside wall of the clean room and framing the window on the outside with jamb members that will reach to the outer surface of the clean room wall. Openings can be framed by using smooth threshold, cap mitered at the corners. The reduction of the number of ledges in the clean room, beyond being an aid to housekeeping, has no measurable effect on the particle count in the clean room atmosphere.

[13] Vinyl sheet goods are not suitable for covering slab on grade. Although sheet goods are preferred for conventional clean rooms because of the number of cracks in a tile floor covering, it is not required in laminar-flow clean rooms, since dust particles collecting in the floor covering joints cannot rise through the air currents to working levels.

[14] Epoxy paints or other special finishes such as baked enamel considered necessary for conventional clean rooms are not necessary for laminar-flow clean rooms, since particulate matter from this source is not significant to the airborne particulate count within the clean room.

[15] This equipment must be carefully designed and built from the standpoint of low noise level while in operation, absence of filter bypass when properly installed, ease of replacement and/or servicing of filters, and low vibration level. Objectionably high noise levels will result from lack of research and development into the problems of moving the high masses of air involved.

[16] There are several manufacturers of this equipment; however, Agnew-Higgins, Inc., 7532 Anthony Ave., Garden Grove, California, has pioneered its development.

training. Access to prefilters shall be through service aisle at rear of plenum chambers.

6.1.3 Final filters. Final filters shall be of the HEPA type (high-efficiency, particulate, air) having an efficiency of 99.97% or more on dust particles 0.3 micron in size or larger by the DOP test. Final filters shall be mounted so as to be replaced through the rear of the plenum chamber, without special tools, by owner's maintenance personnel. Mounting arrangement shall be such that final filters can be individually replaced without disturbing the remaining filters, and design of mounting shall be such that when units are replaced a 100% positive seal is re-established between the filter and its housing. Absence of leaks or bypass shall be determined by means of a light-scattering indicator of an approved type.[17]

6.1.4 Blower motor units. Blower units shall be capable of delivering a rate of flow of air through the prefilter and HEPA filter of 100 ± 25 fpm, as measured at any point on the downstream face of the filter bank from floor to ceiling. Blowers shall be capable of maintaining this rate of flow during an increase of pressure drop across the filter bank of 0.5 inch (water gauge). Motor units shall be capable of continuous operation. They shall have bearings which are permanently lubricated for the life of the bearing. Motors shall be individually protected against thermal overload. All wiring connected with motor units shall be enclosed in metal conduit and adequately grounded. Motor and blower units shall be mounted on vibration isolator mounts so as to minimize vibration. Motors must be easily accessible for servicing.

6.1.5 Filter shields. HEPA filters shall be protected on the clean room side by a perforated metal screen capable of protecting the filters from accidental damage.

6.2 Return air modules. Return damper wall shall be made up of adjustable louvered-type dampers. Louvers shall be adjusted by key or wrench. Lever-type adjustments that may be operated by other than authorized personnel shall not be acceptable. Means shall be provided for access to plenum chamber in back of dampers for periodic vacuuming of floor of return air plenum from within the clean room, as required.[18]

6.3 Service aisle. The service aisle can be an adjoining aisle area, or an adjoining room in the case of the single laminar-flow clean room. In the case of the twin laminar-flow clean room, the service aisle also serves as a supply air plenum. Each will be dealt with in turn below.

6.3.1. Service aisle: Single laminar-flow clean room. A service aisle shall be provided in rear of supply air wall for servicing of prefilters and HEPA filters. Service aisle shall be a minimum of 24 inches in width and shall be provided with lighting and ventilation not connected with the clean air system. (Distribution panel servicing blower and motor units of filter wall may be located in this service aisle—see Section 8.3 below.)

6.3.2 Service aisle: Twin laminar-flow clean room. A service aisle shall be provided in rear of laminar-flow supply modules for servicing of prefilters and replacement of HEPA filters. Service aisle shall be a minimum of 24 inches in width and shall be provided with lighting sufficient for maintenance purposes. Door to service aisle shall be weatherstripped and shall open out, since the service aisle will be used as a plenum through which air will be drawn by the laminar-flow modules from the adjoining return air plenum of the twin room alongside. Warning sign or other means should be used to make sure that maintenance personnel do not open this door while the clean room is in operation. Distribution panels should not be located in this plenum.

6.4 Dust count in clean room. Dust count, as measured anywhere in the first-air areas of the clean room, shall not exceed 100 particles per cubic foot above 0.5 micron, nor 1000 particles above 0.3 micron in size, as measured by a light-scattering dust particle counter (see Performance Tests, Section 13.5).

6.5 Sound level within clean room. The laminar-flow air-handling system must operate at a low noise level in the interest of the comfort of personnel. Excessive noise levels shall be cause for rework or rejection of the equipment.

[17] Refer to discussion pertaining to aerosol photometer monitoring devices in Chapter 9.

[18] Return air damper wall may be spaced away from the return air end of the clean room by a distance sufficient to enable this space to be used for an entryway.

7.0 *Air-Conditioning System*

The air-conditioning system for the laminar-flow clean room includes the heating, cooling, and ventilating systems for the clean room, but does not include the laminar-flow air-handling system described in Section 6 above. It should be noted that the requirements for the air-conditioning system do not include a requirement for the control of airborne particulate matter, this being handled by the laminar-flow air-handling system. Therefore, equipment should be selected according to the requirements of the job aside from the requirements for dust control. Conditions of the job that will govern the selection of equipment and factors of heat load that will govern the sizing of the equipment are given below.

7.1 Size of room. Size of room is given on architectural drawing No.________, which forms a part of this specification.

7.2 Altitude. Altitude of the building in which clean room is to be located is______ feet above sea level.

7.3 Building in which clean room is to be located is (is not) air-conditioned. Air surrounding clean room from which fresh air make-up for clean room will be drawn has a temperature level ranging from______ °F to______ °F dry bulb.

7.4 Condenser of air conditioner shall be of the air-cooled______ or water-cooled______ type. (If water-cooled, 3 gallons per minute per ton of 80°F maximum-temperature water will be made available, plus sewer capacity to dump it or cooling tower capacity for recirculation.)[19]

7.5 Location of air-conditioning system shall be as follows:

______Mounted on floor alongside clean room. (For location refer to mechanical drawing No. ________.)

______Mounted on platform suspended over clean room. (Refer to mechanical drawing No. ________.)

______Mounted on platform on roof of building. (Refer to mechanical drawing No.______ for location.) Compressor / condenser section mounted on platform located______. (Refer to mechanical drawing No.______.) Air-handling unit mounted on floor______ or on platform suspended over clean room______or over aisle area adjacent to clean room____________.

7.5.1 ______number of persons will normally occupy the clean room.

7.5.2 The following heat-producing equipment will be used in the room. (A percentage factor is shown alongside each item to indicate the average usage of the item.)[20]

* * * * *

7.5.3 Lighting level of______ foot-candles is required. (See Lighting, Section 8.1 below.) Heat load from lighting in the clean room may be obtained from electrical subcontractor.

7.5.4 Auxiliary lighting to be used within the clean room will have a total wattage of______ watts.

7.5.5 A temperature of 67°F to 77°F dry bulb must be maintained at all times within the clean room. (If special conditions of temperature must be required as for metrology rooms, specify here.)

7.5.6 Relative humidity within the clean room must be maintained at all times less than 45% relative.[21] (If special conditions of humidity are required, state here.)

7.5.7 Fume exhaust. The following fumes and vapors will be generated inside the clean room

---

[19] The choice of an air-cooled compressor will require a decision as to the means of dumping the waste heat from the condenser coil. If the air-conditioning unit is mounted inside the building where the clean room is located, this waste heat can be ducted to the outside atmosphere. It may be necessary to duct cooling air for the condenser coil into the building to avoid bleeding down the conditioned air from the parent building. The compressor/condenser section can be mounted on the roof outside in the weather to avoid this. In this case, the refrigerant lines can be run down to an air-handling unit located adjacent to the clean room. Refrigerant lines can be concealed as they pass through the upper stories of a building inside a chase surface mounted on a building column.

[20] This should be a listing of electric motors to be used in the clean room, stating the size of the motor and a list of such items as bag sealers, soldering equipment, ovens, with the wattage of each unit. A form for estimating cooling loads for self-contained air conditioners is included at the end of this specification. This form was taken from the Air Conditioning & Refrigeration Institute Application Standard 220 and is acceptable under this specification for sizing air-conditioning equipment.

[21] Normally a value of between 30% and 35% is sufficient for the lower limit of relative humidity. Below this range, static charges on garments become noticeable.

and must be exhausted by hooded equipment. Hoods, exhaust fans, ducting, static dampers, and weather hoods as required shall be furnished by the air-conditioning contractor.[22]

* * * * *

7.5.8 Fresh air make-up. A minimum of 20% of fresh air must be supplied to the air-conditioning system.[23]

7.5.9. Positive internal static pressure. Conditions of 0.05 inch (water gauge) positive static atmospheric pressure shall be maintained within the clean room.[24]

7.6 Platforms. (Describe location and function.)[25]

7.7 Vibration isolation. All moving components of the air-conditioning system shall be mounted on suitable isolators to minimize vibration and noise from this equipment.

7.8 Ductwork. Ductwork connecting the air-handling section of the air-conditioning system to the clean room shall be designed so that cool dry air as needed is delivered to the plenum leading to the laminar-flow supply modules in uniform manner across the entire width of the laminar-flow air stream. Tapered ducts with slot-type discharge openings are acceptable. Return air ductwork for recirculation of air through the air-conditioning unit shall be similarly arranged and shall be located upstream of the air-conditioning supply air duct.[26]

7.9 Fresh air intake. A fresh air intake should be located on the return air duct of the air-conditioning system.[27]

7.10 Fresh air filter. A cartridge-type disposable filter should be located in the fresh air intake opening. If a ladder is necessary, it shall be permanently mounted in place and properly labeled to indicate its use for access to the fresh air intake filter.[28] The filter should be mounted so as to be readily removed without special tools, for replacement. A permanently attached label at the fresh air filter should indicate the frequency with which the filter should be changed and the type and size of filter required for replacement. (This label can also refer to the Maintenance Manual which is provided with the clean room.)

7.11 Reheat section. Operation of the compressor unit of the air-conditioning system should be continuous to provide for continuous dehumidification of air delivered to the clean room. Temperature control shall be achieved by means of reheat controlled by thermostat(s). Reheat shall be ______electric, ______hot water, or ______ steam. (Specify which.) Reheat coils shall be in ______sections.

7.12 Humidifier. The minimum level of relative humidity shall be assured by the use of a suitable humidifier. This shall be located in the supply ductwork leading from the air-conditioning system to the clean room downstream of the reheat coil.[29]

---

[22] A list should be provided here of the equipment which must be furnished with exhaust hoods.

[23] This minimum value may vary with local health codes.

[24] Minimum positive static pressure will be 0.05 inch (water gauge) and will normally be furnished to the room by the evaporative blower fan contained in the air conditioning system. This is sufficient pressure over ambient to ensure that strong currents from outside the room will not enter the clean room atmosphere.

[25] If platforms will be required to carry portions of the air-conditioning system, the owner should furnish to the contractor an architectural drawing of the platform location giving sufficient information for obtaining a building permit for locating the platform as required with respect to the roof-loading calculations of the parent building.

[26] If it is necessary to put supply and return ducts inside the return air plenum of the laminar-flow air-handling system, it is important to keep their cross section as flat as practical with the width being tapered so as to keep the interference which the ducts will present to the return air flow at a minimum. By locating the evaporator coil section of the air-conditioning system adjacent to or above the upper ceiling of the clean room, the length of supply and return ducts can be held to a minimum. Galvanized sheet metal ductwork is acceptable, since all ductwork is upstream of the filters of the laminar-flow air-handling system. Ducts should be externally insulated (if located outside the return air plenum) in accordance with standard commercial practice. Duct sections within the return air plenum of the laminar-flow air-handling system need not be wrapped.

[27] Motor-operated damper may be used on the fresh air intake to vary the percentage of fresh air intake as exhaust hoods are brought into operation in the clean room.

[28] This encourages servicing the prefilters at the proper intervals.

[29] The use of a humidifier to maintain the lower limit of the relative humidity requirement may not be needed in some areas.

7.13 Controls. Location of thermostats and humidistats to control the air-conditioning system shall be as indicated on mechanical drawing No._____. Low-voltage wiring to controls shall be provided by electrical contractor. (See Section 8.0.)

7.14 Exhaust vents. Positive static pressure within the clean room as created by the evaporator coil blower shall be regulated by means of gravity dampers located above the entrance doors of the clean room, as shown on mechanical drawing No. _______.[30]

7.15 Recorders. Temperature and relative humidity indicators shall be provided and located as shown on mechanical drawing No. _______.[31]

8.0 *Electrical System*

The electrical system includes the lighting system, the convenience outlets, the distribution panel, required disconnects for the air-conditioning system and the laminar-flow air-handling system, and wiring to the low-voltage controls of the air-conditioning system.

8.1 Lighting system. Lighting for the clean room in the main enclosure shall be by means of ceiling-mounted fixtures of the type which are serviced from below. Flush-mounted fixtures may be used; however, the Lockheed laminar cross-flow clean room has demonstrated that lights mounted below the ceiling have no effect on the cleanliness of the room. If below-ceiling lighting is used, the lengthwise direction of the fixtures should be parallel to the air flow. The number and location of these fixtures shall be sufficient to give a lighting level of 100 foot-candles minimum at bench height throughout the main enclosure. All wiring to these lighting fixtures shall be enclosed in metal conduit in accordance with local building codes.[32] Lighting for the entryway or change room shall be similar to that of the main enclosure except that a level of 50 foot-candles at 30-inches off the floor is satisfactory.

8.2 Convenience outlets. Convenience outlets shall be of the _______flush-mounted or _______surface-mounted wiremold type. (Specify which.)[33] Type of outlets and their location are indicated in electrical drawing No. _______.

8.3 Distribution panels. Distribution panels for the laminar-flow air-handling system, the lighting system and convenience outlets, and the air-conditioning system shall be located as shown on electrical drawing No. _______. Breakers shall be of the quick-break, quick-make thermal magnetic type for provision of overload protection.[34]

9.0 *Central Vacuum Cleaning System*

A central vacuum cleaning system for clean-down of the clean room and anteroom shall be provided. This shall consist of a vacuum pump, effluent lines, wall inlets, and sets of tools.

9.1 External pump. _______wet or _______dry pickup. (Specify.) This shall be of the _______ continuous-duty or _______ intermittent-duty type. (State which.)[35] The pump shall have a capacity of pulling 70-inches of water at each inlet.

9.2 Effluent lines, Effluent lines shall be of the _______metal or _______plastic type.[36]

[30] Clean room bleed-off for fresh air make-up is often exhausted into the anteroom as a means of keeping the anteroom ventilated.

[31] They may be of the 24-hour electrically driven, 7-day circular chart type with dual pens, surface-mounted on the walls of the clean room; however the type of product in the clean room should dictate whether hard records of temperature and humidity are necessary.

[32] Servicing of light fixtures, as for relamping, can be scheduled during off-hours. The laminar-flow air-handling system should be in operation during relamping. Dust particles generated by maintenance personnel will be quickly removed from the room. Selection of this method of lighting and the type of fixture to be used should be submitted to the building department of the city in which the room will be located for approval prior to issuing of this specification.

[33] The type of outlet chosen should correspond to needs. The continuous wiremold type of outlet may be preferred if it is anticipated that the clean room will be disassembled for movement to another location.

[34] Separate panels for the air-conditioning system may not be required, since their purpose may be served by fused disconnects required by reason of the location of the air-conditioning system.

[35] Intermittent-duty pumps are adequate for the amounts of dirt to be removed from clean rooms. Roof mounting of the pump units will isolate noise from this source from workers in the area. See previous note regarding portable clean room vacuum cleaner.

[36] Choice of type of effluent lines should be governed by whether or not the lines will be exposed to accidental damage. If the effluent lines are externally mounted to

9.3 Wall inlets. Wall inlets shall be flush-mounted on the interior walls of the clean room in locations in the anteroom and main clean room as shown on mechanical drawing No. ________. Inlets shall be provided with a low-voltage switch (if intermittent-duty pump).[37] Wall inlets shall have spring-loaded cover plates equipped with suitable gaskets.

9.4 Tools. Two sets of tools shall be provided, consisting of the following: dry floor brush, round dusting brush, crevice wand, length of hose. Ten feet of hose shall be provided for use in the anteroom. Twenty-five feet of hose shall be provided for use in the main clean room. Bracket for mounting hose.

10.0 *Accessories*

The following accessories shall be provided as a part of this clean room contract:

10.1 Assembly tables. (Specify type.)
10.2 Chairs. (Specify type.)
10.3 Pass-through chambers. Refer to architectural drawing No. ________for size and type.
10.4 Intercom system. (Specify type.)
10.5 Particle counter. (Specify type.)[38]
10.6 Pressure gauges. Pressure gauges shall be provided to indicate pressure drop across the filter wall of the laminar-flow air-handling system to indicate need for changing filters. A pressure gauge shall be provided to indicate the positive internal static pressure within the clean room. These pressure gauges shall be of the type indicated and located as shown on mechanical drawing No. ________.
10.7 Shoe cleaner. (Specify type.)
10.8 Smocks, smock racks. (Specify type.)[39]
10.9 Hats and hat storage cabinets. (Specify type.)
10.10 Clothing lockers or racks. (Specify type.)
10.11 Storage shelves. (Specify type and arrangement.)
10.12 Other.

11.0 *Reports and Records*

11.1 The contractor shall furnish to the procuring activity within 10 days after award of contract and prior to any fabrication and/or installation three complete sets of structural, architectural, electrical, and air-conditioning drawings, together with lighting and cooling load calculations. One set of drawings will be returned to the contractor with the procuring activity's approval or disapproval prior to commencement of work by the contractor.

11.2 Contractor within 10 days after award of contract shall furnish a current projected time schedule to bring up to date the schedule submitted as required in Section 4.3 of these specifications.

11.3 Prior to final acceptance of the work the contractor shall furnish three copies of an operating, spare parts, and maintenance manual covering each major item of equipment. These instructions shall include procedures for lubrication of equipment and manufacturers' specifications and bulletins relating to the equipment and complete operating instructions.

11.4 A condensed set of operating instructions detailing the location and means of turning on and off the major pieces of equipment shall be

---

the walls of the clean room or mounted adjacent to walkways above the clean room, they should be of metal to prevent external damage.

[37] A push-button switch can be located adjacent to each wall inlet. Pilot lights are sometimes used to indicate that the pump is in operation. In some makes of vacuum cleaners, the low-voltage switch is a part of the inlet and is actuated by inserting the vacuum cleaner hose end member into the inlet.

[38] A particle counter should be justified by the designing activity on its planned use. Experience has shown that the contamination levels of these rooms do not change from day to day or even from year to year. Unless the filter bank is seriously disturbed or a highly contaminating operation (which should be obvious to supervisors) is brought into the room, the room contamination level will remain close to the characteristics of the HEPA filters. If clean room certification services can be obtained in which an experienced technician monitors all desired points, such services and procurement of them should be considered at this point.

[39] Knee-length smocks and caps are sufficient for use in laminar-flow clean rooms. Full-length garments, hoods, and booties may be required in conventional clean rooms. The use of smocks and caps in laminar-flow clean rooms is valuable from two standpoints—to help prevent clothing lint, hair, skin flakes, etc., from entering the clean room atmosphere, and for psychological reasons to inspire workers to clean work habits.

mounted on an exterior wall of the enclosure under a suitable protective cover.

12.0 *Warranty*

12.1 The contractor shall warrant that the quality of the workmanship, materials, design, and construction of the enclosure and its associated systems are such that, if operated and maintained in accordance with the manual supplied by the contractor, it will meet all contract specifications including the acceptance tests for a period of 1 year from date of final acceptance. This warranty shall not apply to replaceable items such as fuses, filters, and lamp bulbs, or to loss of refrigerant.

12.2 In the event the enclosure or its associated air-conditioning, lighting, or vacuum cleaning systems fails to meet any specification or test during the warranty period, the contractor shall, within 2 weeks after receipt of notice from the procuring activity of such failure, determine the nature of such failure and take steps to correct the condition at no expense to the procuring activity.

12.3 This warranty provision is in addition to the other provisions of the contract and does not in any way limit or restrict the procuring activity's rights under the inspection clause or any other provision of this contract of other legal remedy.

13.0 *Performance Tests for Laminar-Flow Clean Rooms*

The following performance tests are incorporated in these specifications. These tests shall be run with instruments of an approved nature which shall show evidence of having been recently calibrated. Test instruments shall be provided by the contractor as indicated. Tests shall be run at the contractor's expense and witnessed by a designated member of the owner. Certificate of Performance showing results of the tests shall be furnished by the contractor on acceptance of the clean room.

13.1 Temperature variation over a 24-hour period. This test shall be conducted with a chart-type recorder which has been recently calibrated. The charts for the period of the tests shall become a part of the permanent record of the tests run at the time that the clean room is accepted from the contractor. Results shall show conformity with Section 7.5.5 of this specification.

13.2 Relative humidity. A standard sling-type psychrometer shall be used for this test, and readings should be taken over a half-hour period, both outside the clean room and inside the clean room. The readings shall be recorded until they level out and show consistency, and results shall be within Section 7.5.6 of this specification.

13.3 Positive internal static pressure. This is a function of the air tightness of the room, and any guarantee as to the performance of this test shall be conditional upon a proper evaporator coil fan performance from the air-conditioning contractor, proper installation of gravity dampers, and proper installation of weatherstripping as specified herein. Positive internal static pressure shall be evidenced by an approved type of static pressure gauge. The sensing element of this gauge shall be introduced into the main enclosure under the wiper strip of the entrance door. Result shall show conformity with Section 7.5.9 of this specification.

13.4 Rate of air flow of the laminar-flow air-handling system. This test shall be run across the width and height of the clean room at the supply wall, midway down the clean room, and at the return wall, to determine the rate of flow of the laminar-flow air-handling system. Properly calibrated velocity meters having a range suitable for the rates of flow concerned shall be used in making this test. Results shall show conformity with Section 6.1.4 of this specification.

13.5 Airborne particle count within the room. This test shall be conducted with a light-scattering type of instrument in accordance with the recommendations of the manufacturer of this equipment.[40] Results shall show conformity with Section 6.4 of this specification.

---

[40] Tests made with the light-scattering type of particle counter can be run by using the services of the manufacturer of this type of equipment on a per diem basis. Results of this test shall indicate performance of the clean room within Class 100 of Federal Standard No. 209 as measured at any point within the first air areas of the clean room. Dust counts taken when the room is placed in operation will be dependent on proper work habits and observance of clean room operating techniques as called

13.6 Foot-candles of illumination. This test shall be conducted with a light meter calibrated in foot-candles. Results of this test shall show the illumination at bench level to be equal to or above the minimum specified in Section 7.5.3 of this specification.[41]

13.7 Operating amperage and voltage in the electrical system. This test shall be run with a recently calibrated tong-type ammeter to demonstrate that the equipment is operating at the voltages recommended by the manufacturer of the air-conditioning equipment.[42]

14.0 *Cleanup*

Contractor shall maintain construction site in a clean and orderly condition and shall remove all trash from the premises prior to acceptance of the work.

15.0 *Work by Others*

The following items of work will be performed by others and are outside the scope of this contract:

15.1 All clearing of site prior to commencement of work.

15.2 Any alterations to existing site necessary to accommodate the clean room and its associated components.

15.3 Wiring of electric current to line side of electrical panels.

15.4 Plumbing, including all necessary traps, drain lines, and pumps as needed, between sewer and drain fitting of drain pan below evaporator coil of air-conditioning unit and of humidifier if any.

15.5 Ducting of cooling air to and waste heat from air-conditioning unit as required.

15.6 Connection to supply side of stub-outs through clean room wall of such items as compressed air, gas, water or other services.

16.0 *Fire Protection System* (Optional)

16.1 A manual-reset D.P.D.T. shall be furnished with the air-conditioning system. Firestat shall be located with sensitive element downstream of the evaporator-coil. When the temperature rises to a point above 125°F, one set of contacts shall open and disconnect the blower and reheat circuits while the other set of contacts shall close. The procuring activity will connect the other set of contacts provided in the D.P.D.T. to fire alarm.

16.2 The clean room shall be provided with an automatic fire protection system of the water type, complete from sprinkler heads within the enclosure to manual O.S. & Y. shutoff valve located on the roof of the enclosure in a location as shown on procuring activity's drawing No. ________. Sprinkler heads within the enclosure shall be of the flush type.

Air-Conditioning Calculations

It is recognized that, during the process of preparing a specification for the design and construction of a clean room, air-conditioning cooling loads must be determined. In an effort to assist those persons charged with this responsibility, ARI Standard 2-20 is reprinted here. It is suggested that this standard be read completely, several times before air-conditioning calculations are performed, in order that all factors to be considered in the calculations are properly evaluated. Particular attention should be paid to Section 2, Estimate Form, subheading "Other Heat Sources To Be Inserted at B." Improper evaluation of other heat sources can cause serious errors in these calculations. The result of these errors will be an incorrect estimate of required air-conditioning cooling load or tonnage.

---

out by applicable parts cleaning specifications. When proper operating techniques are employed, laminar-flow clean rooms should in all cases exceed Class 100,000 of Federal Standard No. 209 (which is equal to the Air Force standard clean room, USAF Technical Order 00-25-203, July 1, 1963).

[41] The design specification should state a minimum initial illumination level higher than the illumination level that is desired to be maintained, since the system will degenerate to a certain extent in the early stages of operation. The amount of this decline in light efficiency can be determined in advance and allowed for in accordance with the recommendations of the manufacturer of the lighting fixtures.

[42] This clause will protect the owner against possible overloading of the equipment.

[43] Courtesy of Air-Conditioning and Refrigeration Institute.

ARI STANDARD 2-20[43]

COOLING LOAD ESTIMATE FORM FOR SINGLE-PACKAGE AIR-CONDITIONERS

Section 1. Instructions

1.10 At the bottom of this page are spaces for inserting the summer outside design temperatures. These may be obtained for the principal cities of the United States by referring to the *Heating, Ventilating, Air Conditioning Guide*, published by The American Society of Heating and Ventilating Engineers. Generally, the one design temperature will be adequate to cover the locality handled by any one salesman.

1.20 Insert the information called for in the six job identification lines at the top of the Estimate Form.

1.30 The following numbered paragraphs refer to the item numbers of the Estimate Form:

1. Insert the number of persons to normally occupy the space after the air-conditioning is installed. If all the people are engaged in the same activity, the number should be placed on the proper line. If some are more actively engaged than others, the total number would be properly divided on the two lines. If it is a space which would be occupied by a large number of people for only a few minutes' duration and then a smaller number for the remaining time, use the largest number which would be present for approximately 15 minutes' duration.
2. Insert the maximum total square feet of window area on any one wall of the space exposed to direct sunshine. Refer to Table A and select the proper factor which must be inserted in space indicated. If all of the windows are on the north wall or on a wall shaded completely from the sun by an adjacent building, no figure will appear in this item.
3. Insert the total number of watts in use, not including the watts consumed by appliances listed in Table B. Lights in store showcases contribute heavily to the load and must not be neglected.
4. Use Table B for calculating the heat load due to gas and electrical appliances and motor-driven apparatus. Insert the total in the space indicated in Item 4.
5. After checking the extensions of the first four items, add them and carry this sub-total to space at right.
6. Insert the total square feet of windows not included in Item 2. In Table C select the factor for these windows under the design outside dry-bulb temperature previously established. Insert this factor in space indicated in Item 6.
7. Three lines are provided in this item, as it is quite possible that several wall constructions may be used on a particular space. In each case subtract the area of the windows from the total net wall or partition area. In Table C select the proper wall or partition factors shown under the design temperature already established. Insert these factors on the proper lines at the spaces indicated in Item 7.
8. Insert the total square feet of floor area. Refer to Table C for the factor to be inserted in the space indicated.
9. Insert the total square feet of ceiling area. Refer to Table C for the factor which fits the conditions of the building. Adjust this factor if ceiling is insulated and insert the factor or adjusted factor in space indicated.
10. Use Table D for calculating the ventilation or infiltration cfm. The total number of occupants must equal the number used in Item 1. The infiltration does not include the cfm which will enter the space if doors or windows are permitted to remain open. Insert the cfm in space provided.
    Refer to Table E and select the factor shown under the design outside wet-bulb temperature previously established. Insert this factor in space indicated.
11. After checking the extensions of Items 6 through 10, add them and carry this sub-total to space at right.
12. Add sub-totals, Items 5 and 11. This total is the Btu per hour cooling load. An air-conditioner with capacity equal to or greater than this load must be selected to obtain comfort conditions within the space.

LOCAL SUMMER OUTSIDE DESIGN TEMPERATURES

For City of ______________________ **Dry Bulb** ______F **Wet Bulb** ______F

For Table C use factors under temperature encircled.	**Outside Dry Bulb, F 86 87 88 89 90 91 92 93 94 95 96 97 98 99 100 101 102 103 104**
For Table E use factors under temperature encircled.	**Outside Wet Bulb, F 64 65 66 67 68 69 70 71 72 73 74 75 76 77 78 79 80**

[43] Courtesy of Air-Conditioning and Refrigeration Institute.

COOLING LOAD ESTIMATE FORM FOR SINGLE-PACKAGE AIR-CONDITIONERS[43]

Section 2. Estimate Form

This estimate is suitable for comfort air-conditioning jobs not requiring specific conditions of temperature and humidity.

Customer .... Buyer ....
Address .... Space to be used for ....
Estimate by .... Date .... Approval .... Date ....

1. People .... (Number Sitting or Moving Slowly) .... × 400 = ...
   .... (Number Working, Dancing, or Similar Activity) .... × 660 = ...
2. Windows Exposed to Sun .... (Total Sq Ft) .... × .... **A** = ...
   (Figure this item for the one sun exposure having largest window area.)
3. Lights and Electrical Appliances .... (Total Watts in Use) .... × 3.4 = ...
   (Include in this item only those appliances not listed in Table B.)
4. Other Heat Sources .... **B** = ...
5. Sub-Total—Sum of Items 1 through 4 .... = ——→ ....
6. Windows Not Included in Item 2 .... (Total Sq Ft) .... × .... **C** = ...
7. Walls and Partitions .... Sq Ft—Windows .... Sq Ft = ... × .... **C** = ...
   .... Sq Ft—Windows .... Sq Ft = ... × .... **C** = ...
   .... Sq Ft—Windows .... Sq Ft = ... × .... **C** = ...
8. Floor .... (Total Sq Ft) .... × .... **C** = ...
9. Ceiling .... (Total Sq Ft) .... × .... **C** = ...
10. Ventilation or Infiltration .... (CFM) .... **D** × .... **E** = ————
11. Sub-Total—Sum of Items 6 through 10 .... = ——→ ....
12. Total Btu per Hour Cooling Load to be Used for Selection of Unit—Sum of Items 5 and 11 .... = ————

COOLING LOAD FACTORS

WINDOWS EXPOSED TO SUN-SOLAR RADIATION FACTORS FOR DIFFERENT ORIENTATIONS TO BE INSERTED AT A

Direction Windows Face	NE	E	SE	S	SW	W	NW
Clear Glass (Single or Double) No Protection	110	180	160	105	160	180	110
Shaded Completely by Awnings	30	50	45	30	45	50	30
Light-Colored Inside Shades or Venetian Blinds	65	110	95	60	95	110	65
Glass Brick, No Protection	44	72	64	42	64	72	44

OTHER HEAT SOURCES TO BE INSERTED AT B

		Factor	
Beauty Parlors	Number of Operators	× 2000	= ....
Electric Motors	Total Nameplate HP	× 2800	= ....
† Gas Burners	Number	× 6000	= ....
† Glass Coffee Makers	Number	× 900	= ....
† Coffee Urns—Gas or Electric	Coffee Capacity in Gallons	× 1400	= ....
† Steam Tables—Electric	Sq Ft Area of Top	× 550	= ....
† Steam Tables—Gas	Sq Ft Area of Top	× 1300	= ....
Additional Heat Sources		Btu/Hr	= ————

† Factors for appliances equipped with hood and positive exhaust should be reduced by 50%. Insert Total at **B** ....

WINDOWS, WALLS, FLOORS, AND CEILING TRANSMISSION FACTORS FOR VARIOUS OUTSIDE DESIGN TEMPERATURES—INSERT AT C

Outside Dry Bulb, °F	86	87	88	89	90	91	92	93	94	95	96	97	98	99	100	101	102	103	104
Windows (No Sun)	8	9	10	11	12	13	14	15	16	17	18	19	20	21	22	23	24	25	26
Walls—Heavy Masonry	2	3	3	3	3	4	4	4	4	5	5	5	5	6	6	6	6	6	7
Walls—Average Masonry	3	3	3	3	4	4	4	4	5	5	5	6	6	6	6	7	7	7	7
Walls—Insulated Masonry or Frame	1	2	2	2	2	2	3	3	3	3	3	3	4	4	4	4	4	4	5
Walls—Average Frame	2	3	3	3	4	4	4	4	5	5	5	5	6	6	6	6	7	7	7
Partition—Inside, Single Thickness	5	5	6	7	7	8	8	8	9	10	10	11	11	12	12	13	14	14	15
Partition—Inside, Double Thickness	3	3	3	4	4	4	4	5	5	5	6	6	6	6	7	7	7	8	8
Partition—Display Window Back	11	12	13	13	14	14	15	15	16	17	17	17	18	19	19	19	20	21	21
Glass Brick (No Sun Exposure)	4	4	5	5	5	6	6	7	7	8	8	8	9	9	10	10	10	11	11
Floor	2	2	2	2	3	3	3	3	3	4	4	4	4	4	5	5	5	5	5
Ceiling under Unventilated Attic*	11	11	11	12	12	12	12	13	13	13	13	14	14	14	15	15	15	15	16
Ceiling under Ventilated Attic*	7	7	8	8	9	9	10	10	10	11	11	12	12	13	13	14	14	14	15
Ceiling under Flat Roof*	13	13	14	14	14	15	15	15	16	16	16	17	17	17	18	18	18	19	19
Ceiling under Occupied Floor*	2	3	3	3	3	3	4	4	4	5	5	5	5	6	6	6	6	7	7

* Adjust factor selected from this table if ceiling is insulated. Example: 4″ Insulation—0.2 × Selected Factor = Adjusted Factor.
1″ Insulation—0.4 × .... = ..., 2″ Insulation—0.3 × .... = ..., 4″ Insulation—0.2 × .... = ...

VENTILATION OR INFILTRATION QUANTITY TO BE INSERTED AT D

Calculate requirements for both ventilation and infiltration, and use larger quantity cu ft per minute (CFM). Use no less cfm than required by local ordinance, and no less than amount drawn from space by exhaust fans, if used.

VENTILATION REQUIREMENTS

Smoking	No. Occupants		CFM
None	....	× 7½	= ....
Light	....	× 15	= ....
Heavy	....	× 40	= ....

INFILTRATION

(H) = Room Height, (L) = Length, (W) = Width, (G) = Wall Factor
Room with one outside wall, (G) = 1
Two outside walls, (G) = 1.5
Three or more outside walls, (G) = 2

$$\text{CFM} = \frac{(H)\ldots \times (L)\ldots \times (W)\ldots \times (G)\ldots}{60} = \ldots$$

VENTILATION OR INFILTRATION FACTOR FOR VARIOUS OUTSIDE DESIGN TEMPERATURES IN °F WB TO BE INSERTED AT E

Outside Wet Bulb, °F	64	65	66	67	68	69	70	71	72	73	74	75	76	77	78	79	80
Factor	0	1	3	5	8	11	14	17	20	23	27	30	33	37	41	45	49

* Courtesy of Air-Conditioning and Refrigeration Institute.

REFERENCES

1. Austin, 1/Lt. P. R. *Size Distribution Relationships for Airborne Particulate Matter*, Report 17.0002.04.01 Olmsted AFB, Pa.: MAMES, April 1963.

2. Timmerman, S. W., and Austin, 1/Lt. P. R. *Investigation of Cross-Flow Clean Room Characteristics*. Report 17.0006.16.03. Olmsted AFB, Pa.: MAMES, October 1963.

3. Whitfield, W. J. "State of the Art (Contamination Control) and Laminar Air-Flow Concept." *Conference on Clean Room Specifications*, SCR-652. Office of Technical Services, Department of Commerce, Washington, D. C., May 1963.

4. Timmerman, S. W., and Austin, 1/Lt. P. R. *Laminar Air-Flow Concept for Clean Room Construction*. Report 17.0004.16.01. Olmsted AFB, Pa.: MAMES, July 1963.

5. Timmerman, S. W., and Austin, 1/Lt. P. R. *Potential Heat Loading Problems with Cross-Flow Clean Rooms*. Report 17.0008.16.04. Olmsted AFB, Pa.: MAMES, October 1963.

6. Timmerman, S. W., and Austin, 1/Lt. P. R. *Twin Cross-Flow Design for Clean Room Construction*. Report 17.0004.16.02. Olmsted AFB, Pa.: MAMES, August 1963.

7. Marsh, R. C. "Adaptability of Laminar Air-Flow for Contamination Control." *Conference on Clean Room Specifications*, SCR 652. Office of Technical Services, Department of Commerce, Washington, D. C., May 1963.

8. Agnew, B. *Laminar/Flow Clean Room Handbook*. Garden Grove, Calif.: Agnew-Higgins, Inc., 1963.

Chapter 8. *Laminar-Flow Clean Room Operation*

Introduction

Laminar-flow rooms will solve the problem of airborne contamination, but they will not prevent contact and transfer contamination. No clean room can prevent this. The prevention of contact and transfer contamination is the result of garmenting (including hand and finger covers) and worker disciplines.

With laminar flow it is possible to achieve cleanliness levels that approach the cleanliness level immediately downstream of a HEPA filter. This is especially true in a down-flow room. In a cross-flow room the level achieved in any specific location is dependent on the upstream particle generation. In many cases laminar-flow rooms, especially those of the cross-flow type, will be utilized for airborne contamination protection of components that will not be affected by a cleanliness level several orders of magnitude *dirtier* than the room is achieving. In these cases, because of the wide margin of protection it will be possible to dispense with some of the operational formalities usually associated with clean rooms. Smocks may be used rather than a full suit-up, and in most cases air showers will not be needed. In some cases no protective clothing other than a cap will be needed. The most important result of the elimination of these formalities is the saving of entry time. Time previously used for entry and exit procedures can be converted to production work. In addition, garment cost will be eliminated or considerably reduced. An estimate of these costs is shown in the following breakdown which was considered to be representative of the Air Force clean rooms. Considerable variation could exist from room to room; however, the following times and cost calculations indicated the savings that can be achieved by using a laminar-flow room with minimum personnel suit-up, etc.

LOST TIME – PERSONNEL DECONTAMINATION AND ROBING[1]

Enter clean room from locker area

Travel time from doorway to shoe cleaner operation	4 seconds
Average delay time because shoe cleaner is in operation	20 seconds
Right shoe cleaning	10 seconds
Change of feet	3 seconds
Left shoe cleaning	10 seconds
Lost time because of conversation	20 seconds
Step from shoe cleaner	2 seconds
Walk from shoe cleaner to door of washroom	4 seconds
Open door	3 seconds
Walk from door to basin	4 seconds
Establish water temperature	7 seconds
Wash hands	60 seconds
Lost time because of conversation	60 seconds
Wash face	30 seconds
Dry hands and face	45 seconds
Walk from basin to door	4 seconds
Open door	3 seconds
Walk to clothes rack or locker	4 seconds

[1] MAMES, Olmsted Air Force Base, Pennsylvania.

Open locker, remove garment from storage	5 seconds
Open garment package and take out garment	10 seconds
Visually check garment	6 seconds
Put on garment	10 seconds
Lost time because of conversation	60 seconds
Check cap	3 seconds
Put on cap	4 seconds
Dispose of garment bag and close locker, etc.	10 seconds
Walk to air shower	4 seconds
Average delay time because shower is in operation	12 seconds
Open air shower door	3 seconds
Remain in air shower	20 seconds
Open air shower door	3 seconds
Enter clean room	
	443 seconds

Exit clean room

Walk from clean room door to clothes rack	4 seconds
Take off garment	7 seconds
Hang up garment	7 seconds
Lost time because of conversation	30 seconds
Take off hat	3 seconds
Hang up hat	3 seconds
Walk to door	4 seconds
Open door	3 seconds
	61 seconds

Total lost time for entering and exiting clean rooms is approximately 8½ minutes.

Daily schedule for entering and exiting clean room

ENTER	EXIT
Beginning of shift	Coffee break
Return from coffee break	To use toilets
From using toilets	Lunch
Return from lunch	To look at T.O., obtain instructions, etc.
Return from looking at T.O.	Coffee break
Return from coffee break	End of shift

An average of six trips in and out of the clean room per person per day amounts to 8½ minutes $\times$ 6 = 51 minutes of lost time per day. At $3 per hour, this amounts to approximately $665 per year per person.

LOST TIME – PERSONNEL CLEAN ROOM CONTROLS

Wiping off bench top each time employee returns to work from outside clean room (six times); 2 minutes each wiping	12 minutes
Inhibited personnel actions during work to prevent contamination of the product. This varies from 30 to 60 minutes	35 minutes
Writing precautions to prevent contamination of the room	10 minutes
Controls necessary in supervisor-personnel instructions	15 minutes
	72 minutes

Total lost time is approximately 1 hour 12 minutes. At $3 per hour, this amounts to approximately $935 per year per person. To provide garments for one person for one year costs $100.

OPERATIONAL COST COMPARISON

	STANDARD CLEAN ROOM	LAMINAR-FLOW CLEAN ROOM[2]
Lost time – personnel decontamination	$665/year/person	0
Lost time – clean room controls	$935/year/person	0
Garment rental costs	$100/year/person	0
Total cost	$1600/year/person	0

The result of this relaxing of controls may have a detrimental effect on the employees' mental attitude. (See Psychological Benefits, Chapter 6.) Supervisors must be aware of this effect. Remember, laminar-flow rooms do not solve all contamination problems. They only allow us to concentrate on those problems previously masked by airborne contaminant problems.

[2] For this comparison, no garments were to be used in the Laminar-flow room.

Down-Flow Room Operation

The operating procedures necessary to ensure adequate airborne contamination control are almost nonexistent in a down-flow room. As has been discussed in Chapter 7, the down-flowing air isolates every operation in the room by a curtain of air streamlines. The design of the room precludes worker control except where he would interfere with the air flow to the critical item or where he would induce contaminants into the air flow over the critical item. Head covers, smocks, and hand or finger covers may be necessary if extremely critical items are being overhauled. The use of shoe cleaners, tacky mats, or air showers will not be necessary.

The prefilters directly under the flooring grille will be an important maintenance item. Vacuuming should be done weekly if prefilters are the washable type. Washing should be a quarterly operation. There is no substitute for experience, however. The optimum cleaning cycle may be determined by observing the loading of the filters. Throwaway filters may be changed in accordance with manufacturers' recommendations. If desired, both types of filters may be equipped with a sensor to "announce" when the dirt has caused a predetermined pressure drop. This would indicate that action such as cleaning or changing filters is necessary. A similar device may be installed on the HEPA filter bank.

In a down-flow clean room everything below the bench level should be considered contaminated. Although this is not true in every case, it is a good rule to follow. Horizontal flat areas (bench tops)

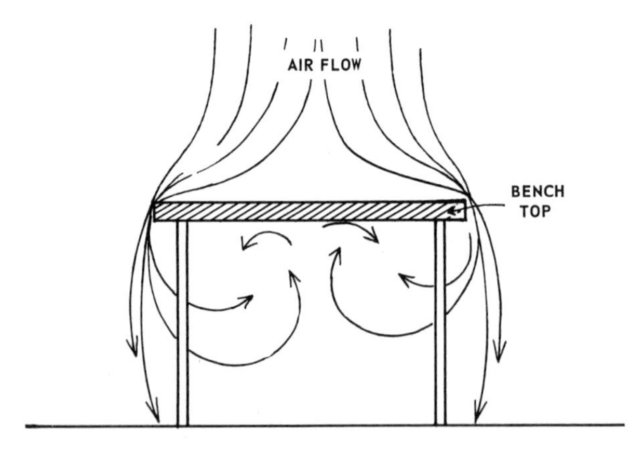

FIGURE 8-1. Air flow around an open bench in a down-flow clean room.

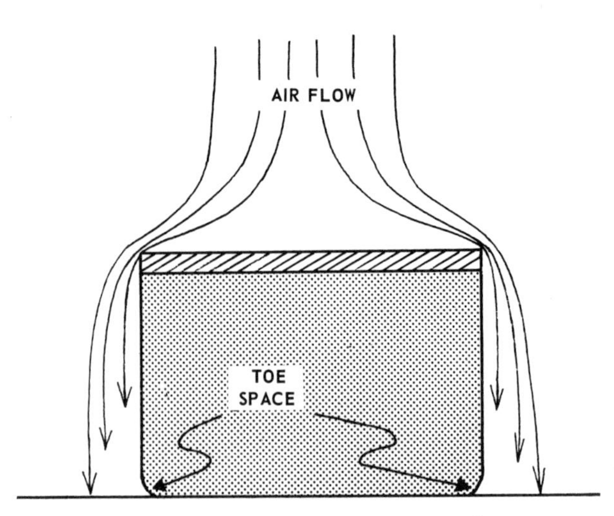

FIGURE 8-2. Air flow around a closed bench in a down-flow clean room.

with an exposed underside will allow turbulent conditions to exist below the exposed surface. (See Figure 8-1.) This will not be a source of contamination; however, it will be possible to have a collection of contamination there while a contaminant-generating operation is taking place above. When the generation is stopped, the turbulence still exists, but it is clean turbulence and of no significance. Since some down-flow rooms will be utilized for extremely critical components, this situation may be eliminated by enclosing the bench to the floor. (See Figure 8-2.)

Cross-Flow Room Operation

Since the maximum cleanliness level achieved by a cross-flow room is not always necessary, the operational techniques can be varied to meet the requirements. As has been discussed previously, the level of cleanliness at any given location in a cross-flow room is dependent on the contamination generated upstream of the location. Use of a cross-flow room to ensure a contamination level several orders of magnitude greater than that produced by a HEPA filter allows the operators to take some liberties with operational controls. If, however, the capacity of the cross-flow room must be fully utilized, then it will be necessary to protect downstream areas from as much contamination as possible. This can be accomplished by using techniques discussed in Conventional Clean Room Operation, Chapter 6, and by donning complete clean room garments including shoe covers and hoods. At this point, it would probably be more advantageous to utilize the down-flow principle for ultimate cleanliness.

The portion of the cross-flow room in the "first-pass air" (adjacent to the filters) will be as clean a work area as possible. The most critical work should be accomplished here. The next most critical work should be next downstream, etc. Any contaminant-generating operations necessary in the clean room should be accomplished at the room exit. If toxic vapor is involved, it should be kept out of the recirculating air stream by a localized exhaust system. The cleaning room at the AiResearch Division of the Garrett Corporation discussed in the previous chapter was utilized entirely for cleaning operations. The room exit air was not recirculated. Paper work may also be accomplished at the "exit" end of the room.

Room entry should be accomplished at the "exit" end of the room. Walking adjacent to the air exit wall will allow any loose particulate matter carried in from a contaminated area to be exhausted without degrading the room. Heavy particulate matter that falls out and is not carried out with the air flow will settle to the floor. This action will occur throughout the room. Activity, such as walking, will reintroduce the floor contaminants into the air stream. The heavier particles will immediately fall out because of their weight. Ground-up smaller particles will be carried out in the air flow adjacent to the floor. The horizontal stratification of the air will thus protect the working area of the room from this reintroduced particulate matter. So that the floor will not become a problem, it is recommended that it be cleaned with a mild detergent and water at least once per week. The frequency of cleaning depends on the room population. This cleaning should be done when the room is not in operation. Other periodic cleaning, such as walls, ceilings, and lights, should be done as needed and in a similar manner. Once or twice a year would be adequate in most cases.

The most important maintenance operation in a cross-flow clean room is the cleaning or changing (depending on the type of filter) of the prefilters. Here again the schedule must be determined by filter loading. A good starting point is four times a year. HEPA filters should be changed when the

FIGURE 8-3. Darkened cross-flow clean-room smoke tests at General Dynamics, Pomona, Calif., showing undisturbed flow. *Courtesy General Dynamics Corp.*

pressure across them increases by 1.0 inch (water gauge). One cross-flow room operator estimates that his HEPA filters will last eight years. This shows the advantage of good prefilters and good maintenance of the prefilters. This room, incidentally, was in operation for over a year and was run 24 hours a day when the estimate was made.

Cross-flow room equipment should be as streamlined as possible to allow smooth passage of air around it. Workbenches should allow air to pass under them if possible. For some layouts, staggering work stations perpendicular to the flow will yield another row of "first-pass" work stations and will also tend to limit contamination build-up from filter end to exit.

Figure 8-3 shows the General Dynamics cross-flow clean room darkened. There are two lights in the picture—one on the right and one on the left. They are pointing at each other. The man on the right has a smoke generator similar to that shown later in Figure 13-2 with the additional feature of being operated by a small aquarium pump. The smoke illuminated by the lights can be seen following the streamlines out of the room. Since the smoke generator introduces the smoke at a high velocity and not in a fine jet, a number of streamlines are affected and carry the smoke. In addition, the individual was not able to hold the unit steady enough to prevent some scattering. In spite of this, the flow is contained well. Note that the beam from the lights cannot be seen except where it shines on the smoke. If much dust were present, the light beam could be seen. This is a striking demonstration. A light beam cannot be seen in a laminar-flow room. The object it illuminates will of course be seen, but the beam itself is invisible. Figure 8-4 shows how an object in the path of contaminants caused them to flow around the object and re-form downstream. There is some breaking up of the smoke, but the expanded contaminant-laden area continued to move toward the exit. When the smoke generation was stopped, the air downstream cleaned up in a few seconds.

The AiResearch Division of the Garrett Corporation performed a unique test by shutting off the air flow in its large (40 by 80-foot) cross-flow room and releasing a smoke bomb. When the room was completely full of smoke and generation had ceased, the air flow was turned on. It took 20 seconds to effectively purge the room. Complete (absolutely no trace of smoke) purging took 57 seconds. When the time it takes to bring the blowers up to speed and the time required to overcome the inertia of the air in the entire system are considered, this is an amazing demonstration. Operational recovery is so fast that a smoke bomb would look like a "dud." The smoke is carried off as quickly as it is generated. This is the secret to the success of the cross-flow room. It is the reason that low levels of contamination are reached at the "exit" end of the room.

Cross-Flow Clean Room Contamination Levels[3]

In September 1963, a study was undertaken by MAMES, Olmsted Air Force Base, Pennsylvania, to investigate and determine the characteristics of existing cross-flow clean rooms. There has been much discussion concerning the variation in contamination level and the ability of these rooms to handle heat loads. In order to resolve these questions, experiments were performed in the cross-flow clean room and the decontamination room of the AiResearch Division of the Garrett Corporation, the cross-flow clean room of General Dynamics Corporation, and the cross-flow clean room of the Lockheed Missiles and Space Company.

FIGURE 8-4. Disturbed air-flow tests show smoke separation and formation around objects in the air stream. *Courtesy General Dynamics Corp.*

[3] Abstracted from reference *1*.

A summary of construction features of these four facilities is given below:

1. *AiResearch Division, Garrett Corporation, Los Angeles, California:*

   Figure 7-39. Size 40 by 80 feet (3200 square feet)
   Construction features:
   a. New construction in existing building
   b. Plasterboard walls and ceiling
   c. Vinyl sheet flooring
   d. Cloth-covered walls and ceilings painted with epoxy paint
   e. Hung ceiling
   f. Air returned between ceilings
   g. Custom filter wall and blower system, with HEPA filters as the final filters
   Use: Assembly and test of Apollo environmental systems.

   Figure 7-45. Size 20 by 30 feet (600 square feet)
   Construction features:
   a. New construction in existing building
   b. Plasterboard walls and ceilings
   c. Grated floor with some vinyl sheet
   d. Cloth-covered walls and ceilings painted with epoxy paint
   e. Hung ceiling
   f. 100% fresh air
   g. Custom filter wall and blower system with HEPA filters as the final filters.
   Use: Decontamination and cleaning of parts.

2. *General Dynamics, Pomona, California:*

   Figure 7-29. Size 35 by 17 feet (595 square feet)
   Construction features:
   a. New construction in existing building
   b. Plasterboard walls and ceiling

c. Vinyl sheet flooring
d. High-quality enamel paint
e. Hung ceiling
f. Air returned between ceilings
g. Modular filter wall construction using HEPA filters as the final filters.

Use: Miniature gyro assembly and testing.

3. *Lockheed Missiles and Space Company, Van Nuys, California:*

Figure 7-31. Size 33 by 42 feet (1386 square feet)
Construction features:
a. Modification of existing room
b. One plywood wall added
c. Original asphalt tile flooring
d. High-quality enamel paint
e. Original hung ceiling
f. Ducted air return
g. Modular filter wall construction with HEPA filters as the final filters.

Use: Assembly and testing of rocket fuel transfer consoles.

The conclusions drawn from this investigation are listed as follows:

1. The operating contamination level of cross-flow clean rooms varies from end to end with up-stream activity. When maximum activity is taking place upstream, the dirtiest point in these rooms has a contamination level approaching that of the Air Force clean work station in operation.

2. The "at-rest" contamination level of cross-flow clean rooms is approximately equal to the Air Force clean work station at rest.

3. Cross-flow clean rooms control room contamination levels more effectively and efficiently than any existing Air Force conventional clean room.

4. Cross-flow clean rooms provide an even temperature and humidity distribution throughout their entirety. (Note excessive heat load problems as described in Cross-Flow Room Design, Chapter 7.)

5. Cross-flow clean rooms are recommended for Air Force clean room construction.

Before presenting the data taken during this investigation, it is important to emphasize several points again. Since laminar flow stratifies the air in the room, particle counts taken will represent the contamination in one streamline. If readings are to be taken to determine the contamination at the "downstream" end of the room, the counter probe must be placed in the affected streamlines.

Special attention was paid to the location of the monitoring instruments during each set of readings. When measuring downstream contamination during these tests, the counter was placed in the area where the most upstream activity (contamination) was taking place. In addition, a number of tests were made in which a large amount of contamination was created upstream of the counter. This was accomplished by an individual doing vigorous physical activity. Such activity would not normally be done in a clean room. Other tests were conducted which simulated worker actions.

Experimental Data

The following data are common to curves AR-1 through AR-16:

Date: 24 Sept. 1963

Place: Laminar cross-flow clean rooms, AiResearch Manufacturing Company, Division of Garrett Corporation, Torrance, Calif.

Persons Performing Tests: 1st Lt. Philip R. Austin, Clifford F. Frith, and Stewart W. Timmerman.

Instruments Used: All curves were obtained by a Royco particle counter, PC200A, operated by William Zinky and Jack Lawler of Royco Instruments, Palo Alto, Calif.

Temperature and Humidity

	Filter End of Room	*Middle of Room*	*Exit End of Room*
Dry-bulb temperature, °F	71	72½	72½
Wet-bulb temperature, °F	58	58½	58¾
Relative humidity, %	45	42	42

Clean Room Clothing Worn: Head coverings, foot coverings, plastic gloves, and smocks. (The visitors to this room wear smocks; however, the operating personnel wear coveralls of 100% nylon.)

Curve AR-1 (Figure 8-5)

Time: 1002 hours

Place: Cross-flow clean room (40 by 80 feet). The position monitored was 3 feet from the filter bank on the right side of the room as one faces the filter bank. The filter monitored is shown in Figure 7-37 as the third filter from the right wall and the second filter from the floor.

Sample Characteristics

Height of sample: 32 inches from floor

Length of sample: Each channel was sampled for 3 minutes.

Sample rate: 0.01 cfm

Multiplication factor: 33

Observations on Curve: Three readings were taken for this curve. All particles greater than 0.32, 0.50, and 1.0 micron were recorded. Only one count at 0.32 micron and one at 0.50 micron were recorded. No count was recorded for 1.0 micron and larger. The air at the monitoring point is essentially the same as when it enters the room through the HEPA filters.

Curve AR-2 (Figure 8-5)

Time: 1015 hours

Place: Equidistant from filter bank and room air exits on centerline of cross-flow clean room (40 by 80 feet).

Sample Characteristics: Same as for AR-1.

Observations on Curve: Three readings were taken for this curve. All particles greater than 0.32, 0.50, and 1.0 micron were recorded. No count was recorded for 1.0 micron and larger. During this test, two men were working direct-

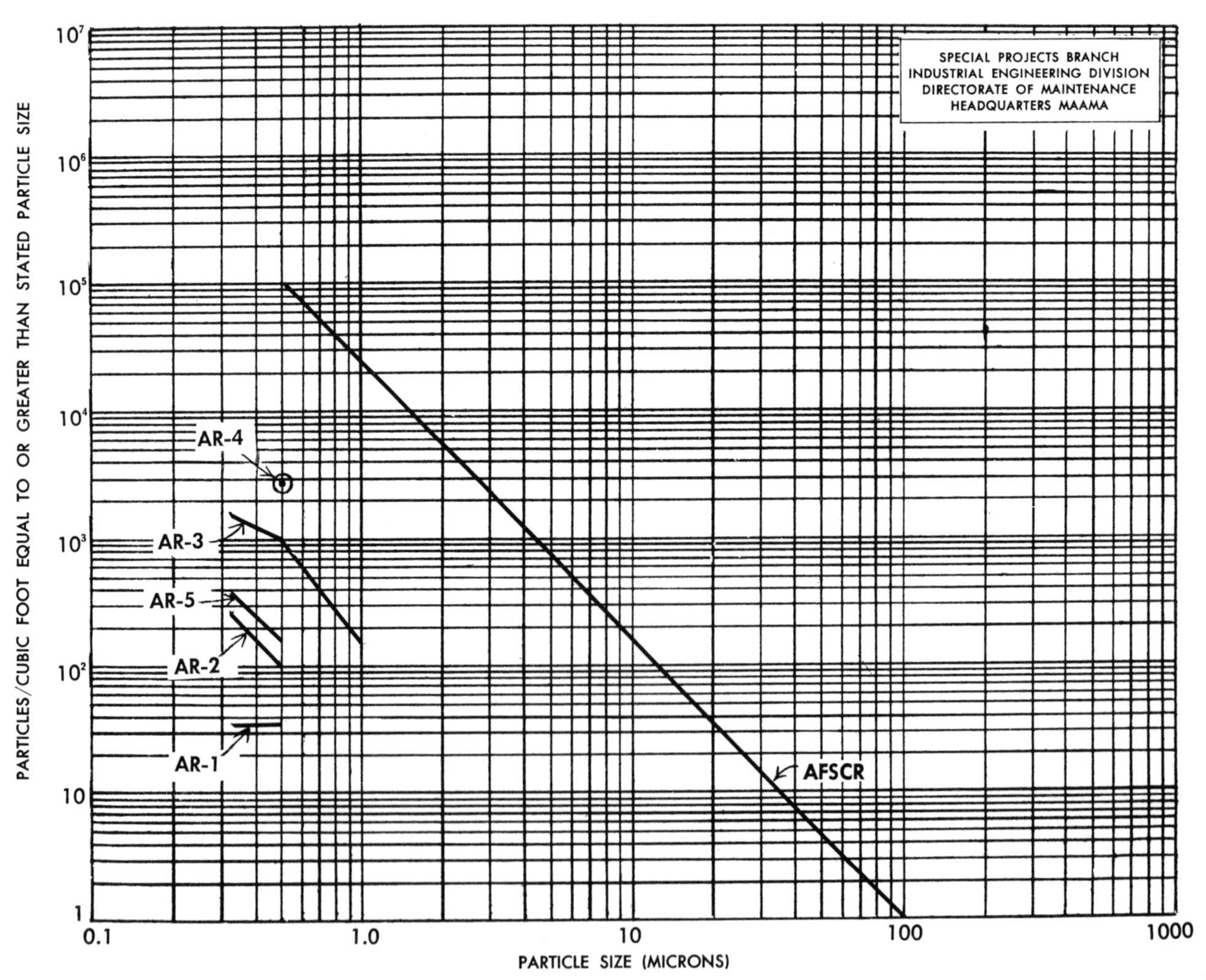

FIGURE 8-5.

ly upstream from the counter. The conditions existing during this sampling are equal to the Air Force standard clean work station (at-rest) limit. (See Figure 14-3.) Note that the slope of this curve is parallel to the AFSCR curve.

Curve AR-3 (Figure 8-5)

Time: 1030 hours

Place: Cross-flow clean room (40 by 80 feet) at a position equidistant from filter bank and room air exits, and in line with row of test stands on left side of room as one faces the filter bank. Upstream of this counter were a cryogenic 0_2 test stand and a high-pressure (5000-psi) test stand.

Sample Characteristics: Same as for AR-1

Observations on Curve: During this sampling, four men were performing their tasks at the test stands with intermediate movement to and from their work stations. Readings were obtained for all particles greater than 0.32, 0.50 and 1.0 micron. The conditions existing during this sampling are equal to the Air Force standard clean work station (operational) limit. The slope of this curve is essentially parallel to the AFSCR curve.

Curve AR-4 (Figure 8-5)

Time: 1040 hours

Place: Same as for AR-3

Sample Characteristics: Same as for AR-1

Observations on Curve: One reading was taken for this curve. The same personnel conditions existed during this test as for AR-3; however, a chair was turned over, the cushion was adjusted, and then it was moved away from the test stands. As noted by the plot in Figure 8-5, this action produced more contamination than when four men were working at the bench as shown in AR-3.

Curve AR-5 (Figure 8-5)

Time: 1045 hours

Place: End of cross-flow clean room (40 by 80 feet) at a position 7 feet from room air exits and on the same streamline as was monitored in AR-3 and AR-4.

Sample Characteristics: Same as for AR-1.

Observations on Curve: Upstream of the counter were a low-pressure test stand, a cryogenic 0_2 test stand, and a high-pressure (5000-psi) test stand. Seven people were directly upstream of the counter, working at these test stands and essentially in line with each other. They were also on the same streamline as was being monitored by the particle counter. There was little movement to and from each work station. Two channels were monitored for this curve. The results show that the conditions existing were slightly greater than those existing in an Air Force standard clean work station at rest. Note that the slope of this curve is also parallel to the AFSCR curve (Figure 14-3).

Curve AR-6 (Figure 8-6)

Time: 1055

Place: Cross-flow clean room (40 by 80 feet) at a position 5 feet from the room exit, approximately the center of the room.

Sample Characteristics

Height of sample: 32 inches from floor

Length of sample: 0.3 minute

Rate of sample: 0.01 cfm

Multiplication factor: 333

Observations on Curve: No personnel or particle generation operations were upstream during this test other than the test personnel. This test was performed to determine the magnitude of particles generated when a person stands up and sits down at his work place. A chair was placed 8 feet directly upstream from counter. Mr. S. W. Timmerman stood up, walked around the chair, and sat down twice during a 0.3-minute cycle. The value obtained during this test is less than the requirements for an Air Force standard clean work station in operation.

Curve AR-7 (Figure 8-6)

Time: 1057 hours

Place: Same as for AR-6

Sample Characteristics: Same as for AR-6

Observation on Curve: The same type of test was performed for this reading as for AR-6. Roger Arrowsmith of AiResearch stood up, walked around a chair, and sat down twice.

The chair was placed 6 feet in front of the counter, rather than 8 feet as in the previous test. The value obtained during this test was less than that for an Air Force standard clean work station in operation.

Curve AR-8 (Figure 8-6)

Time: 1059 hours
Place: Same as for AR-6
Sample Characteristics: Same as for AR-6
Observations on Curve: Roger Arrowsmith was 6 feet upstream of counter. This experiment required the subject to clap his hands slowly at once per second, with his hands two feet apart in the extended position. The values obtained during this test were less than that required for an Air Force standard clean work station in operation.

Curve AR-9 (Figure 8-6)

Time: 1101 hours
Place: Same as for AR-6
Sample Characteristics: Same as for AR-6
Observations on Curve: Lt. P. R. Austin performed jumping-jacks 8 feet upstream from the counter. The jumping-jacks were performed for a period of 40 seconds in which two channels (0.32 micron and 1.0 micron) were moni-

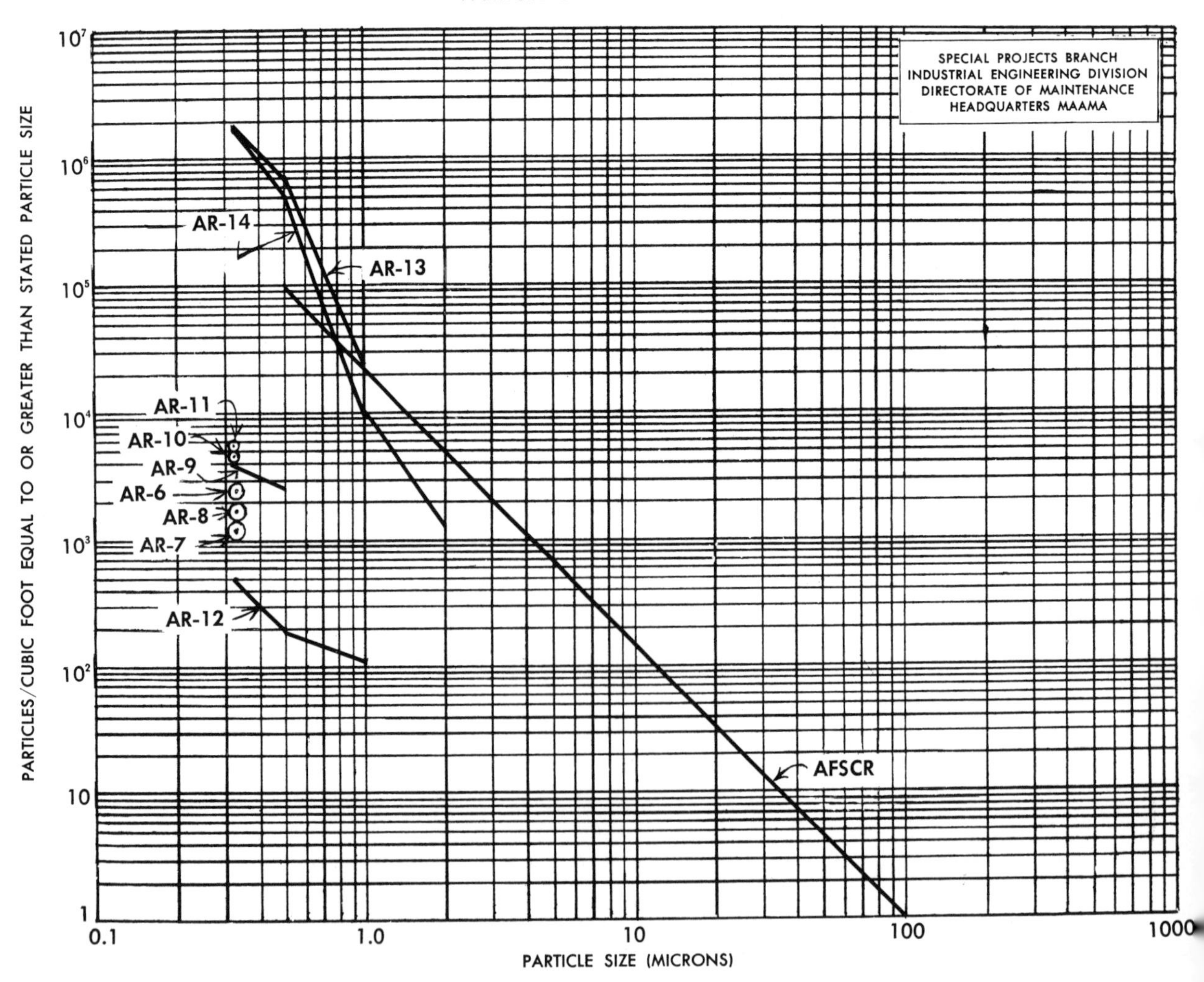

FIGURE 8-6.

tored. The contamination produced during these exercises was greater than requirements for an Air Force standard clean work station in operation, but less than the former Air Force Class IV requirement by a factor of 3. It should be noted that the contamination level produced by these exercises decreased as soon as the exercises ceased.

Curve AR-10 (*Figure 8-6*)
Time: 1104 hours
Place: Same as for AR-6
Sample Characteristics: Same as for AR-6
Observations on Curve: Lt. P. R. Austin stood 4 feet upstream of the counter and vigorously rubbed his clean room garments. The contamination level produced was slightly more than that for AR-9 (jumping-jacks). This indicates that the particles counted in AR-9 and AR-10 came predominantly from the clean room garments.

Curve AR-11 (*Figure 8-6*)
Time: 1106 hours
All conditions and observations the same as for AR-10.

Curve AR-12 (*Figure 8-6*)
Time: 1108 hours
Place: Cross-flow decontaminating room (20 by 30 feet). Counter was placed approximately in the center of the room. (See Figure 7-45.)
Sample Characteristics
Height of sample: 32 inches from floor
Length of sample: Each channel was sampled for 1 minute.
Rate of sample: 0.01 cfm
Multiplication factor: 100
Observations on Curve: Three readings were taken for this curve. All particles greater than 0.32, 0.50, and 1.0 micron were recorded. Three persons were working upstream at normal task. The values received during this test are less than those required for an Air Force standard clean work station in operation. Note that this curve is essentially parallel to the AFSCR curve.

Curve AR-13 (*Figure 8-6*)
Time: 1120 hours
Place: At the exit of a clean room tunnel approximately 6 feet wide by 12 feet long by 8 feet high. The air from this tunnel dumped directly into the general building work area. Two HEPA filters (4 by 2 feet each) were placed at one end of the tunnel. The air passed directly over a fluid test stand.
Sample Characteristics: Same as for AR-12
Observations on Curve: The air existing from the filters across the bench provided a clean work area in the proximity of the filters. The air exiting from this tunnel showed a high contamination level, however, as is shown in this curve. The filters covered only a portion of the rear wall. These filters were flush with the ceiling and one side of the tunnel wall. In this type of configuration, aspiration of dirty air into the filtered air stream will take place. It is believed that air was being drawn in from floor level into the clean air stream and then being blown over the bench to the exit of the tunnel. As a result, the contamination level of this room exceeded AFSCR curve.

Curve AR-14 (*Figure 8-6*)
Time: 1130 hours
Place: At the exit of a clean room tunnel approximately 10 feet wide by 20 feet long and 8 feet high. This tunnel was approximately 40 feet from the tunnel of AR-13. Two groups of two filters (4 by 2 feet each) were installed at one end of this tunnel. Each of the two groups of filters was divided by a 1-foot glass pane in the center of the rear wall. Each group of filters was flush with the ceiling and tunnel wall. On one side of this room two fluid test stands were installed.
Sample Characteristics: Same as for AR-12.
Observations on Curve: Same as for AR-13.

Curve AR-15 (*Figure 8-7*)
Time: 1135 hours
Sample Characteristics: Same as for AR-12
Place: Four feet from filter in same clean room tunnel as for AR-14. The counter was on the left side of the tunnel next to the hydraulics test stand. The test tube was at bench level for each of curves AR-13, AR-14, and AR-15. This curve showed similar characteristics to AR-13 and AR-14 in that floor air which was

of the same quality as the general facility area was drawn into the clean air stream. However, the monitoring probe was not deep enough into the clean air stream to prevent reading the aspired particles drawn into the stream.

Curve AR-16 (Figure 8-7)

Time: 1140 hours

Place: Open facility area between two clean room tunnels mentioned for AR-13 and AR-14.

Sample Characteristics: Same as for AR-12

Observations on Curve: Contamination level in this area is greater than the AFSCR curve. It is also greater than the contamination level recorded in both clean room tunnels. The characteristics of curve AR-16 and curves AR-13, AR-14, and AR-15 are similar to the slope of the curves discussed in Chapter 2. Here it was found that the particles in the small particle size range between 0.3 and 2.0 microns tend to accumulate and vary from Stoke's law. This is because the significant forces on particles of

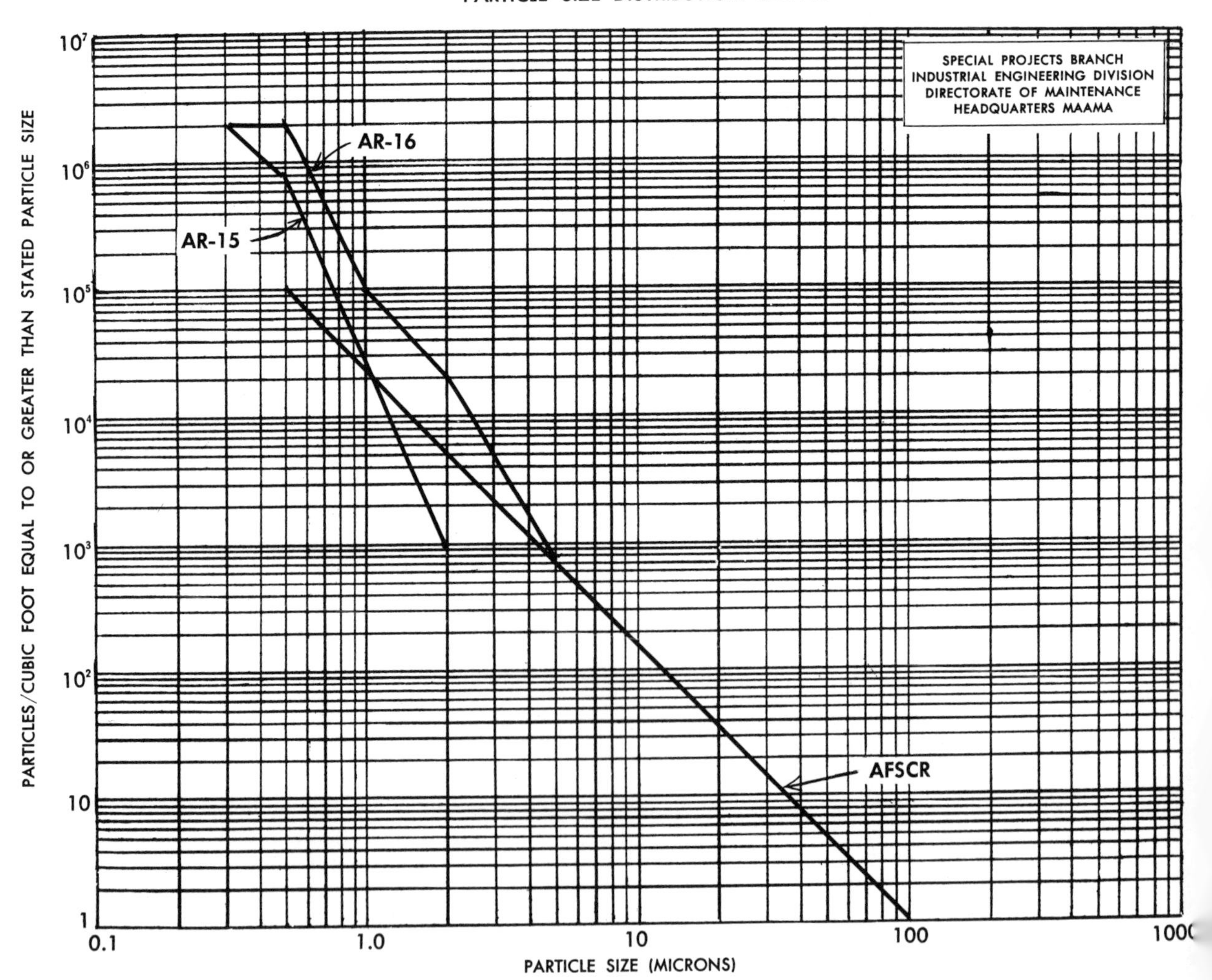

FIGURE 8-7.

this size range are no longer gravitational forces but are aerodynamic forces. Note that there is a slight change of slope after 2.0 microns and that larger particle size distribution does follow the AFSCR curve.

The following experiments were performed with a Royco 230 aerosol photometer in the AiResearch cross-flow clean room (40 by 80 feet). This photometer operates on the principle of light scattering and measures the relative mass of contaminants being sampled rather than amount of contaminants in discrete size ranges. Its sensitivity to low concentration of particles is made possible by a logarithmic scale deflection. Scale deflections are from 0.001 to 1.0 and are relative. This device has a rapid response to change in contamination level being sampled.

At 1000 hours the photometer was placed 5 feet from the filter bank on the bench paralleling the right wall as one faces the filter bank. The streamline monitored issued from the filter which was the first from the right wall and the second from the floor. After calibration of the instrument, readings were taken. No significant scale deflection was noted. Barely perceptible scale deflection from 0.001 to 0.002 took place. This test was continued during a 20-minute interval in which no noticeable deflection of the meter took place. This indicated that almost no particles greater than 0.32 micron were entering the room through the filter.

At 1020 hours the photometer was placed approximately half-way between the filter bank and room air exits on the workbench paralleling the right wall. One man was performing his assigned task at the bench upstream of the photometer. The level indication for a 10-minute period of time was 0.002, which showed almost no particles greater than 0.32 micron to be present. This reading was also the same as taken at the filter bank. A deflection up to 0.08 was recorded, however, when contamination was artificially introduced into the monitored streamline by lightly brushing the arm of the garment.

At 1030 hours a check of several filters in the filter bank was made. No pinhole leaks or sealing leaks were found. This indicated that, by proper selection and installation of filters, a very low room contamination level can be achieved.

The following data are common to curves GD-1 through GD-11:

Date: 25 Sept. 1963

Place: Laminar cross-flow clean room, General Dynamics Corporation, Pomona, Calif.

Persons Performing Tests: 1st Lt. Philip R. Austin, 1st. Lt. Clifford F. Frith, and Stewart W. Timmerman.

Instrument Used: All curves were obtained by a Royco particle counter, PC200A, operated by William Zinky and Jack Lawler of Royco Instruments, Palo Alto, California.

Temperature and Humidity: Dry-bulb temperature, 76°F; wet-bulb temperature, 60°F; relative humidity, 38%. Note that readings were constant throughout room.

Clean Room Clothing Worn: Head coverings, foot coverings, and coveralls.

Curve GD-1 (Figure 8-8)

Time: 1035 hours

Place: Three feet from air exits of room on right-hand side of room, approximately 6 feet from right wall.

Sample Characteristics

Height of sample: 32 inches from floor

Length of sample: Each channel was sampled for 1 minute.

Sample rate: 0.01 cfm

Multiplication factor: 100

Observations on Curve: There was light activity upstream of the counter. One man was moving about. The values received for this test showed a contamination level in small particle sizes to be less than the requirement for an Air Force standard clean work station in operation.

Curve GD-2 (Figure 8-8)

Time: 1038 hours

Place: Same as for GD-1

Sample Characteristics: Same as for GD-1

Observations on Curve: There was light activity upstream of the counter. Two men were moving about. Note that this value is slightly greater than that for GD-1 and is approximately equal to the requirement of an Air Force standard clean work station in operation.

Curve GD-3 (Figure 8-8)

Time: 1041 hours

Place: Same as for GD-1

Sample Characteristics:

Height of sample: 32 inches from floor

Length of sample: Each channel was sampled for 3 minutes.

Rate of sample: 0.01 cfm

Multiplication factor: 33

Observations on Curve: Four men were standing 3 feet upstream from counter discussing a problem. Little bodily motion was taking place. Note that the value recorded as one point is less than the requirement for an Air Force standard clean work station in operation.

Curve GD-4 (Figure 8-9)

Time: 1045 hours

Place: Same as for GD-1

Sample Characteristics: Same as for GD-3

Observations on Curve: Four men were working at their work stations 15 feet upstream of particle counter. One man was moving about back and forth across the streamline being monitored. Note that the contamination level approximates that of GD-3. Also, this curve is

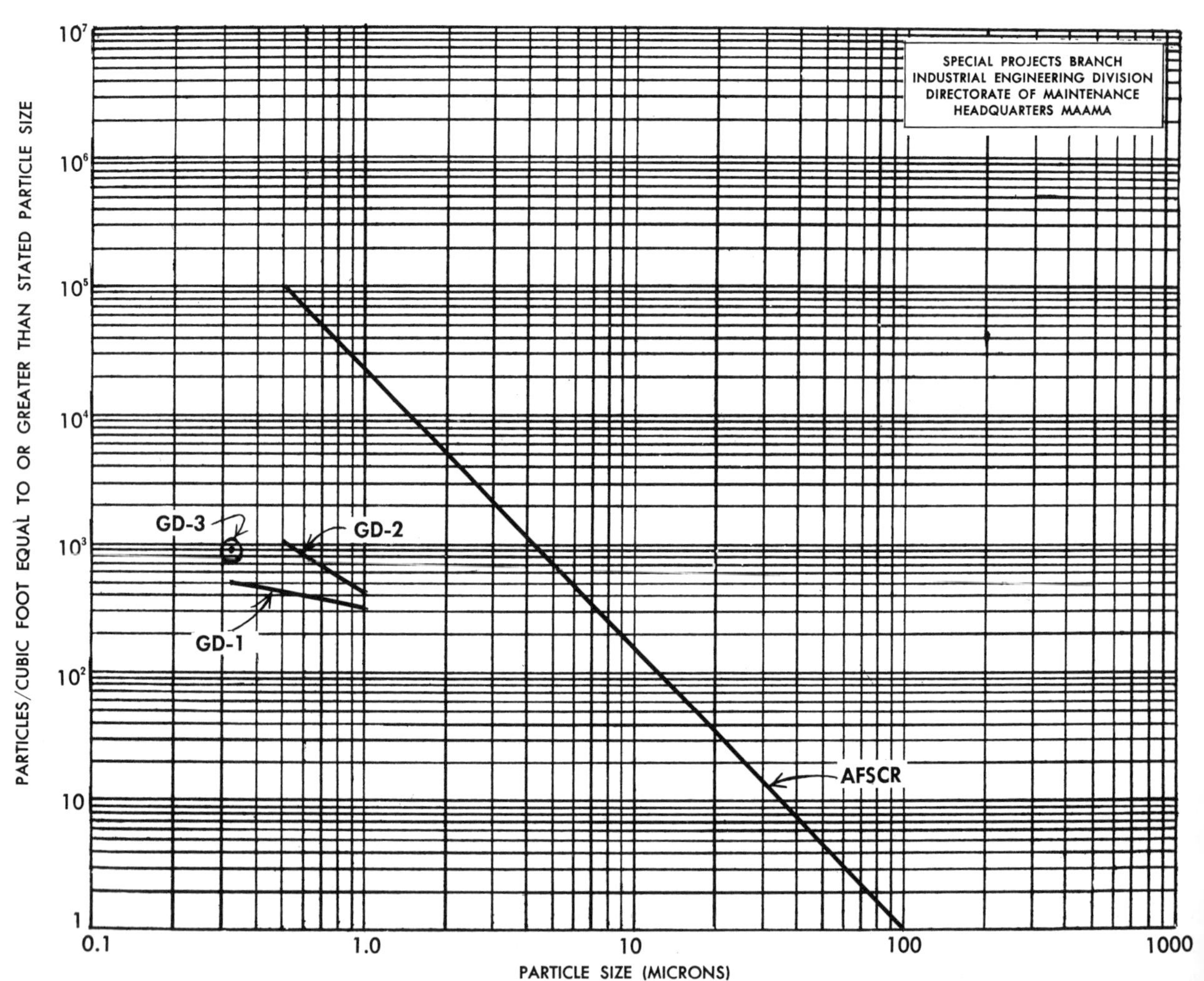

FIGURE 8-8.

parallel to the AFSCR curve. The values received for this curve are less than those required for an Air Force standard clean work station in operation.

Curve GD-5 (Figure 8-9)

Time: 1057 hours

Place: Same as for GD-1

Sample Characteristics

Height of sample: 32 inches from floor

Length of sample: Each channel was sampled for 0.3 minute.

Sample rate: 0.01 cfm

Multiplication factor: 333

Observations on Curve: Lt. P. R. Austin clapped hands at a rate of two beats per second which included hand-shearing motions as well as clapping such as is experienced in the clashing of cymbals. Notice that this curve is slightly greater than that required for the Air Force standard clean work station in operation.

Curve GD-6 (Figure 8-9)

Time: 1100 hours

Place: Four feet from filter bank and 6 feet from right wall as one faces the filter bank.

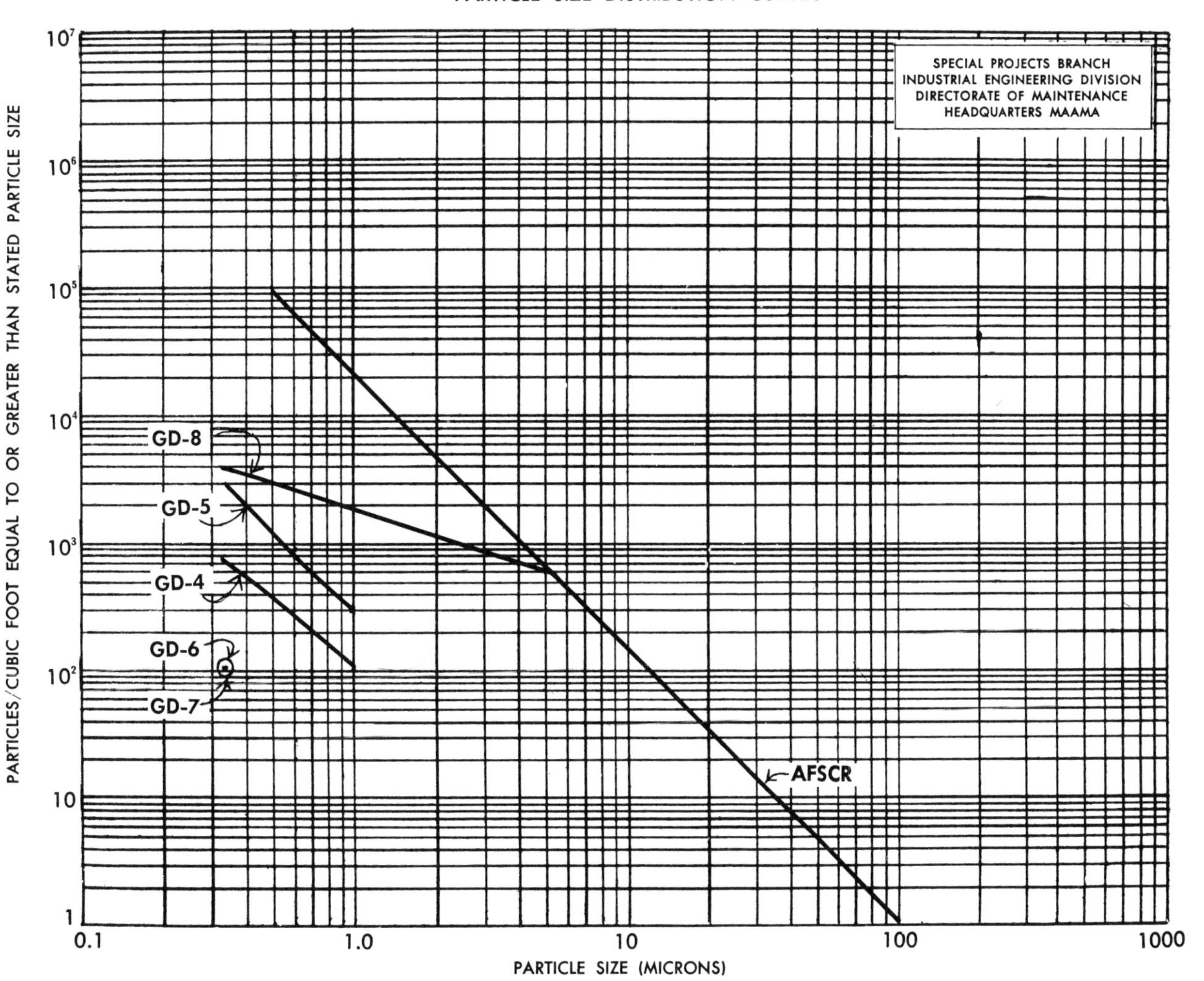

FIGURE 8-9.

Sample Characteristics
Height of sample: 32 inches from floor
Length of sample: Each channel was sampled for 3 minutes.
Rate of sample: 0.01 cfm
Multiplication factor: 33
Observations on Curve: Readings were taken on the 0.32- and 1.0-micron channels. The counter was operating on total mode. No counts were recorded for particles 1.0 micron in size and larger. Value recorded has a lower contamination level than is required by the Air Force standard clean work station at rest.

Curve GD-7 (Figure 8-9)
Time: 1105 hours
Place: Same as for GD-6
All observations and conditions the same as for GD-6.

Curve GD-8 (Figure 8-9)
Time: 1110 hours
Place: Same as for GD-1
Sample Characteristics
Height of sample: 32 inches from floor
Length of sample: Each channel was sampled for 0.3 minute.

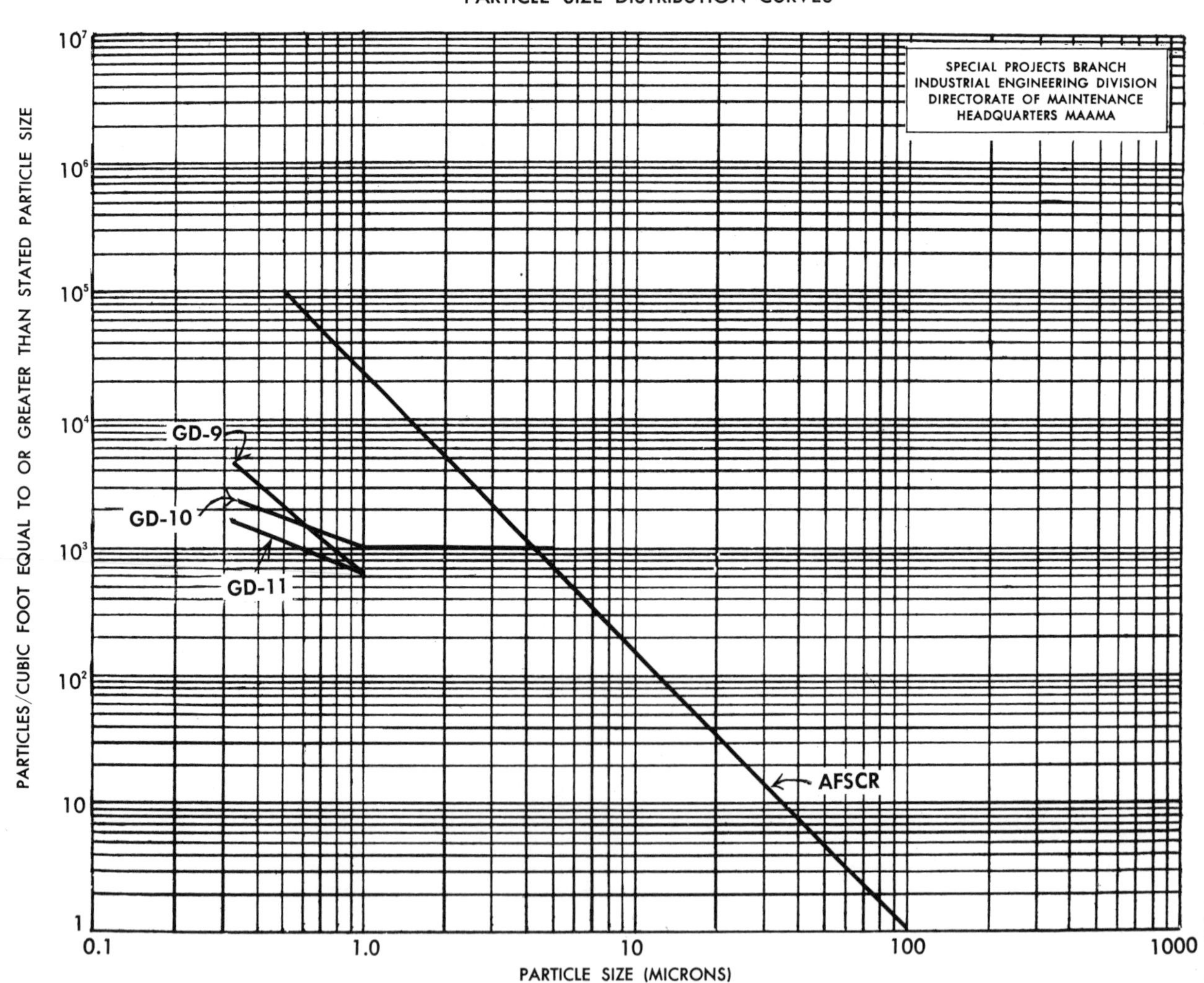

FIGURE 8-10.

Sample rate: 0.01 cfm
Multiplication factor: 333
Observations on Curve: This test was performed to determine the amount of contamination produced by a man doing calisthenics. Lt. C. F. Frith performed jumping-jacks 6 feet upstream of the particle counter which was monitoring size ranges for 0.3, 1.0, and 5.0 microns. Notice that this curve is linear. The predominant number of these particles is of the larger size. Previous tests have shown that this curve will tend to become parallel with the AFSCR curve in the larger particle size range.

Curve GD-9 (*Figure 8-10*)
Time: 1115 hours
Place: Same as for GD-8
Sample Characteristics: Same as for GD-8
Observations on Curve: This test was performed to see how much contamination was produced by a man getting up from his chair, moving away from his work station, and then coming back and sitting down on the chair. This was done by Lt. P. R. Austin with a chair 6 feet upstream of the counter. Four cycles were performed every 20 seconds, each cycle consisting in rising from the chair, moving around the chair, and sitting back down on the chair. Points were recorded for the 0.32-, 1.0-, and 5.0-micron channels which were set on total mode counting. No particles larger than 5.0 microns were recorded. Notice that the curve is essentially parallel to the AFSCR curve. The value recorded in this curve is slightly more than that required by the Air Force standard clean work station in operation.

Curve GD-10 (*Figure 8-10*)
Time: 1117 hours
Place: Same as for GD-8
Sample Characteristics: Same as for GD-8
Observations on Curve: This test was performed to determine the quantity of particles generated when a clean room garment was brushed. The type of clothing being worn in this facility is as shown in Figure 7-29. Complete overalls and head coverings with shoe covers are worn. Lt. P. R. Austin brushed front, back, arms, and legs during this test. Notice that proportionately larger particles are generated during such actions.

Curve GD-11 (*Figure 8-10*)
Time: 1130 hours
Place: Same as for GD-8
Sample Characteristics: Same as for GD-8
Observations on Curve: Eight people were monitored upstream of the counter. These people were performing their assigned work functions with light activity taking place. Several people were discussing a problem, while the others were working at their work stations. The value recorded in this curve was slightly more than that required in the Air Force standard clean work station in operation.

Experiments were performed with a Royco 230 aerosol photometer in the General Dynamics cross-flow clean room. No significant photometer scale reading or deflection was noted during the tests to measure the mass concentration of airborne contaminants at the filter bank, the middle of the room, and the exit of the room. These tests reinforced the data taken with the Model PC200A, which showed an extremely low contamination level throughout this room.

The following data are common to curves L-1 through L-4:
Date: 26 Sept. 1963
Place: Laminar cross-flow clean room, Lockheed Aircraft Corporation, Van Nuys, Calif.
Persons Performing Tests: 1st Lt. Philip R. Austin, 1st Lt. Clifford F. Frith, and Stewart W. Timmerman.
Instrument Used: All curves were obtained by a Royco particle counter, PC200A, operated by William Zinky and Jack Lawler of Royco Instruments, Palo Alto, Calif.
Temperature and Humidity: Dry-bulb temperature, 73½°F; wet-bulb temperature, 58½°F; relative humidity, 39%.
Clean Room Clothing Worn: Head covering and smocks.

Curve L-1 (*Figure 8-11*)
Time: 1019 hours
Place: Two feet from filter bank and approxi-

mately 7 feet from the left wall as one faces the filter bank. The filter monitored during this experiment can be shown in Figure 7-30 as the second filter from the floor and the third filter from the left side of the room.

Sample Characteristics
- Height of sample: 32 inches from floor
- Length of sample: Each channel was sampled for 3 minutes.
- Rate of sample: 0.01 cfm
- Multiplication factor: 33

Observations on Curve: Two channels were monitored during this test. The counter was on total mode, and all particles greater than 0.32 and 0.5 micron were monitored. Notice that the curve is parallel to the AFSCR curve. The values recorded during this test are of lower contamination than is required by the Air Force standard clean work station at rest.

Curve L-2 (Figure 8-11)
- Time: 1035 hours
- Place: Same as for L-1
- Sample Characteristics
  - Height of sample: 32 inches from floor
  - Length of sample: Each channel was sampled for 1 minute.
  - Rate of sample: 0.01 cfm

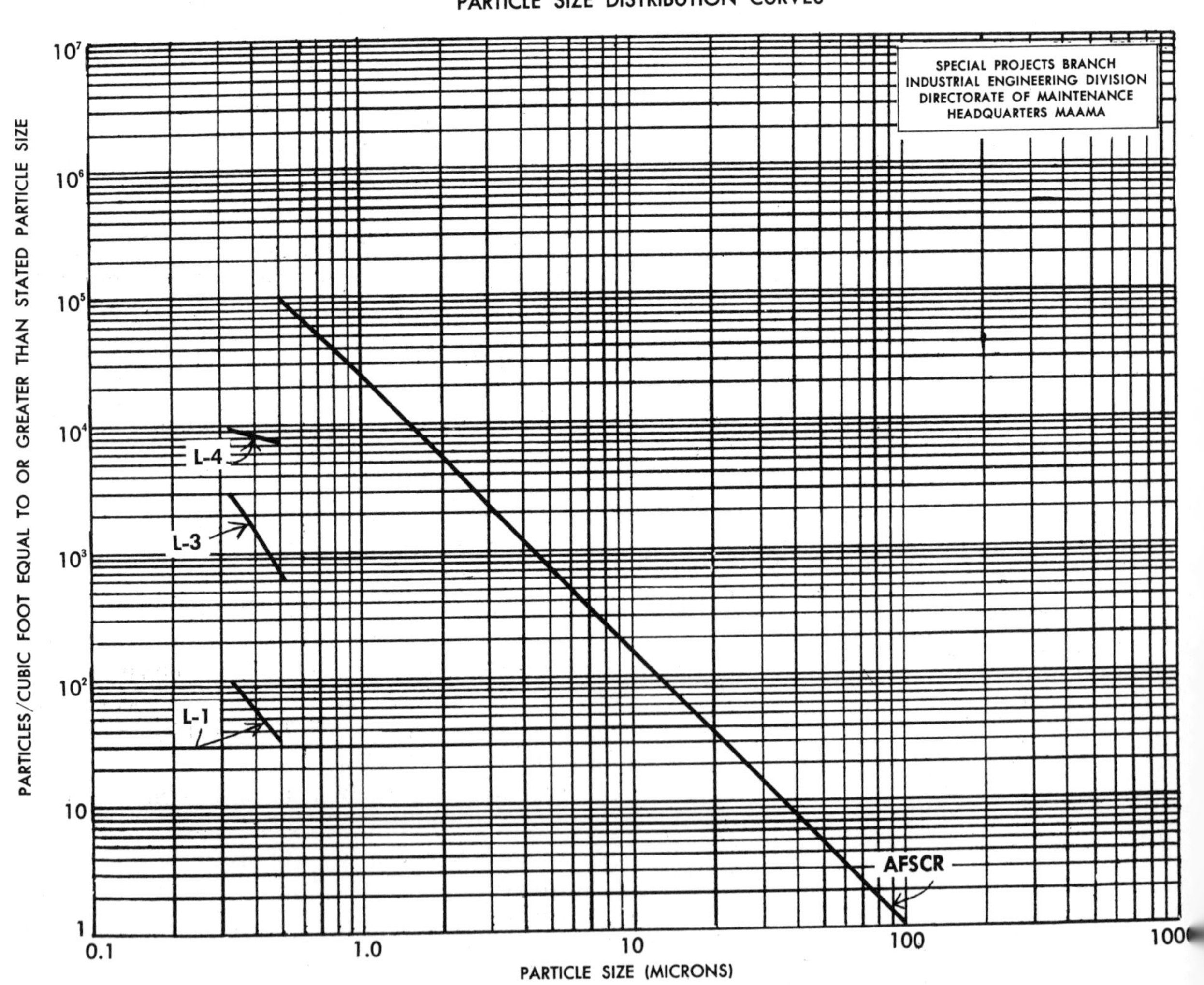

FIGURE 8-11.

Multiplication factor: 100

Observations on Curve: After curve L-1 was taken, the counter time setting was changed to 1-minute sampling periods and allowed to continue to sample the air. At approximately 1030 hours, the counter again was observed, and no particles were being recorded on either channel. At 1035, a recording of both channels indicated zero counts for particles larger than 0.32 and 0.5 micron. This curve does not appear on the chart, since the scale does not allow plotting. These data are significant, however, since they show that for periods of time no particles greater than 0.32 micron can be recorded in front of HEPA filters. It should also be noted that working personnel had not been in this room for several days, owing to a change in workload. This may account for the very low contamination recorded at the filters. The characteristic of these filters, however, is to be 99.97% efficient by volume on 0.3-micron particles.

urve L-3 (Figure 8-11)

Time: 1043 hours

Place: Dress-up area at exit of room. Counter was placed 2 feet from the return air grilles.

Sample Characteristics

Height of sample: 32 inches from floor

Length of sample: Each channel was sampled for 0.3 minute.

Sample rate: 0.01 cfm

Multiplication factor: 333

Observations on Curve: Three men entered the clean room and began donning smocks and head coverings. These men were approximately 6 feet upstream of the counter. Notice that this curve is essentially parallel to the AFSCR curve. The contamination level was less than that required by the Air Force standard clean work station in operation.

rve L-4 (Figure 8-11)

Time: 1047 hours

Place: Same as for L-3

Sample Characteristics: Same as for L-3

Observations on Curve: Lt. P. R. Austin was 6 feet upstream of counter. Garments were brushed and rubbed lightly. Notice that the slope of the curve is similar to that of GD-10 and approximately the same magnitude as AR-10.

Experiments were performed with a Royco 230 aerosol photometer in the Lockheed cross-flow clean room. No significant scale reading or deflection was noted, however, during the tests performed at the filter bank, in the middle of the room, or at the exit of the room.

Application of Laminar Flow to Operating Rooms

An operating room utilizing laminar flow could have an atmosphere many times as clean as that in the most modern operating room, thus immensely advancing sterile procedures.

A great deal of time and effort has been expended over the last decade to control the level of bacteria present in the air in all types of medical facilities, including operating rooms. This has been necessary since airborne bacteria create a high infection rate in both surgical and other hospital facilities. The chief organism which is responsible for postoperative infections and for many other hospital type epidemics is hemolytic staphylococcus aureus (the "staph germ"). This organism causes approximately 90 per cent of the infections which occur in hospitals because it is of such a size (approximately 0.5 micron) that it will not readily drop out of the air and, yet, a single individual is likely to carry these bacteria by the thousands on his skin, and even a single pimple will produce millions of bacteria. On the outside of the body these bacteria cause little damage, but in a wound or incision they create an infection which is not amenable to treatment by antibiotics. A conventional operating room will produce an average mortality rate of about 1.6 per cent because of postoperative infections alone.*(2)*

The capability of a laminar-flow clean room in reducing microbiological contamination has been partially investigated. Dr. Clapper of the Lovelace Foundation performed colon resection on a dog in one of Sandia's laminar-flow rooms. Figure 8-12 shows Dr. Clapper and his assistant preparing for the operation in front of the clean room. This room is one of the original evaluation models and could be considered a combination cross-flow and down-flow room. Air is brought in through HEPA filters along one wall behind a work bench and exited through the floor below the bench. (See Chapter 7.)

FIGURE 8-12. Equipment to be used by Dr. Clapper of Lovelace Foundation in performing a dog colon resection operation in a laminar-flow room. *Courtesy Sandia Corp.*

The colon resection was chosen because it is an extremely "dirty" operation (from a bacteriological standpoint). The contents of the bowel are exposed to the air in the room. Figure 8-13 shows the bench prepared for the operation. Note the filter bank behind the bench and the grilled floor. Figure 8-14 shows the operation about to begin; the circular objects are plates containing blood agar nutrient. Bacteria hitting these plates can be readily detected.

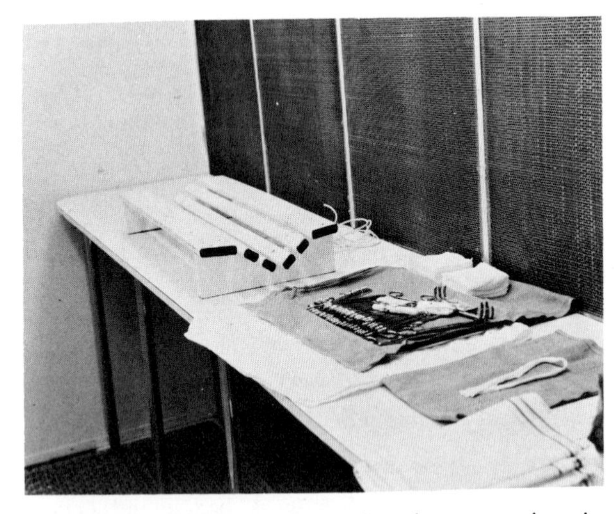

FIGURE 8-13. Bench prepared for dog operation in Sandia portable clean room. *Courtesy Sandia Corp.*

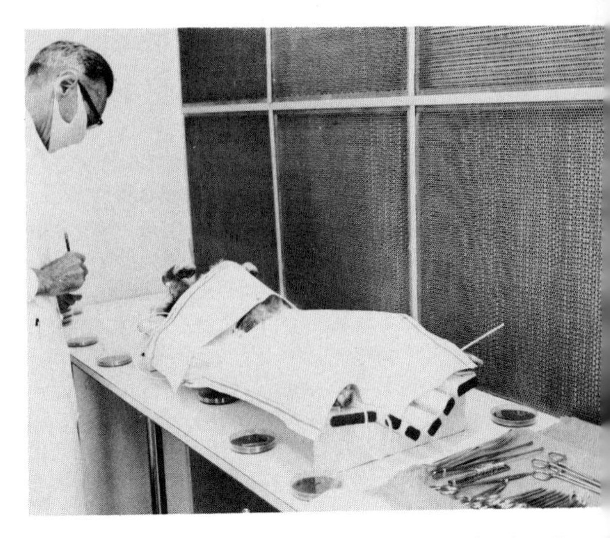

FIGURE 8-14. Operation on dog about to begin. *Cour tesy Sandia Corp.*

The plates were exposed during the entire operatior about one-half hour. The results of the test showe that contamination existed only downstream fror the dog and the doctors. (See Figure 8-15.) Ther was no lateral movement of the bacteria, and th air at the site of the operation remained sterile Furthermore, the areas where contamination ord narily exists in a conventional operating room wer maintained at a much lower contamination leve This may be explained by the dilution effect pro duced by the high rate of air flow. A super-clea operating room, using laminar-flow principle

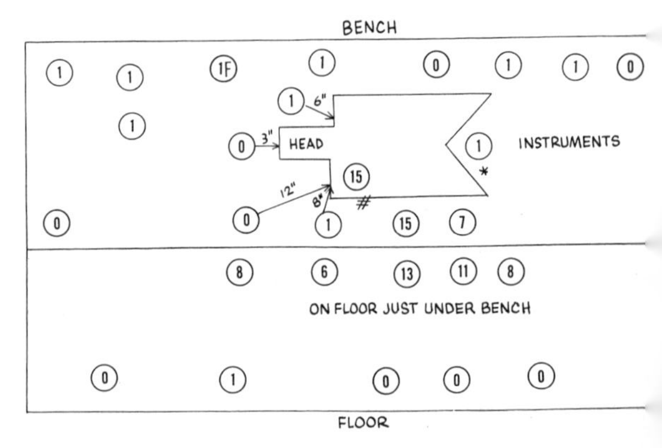

FIGURE 8-15. Bacterial fallout on blood agar plat during a half-hour colon resection on a dog. *Cou tesy Sandia Corp.*

promises spectacular improvements in operating environments.

The ideal operating room would use down-flow, since this would carry the bacteria from the patient down and out the floor. This would place the doctor in a protected atmosphere above the patient. "Suiting-up" and "scrub-down" would prevent the doctor from contaminating the patient. A down-flow room would not require a complete "scrub-down" after a "dirty" operation. Such procedures close down an operating room for at least an hour while the entire room is scrubbed with a germicide. In a laminar-flow room the next operation could proceed with a minimum of room preparation, almost immediately. A super-clean operating room using this principle promises spectacular improvements in operating environments and utilization.

REFERENCES

1. Timmerman, S. W. and Austin, 1/Lt. P. R. *Investigation of Cross Flow Clean Room Characteristics*. Report 17.0006.16.03. Olmsted AFB, Pa.: MAMES September 1963.

2. Marsh, R. C. "Adaptability of Laminar Air Flow for Contamination Control." *Conference on Clean Room Specifications*. SCR-652. Office of Technical Services, Department of Commerce, Washington, D. C., May 1963.

Chapter 9. *Clean Room Monitoring*

Introduction[1]

Monitoring of a clean room can present many problems to those performing the monitoring if they lack understanding of the factors influencing the clean room environment. These factors must be considered in order to interpret the monitoring data properly.

Contamination levels will vary throughout a clean room. This is caused by the following factors: Filtered air is entering at one or more locations; contamination is being generated in various amounts throughout the room; and contaminated air is exiting the room at one or more locations. The highest level of contamination is not necessarily at the air exit points, since air from a highly contaminated area may be diluted with filtered air prior to exiting the room. Higher and lower levels of contamination can thus readily exist within a given room. The areas of most concern are those immediately surrounding the product. It would be almost impossible to monitor all work areas continuously. The area, or areas, that are the most highly contaminated can be determined by statistically sampling the room. These areas should be monitored several times a day. Other areas should be monitored several times a week. The exact requirements for monitoring must be determined on an individual basis.

The temperature within a room varies from point to point. This temperature variance is sometimes referred to as the temperature gradient within the room. Since cool air is entering the room from the air conditioner and heat is being liberated to the air from people and equipment, different levels and regions of temperature are to be expected throughout the room. Unless a product is very sensitive to the rate of temperature change, temperature can be monitored at any convenient spot. If necessary, an alarm system may be placed at the air duct entrance, or within the air duct to the room, to warn of any sudden malfunction of the air-conditioning system.

Low humidity can become troublesome if it is allowed to reach a level where static charges are generated by clean room personnel or where metallic oxidation (rusting) may be a problem. Generally speaking, a humidity level of no less than 30% is desired. The humidity level can be as flexible as that used for temperature. Many clean rooms are functioning at humidity levels of less than 30%. This is possible only because the ambient humidity is very low and the rooms are experiencing no difficulty with static electricity. Relatively few products are so sensitive to humidity that a specific humidity tolerance must be maintained. For those items where humidity tolerance is critical, special control measures should be employed.

Particle Monitoring[2]

Various techniques may be applied to monitor the contamination level of a controlled-environment facility or a clean work station. These methods contain varying amounts of automaticity. The basic method employed is the membrane filter sampling technique used in conjunction with a microscope of at least 100×. This method is called the "Manual Method for Sizing and Counting Airborne Particulate Contamination in Clean Rooms and Other Dust-Controlled Areas," and it covers a

[1] Abstracted from reference *1*, p. 4-1.

[2] *Ibid.*, pp. 4-1 and 4-2.

procedure for counting and sizing airborne particulate matter 5 microns and larger.

A valid check can be made of an average clean room by using a 100× microscope in conjunction with the curves in Chapter 2. The clean work station and super-clean atmospheres will require a different monitoring technique. Particles of less than 5 microns may be counted by using a microscope of greater than 100×. When counting in the submicron range, caution must be used in determining the background count of new filters. New filters have a certain amount of contamination on them when received, which is called background count. The amount of this contamination must be recorded and subtracted from the final count after use. Experience has demonstrated that an average background count from a sample of four per one hundred new membrane filters is representative and gives results required. This procedure requires an advanced microscopist and a more exacting laboratory technique, however.

Emphasis must be placed on the accuracy of the person reading the samples. Personnel must be trained and qualified before attempting to validate the particle count of a contamination-controlled space. Proper illumination is of vital importance. Both the intensity and the angle of the light beam must be adjusted for best results.

The membrane filters should be counted in an environment in which the contamination level is similar to or less than that measured by the filter. This will lessen the probability of fallout or particulate matter on the filter during the counting process.

The "Tentative Method for Sizing and Counting Particulate Contamination in Clean Rooms and Other Dust-Controlled Areas" (ASTM F25-63T) or the "Procedure for the Determination of Particulate Contamination of Air in Dust-Controlled Spaces by the Particle Count Method" (SAE ARP 743, August 30, 1962) may be substituted for the technique described in this chapter.

Automated methods of counting particles may be used as a supplement to the manual method but should not be wholly substituted for it. In general, electronic particle counters are effective in the range from 0.5 to 5 microns. Automated particle counters, as opposed to microscopic methods, have the advantages of speed and ease of count. They remove the tedious work of counting particles, but often they do not show the entire airborne contaminant level and make-up of the environment. Some of their disadvantages are the level of skill required to maintain these units in operation and the accuracy of their count. If automated counting methods are to be used, these units should be field-calibrated daily, or more frequently as necessary. They should also be checked at least once daily against the manual method for general agreement if the automated counter reading will be used to determine room shutdown.

Logic should be used in determining room shutdown. An occasional peaking of the contaminant level within a room is permissible for a few minutes' time. Continual peaking of the contaminant level indicates improper exhaust of contaminant-producing operations or excessive movement in a "dirty" clean room. Both conditions are unacceptable in a clean room and must be corrected. Contaminant levels that are continually above operational standard limits are not to be tolerated and may indicate a faulty filter system, a negative room pressure, or a continuous particle generation operation within the room. Figure 9-1 shows typical contaminant levels during a 24-hour period.

A qualitative identification of airborne contaminants should be made where room contamination levels remain above operational standard limits. This identification should be made so that the source of contamination can be traced and eliminated. A visual identification of airborne particulates may be made by use of a microscope in conjunction with a filter sampling technique. If visual identification of particulate matter is impossible by this method, qualitative chemical analysis should be performed.

The manual method (5 microns and larger) will be adequate for the level of cleanliness as required in conventional clean rooms; however, when checking a cleaner atmosphere such as a down-flow or cross-flow room or a clean work station, this method has certain limitations. So few particles of 5 microns and larger will be present that the manual method may not pick up enough of these particles to produce a statistically valid determination of the contaminant level. A quantitive check of super-clean atmospheres must be made with automatic equipment measuring the range from 0.5 to 5 microns. It can be determined whether the contamination level is acceptable by using a deductive process. This procedure checks the filters for leaks, uniformity of air flow, and air velocity. If the filters pass this test, then it can be deduced that the contaminant level is satisfactory. Similar logic may be used to check a laminar-flow room. Additional manual checks should be made upstream from work stations in a cross-flow room to determine if excessive particles are being generated within the room.

Temperature Monitoring[3]

Temperature monitoring may be achieved by the use of conventional temperature-monitoring devices, the simplest of them being a conventional Fahrenheit thermometer. More-automated devices may be used as a supplement to the thermometer, but these devices should be checked at least daily against the thermometer. Alarm devices may be installed with the automated devices. Normally, hourly checks of temperature will be sufficient, since supervisors can be expected to notice unusual variations which may occur between checks.

If the product being worked on is extremely sensitive to temperature rate of change, it may be necessary to monitor this value with an automated temperature-recording device. In such cases the temperature probe should be in the proximity of the product where temperature rate of change is critical. Warning or alarm devices can be employed if it is determined that the product is sensitive to temperature rate of change.

Humidity Monitoring[4]

Humidity monitoring may be achieved by use of a conventional wet- and dry-bulb thermometer used in conjunction with a psychrometric chart.

[3] *Ibid.*, p. 4-3.

[4] *Ibid.*, p. 4-3.

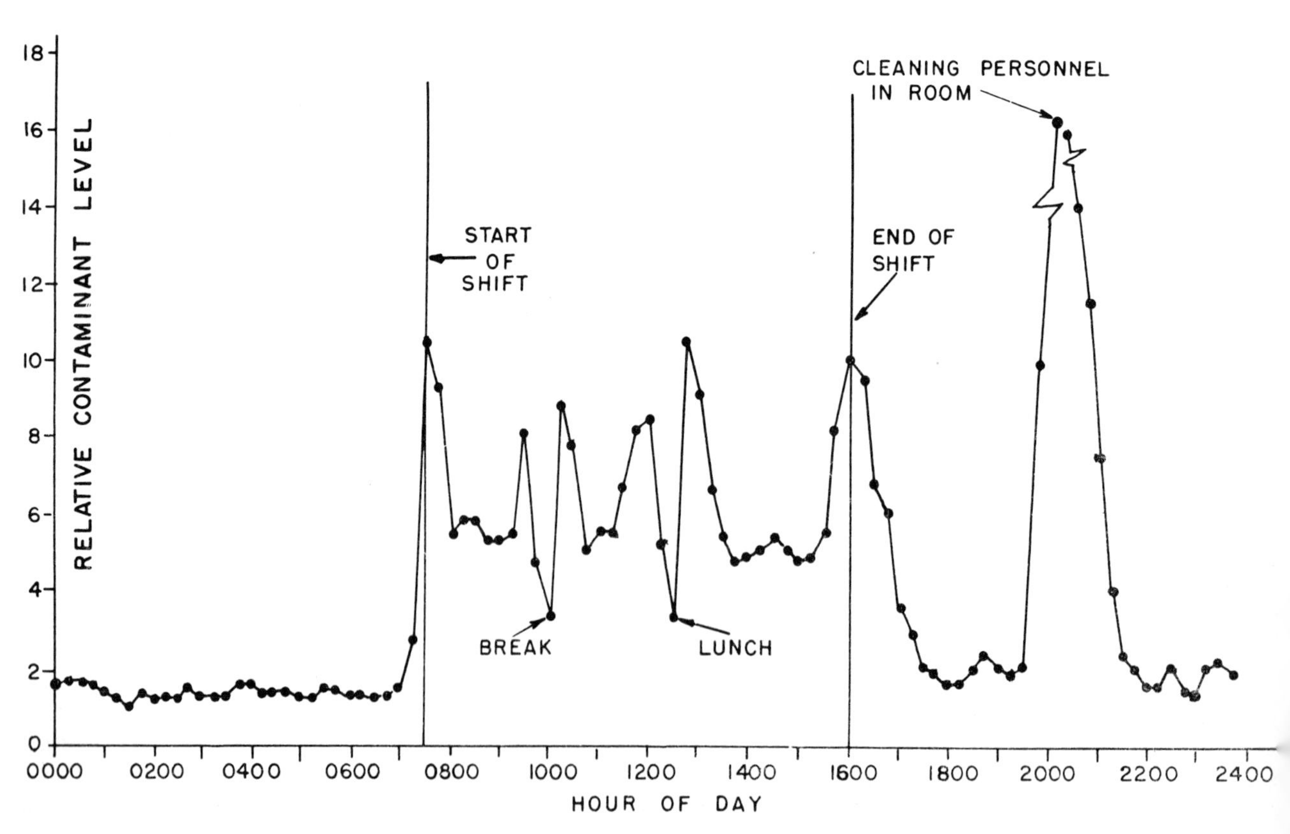

FIGURE 9-1. Typical clean room contamination levels.
U. S. Air Force Technical Order 00-25-203

More-automated devices may be used as a supplement to the wet- and dry-bulb thermometer. If such devices are employed, they should be checked against a wet and dry thermometer at least once weekly.

Pressure Monitoring

Pressure monitoring may be achieved by means of a simple U-tube manometer with each opening vented in such a manner that the pressure differential is measured between the clean room and its outside surroundings. An ordinary pressure differential gauge capable of measuring several inches of water pressure may be substituted for the manometer.

Contamination Monitoring

Contamination monitoring is the most difficult monitoring problem of clean room operation. Many clean rooms have been temporarily shut down because indicated contamination levels were greater than acceptable. In many cases such shutdowns could have been avoided if proper contamination monitoring equipment and techniques had been employed. In an attempt to shed as much light as possible on this subject, the remainder of this chapter will be devoted to this topic.

Selection of Samplers

Many types of air samplers and modifications thereof have been described in the literature, each of which has been designed for individual needs and specific conditions or redesigned in an attempt to improve its efficiency. There is still a need for improvement of existing air samplers.

When selecting a sampler for a specific air-sampling program, many factors must be considered, but first one must have a clear understanding of the type of information desired and the particular determinations to be made. For instance, is information desired on (1) one particular size of contaminant, or on all sizes that may be present in the air, (2) the concentration of these particles, (3) the change of concentration with time, (4) the size distribution of the collected particles, or (5) a combination of these points? Furthermore, are the results on concentrations to be qualitative or quantitative?

Factors to be considered before selecting a particular sampler are:

1. Size and type of the particles to be sampled.
2. Sensitivity of particles to sampling.
3. Assumed concentrations and particle size.
4. Volume of air to be sampled and length of time sampler is to be continuously operated.
5. Background contamination.
6. Ambient conditions.
7. Sampler collection efficiency.
8. Effort and skill required to operate sampler.
9. Availability and cost of sampler.
10. Availability of auxiliary equipment and facilities, such as vacuum pumps or lines, electricity.

The continued sophistication, development, and requirements of clean rooms has brought about the need for measuring the concentration of airborne particulate matter in such areas. Not only is the concentration or quantity important, but the size and nature of this matter must be known. An ideal monitoring instrument*(2)* might be visualized as one that can count, size, and identify particulate matter on a continuous basis with immediate data readout. Of course, such a device must be economically constructed, and therefore the production of the ideal monitor will be tempered by economics. Many methods and much equipment have been designed and developed over the years in an attempt to define airborne particulate matter accurately. Filtration, impaction, light-scattering, microscopic analysis, and sedimentation are some of the more common methods of measuring and counting aerosol particles. None of these methods qualify as an ideal method in its present form. Currently, much work is being performed to improve the adequacy and correlation of these methods.

Contaminant monitoring in very clean areas presents the problem of sensing extremely small amounts of particulate matter. This problem can become so acute that it is possible for an operator accidentally to introduce more contamination into the monitoring device than is introduced by the atmosphere being sampled. Sampling locations within a clean room must be considered carefully, since there is usually a great deal of variation in contamination concentrations within an area. As a result, it may be necessary to sample a number of areas in a room to obtain a representative contamination level for a room. The samples should be taken during identical time periods or as close together in time as possible, since contamination levels of areas do vary at different times(*3*).

When comparing the different airborne-dust monitoring methods in order to select the best one for a clean room monitoring program, several factors must be considered. First, what type of information is necessary to perform the monitoring function adequately? Second, what compromises, if any, will be accepted because of economic demands?

In the following discussions it will be shown that each method yields different information. The choices to be made are (*2*):

1. An instantaneous sample with delayed readout, or a continuous sample with instantaneous readout.
2. A level indication.
3. An individual particle count with size information.
4. Size, count, and information on particle shape, nature, and material.

Often the real problem is one of deciding which techniques or instrument will do the job most accurately, quickly, simply, or inexpensively.

Counting of contaminant or particulate matter by microscopy is probably the oldest and simplest method known. The particulate matter is collected on membrane filters, prepared slides, or other surfaces and then positioned beneath the microscope for counting, sizing, and identification when desired. Of course, this method has disadvantages when compared to the automaticity of some other methods, but it represents one of the least expensive methods for counting. Some of the objections raised against microscopic work is that it is tedious, is time-consuming, and depends greatly on operator technique, visual acuity, and judgment. This method is still one of the best tools for particle counting, however. The most automatic device cannot provide all the information that may be obtained by microscopic observation of the particles themselves. Characteristics such as shape, density, color, and frequency of particle type, which are invaluable in tracing the source of a particular contaminant, cannot be observed by any other single method.

Sizing and Counting Airborne Contaminants[5]

Outline of Method

The following manual method covers a procedure for counting and sizing airborne particulate matter 5 microns and larger in clean rooms and other dust-controlled areas. The sampling areas are specifically those with contamination levels typical of clean rooms and dust-controlled areas designed for electronic and aerospace work. It is not a method for dust counting where isokinetic sampling is a factor.

This method is based on the microscopic examination of particles impinged upon a membrane filter with the aid of a vacuum. The number of sampling points is proportional to the floor area of the enclosure to be checked. The apparatus and facilities required are typical of a laboratory for the study of microparticle contamination. The operator must have adequate basic training in microscopy and in the techniques of particle sizing and counting.

Definitions

a. The major projected dimension of a particle is designated as the particle size.

b. The standard unit of length for sizing purposes is the micron (μ), which is 0.001 mm or 0.00004 inch.

c. Only particles with a measurable length greater than 5 microns are to be counted.

d. A fiber is considered a particle, no distinction being made with respect to length/width ratios.

Apparatus Required

a. Aerosol open-type filter holder (Figures 9-2 and 9-3).

b. Vacuum pump or aspirator capable of producing a vacuum of 500 torr (500 mm Hg) (Figures 9-4 and 9-5).

[5] Abstracted from reference *1*, Appendix IV. This method was originally modified from the "*Proposed Tentative Method for Sizing and Counting Airborne Particulate Contamination in Clean Rooms and Other Dust-Controlled Areas*" (ASTM F25-63T). This method was jointly proposed by the Sampling and Airborne Sub-Committees of the ASTM F-1-X Contamination Committees. The initial draft was presented for discussion at the St. Louis and Washington winter meetings, 1962.

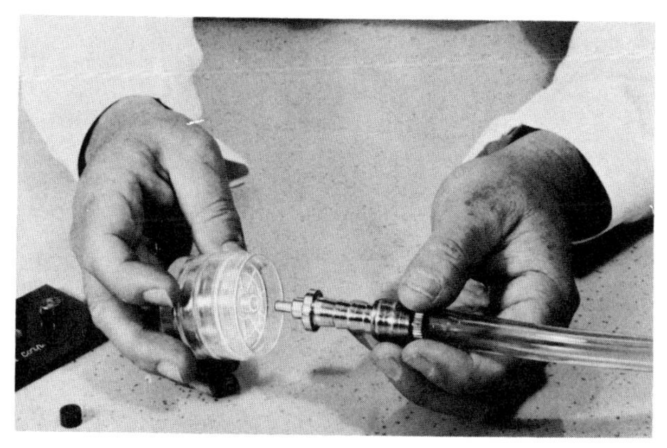

FIGURE 9-2. Millipore aerosol analysis monitor. *Courtesy Millipore Filter Corp.*

FIGURE 9-3. Gelman open filter holder. *Courtesy Gelman Instrument Co.*

FIGURE 9-4. Millipore vacuum-pressure pump. *Courtesy Millipore Filter Corp.*

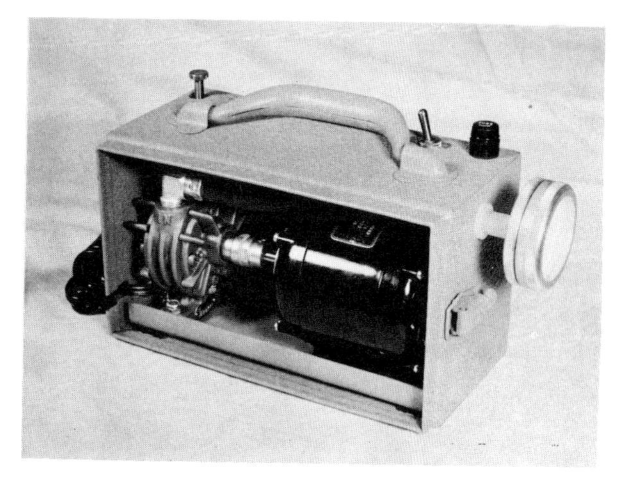

FIGURE 9-5. Gelman bantam air sampler. *Courtesy Gelman Instrument Co.*

c. Flowmeter with 10-liter per minute capacity or 10-liter per minute orifice.

d. Membrane filters, contrasting, 0.80 micron or smaller pore size, with imprinted grid.

e. Glass microscope slides, 50 by 75 mm, or 47-mm plastic disposable Petri dishes.

f. Forceps with unserrated tips.

g. Binocular microscope with ocular-objective combinations to obtain 40/45× and 90/100× magnifications. Latter objective shall have numerical aperture of 0.15 minute (Figure 9-6).

h. Manual counter (two-gang).

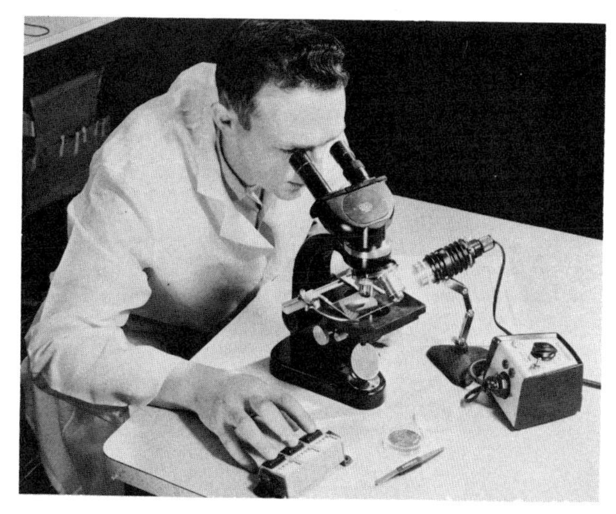

FIGURE 9-6. Particles examined microscopically to determine the amount of contaminant present in stated size ranges. *Courtesy Millipore Filter Corp.*

i. Microscope lamp, 6 volts, 5 amp variable intensity (Figure 9-6).

j. Micrometer eyepiece with movable scale or ocular micrometer reticle.

k. Stage micrometer, standard 0.01- to 0.1-mm scale.

Sampling Procedure

a. The sample shall be collected by impinging airborne particles on a membrance filter which has a known effective filtering area. The filter surface is to be vertical (filter holder horizontal) with respect to the floor.

b. Standard sample for this procedure shall be 10 cubic feet (283 liters). The sample size may be adjusted for specific conditions, however.

c. Sample shall be taken at waist level (36 to 40 inches from the floor) or at bench level unless area is limited. General sampling points are as designated on the sampling plan in Figure 9-7. The number of samples for averaging is a function of the floor area of the space being sampled.

d. Samples can be taken at the respective locations illustrated on the sampling plan in Figure 9-7. Sample at 1 for areas of cabinet size. Sample at 1′ and 2′ for areas less than 150 square feet. Sample at 1, 2, 3, 4, and 5 for areas to 1000 square feet. For areas larger than 1000 square feet, increase sampling by four locations per 1000 square feet. If desired, for an average room dust count, a single sample may be taken for 5½ minutes at each of the five designated sampling points.

e. Locations are approximate. Location 1 is area center, 1′ and 2′ are centers of triangles on respective bases. Locations 2, 3, 4, and 5 are half-distances from center to respective corners on area diagonals, as shown in sampling plan.

f. Operating conditions should dictate number and location of samples. Each critical work position within a clean room should be monitored. Past experience has shown that these work positions should be checked daily, or more often, and during periods of most activity.

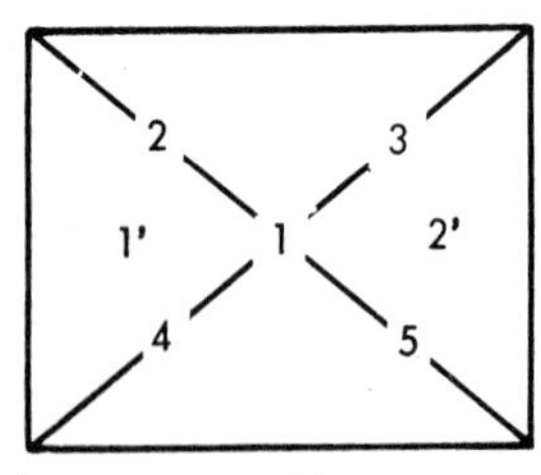
2
3
1'
1
2'
4
5
SAMPLE AT 1' AND 2' FOR AREAS LESS THAN 150 FT2
LARGER AREAS TO 1000 FT2, USE 1,2,3,4 & 5 AVERAGE READINGS.

FIGURE 9-7. Clean-room sampling plan. *USAF Technical Order 00-25-203.*

Preparation of Apparatus

a. Prior to sampling, dirt and dust are to be removed from the filter holder by washing in a free-rinsing detergent, ketone-free isopropyl alcohol, and reagent-grade petroleum ether (30° to 60°C boiling range).

b. The laboratory equipment and area used for counting and sizing the airborne particulate are to be maintained in a condition of cleanliness paralleling or superior to that of the area sampled. Plastic microscope hoods have proved satisfactory as covering in the absence of a laboratory.

c. Personnel performing sizing and counting operations are to be equipped with garments consistent with good practice.

d. Microscope slides and Petri dishes are to be cleaned and prepared for preserving membrane filter and specimen. Lens tissue properly used is satisfactory for this operation.

e. Hazardous chemicals employed in the method are to be handled with recognized precautions.

f. Background count on membrane filters shall be established by examining each filter used for referee purposes. Examination at 40 to 50× through a bench or stereo microscope will reveal low or high background count.

g. For routine work, an average background count may be used by counting four filters per box of one hundred. If the background count approximates 10%, or greater, of the sample count, each individual filter should have a background count established.[6] This background count should be subtracted from the sample count.

h. Acceptable filters shall be placed in clean and identified Petri dishes for test use and covered.

Procedure

a. With the aid of laboratory pressure rubber or plastic tubing, connect the filter holder to the vac

[6] If the background count is estimated to be greater than 10% of the total count from a 10-cubic foot specimen, a larger sample (15 or 20-cubic foot volume) may be used.

uum train which includes filter holder, 10-liter per minute limiting orifice or (and) 10-liter per minute flowmeter, and source of vacuum (vented outside sampling area).[7]

b. With clean unserrated forceps, carefully remove membrane filter from Petri dish and place, with grid side up, on screen support of filter holder (Figure 9-8). Twist locking ring in place to secure filter.

c. When in the sampling area, place the filter holder in a horizontal position, filter surface vertical, 36 to 40 inches from floor level for purposes of sampling. Apply vacuum, and adjust to flow of 10 liters per minute or other desired flow. A standard vacuum gauge will not suffice for maintaining correct flow. Either a rotometer (flowmeter) or limiting orifice with manometer is required. When using the orifice, no adjustment is necessary. The pump should be checked with the manometer, however, to assure its ability to maintain a vacuum of 500 torr or better while sampling.

d. Remove the filter from the holder with forceps and place it on a clean glass slide in preparation for counting. If the filter cannot be counted immediately, place it in a clean Petri dish for transport to the microscope counting area.

e. Microscopic Analysis Procedure

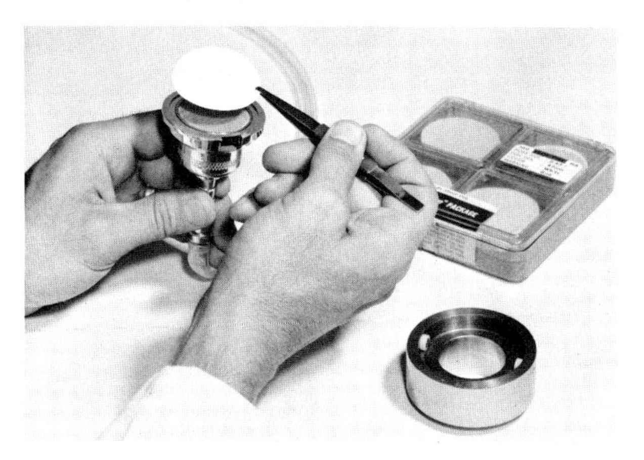

FIGURE 9-8. Placing Millipore filter on base of filter holder. Locking ring will hold filter. *Courtesy Millipore Filter Corp.*

[7] For low-contamination areas, a flowmeter with a 1-cfm capacity may prove more satisfactory for taking a larger sample in less time.

1. Place the ocular micrometer in one eyepiece. Using a stage micrometer, calibrate the measuring eyepiece (ocular micrometer) for each magnification.

2. Place the microscope slide or Petri dish containing the specimen under the microscope. The Petri dish cover must be removed.

3. Adjust the microscope lamp intensity and direct it on the specimen from an oblique position to obtain maximum definition for sizing and counting. High-intensity illumination is a critical requirement. The angle of the light beam is very significant for defining different types of contamination.

4. Knowing the subdivisions of the stage micrometer, size the divisions of the measuring eyepiece from it.

5. A magnification of approximately 100× will be required for counting particles 5 microns and larger. Greater magnification may be advantageous for identification of particles.

6. Particles are to be counted and tabulated in three size ranges: All particles between 5 and 15 microns; all particles between 15 and 25 microns; all particles greater than 25 microns; also number of fibers.[8] Particles smaller than 5 microns are not to be counted by this method. The size of a particle is determined by its greatest projected dimension. Fibers are counted as particles.

f. Method of Counting Particles

1. Adjust microscope focus and lamp position so that maximum clarity of filter surface and particle definition is obtained.

2. The largest projected dimension of the particle determines the size category of the particle.

3. Use the counting plan as shown in Figure 9-9. Count ten grid squares or unit areas within different grid squares as indicated in the counting plan of Figure 9-10.

4. After counting ten squares or unit areas, if the total number of particles in each size range does not equal or exceed 50, count additional squares or unit areas until the following statistical requirement is met: $F_n \times N_t = 500$, where F_n is the number of grid squares or unit areas counted, and N_t is the total number of particles counted in F_n areas. If this requirement is not met for all size ranges after fifty

[8] Fibers will be included in their particle size range for computing the particles per cubic foot.

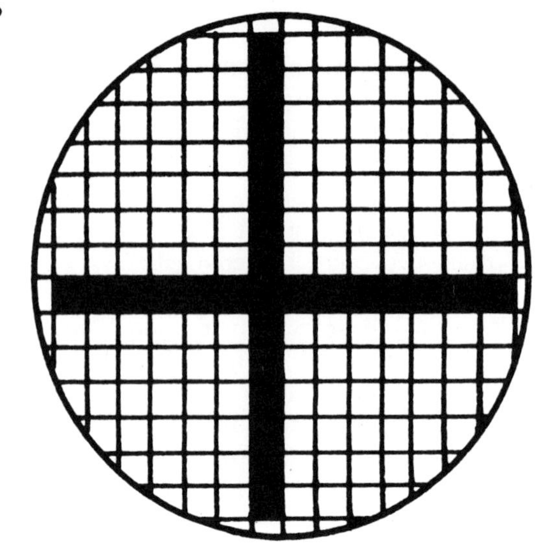

FIGURE 9-9. Double-diameter counting plan. The shaded area is employed. *Courtesy Millipore Filter Corp.*

areas have been counted, or 50% of the total effective filtering area, it will be necessary to increase the sample volume. Extreme caution must be maintained when examining the effective filter area, owing to no visual evidence of boundaries. *Note:* The equation $F_n \times N_t = 500$ must be met for each size range. It may, therefore, be necessary to tabulate the three separate ranges (5 to 15 microns, 15 to 25 microns, > 25 microns) in the first ten areas to satisfy the equation for each range, and then count only the particles greater than 25 microns in additional areas to get valid results for the third range. A lower magnification may be used to count the particles greater than 25 microns, but this is not recommended.

5. To obtain the total number of particles, count ten or more grid squares or unit areas on the filter

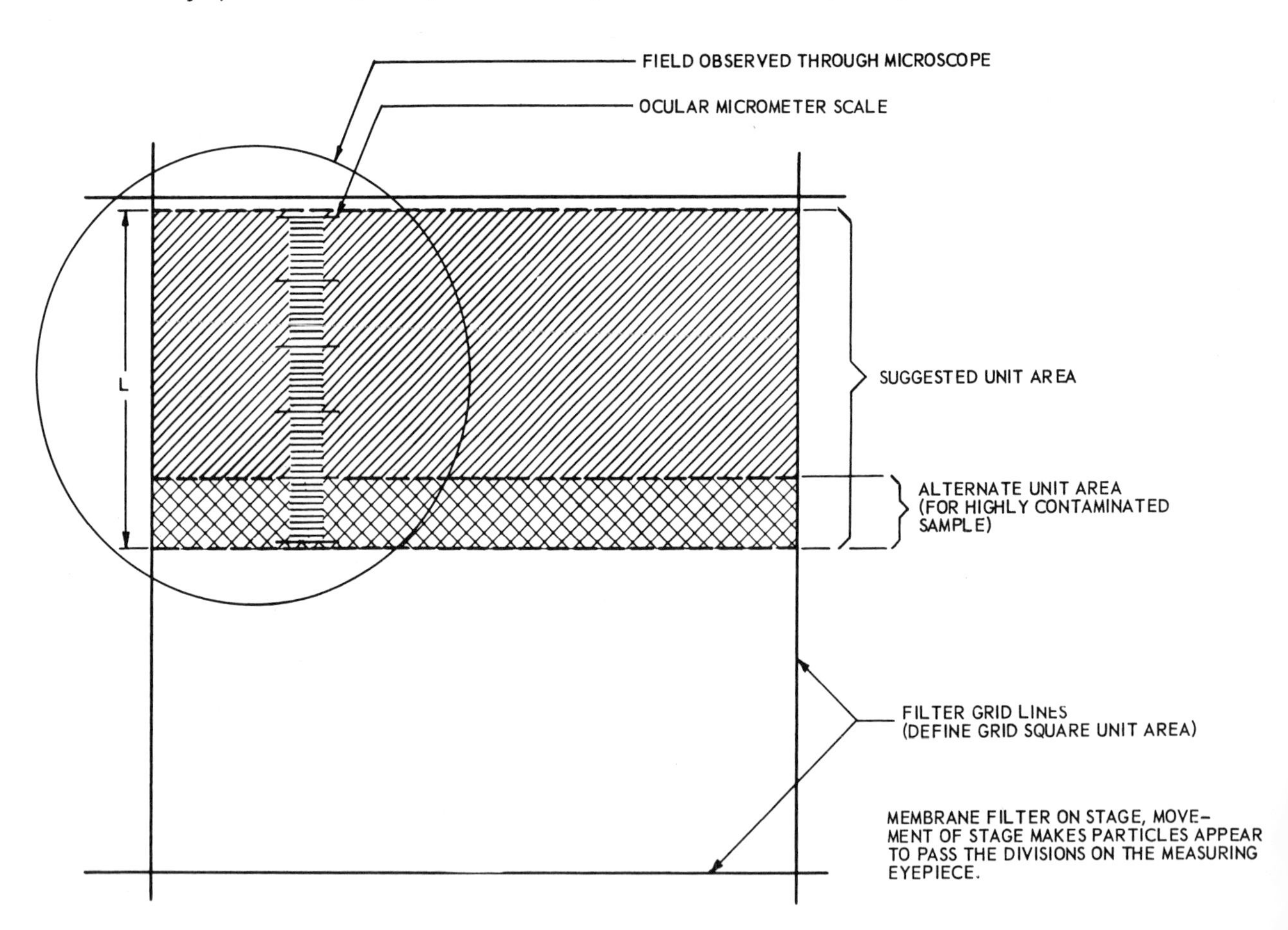

FIGURE 9-10. Alternative unit areas. *USAF Technical Order 00-25-203.*

disk. From this count, calculate the total number of particles that would be present on the total effective filtration area of grid squares.

6. Select unit areas for counting so that the average total number of particles in a unit area does not exceed 50 to 60 particles. (See Figure 9-10 for alternative unit areas.)

7. If a particle lies on the upper or left boundary line of a counting area, count this particle as if it were within the boundaries of the counting area.

8. Start and finish a selected grid square or unit area by sizing and counting from the left edge of a grid line, scanning exactly one grid square width as the operation continues from left to right. Optional unit areas are: (*a*) a grid square; (*b*) a rectangle defined by the width of a grid square and by the calibrated length of the ocular micrometer scale; (*c*) a rectangle defined by the width of a grid square and a portion of the length of the ocular micrometer scale.

9. Scan the unit area for particles by manipulating the stage so that particles to be counted pass under the ocular micrometer scale. Only the maximum dimension of the particle is regarded as significant; for particles improperly oriented relative to the ocular micrometer scale, estimate the maximum dimension. The eyepiece containing the ocular micrometer should not be rotated to size specific particles. Using a manual counter, count all particles in the selected area which are in the range of 5 microns and greater, as indicated by the ocular micrometer scale. Record the number of particles in each size range in each unit area counted, in order to have a record of the number of unit areas and the particles counted to meet requirements of paragraph (4). The sample worksheet (Figure 9-11) will assist in counting and computing the particle count.

Calculations

a. Calculate the total number of particles in a given size range on the filter, in accordance with the formula

$$P_t = N_t \times \frac{E}{n \times A_f} \qquad (9\text{-}1)$$

where P_t = the total number of particles of a size range on the filter.

N_t = the total number of particles counted in n unit areas.

n = the number of unit areas counted.

A_f = the unit area, in square millimeters.

E = the effective total filter area, in square millimeters.

Results should be expressed for each size range in particles per cubic foot of sample by dividing the P_t by the sample size (10-cubic foot standard):

$$P/\text{ft}^3 = \frac{P_t}{10} \qquad (9\text{-}2)$$

Final results are in particles per cubic foot of sampled atmosphere, in size ranges determined. (See sample worksheet, Figure 9-11.)

b. Ready comparison of particle distribution is possible by plotting size counts on log-log graph paper and comparing with the standard plots as given in Chapter 2. This may be accomplished by adding the particles per cubic foot above each size range and plotting the data on graph paper. For example, adding all the ranges will give the total particles per cubic foot greater than 5 microns. Skipping the first range will give the total particles per cubic foot greater than 15 microns, etc.

Precision and Accuracy

a. The precision and accuracy of this method can be no higher than the sum total of the variables. In order to minimize the variables attributable to an operator, a trained microscopist technician is required. Variables of equipment are recognized by the experienced operator, thus further reducing possible error.

b. A periodic check of the microscopist with a check-slide[9] should be performed by individual laboratories to obtain quality results.

c. For training personnel, specimens of low to medium concentration may be prepared on a grid filter and preserved between microslides as standards for a given laboratory.

d. Analysis for particles in the 0.5- to 5.0-micron size range may be achieved by employing transmitted light techniques, after rendering the white filter transparent by placing the filter on immersion oil of refractive index 1.515. A magnification of at

[9] A commercially available precounted membrane filter mounted in a glass slide (Millipore Filter Corporation)

least 500× is required, and the background count as described above must be obtained.

e. This method can be adapted for projection microscopic analysis by the use of a white filter, transmitted light, and a properly marked projection screen. The projection techniques should be checked against a direct microscope count, because the optics of projection equipment are sometimes inadequate for resolution of small particles.

Sampling Time

Should air samples be taken in places other than clean rooms, these samples must be large enough to be measurable and representative. In general, the following sizes are suitable:[10]

	Sample	*Rate**	*Time**
Clean rooms	10 cu ft =	10 liters/min	for 28 min
Country air	5 cu ft =	10 liters/min	for 14 min
City air	1 cu ft =	1 liters/min	for 28 min
Factory air	0.5 cu ft =	0.5 liters/min	for 28 min

* Established values obtained with Millipore filter equipment. Higher sampling rates and shorter sampling times can be used if the resulting air sample is representative of existing conditions.

[10] See Millipore Filter Corporation brochure.

PARTICLE COUNT DATA

ROOM NR	CLASS	SOURCE	VOLUME	FILTER TYPE	TIME/DAY/MONTH/YEAR	COLLECTED BY	COUNTED BY
HIG	III	Pump	10CuFt	0.8μ	0945/5/April/63	Price	Garnett

MAG. X	PARTICLE SIZE μ	AREA PER FIELD MM² A	PARTICLES COUNTED IN EACH RANDOMLY SELECTED FIELD										FIELDS COUNTED B	PARTICLES COUNTED TOTAL C	X FACTOR D = TOTAL AREA / A X B	PARTICLES IN SAMPLE E = CD	BACKGROUND F	PPCF (E · F) / VOL
100	5-15	3.08	8	5	4	7	10	5	9	11	6	3	10	68	960 / 3.08x10 = 31.2	2122	101	202
100	15-25	3.08	2	0	0	3	4	1	0	2	2	0	20	29	960 / 3.08x20 = 15.6	452	40	41
			1	4	1	2	1	2	3	0	0	1						
100	>25	9.49	1	2	0	0	3	4	2	1	1	1	20	25	960 / 9.49x20 = 5.1	128	10	12
			2	1	1	0	0	1	3	0	1	1						
100	Fibers	9.49	1	0	0	0	0	1	0	0	2	0	20	7				
			1	0	1	0	0	0	0	1	0	0						

COMMENTS

1. Ten grid squares were counted for the background. The total background count was multiplied times 10.1 in each size range to give background (F).
2. A flow meter was used to measure sample (10 cubic feet-10 minutes).
3. Fibers which are separately listed are also included in the >25 count.

FIGURE 9-11. Sample worksheet. *U. S. Air Force Technical Order 00-25-203*

Where large numbers of relatively noncritical samples must be taken, use of conventional filters and filter holders will afford a small saving in materials.

Isokinetic Sampling in Ducts

Often, by reason of the total flow, the allowable pressure drop, or the physical dimensions of the system (as in air-conditioning ducts), it is impracticable to sample the entire flow. Because of low viscosity, these gas streams present special sampling problems which may disturb results.

To collect a representative sample of contamination from a ducted air stream, insert a probe, coupled to a filter holder equipped with a limiting orifice, and connected to a vacuum source (Figure 9-12). Isokinetic sampling demands that the gas *linear velocity at the probe opening match that in the duct.* Equal velocities may be achieved by a proper ratio between the probe opening and the limiting orifice dimension:

$$\frac{\text{Flow rate in duct}}{\text{Duct cross-sectional area}} = \frac{\text{Flow rate in probe}}{\text{Probe cross-sectional area}} \quad (9\text{-}3)$$

Failure to match probe and duct velocities (Figure 9-13) will cause a distortion of results favoring either large particles (probe velocity lower than duct velocity) or small particles (probe velocity higher than duct velocity). Probes should have thin walls, sharp leading edges, as large an inner diameter as practicable (minimum 0.25 inch), head directly upstream, and be bent at a minimum radius of 1 inch.

Anisokinetic distortions are insignificant in most

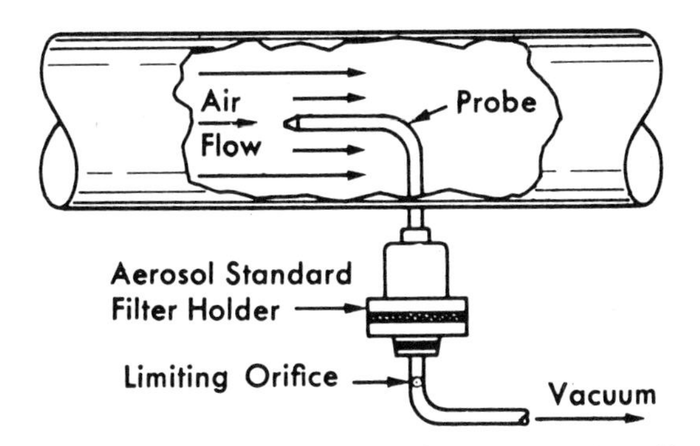

FIGURE 9-12. Isokinetic sampling from a duct. Sampling rate and probe dimensions carefully adjusted. *Courtesy Millipore Filter Corp.*

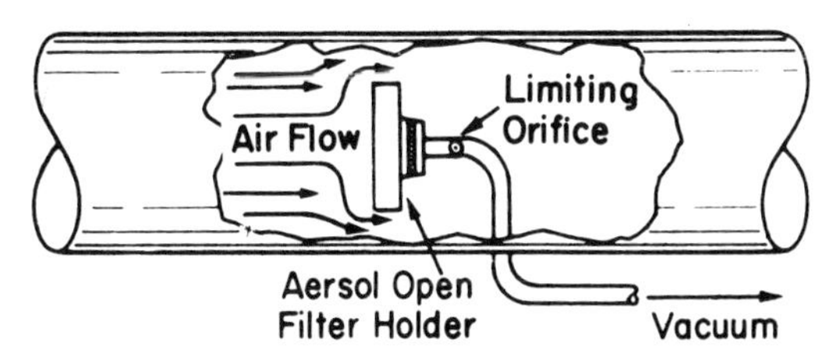

FIGURE 9-13. Faulty sampling from a ducted gas stream caused by using an open-type holder. Large particles scrubbed from filter by air passage; small particles largely diverted. *Courtesy Millipore Filter Corp.*

liquid systems, since particles tend to follow the flow of the liquid of higher viscosity.

Isokinetic conditions are important, from a practical standpoint, only when these three factors apply: (1) The fluid is flowing at relatively high velocity (typical of gasses). (2) The fluid is of relatively low viscosity (cryogenic fluids or gases). (3) Large particles (greater than 25 microns) are present in the fluid and of concern in the analysis.

Dry-Slide Settling Technique *(4)*

In some particular cases, dust monitoring by the "dry-slide settling technique" may be desirable. The following paragraphs will briefly discuss microscope slide preparation, apparatus, procedures, and results of this technique.

Slide Preparation

When monitoring clean rooms and areas by the dry-slide settling technique, clean slides and slide covers are essential to accurate particle counting and sizing. Unless a high degree of cleanliness is achieved, a preliminary particle count of the slide must be made before sampling. Also, slide cleaning and mounting must be done in a very low-count airborne contamination space such as a clean work station. A standard 2- by 3-inch glass microscope slides and 43- by 50-mm covers, No. 2 thickness, can be used. The slides and covers should be carefully cleaned before mounting by scrubbing them in a water-detergent solution most liquid household detergents are satisfactory. The water used in this solution must be carefully filtered and deionized or distilled. After the slides and covers have been carefully scrubbed, rinse in two water baths, followed by an alcohol bath. The slides are then placed in a covered dish to dry. The rinse water must also be filtered and deionized or distilled. After approximately twenty slides have been rinsed, the alcohol should be refiltered. The water rinse baths should be changed at this time. After the slides and covers are dry, they are mated. This is done by placing a slide on a clean horizontal surface and centering a slide cover on the slide. Clear cellulose tape is then used to secure one end of the slide cover to the slide; this piece of tape later serves as a hinge for the cover during sampling. Another short piece of tape is used to fasten the other end of the cover to the slide. The slide assembly should be placed in a clean covered container for storage or transit to the area to be sampled.

A glass tube is used to maintain a relatively still air column above the microscope slide during sampling periods. Such a tube allows free access for positioning and mounting of the slide. A tube 8 inches long and 4 inches in diameter is sufficient; however, the length-to-diameter ratio of the tube is arbitrary. The surfaces of this tube must be carefully wiped with a "lint-free" cloth just before use, to remove loose particulate matter.

Location of Slide for Sampling

This method of monitoring, like almost all methods, covers the immediate area of the microscope slide. This characteristic must be carefully considered when locating the slide in an area to be sampled. Since particulate matter concentrations vary considerably within most areas, areas of interest must be sampled individually to obtain accurate results. An entire area is evaluated by locating slides near various operations in the area, as well as in inactive areas.

Sampling periods are varied to meet the monitoring requirements of an area. Samples are usually taken during work periods; however, samples are taken periodically to monitor the clean-down capabilities of an area. A minimum sampling period of 4 hours is recommended to monitor very clean areas.

Mounting of Slide

At the completion of the sampling period, the cover is lowered slowly to avoid disturbing the collected particulate matter. After the cover is lowered, the still-air tube is removed. This allows free access for mounting the slide. Before removal of the slide from the area, the remaining three sides of the slide cover should be taped to the slide. The slide is now ready for microscopic evaluation. During handling or storage, the slide is kept in a horizontal position.

Sandia Corporation has found that, when this method is employed, a comparator-type microscope used to count and size particulate matter is best. A diagram of the optical system is shown in Figure 9-14. This microscope is equipped with a 7-inch ground-glass viewing screen which is ruled in square millimeters. Dust field magnifications of 70 to 1200× are possible. This unit is also equipped with a precision micrometer stage for convenient slide manipulating during counting.

Normally, a power of 125× is sufficient. At this power each millimeter on the microscope screen equals 8 microns on the slide. When needed, higher

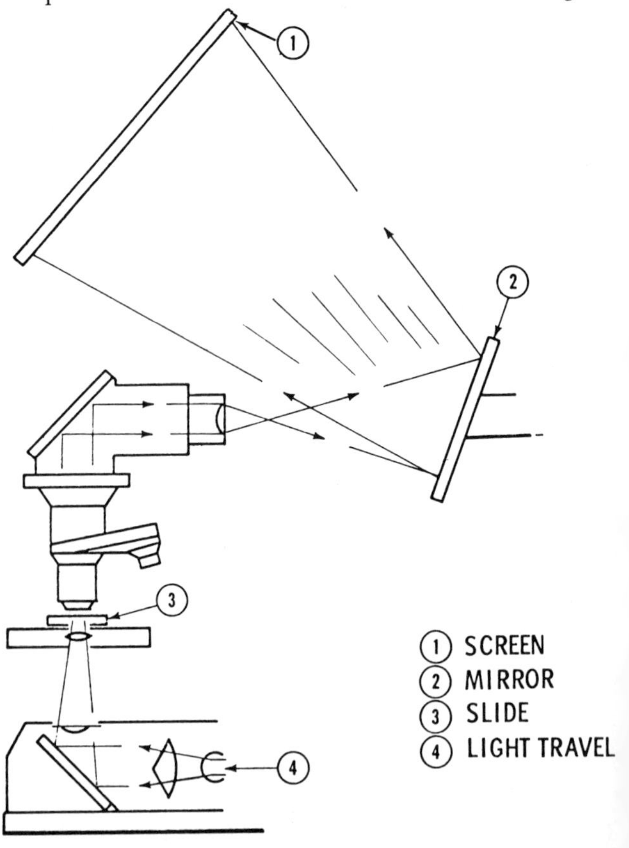

FIGURE 9-14. Microscope optical system. *SCTM 87-61 (25), Sandia Corp.*

power magnifications are used to aid in individual particle identification. At present, thirty microscopic fields are randomly selected and counted. A microscopic field is specified as the slide area displayed on the 7-inch screen. Since the complete area of the screen is marked in 1-millimeter squares, particles are conveniently sized over an entire field with little or no slide manipulation.

Particle counting by size requires some additional time for counting; however, the distribution data obtained are valuable in describing an area. Actual experiences in clean room operation have shown that this information is also valuable in determining contamination sources. After a few samples have been taken in a particular area, a typical particle size distribution for the area is quickly established. Figure 9-15 shows the typical distribution of two different areas(*4*) obtained by Sandia Corporation. The dry slide technique has not found widespread acceptance with clean room operators.

Cascade Impactor (Casella)

Air drawn into the cascade impactor *(5, 6)* is passed through four slit-type jets arranged in series.

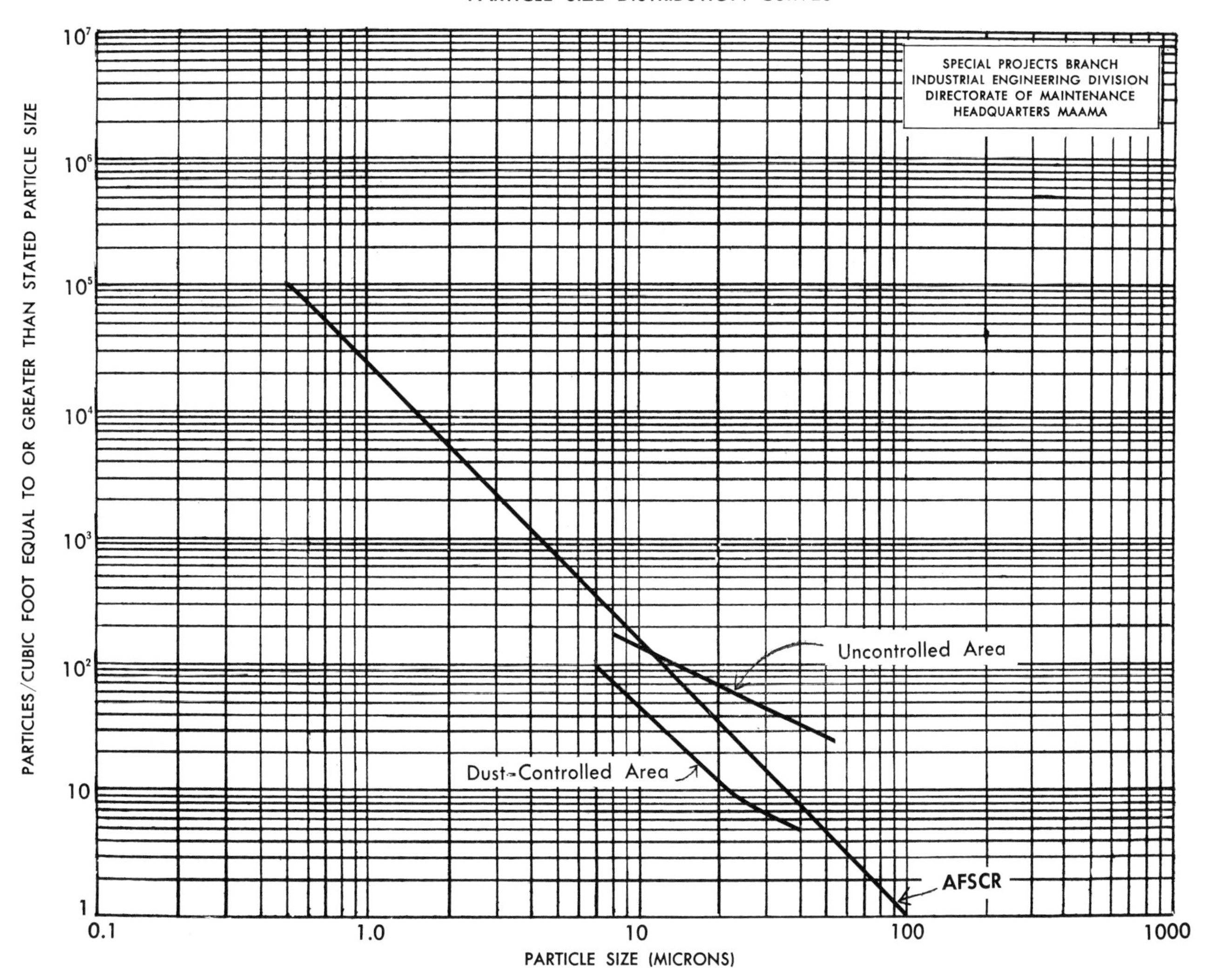

FIGURE 9-15. Dry-slide technique particle size-distribution curves.

Each jet is directed against a glass slide. The successive jets decrease in area so that at each stage the sampled air is accelerated to a higher velocity. This results in particles of decreasing size range being impacted on successive slides.

The clearance between the face of the jet and the slide also varies. The first jet is chamfered so that there is a clearance of 1 mm on the upstream side and 6 mm on the downstream side. The second jet is chamfered at 45° with the lower edge nearly touching the slide. The third and fourth jets are not chamfered and have clearances approximately equal to the slot width. A filter paper sampler may be added to serve as a fifth stage. The inlet tube terminates in the first jet. The dimensions of the jet, approximate speed of the air passing through the jet, mass median diameter (MMD), and maximum particle size impacted on the slides by each jet at an air-flow rate of 17.5 liters per minute are shown in the Table 9-1.

Membrane Filters

Having discussed several manual collecting and counting procedures requiring the use of membrane filters, it might be well to now discuss these filters in more detail. Membrane filters are porous membranes composed of pure and biologically inert cellulose esters. These filters perform primarily as simple screen-type filters or sieves. Many distinct pore-size types are currently produced ranging from 5 microns downward in pore size to 10 millimicrons. Each type retains on its surface, from liquids or gases passed through it, all particles that exceed the pore size in dimension. This absolute surface retension makes possible the extraordinary precision of those analytical procedures that require examining, counting, sizing, or identifying the retained particles.

Curves of high-pressure mercury intrusion test data[11] reveal an extraordinary uniformity of pore size throughout each filter. Figure 9-16 shows typical results for the 0.45-micron Millipore filter. Pore sizes in the sample vary from 0.43 to 0.47 micron, with the mean pore peaking at 0.45 micron. The filter specifications, therefore, are designated as 0.45 ± 0.02 micron.

Pores that penetrate the filters pass directly through the average 150-micron depth of the filter with a minimum of cross-linkage. Each square

[11] Skau-Ruska mercury intrusion measurements of pore radius are taken in which the formula $pr = -2\gamma \cos\theta$ relates pressure and pore radius to the coefficient of surface tension of mercury and its contact angle with respect to the filter matrix.

TABLE 9–1

AIR JET COMPARISON (7)

Jet	*Dimensions (cm)*	*Air speed (meters/sec)*	*Mass median diameter* (microns)*	*Maximum particle size of each jet (microns)*
1	1.9 × (0.6–0.7)	2.4	—	200
2	1.4 × 0.20	11.1	12	20
3	1.4 × 0.075	28.8	4	7
4	1.4 × 0.027	83.0	2	2.5

* MMD for No. 1 jet depends on maximum size present in aerosol.

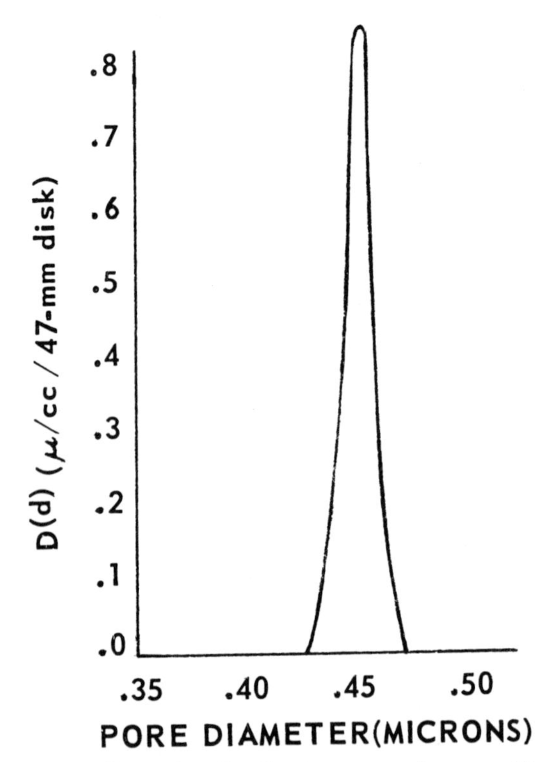

FIGURE 9-16. Pore size-distribution curve for type HA Millipore filter (0.45 micron) derived from high-pressure mercury intrusion test data. *Courtesy Millipore Filter Corp.*

TABLE 9–2

MILLIPORE FILTER SOLUBILITY CHARACTERISTICS

(In normal filtration exposure)

Solvent	*Effect on filter*	*Solvent*	*Effect on filter*
Hydrocarbons		*Esters*	
Pentane	None	Methyl acetate	Dissolves
Hexane	None	Ethyl acetate	Dissolves
Petroleum ether	None	Propyl acetate	Dissolves
Benzene	None	Butyl acetate	Dissolves
Toluene	None		
Xylene	None	*Miscellaneous Organic*	
		Pyridine	Dissolves
Halogenated Hydrocarbons		Dimethyl formamide	Dissolves
Methylene chloride	Shrinks	Unsymmetrical dimethyl hydrazine	Dissolves
Ethylene chloride	None	Nitrobenzene	Dissolves
Carbon tetrachloride	None	Ethylene glycol	None
Trichlorethylene	None	Varsol†	None
Freon TF*	None	Cobehn‡	None
Dichloroethane	None	Mineral spirits	None
Alcohols		Turpentine	None
Methanol	Dissolves	Kerosene	None
Ethanol	Swells	JP–4	None
Propanol	Distorts	JP–5	None
Isopropyl alcohol	None	*Oils*	
Butyl alcohol	None	Silicones	None
Glycerol	None	Silicodynes	None
Ether Alcohols		Petroleum-base hydraulic fluid	None
Carbitol	Dissolves	Phosphate esters	Swells§
Methyl Cellosolve	Dissolves	Silicate esters	Swells
Butyl Cellosolve	Dissolves	Terresso V–78†	None
		Natural oils	None
Cryogenic Liquids			
Liquid oxygen	None	*Acids*	
Liquid nitrogen	None	Glacial acetic acid	Dissolves
Liquid helium	None	10% acetic acid	None
Liquid hydrogen	None	6*N* hydrochloric acid	None
Ketones		6*N* sulfuric acid	None
Acetone	Dissolves	6*N* nitric acid	None
Methyl ethyl ketone	Dissolves	*Alkalies*	
Methyl isobutyl ketone	Dissolves	6*N* sodium hydroxide	Disintegrates
Cycohexanone	Dissolves	6*N* ammonium hydroxide	None
Diacetone	Dissolves		

* Registered trademark of the DuPont Company.
† Registered trademark of Esso Standard.
‡ Registered trademark of Cobehn Corporation.
§ Swells at 25°C; dissolves at elevated temperatures.

centimeter of the filter contains millions of these capillary pores. Pore volume occupies approximately 80% of the total filter volume.

Membrane filters exhibit typical properties of cellulose esters with respect to solubility and chemical resistance, as shown in Tables 9-2 and 9-3. They are not attacked by water, dilute acids and alkalies, aliphatic and aromatic hydrocarbons, halogenated hydrocarbons, or nonpolar liquids. These filters are soluble in ketones, esters, ether alcohols, and nitroparaffins, and are attacked by strong alkalies.

The membrane filter manufactured by Millipore is stable in a dry state at temperatures up to 125°C in the presence of oxygen. Gradual decomposition

Table 9–3

GELMAN MEMBRANE SOLVENT COMPATIBILITY TABLE

(Minimum 20-hour test at 20°C)

Solvent	*Solvent Concentration (%)*	*A M*	*G M Gravimetric*	*Protein Enrichment*	*Solvent Resistance*
Halogenated Compounds					
Methylene chloride	100	None	Shrinks	Shrinks	None
Chloroform	100	None	None	None	None
Carbon tetrachloride	100	None	None	None	None
Ethlylene chloride	100	None	None	None	None
Trichloroethylene	100	None	None	None	None
Perchloroethylene	100	None	None	None	None
Dichlorobenzene	100	None	Swells	None	None
Monochlorobenzene	100	None	Swells	None	None
Freon TF*	100	None	None	None	None
Hydrocarbons					
Benzene	100	None	Swells	None	None
Pentane	100	None	None	None	None
Cyclohexane	100	None	None	None	None
Hexane	100	None	None	None	None
Toluene	100	None	None	None	None
Pentane	100	None	None	None	None
Xylene	100	None	None	None	None
Petroleum ether	100	None	None	None	None
Ether alcohols					
Butyl Cellosolve	100	Dissolves	Dissolves	Dissolves	None
Methyl Cellosolve	100	Dissolves	Dissolves	Dissolves	None
Carbitol	100	Dissolves	Dissolves	Dissolves	None
Alcohols					
Methanol	100	Dissolves	Dissolves	Dissolves	None
	90	Swells	Swells	Dissolves	None
	70	None	None	None	None
Ethanol	96	Swells	None	Swells	None
	70	None	None	None	None
Propanol	100	Distorts	Distorts	Distorts	None
Isopropyl alcohol	100	None	None	None	None
Butyl alcohol	100	None	None	None	None
Amyl alcohol	100	None	None	None	None
Diethyl carbinol	100	None	None	None	None
Hexyl alcohol	100	None	None	None	None
Isobutyl alcohol	100	None	None	None	None
Octyl alcohol	100	None	None	None	None
Glycerol	100	None	None	None	None
Phenol	100	None	None	None	None
Acids					
Acetic acid	96	Dissolves	Dissolves	Dissolves	None
Acetic acid	30	None	Swells	None	None
Acetic acid	10	None	None	None	None
Aqua regia	100	None	Dissolves	None	Dissolves
(boiled 30 min)	100	Dissolves	Dissolves	Dissolves	Dissolves
Nitric acid	70	Dissolves	Attacks	Dissolves	Dissolves
	25	None	Attacks	None	None
	20	None	Attacks	None	None
	15	None	Attacks	None	None
	6*N*	None	None	None	None
Hydrochloric acid	32	Dissolves	Dissolves	Dissolves	Dissolves
	25	Distorts	Dissolves	None	Dissolves
	20	None	Distorts	None	None
	15	None	Distorts	None	None
	10	None	None	None	None
Sulfuric acid	96	Dissolves	Dissolves	Dissolves	Dissolves
	25	Distorts	Dissolves	None	Dissolves
	20	None	Distorts	None	None
	15	None	None	None	None
Formic acid	commercial	None	None	None	None
Phosphoric acid	50	Swells	Swells	None	None
	25	None	None	None	None
	20	None	None	None	None
	15	None	None	None	None
Ketones					
Acetone	100	Dissolves	Dissolves	Dissolves	None
Methyl isobutyl ketone	100	Dissolves	Dissolves	Dissolves	None
Diacetone alcohol	100	Dissolves	Dissolves	Dissolves	None
Cyclohexanone	100	Dissolves	Dissolves	Dissolves	None
Methyl ethyl ketone	100	Dissolves	Dissolves	Dissolves	None
Esters					
Methyl acetate	100	Dissolves	Dissolves	Dissolves	None
Ethyl acetate	100	Dissolves	Dissolves	Dissolves	None
N-Butyl acetate	100	Dissolves	Swells	Dissolves	None
Cellosolve acetate	100	Dissolves	Dissolves	Dissolves	None
Phosphate esters	100	Dissolves	Dissolves	Dissolves	None
Miscellaneous Organic					
Ethylene glycol	100	None	None	None	None
Propylene glycol	100	None	None	None	None
Methyl pyrrolidine	100	None	None	None	None
Petroleum ether	100	None	None	None	None
Turpentine	100	None	None	None	None
Kerosene	100	None	None	None	None
Aniline	100	Distorts	Dissolves	None	None
Decalin	100	None	None	None	None
Diethylene glycol	100	Dissolves	Swells	Dissolves	None
Dioxane	100	Dissolves	Dissolves	Dissolves	None
Glycerine	commercial	None	None	None	None
Bases					
Ammonium hydroxide solution	25	Dissolves	None	Dissolves	Distorts
	10	Dissolves	None	Distorts	None
	5	Distorts	None	None	None
Sodium or potassium hydroxide	50	Dissolves	Dissolves	Dissolves	Dissolves
	3	Dissolves	Distorts	Dissolves	Dissolves
	1	Distorts	None	Distorts	None
Oils and Fuels					
Mil H–5606–A	commercial	None	None	None	None
MIL H–6083–B	commercial	None	None	None	None
MIL F–17111	commercial	Swells	Swells	Swells	None
Silicate esters	commercial	None	None	None	None
Silicone oils	commercial	None	None	None	None
MIL H–7083–A	commercial	None	None	None	None
JP–4	commercial	None	None	None	None
JP–5	commercial	None	None	None	None
Natural oils	commercial	None	None	None	None

* Registered trademark of the DuPont Company.

takes place in air at temperatures above 125°C. These filters may be used in oxygen-free atmospheres at temperatures up to 200°C. The flash point of the filter is in excess of 200°C. They have been employed successfully for filtering cryogenic materials at temperatures as low as −200°C. No change in pore size, flow rate, or other properties is apparent as a result of prolonged storage of the filters at normal room temperatures.

In gas filtration, substantial electrostatic charges are generated and held by the filter because of the enormous specific surface and high resistivity. This negative charge prevents the passage of particles far smaller in dimension than the filter pore size. In liquid filtration, a high percentage of particles smaller than the filter pores are also retained by secondary valence (van der Waals) forces, by random entrapment in the slightly tortuous pores, and by build-up on previously retained particles.

White Millipore filters become transparent when their pores are filled with an immersion oil of matching refractive index. This property permits examination of particles on the filter surface by common transmitted light microscopy methods, with or without oil immersion objective lenses. The approximate refractive index for the filter is 1.5. This filter is an integral structure containing no fibers or particles that can work loose to contaminate a filtrate. It produces no ionic reaction with compatible fluids. If properly supported, Millipore filters will withstand differential pressure of at least 10,000 psi without significant distortion of the pore structure. They require no treatment prior to use and are disposable after use.

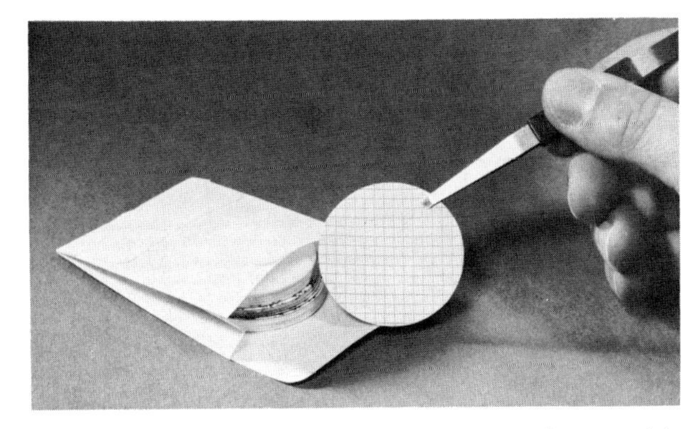

FIGURE 9-17. A Millipore filter with imprinted grid-marked top surface which divides the effective filtration area of a 47-mm disk into one hundred grid squares. *Courtesy Millipore Filter Corp.*

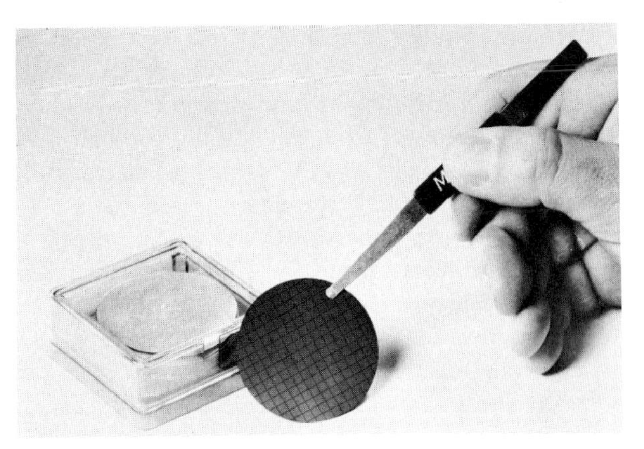

FIGURE 9-18. A dark-background Millipore filter. *Courtesy Millipore Filter Corp.*

Millipore filters are available with plain or imprinted grid-marked top surfaces (Figures 9-17 and 9-18). Grid lines are spaced 3.08 mm apart, forming squares each of which equals one-hundredth of the 9.6 sq cm of effective filtering area of a 47-mm diameter. Filter counts of particles falling within n grid squares may be multiplied by the factor $100/n$ to obtain a statistically accurate total count of all particles on the filter surface.

Some commercially available membrane filters are listed in Table 9-4. Figures 9-19 through 9-21

TABLE 9-4

SOME COMMERCIALLY AVAILABLE MILLIPORE FILTERS

Type	*Pore Size (microns)*
SM	5.0 ± 1.2
SS	3.0 ± 0.9
RA	1.2 ± 0.3
AA	0.80 ± 0.05
DA	0.65 ± 0.03
HA	0.45 ± 0.02
PH	0.30 ± 0.02
GS	0.22 ± 0.02
VC	100m ± 8m
VM	50m ± 3m
VF	10m ± 2m

graphically display some properties of these filters.

Millipore field monitors are disposable, plastic filter holders. A Millipore filter disk is sealed tightly at its margin between the top and bottom halves of the monitor (Figure 9-22) so that fluids may be passed readily through the unit, leaving their contaminants on the filter surface. A cellulose pad is placed beneath the filter for support and to distribute fluid flow over the entire filter surface. The effective filtration area of a field monitor is 9.6 sq cm. The top half of the monitor may be taken off after use to expose the filter for examination or removal.

Gelman Instrument markets a disposable filter holder called Dispoz-It (Figure 9-23).

Field monitors may be used in virtually all Millipore analytical procedures with a minimum of apparatus. They are ready for application as received, and their disposable configuration leaves nothing to clean up after use. All monitors are assembled in an ultraclean environment so that background particle counts will be minimized. (See Figure 9-24.) Four basic types of field monitors are available.

Contamination analysis monitors, molded of fuel-resistant Tenite plastic (Figure 9-25), are supplied with grid-marked or plain type AA white or black filters for use in the special Millipore bomb sampler. A special "thick" underlying support pad is supplied with these monitors, since they are usually used at higher pressure differentials. Contamination monitors may also be purchased disassembled so that the filter tare weight can be taken before use in a gravimetric analysis of fluid contaminant.

Control of Air-Sampling Rate[12]

For sampling to be quantitative in nature, the amount of air passing through the samplers must be known. The rate of flow for each sampler may be determined prior to the utilization of the device

[12] Abstracted from reference 7, pp. 11-13.

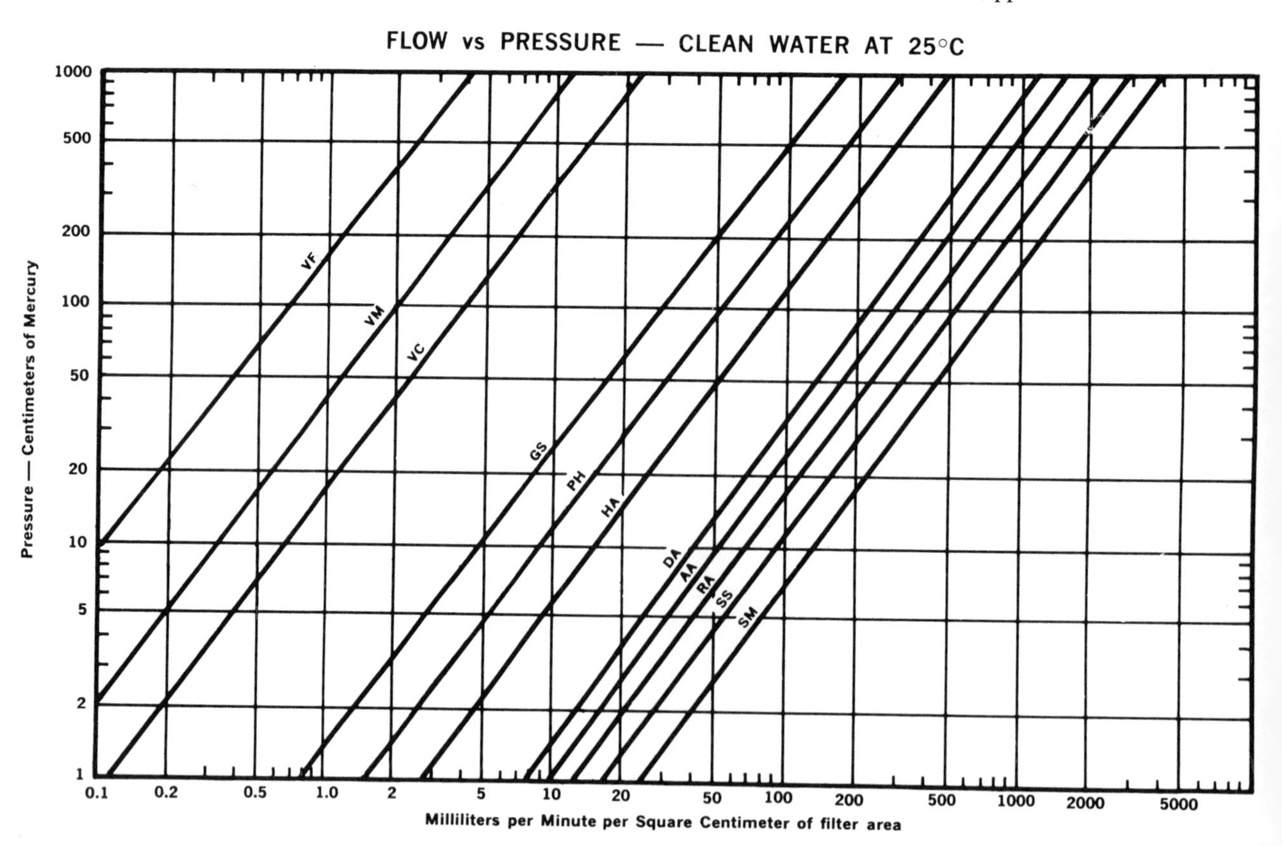

FIGURE 9-19. Flow versus pressure, clean water at 25°C. *Courtesy Millipore Filter Corp.*

for collecting air samples. Many devices for metering the flow are available; three are described here. The simplest but most expensive method is the use of a calibrated flowmeter connected in the vacuum line between the sampler and vacuum source. A somewhat less expensive method is the use of a manometer or a vacuum gauge and a regulating valve. To utilize this method, a calibrated flowmeter is first connected to the inlet of the sampler for calibrating the manometer. One side of a U-tube manometer or vacuum gauge is connected to the vacuum line between the sampler and the source of vacuum. The other side of the manometer is open to the atmosphere. With this system in operation, the amount of air passing through the sampler for a particular manometer reading is determined from the flowmeter and regulated by a bypass valve, preferably of the needle type, located on the vacuum inlet to the pump. In subsequent utilization of the sampler for collecting airborne particulates, the flowmeter is not included in the system. The rate of flow is maintained by adjusting the vacuum to the same manometer reading recorded for the desired flow rate. This calibration will be accurate as long as the resistance of the sampler does not change.

The third method of metering air flow, which eliminates the need of individual flowmeters for samplers when a number are in use, is the insertion of a capillary tube in the vacuum line. This tube may be used as a critical orifice to keep the sampler flow at the desired rate. This is based on the fact that the velocity of a gas flowing through an orifice will reach a maximum or acoustical[13] velocity when the critical pressure is reached. The theory applies to orifices in a thin flat surface, but for all

[13] Commonly referred to as the speed of sound, or Mach 1.

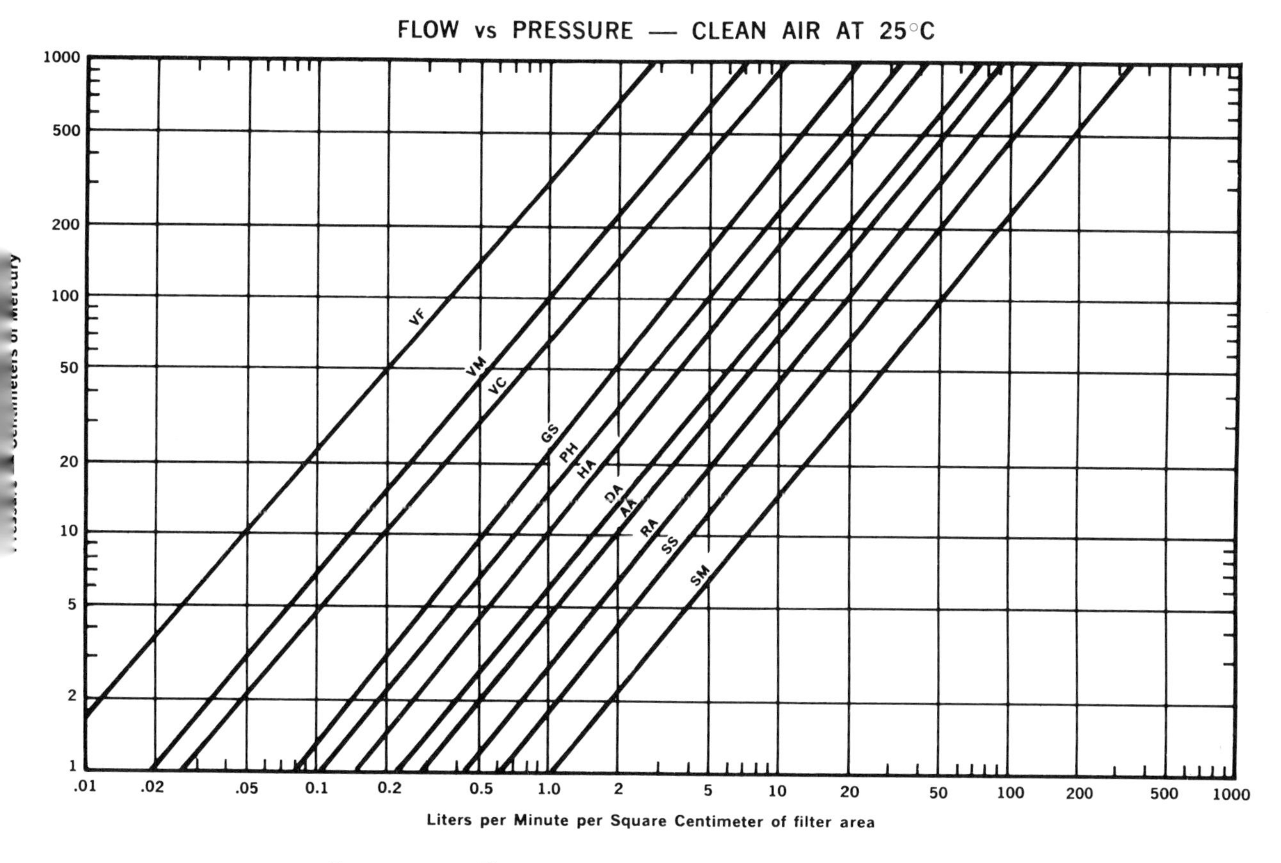

FIGURE 9-20. Flow versus pressure, clean air at 25°C.
Courtesy Millipore Filter Corp.

practical purposes it is also applicable to short lengths of capillary tubing. The critical pressure ratio is represented by the ratio of the downstream absolute pressure to the upstream absolute pressure. This critical ratio is approximately 0.53. When a vacuum is applied to the downstream side, the flow

FLOW RATE vs VISCOSITY

Clean Liquid at 70 centimeters of mercury (13.5 psig) differential pressure

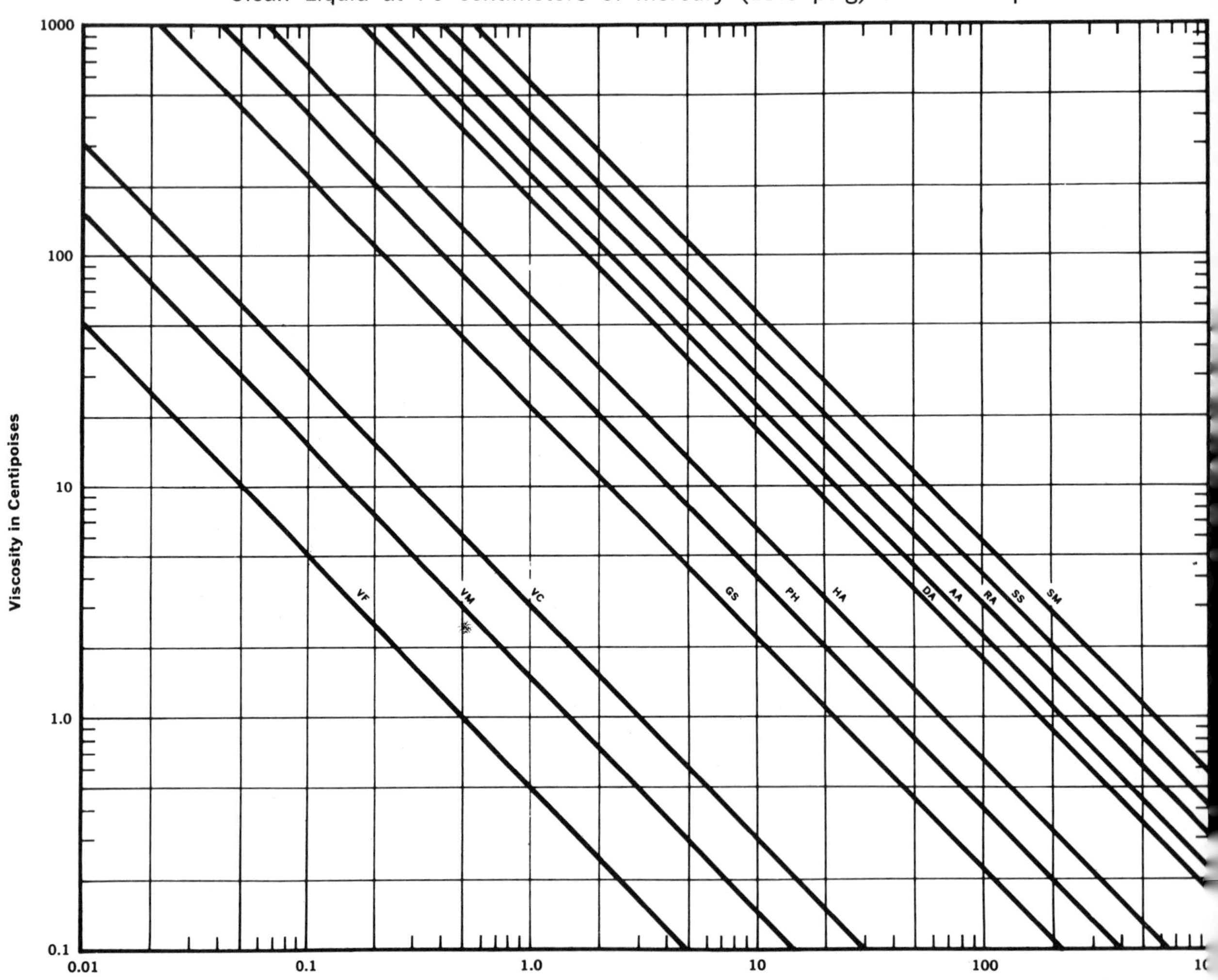

FIGURE 9-21. Flow rate versus viscosity. Curves reflect approximate initial flow rates through Millipore filters for *clean* liquids. Allowance must be made for progressive reduction of flow rate due to filter clogging by fluid contaminants. To convert milliliters per minute to U.S. gallons per minute, divide milliliters per minute by 3785. To convert centistokes to centipoises, multiply centistokes by liquid specific gravity. Flow rate is a linear function of pressure differential (neglecting the flow-limiting effect of specific filter holder design). To calculate approximate flow rates at differential pressures other than 70 cm Hg (13.5 psig), multiply curv readings by

$$\frac{\triangle \text{ P (in cm Hg)}}{70} \text{ or } \frac{\triangle \text{ P (in psi)}}{13.5}.$$

To calculate approximate liquid flow rates throug Millipore filter holders, multiply curve readin by the filtration area factor. *Courtesy Millipor Filter Corp.*

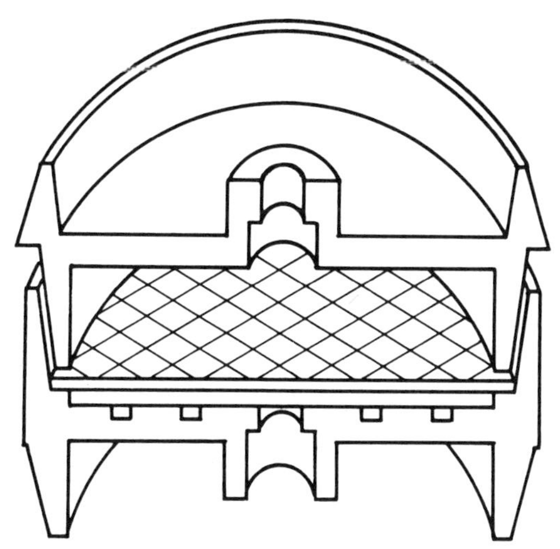

FIGURE 9-22. Cross-sectional view of Millipore field monitor showing construction. *Courtesy Millipore Filter Corp.*

FIGURE 9-24. Aerosol monitors used to detect airborne contaminants where Millipore filters are cut, assembled, and packaged. *Courtesy Millipore Filter Corp.*

through the orifice will increase until this pressure ratio is reached. Increasing the vacuum further will not increase the flow, no matter how high it may go, provided the upstream conditions do not change (Figure 9-26). This means that constant flow can be maintained through a critical orifice without the necessity of having a constant vacuum as long as one uses a vacuum source of sufficient capacity so that the downstream pressure is always less than

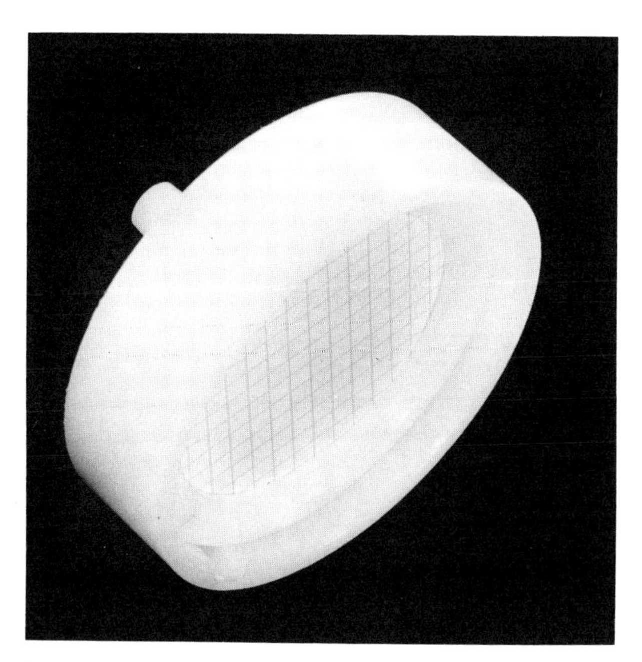

FIGURE 9-23. Gelman DISPOZ-IT disposable filter holder. *Courtesy Gelman Instrument Co.*

FIGURE 9-25. Millipore contaminant analysis monitor. *Courtesy Millipore Filter Corp.*

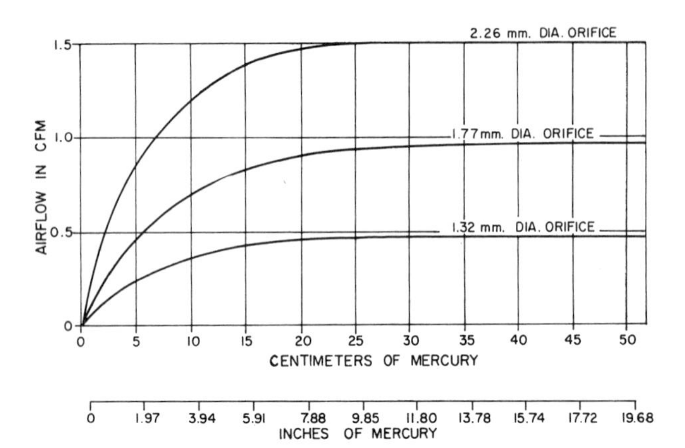

FIGURE 9-26. Critical air flow through orifices. *U. S. Public Health Monograph 60.*

half the upstream pressure. How much less than 0.53 this ratio is does not matter.

An orifice may be cut from a glass or metal capillary tube in a convenient length (2 inches). The outside diameter should be large enough to fit snugly inside the vacuum tubing, and the inside diameter should be of a size to give approximately the desired flow. The exact flow through this orifice must be accurately measured, care being taken to do this in the same arrangement in which it will be used so that there will be no change in conditions when samples are taken. To measure or calibrate the orifice, proceed as follows: Place the orifice in the vacuum line between the sampler and the vacuum source, and connect a standard flowmeter to the inlet of the sampler to measure the sampling rate accurately. Connect a mercury manometer across the orifice, and adjust the vacuum so that the pressure differential is 38.0 cm Hg or above. The air flow is indicated on the standard flowmeter, and if this value is too high or too low, repeat this procedure using another orifice with a different diameter until one is found giving the desired flow. During each measurement, make certain that the pressure drop is at least 0.5 atmosphere. After the proper orifice diameter has been determined, more orifices of the same length may be cut from the same tube, but each of these should be calibrated separately, since the capillary diameter is often not constant through the length of the same tube. If a glass capillary is used and the diameter is larger than desired, it may be reduced by holding one end in a burner flame until the opening at the end is constricted. The flowmeter is not needed after the orifices have been calibrated.

Basic Requirement for Automatic Monitoring *(8)*

A problem that has been a favorite topic of discussion for some time has been that of reliability and need for automatic monitoring. Both digital and analog light-scattering devices have been developed for automatic particle monitoring. Although attempts have been made to produce various types of automatic devices commercially, few of them have come to fruition.

The question to be asked is, "What is the basic requirement for automatic monitoring of a clean room?" The first and most important requirement is that automatic particle monitoring should be performed in areas where other techniques are either inaccurate, inadequate, inefficient, or costly, or where greater reliability, repeatability, and accuracy are needed. Automatic particle counters are necessary in areas where the transient contaminant level must be known. Generally speaking, areas that permit few large-size particles—that is, particles greater than 5 microns—may require automatic counting. Studies *(9-11)* indicate that there is a fairly linear relationship for airborne contaminants when plotted on log-log paper. (See Chapter 2.)

Automatic monitoring devices have application in other areas also—areas where smaller particles will affect the production or operation of the product and where these particles cannot be adequately monitored by manual counting techniques. Automatic counting devices may have one of their best applications on assembly lines. An example might be in the production of color television tubes where airborne contaminants can greatly affect the three-dot color deposition operation. Automatic monitoring devices provide rapid feedback information on airborne contaminant levels. They also provide a hard record of the contamination level during various intervals of time. A hard record is meaningless, however, if the information obtained is never used. Indiscriminate use of automatic particle counting can be a very costly burden to an operation.

The type of operation performed in the majority of facilities will not require automatic digital counting techniques. The level of contamination can be adequately determined by means of manual counting techniques or by the calibration of inexpensive analog counting techniques by digital counting equipment. Thus it appears that one digital counting device will be able to support a number of clean room facilities and would be used primarily for calibration of analog devices, certification of rooms, and random contamination level checks for clean rooms. For very critical areas where contamination must be maintained at extremely low levels, digital counting techniques may be needed.

With the advent of laminar-flow facilities and clean work stations, low levels of contamination can be adequately provided. Once these facilities are checked for leaks and are shown to be in proper operation, few additional checks will be needed; however, when checks are made, they must be performed with an instrument that is extremely sensitive to change in contamination level. In other words, the device must have a quick response, since, in this type of facility, filters will be scanned for pinhole leaks producing high contamination streamlines. Thus, the requirements for automatic monitoring will depend on the type of facility to be monitored, the type of items being worked on, and the nature of the work performed.

Automatic Particle Counters

Methods of sampling dust by collection on surfaces or in a liquid medium by impaction, impingement, or settling form a large group. Details of instruments based on these methods are readily available in many publications(*12-15*). No one of these methods is ideal for all purposes, but each is useful for measurement under specific conditions. Some of the methods may seem inefficient when subjected to exacting or comparative laboratory tests(*16*), but the purposes for which they were designed should be remembered, and their usefulness should not be unduly discounted.

Many systems have been proposed and tried for automatic detection of particulate matter. Measurement of particles in flight has long been recognized as a desirable goal. If this could be accomplished by an automatic instrument that, unattended, would make a continuous record of size and number of dust particles, much valuable information could be obtained at a tremendous saving in labor. An obvious approach to measuring particles in flight is to have the particles intercept a light beam and then measure either the obscuration of transmitted light or the amount of light scattered by individual particles. Successful development of this method has resulted only after much effort by a number of investigators. It had to await refinement of the theory of light-scattering by fine particles and development of highly specialized optics and electronic equipment.

The most commercially successful systems designed for optical detection of submicron and micron particles are based on the theory of light-scattering. The theory for the scattering of monochromatic light by spherical particles was developed by Mie in 1908(*17*) and by Debye in 1909(*18*, *19*). Not until 1947, however, did Gucker *et al.*(*20*) successfully apply this theory in a machine capable of counting 1200 1-micron particles per minute. Gucker and Rose(*21*) improved on this first machine in 1954, and Fisher *et al.*(*22*) produced a similar instrument called the aerosoloscope in 1955.

The first counter used forward-angle scattering because, for all but the smallest particles, this far exceeds the scattering at any other angle. The next instrument employed right-angle scattering in order to reduce the background light to the low level required for maximum sensitivity to small particles. The Mie theory of light-scattering dictates a marked irregularity of the radial light-scattering function. A right-angle counter and photometer of great sensitivity was built by O'Konski and Doyle in 1955; they found that it gave a response linear with the square of the particle radius over the range 0.16 to 0.50 micron.

Based on the above remarks, there might appear to be a discrepancy between the Mie theory and the experimental results. Gucker and Rose (1955) calculated the theoretical response curves for isotropic spheres in four different optical systems of increasing complexity. The theoretical response curves for right-angle scattering were found to have only minor deviations from linearity with particle radius squared, provided that white light was used. White light smooths out many of the minor fluctuations of the monochromatic response curves. A further smoothing of the response curve is obtained if the scattered light is collected over a wide angle,

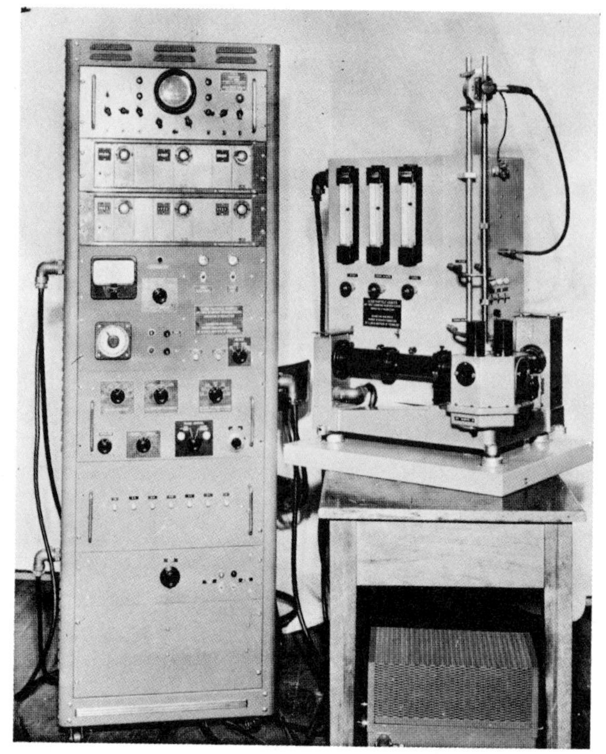

FIGURE 9-27. Armour Research Foundation particle counter. Small cabinet houses aerosol-handling and optical systems, and photomultiplier with preamplifier; large cabinet houses electronic and readout systems. *Courtesy Air Engineering*

which can be accomplished by using a low *f*-number lens. Unpublished work by Royco Instruments Company shows that this relation holds for particles up to 27 microns in diameter at least and is not greatly affected by the refractive index of the particle.

ARF Particle Counter

The Armour Research Foundation (ARF) particle counter,[14] based on the principle described by Gucker *et al.*(*20, 23*) and developed by Katz *et al.* (*24*), employs a multiplier phototube to measure light pulses scattered by individual particles. These pulses are electrically amplified and counted. Because the amount of light scattered is proportional to the square of the particle diameter, size-distribution data are obtained. With this instrument, the sample of air containing the suspended particles may be diluted if necessary to permit electronic counting of individual particles at a rate of 12,000 per minute or less, to keep coincidence error[15] below 3.5%.

The instrument is shown in Figure 9-27. The smaller cabinet houses the aerosol-handling system, the optical system, and the photomultiplier with preamplifier. The larger cabinet houses the electronic and readout systems. The aerosol is drawn into the instrument at a rate of 13.2 liters per minute by a vacuum pumping system. When the aerosol concentration exceeds 1000 particles per cubic

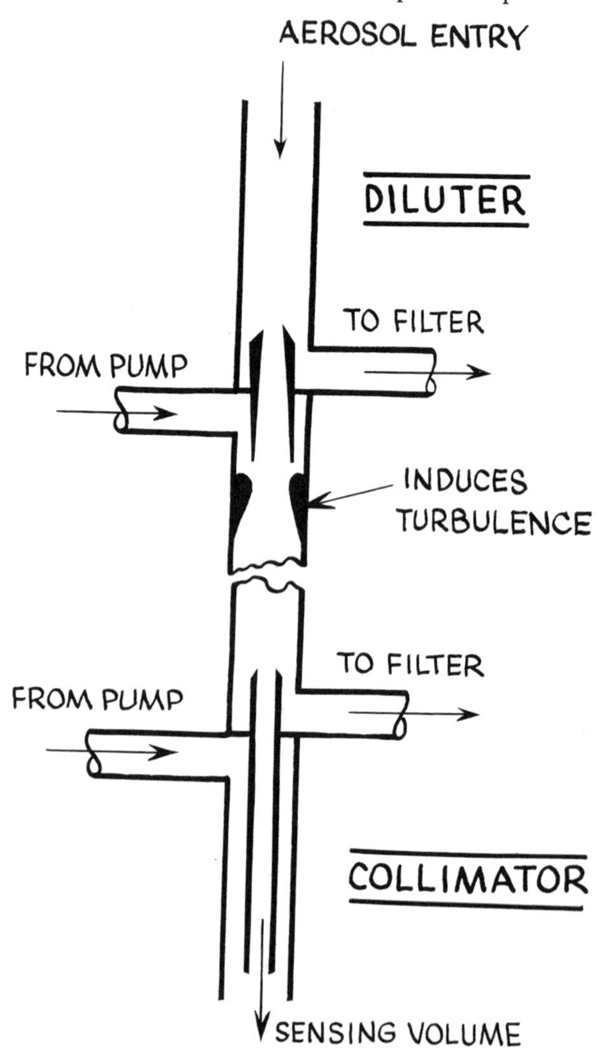

FIGURE 9-28. Diluter and collimator(*25*).

[14] This unit is not commercially available.

[15] Coincidence error results when two particles are in the sensing zone but are counted as one.

centimeter, a diluter is provided to reduce it to one-eleventh of its original concentration. Figure 9-28 shows the dilution stage and collimating stage for delivering a cylindrical stream of aerosol particles of the proper concentration to the optical detection region. For monitoring clean rooms, the diluter is unnecessary.

The air to be sampled enters a collimator, where a representative fraction flows down a central tube, while the balance is routed through a submicron particulate filter to rejoin the areosol as an annular clean air sheath. The collimated aerosol continues down through the detection zone and out the exhaust. It travels at 11 fps through the aerosol-handling section and is present in the detection region for about 300 microseconds. At the working concentration, particles are detected individually.

Figure 9-29 shows how the light scattered at right angles by an individual particle is focused on a photomultiplier tube. The intensity of the light is dependent on the size and the scattering coefficient of the particle. Right-angle scattering has two advantages over forward scattering: (1) it is easier to trap and eliminate extraneous light, with the result that the apparatus is simpler to build; and (2) the intensity of the scattered light is approximately proportional to the square of particle diameter,

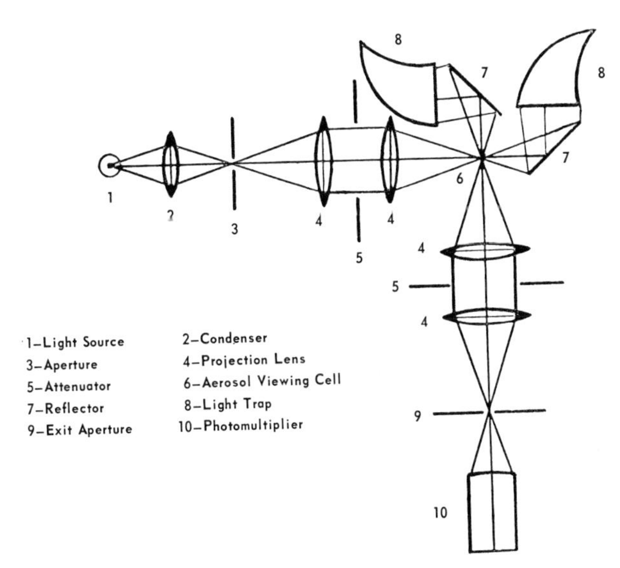

FIGURE 9-29. Typical optical system of a light-scattering airborne particle detector(*2*).

which is not true for forward-scattered light. On the other hand, the forward-scattering principle, because of its greater sensitivity, may be better for very small particles.

The particles are illuminated by a ribbon-filament tungsten lamp, and the light component scattered at 90° is collected by the photomultiplier. The photomultiplier generates a pulse for each particle counted. The height of the pulse is a measure of particle size. The signal pulse leaving the photomultiplier is sent to a six-channel pulse-height discriminator, separating the pulses into groups so that the number in each group can be recorded by a digital readout system.

The speed with which individual particles can be counted is limited by the response of the register system to 12,000 counts per minute per channel. To minimize coincident counting, however, the total rate should not exceed 12,000 particles per minute. The electrical pulses resulting from the scattered light falling on the photomultiplier tube are amplified and then sorted according to pulse height into six channels corresponding to six size ranges of aerosol particles, from about 0.3 to 64 microns. The pulse-height discriminator is adjustable so that the largest particle detected is either eight or sixty-four times the smallest detected.

The light-scattering particle counter is probably the fastest and most convenient method for measuring contamination in a clean room. As Lieberman *(26)* points out, however, it is costly and requires appreciable maintenance. Other problems associated with the light-scattering technique, as pointed out by Lieberman, are as follows: (1) the sample must be large enough to permit counting of a statistically representative sample of all sizes of interest; (2) the scattering coefficient of particles being sampled must be known (a compromise empirical solution to this problem is to assign a mean scattering coefficient for the materials normally encountered in a given clean room); (3) particles, especially the larger sizes, may be lost to the walls of the sampling tube, especially at bends, and to other parts of the instruments; (4) errors may result from coincident counting when the particle count rate is high; (5) proper interpretation of the data, which applies also for other methods of monitoring, is a serious problem (probably the most serious).

Royco Particle Counter

To provide an automatic particle counter and sizer for commercial use, a number of refinements were necessary beyond those incorporated in the experimental models. Several models of a counter produced by Royco Instruments are shown in Figure 9-30.

In later models of this instrument, airborne particles are passed through the sensing region of the optical system shown in Figure 9-31. The region is intensely illuminated by a beam of white light. The suspended particles scatter a portion of the light, a fraction of which is picked up, at 90° to the axis of the beam, by a lens system and proceeds to a photomultiplier tube. The light pulses from individual particles are transformed to electrical pulses. The pulses are amplified and sent to upper- and lower-level discriminators for counting. A block diagram of the Royco PC-200A particle counter is shown in Figure 9-32.

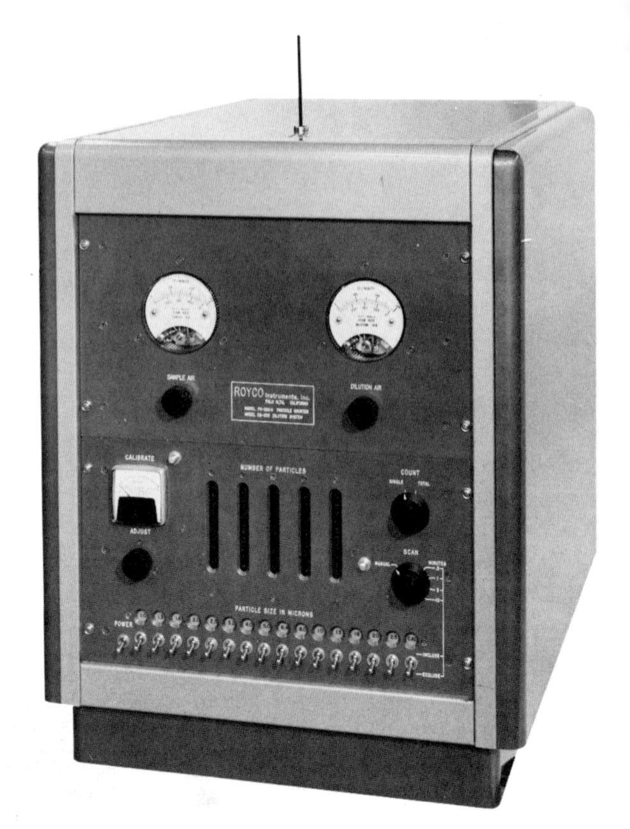

FIGURE 9-30. *A*, Royco Model PC-200A. *B*, Royco Model PC-202 (Model 200 with dilution system). *C*, Royco Model PC-200A with print-out. *D*, Royco Model 300 (liquid particle counter). *Courtesy Royco Instruments, Inc.*

The method described assumes that the intensity of scattered light from an individual particle is proportional to the size of the particle. Light-scatter theory states that, for a given wavelength of incident light, angle of scatter, and refractive index of the particle, the scatter intensity, I, is a function of the particle radius to the power p, as follows:

$$I \propto r^p \qquad (9\text{-}4)$$

Actually, it is known that the value of p varies according to particle size, being about 2 for particles of 0.4 to about 1 micron in diameter, and about 1 for particles larger than 1 micron. The value I also depends on the refractive index of the particle.

Since both particle size and refractive index may vary in atmospheric dusts, some error will be present in the final data.

In practical use, a number of things can happen to the optical system to alter the amount of light scattered by an individual particle. For example, the light bulb darkens with use, or lenses may become dirty. Such changes are usually slow. A means of compensating for them is provided by a mechanically pulsed light beam of calibrated intensity that uses the same optical system as is employed for lighting the particles. By occasionally adjusting proper gain controls, compensation can be made for any changes in the system.

Elimination of stray light and electronic noise, in order to obtain maximum sensitivity, has been a problem for all designers of this type of equipment. The use of right-angle scattering is superior to the use of other angles in this respect. Good engineering design, proper selection of components, and attention to detail all help to reduce noise, although it can never be eliminated. Some scattering of light from air molecules in the light path will occur. A typical response is as follows:

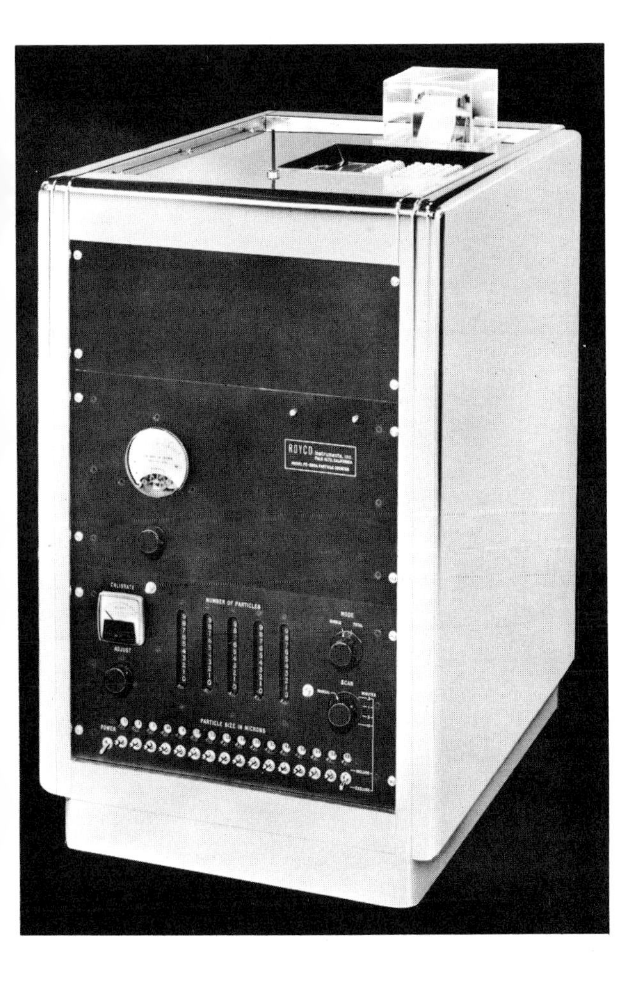

Source of Response	*Signal Level at Output of Phototube Preamplifier*
Dark current of phototube and electrical noise in instrument; light off	0.5 mv
Light cell filled with helium; light on	6.0 mv
Light cell filled with air; light on	20.0 mv
Single 0.32-micron particle in cell suspended in illuminated air	63.0 mv

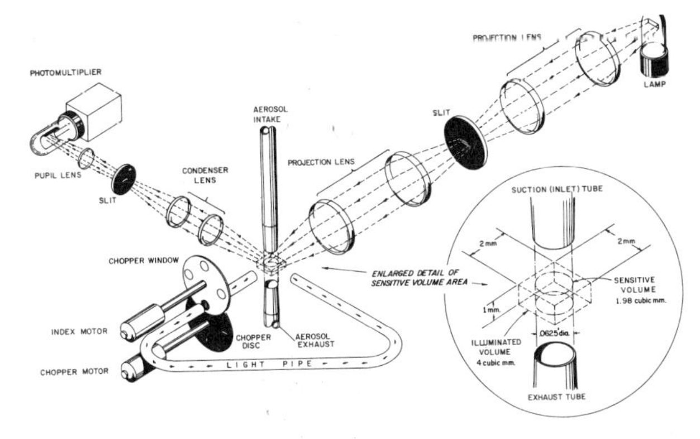

FIGURE 9-31. Exploded view of the operation of a light-scattering particle counting instrument. *Courtesy Air Engineering*

The sampling rate should be as large as possible. Practical considerations that limit the rate are the speed at which the counting mechanisms can be operated and the loss of counts by particles obscuring each other in the light path.

Particles passing through the light path less than 1 millisecond apart tend to be counted as a single particle, which results in a coincident loss. Loss of count can be made negligible for all practical purposes for particle concentrations up to 10,000 per minute *(27)* in any single size range, at air flow rates of 200 cc per minute. Higher concentrations can be measured in the sample and counted by employing a dilution system that supplies known ratios of particle-free air.

Because each particle is counted as an individual, there is little difference in the accuracy whether incoming air contains, on the average, one particle or several million particles per cubic foot.

Not all size ranges are counted simultaneously. Rather, each size range is counted for a definite interval, and a stepping switch transfers the light pulses over a series of ranges, or it may be set to count continuously in a single size range.

The number of size ranges in which particles can be measured may be divided into any reasonable number. The maximum number is a function of the resolution of the instrument. Fifteen ranges are conveniently divided as shown in Table 9-5.

The nominal diameter of particles in each succeeding range increases by about 26%, in accordance with the formula

$$\text{Log}_{10} \frac{(D_n)}{(D_1)} = 0.1(n - 1), \qquad (9\text{-}5)$$

where n is the channel number.
Thus, for channels 1 and 15,

$$\text{Log}_{10} \frac{(D_{15})}{(D_1)} = 1.4 \quad \text{or} \quad \frac{(D_{15})}{(D_1)} = 25 \qquad (9\text{-}6)$$

This corresponds to a measurement of particles with a volume ratio of about 15,850/1.

Packaging of all components into an assembly that is reasonably portable is highly desirable. Samples are collected through a small single-entry tube. It is essential not to pass samples through long con-

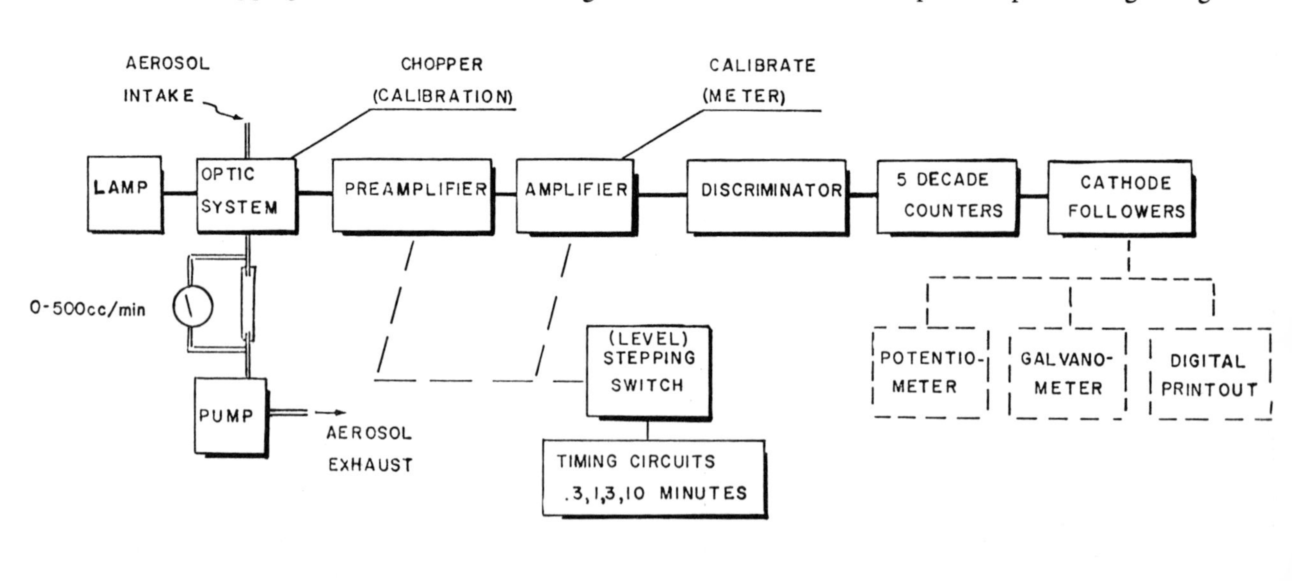

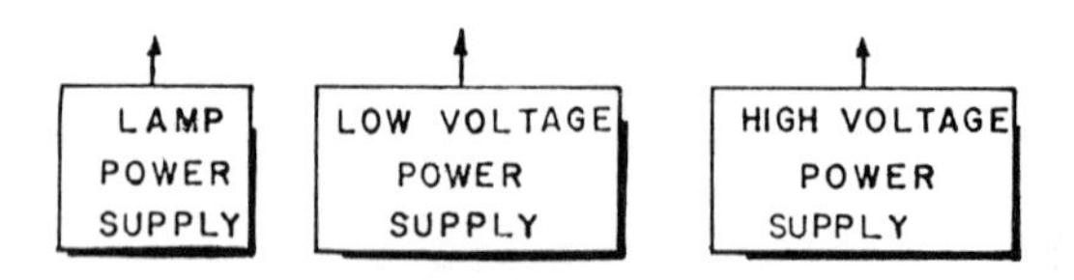

FIGURE 9-32. Block diagram of Royco PC200A particle counter. *Courtesy Royco Instruments, Inc.*

TABLE 9–5

PARTICLE SIZE RANGES*

Range No. (*n*)	*Micron Size, Panel Reading* (*D*)	*Size Range* (μ)	*Signal Level at Preamplifier Output to Initiate Count* (*volts*)
1	0.32	0.316 – 0.398	0.0631
2	0.4	0.398 – 0.501	0.100
3	0.5	0.501 – 0.631	0.158
4	0.64	0.631 – 0.794	0.251
5	0.8	0.794 – 1.0	0.398
6	1.0	1.0 – 1.26	0.631
7	1.3	1.26 – 1.585	1.0
8	1.6	1.585 – 1.995	1.585
9	2.0	1.995 – 2.51	2.51
10	2.5	2.51 – 3.16	3.98
11	3.2	3.16 – 3.98	6.31
12	4.0	3.98 – 5.0	10.0
13	5.0	5.0 – 6.31	15.85
14	6.4	6.31 – 7.94	25.1
15	8.0	7.94 – 10.0	39.8

* From *Air Engineering*

ductors. There is always the possibility of contamination from the conductor or loss of particles to the walls. It is thus desirable to place the instrument as close as possible to the sampling site.

Instrument Development

The successful development of instruments for automatic counting and sizing of dust opens possibilities for displacing many of the previous, more laborious methods. The complexity and expense of the automatic instruments ordinarily will not justify their purchase for occasional use. Further, they do not provide information on the composition of dust particles. If particles are desired for analysis, they must be collected by some of the more conventional methods. A continuous recording sampler can be useful, however, in selecting the best times and locations for selecting spot samples for identification.

It is rare that dust is uniformly mixed in outdoor air or in an enclosure. As a consequence, any single small sample of air is not likely to represent the true facts of concentration or size. This is especially true when concentrations change with time. Errors by a factor of 10 or more may arise from the choice of improper sampling periods. Sampling periods are important when applied to air within enclosures. The time scale that has to be considered depends on the particular problem.

There are a number of highly pertinent aspects of sampling, interpretation of results, and correlation of measurement data with practical phases of manufacturing that are not covered in this discussion. The problem of developing confidence in the change-over from one method of particle measurement to another is not easy to solve. This is especially true if there has been a long period of experience with one method.

Calibration of an automatic particle counter should be according to manufacturer's instructions. To perform a zero-count check on a Royco counter, a 100-millimicron membrane filter is put on the input tube. The air-flow valve is opened and adjusted to the proper air-flow rate. The counter is programed to the total mode, counting all particles greater than 0.5 micron. The instrument should read zero. If counts are registered, the instrument should be allowed to purge itself with the membrane filter in place until a zero count is reached. This procedure may also be accomplished by purging the cell with clean dry helium or nitrogen at 10 psig. This procedure should always be repeated when the counter is placed in an area where the particle concentration is expected to be less than that of the area previously sampled.

When a count of the total number of particles greater than some minimum size is desired, the instrument should be set to total mode and programed to count repeatedly all particles greater than the desired lower size limit. When a particle size-distribution curve is desired, the instrument is set to total mode and programed to step automatically through the desired size spectrum. This will yield a cumulative particle size-distribution curve.

For spot sampling, ten 1-minute counts should be made at each location, and an average taken. For continuous sampling, the average of any three successive counts around any specific time should be reported as the particle count at that time.

The indicated particle concentration may be calculated as follows:

$$N_i = \frac{N}{F \times t} \qquad (9\text{-}7)$$

where N_i = indicated number of particles per cubic foot.
N = number of particles counted.
F = flow rate, in cubic feet per minute.
t = scan time, in minutes.

Flashes of light in the illuminated zone may overlap by random coincidence. Calculation by statistical methods of random processes shows that the indicated concentration is related to the actual concentration as follows:

$$N_a = \frac{N_i}{e^{-VN_i}} \qquad (9\text{-}8)$$

where N_a = the actual concentration, in particles per cubic foot.
V = optical sensor volume, 0.6×10^{-7} cubic feet.
N_i = indicated number of particles per cubic foot.
e = 2.7183, the base of natural logarithms.

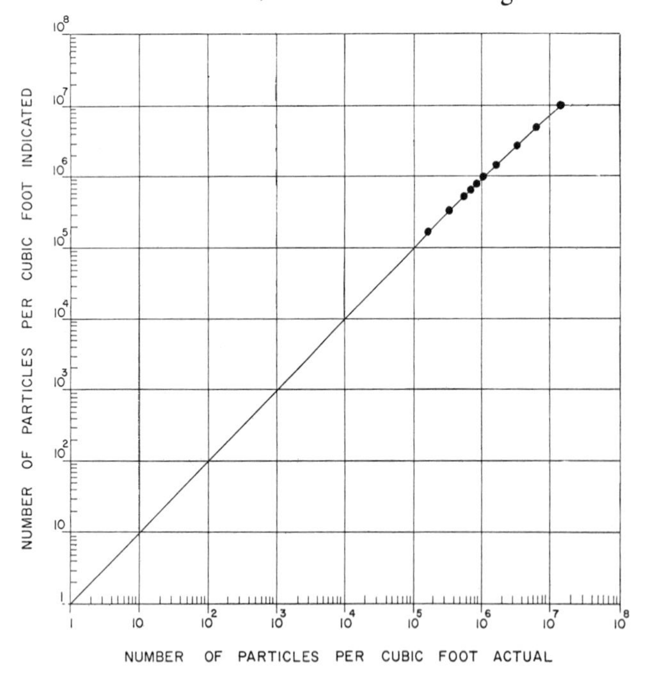

FIGURE 9-33. Number of particles indicated versus number of particles actual. *Proposed ASTM Procedure for Automatic Particle Counters*

A graph of N_i versus N_a is shown in Figure 9-33.

Concentration correction for total indicated particulate concentration of 100,000 particles per cubic foot is less than 0.6% and may be neglected.

An experiment *(28)* was carried out by Dutch, of Litton Systems, to check the error introduced by upscaling the measured particle volumes of a Royco counter, Model PC-200A, to 1 cubic foot. This information is shown in Figure 9-34, where the air-sampled volumes are plotted against particle counts. As the air samples increased, the sum of particle counts from 0.3 to 8 microns also increased, and, when plotted, a straight-line function was obtained. It would be expected that by doubling the sample size the particle counts would also double. This, however, was not the case. The experimental line showed a 20% deviation from the expected line. The counts were carried out in a room where particle contamination was extremely high. In clean rooms where the particle counts are relatively low, the deviation is less, since the coincidence factor (representing the passage of several particles through the optical system at the same time) is lower.

Prior to monitoring the dust-free area, the repeatability of particle counts with the Royco PC-200A particle counter was also checked. This information is shown on Table 9-6. The air-sampling rate was set at 0.01 cfm, and the particles were counted for a period of 0.3 minute. The instrument setting was at total mode (counting the sum

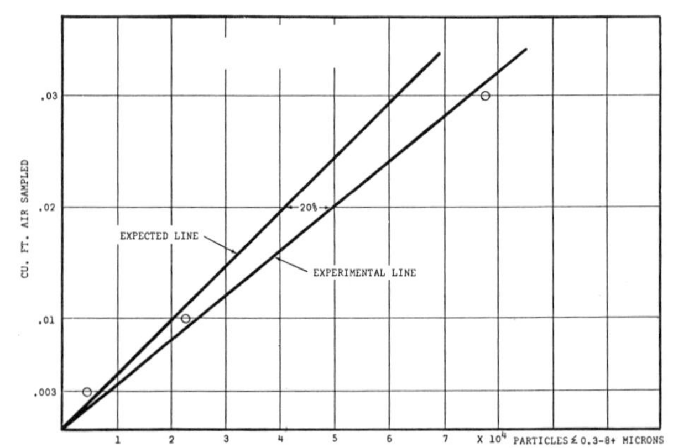

FIGURE 9-34. Variation of particle counts with sample size(*28*).

of all particles ranging from 0.3 to 1.0 micron). The seven determinations produced an average error of 12.5%. The error due to upscaling to 1 cubic foot is a maximum of 20% and the error due to lack of repeatability is a maximum of 12.5%. This gives us a total maximum error of 32.5%.

Comparison of Manual Counting Procedure with Automatic Light-Scattering Device

To date, a number of attempts have been made to correlate manual counting techniques with automatic light-scattering devices. Most recently, Autonetics performed a study under the direction of M. J. Killion to determine the comparison of the automatic counter method with the microscopic method for counting dust samples. Autonetics Report CT-4-3-1, April 2, 1963, stated that the primary concern of this investigation was to compare the Royco PC-200A automatic particle counter with the microscopic method presently used for counting and sizing airborne contamination. A similar study had been made by Autonetics in 1961.

TABLE 9–6

REPEATABILITY OF PARTICLE COUNTS (28)

(Air sample: 0.01 cfm. Counting time: 0.3 min. Counting: total mode 0.3 to 1.0 microns. High concentration)

Room	*Particle Counts per Cubic Foot of Air*	*Per Cent Error*
1	2.6×10^5	12.6
2	4.3×10^5	10.4
3	5.2×10^4	13.5
4	8.0×10^5	10.4
5	2.6×10^6	15.3
6	1.2×10^6	14.6
7	9.7×10^5	10.6
Average error	$5.0 \times 10 - 3.0 \times 10^6$	12.5

Error due to upscaling to 1 cubic foot	20%
Error due to lack of repeatability	12.5%
Maximum total error	32.5%

In their investigation and analysis of dust samples, Autonetics found a wide variation among operators in reading the dust count membrane filters. Therefore, for their comparison study an operator who represented the statistical average of all the operators was employed to read the dust samples. In this study, one hundred and thirty samples were taken simultaneously by both automatic counting and manual sampling methods. The conclusions drawn from this study were that the two methods are interchangeable for the size range above 5 microns. A negative deviation of 1.8% between the two methods was observed.

In this study, a positive deviation of 10 to 15% was noticed between the black and white membrane samples. A further discussion in this report showed that Autonetics could effect a cost saving if automatic sampling equipment was used to monitor and count airborne particulate matter. This was brought out by the comparison study showing that the automatic and microscopic counting methods were interchangeable. The cost of four technicians at an average hourly wage of $2.45 per hour over a two-year period would amount to $44,512. The equipment and membrane filters for taking these manual samples would amount to $8692. During this period these four technicians would take 20,800 samples. Thus the cost per sample would be $2.65. A like comparison was made for automatic counting devices. The cost of four sensing units and a complete master control system installed for the automatic sampling method would be $46,000. One technician would be required to operate this equipment, at a salary of $11,128 for a two-year period. The automatic equipment would take 48 samples per shift. Thus in the two-year period 24,960 samples would be taken, and the cost per sample would be $2.29. After the initial two-year period, the cost per sample for the microscopic method would drop to $2.23, in comparison with a drop to $0.44 per sample with the automatic counter. Autonetics thus would realize a cost savings of $1.79 per sample, or $47,174 per year. It was pointed out in the report that this value was only an estimate in that overhead and maintenance costs were completely ignored. Only the actual salaries and cost of filters and equipment were used.

One aspect must be considered in contamination

monitoring. No matter how simple and effective, or sophisticated and accurate, a particular monitoring system is, it is of no benefit unless the people who operate it are sufficiently trained. Both equipment limitations and the human element must be clearly understood. As long as counting judgment is a function of an individual, some arbitrary counts will exist. People are not infallible. This applies particularly to the exacting field of particle monitoring. Also, training programs should be conducted to acquaint fully those who are charged with monitoring with the causes and effects of contaminants.

Calibration of Particle Counters

Standardization of the particle counter provides a comparison of results obtained when the instrument sizes monodisperse aerosols or an aerosol with a known particle size distribution. The standardization method consists in preparation of an aerosol with known size distribution and measurement of this aerosol size distribution with the counter.

A dispersion of a polystyrene latex hydrosol provides the most readily available standard. Latex particles are available in the size range from 0.3 to 4 microns with standard deviations in particle size of approximately 1%. Particles of latex and other materials are available in larger sizes with much larger standard deviations. Standard polystyrene latex particles produced by the Dow Chemical Company Physical Research Laboratories, Midland, Michigan, have been found satisfactory for this purpose. These particles are sized by Dow Chemical Company with an electron microscope that has been calibrated against primary standards. The number of measurements made on the standard particles and the standard deviation from the indicated size are given for each lot of sample particles. Particles composed of other materials can also be used if the size range is known.

An apparatus for dispersion of a latex hydrosol consists of an atomizer, an aerosol mixer tube, an air pump, two membrane filters with 100-millimicron pore size, and an air drier, as shown in Figure 9-35. Filtered air is supplied to the atomizer at approximately 5 psi. A latex solution of approximately 10^7 particles per cubic centimeter and water is placed in the atomizer. The resulting aerosol, consisting of filtered air, latex particles, and water droplets, is turbulently mixed with approximately 20 liters per minute of air that has been passed through a drier containing approximately 1 pint of calcium sulfate desiccant crystals. A volume of approximately 100 ml per minute of the output aerosol is sampled by the particle counter to be standardized.

This simple method will produce an aerosol with approximately 90% of the particles in a single size range when employed with latex particles that have a 1% standard deviation. The aerosol may contain particles both above and below the standard particle size, owing to particle agglomeration, fracturing of particles in the atomizer, incomplete drying in the aerosol mixer, and the presence of particles that are passed by the filters. Standardization is sufficient, however, if the spectrum of sizes recorded shows a definite peak at the size range of the standard latex particle.

It is not recommended that calibration be performed with other than the latex particles described in this chapter. If it is necessary to use other particles for prime calibration, or to check the cali-

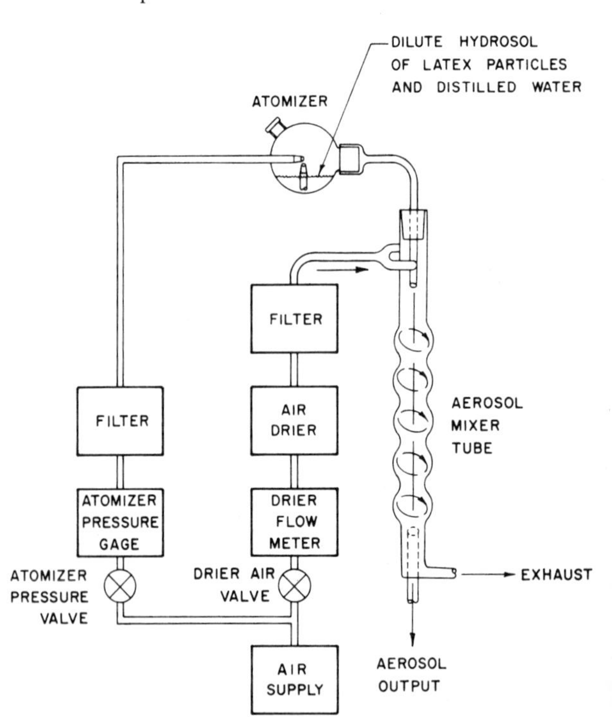

FIGURE 9-35. Apparatus for Dispersion of Latex Hydrosol. *Proposed ASTM Procedure for Automatic Particle Counters*

bration with large particles not covered in Figure 9-36, approximate expected distribution calculations can be made from the standard deviation of the known-size particle sample used. Table 9-7 shows the percentage of all particles falling outside the range bounded by various size deviations. The expected distribution calculations will not be applicable unless the standard deviation used has been accurately determined by the producer of the sample and definitely applies to the particular sample being used.

In conjunction with the previously mentioned Litton experiment, it was necessary to calibrate the Royco particle counter with micron-sized polystyrene particles. These particles were nebulized into the instrument and counted. Figure 9-37 shows Royco nebulizing equipment which can perform this function. The experimental results are shown in Figure 9-38. The particle counts in given size ranges, made at single-mode instrument settings with an air-flow rate of 100 cc per minute, were plotted against particle diameters as indicated by individual instrument channel readings. Figure 9-38 shows that a peak concentration is obtained at the 1.0-micron instrument setting. The calibrated average particle size of these polystyrene heads is 1.17 microns in diameter. Thus a maximum error of 0.1 micron in calibration is to be expected.

Photometers

An aerosol photometer measures the amount of light scattered simultaneously by a large number of

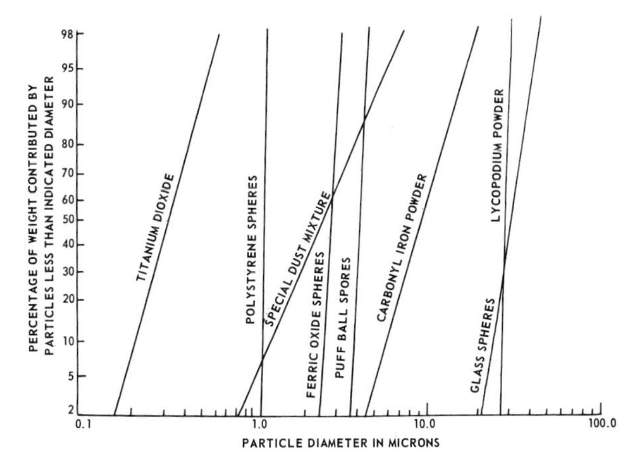

FIGURE 9-36. Particle diameters in solid materials. *Courtesy Royco Instruments, Inc.*

TABLE 9-7

CALCULATING EXPECTED PARTICLE SIZE DISTRIBUTION BASED ON STANDARD DEVIATION VALUE FOR THE PARTICLE CONCERNED

Ratio: (*Particle Size Deviation Used for Calculation* / *Standard Deviation of the Particle*)	*Percentage of All Particles Falling Outside the Range:* (*Average Size* ± *Corresponding Deviation*)
0.674	50.0
0.7	48.4
0.8	42.4
0.9	36.8
1.0	31.7
1.1	27.1
1.2	23.0
1.3	19.4
1.4	16.2
1.5	13.4
1.6	10.9
1.7	8.9
1.8	7.2
1.9	5.7
2.0	4.6
2.1	3.6
2.2	2.8
2.3	2.1
2.4	1.6
2.5	1.2
2.6	0.93
2.7	0.69
2.8	0.51
2.9	0.37
3.0	0.27
3.1	0.19
3.2	0.14

particles rather than light from individual particles. As such, it can be considered an analog counting device. The chief utility of an aerosol photometer is in measuring change in aerosol concentration from place to place (such as before and after a filter) or from time to time at the same location.

An example of a forward-scattering aerosol photometer is the Sinclair-Phoenix photometer. Models of this photometer are shown in Figure 9-39. Figure 9-39*A* is a photometer having logarithmic re-

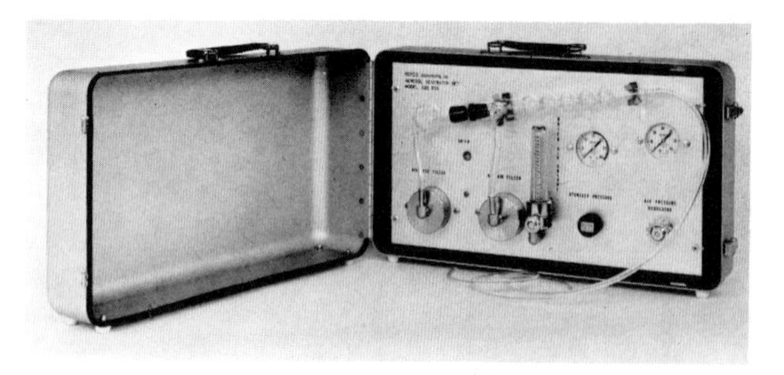

FIGURE 9-37. Royco Model AGS 255/256 aerosol generator. *Courtesy Royco Instruments, Inc.*

sponse. Figure 9-39*B* is a photometer having linear response, and Figure 9-39*C* is a console model of that shown in Figure 9-39*B* but with a 10-inch recorder and its exhaust filtered with a HEPA filter.

The basic diagram of this photometer is shown in Figure 9-40.

A block diagram of the Royco Model 230 aerosol photometer (29) is shown in Figure 9-41. This instrument consists of an air-flow system, a lamp, an optical sensor, a phototube with associated electronic circuitry, a filter and valve for rapidly purging the cell, a calibration probe, and a panel meter. The photometer utilizes a right-angle-scatter dark-field sensor to monitor the aerosol under test continuously. Zinky states:

Ideally when there are no particles in the air streams, the phototube will see total darkness. When particles are present in the air stream, light scattered from the particles is collected by means of a phototube that

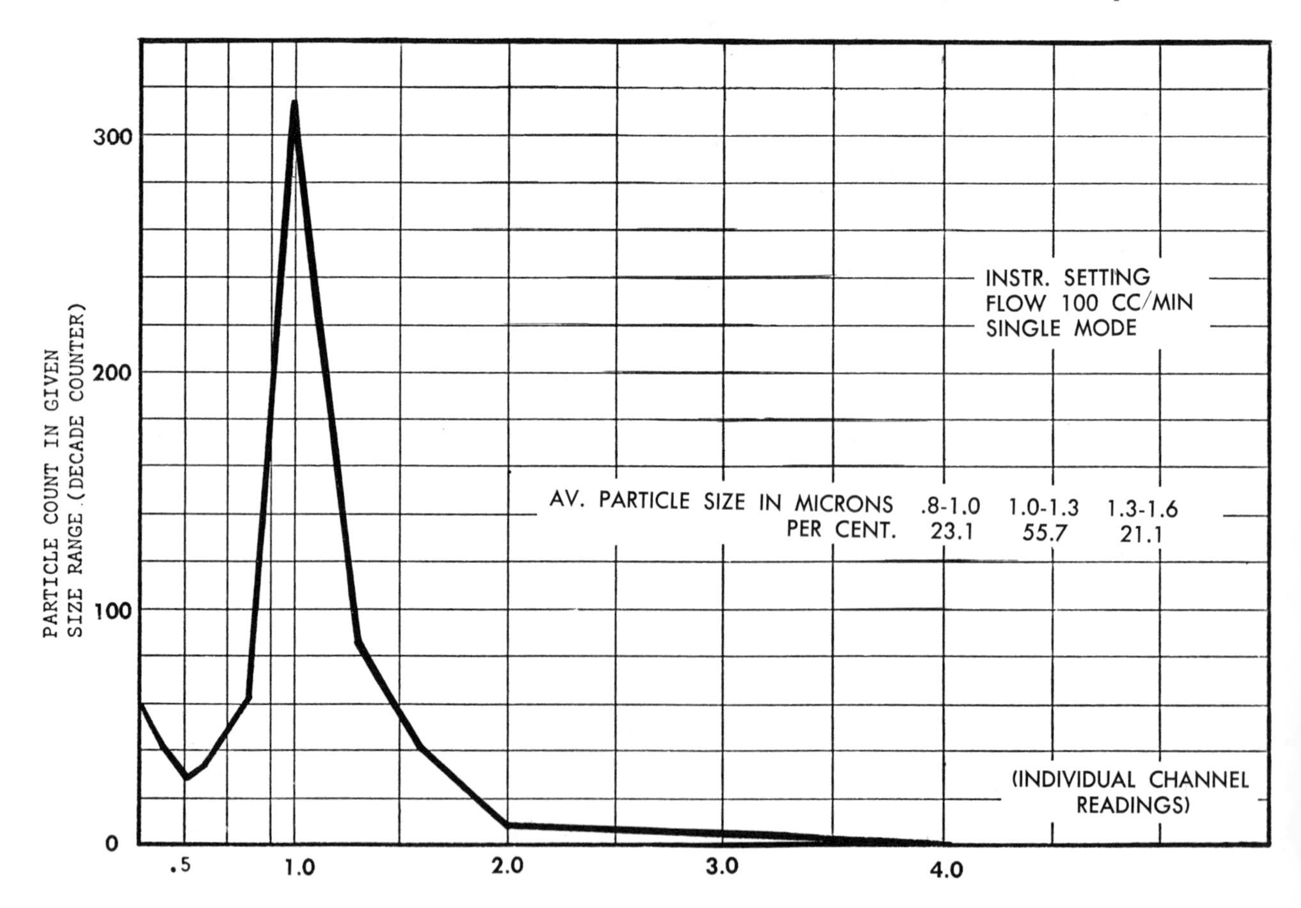

FIGURE 9-38. Calibration of Royco particle counter (*28*).

produces an electrical response. The magnitude of this scattered light is indicated on the front panel meter.

The sensor is designed to monitor continuously a flowing gas stream, and to detect minute changes in

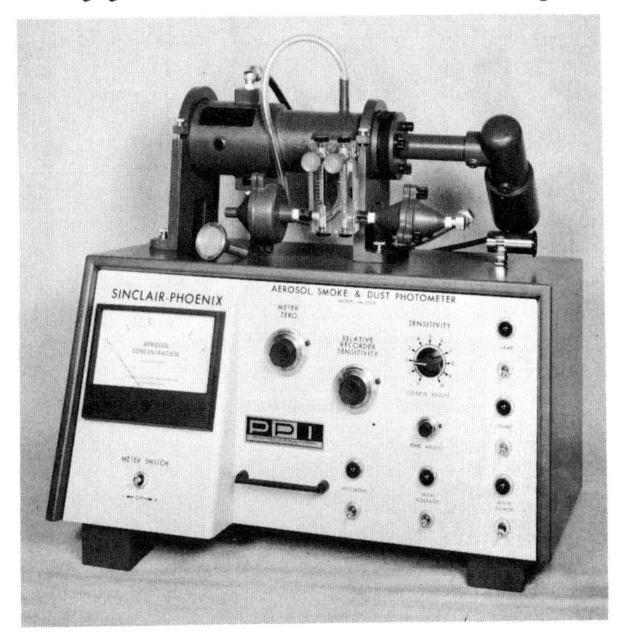

FIGURE 9-39. *A,* Sinclair-Phoenix aerosol photometer, Logarithmic Model JM-2000. *B,* Sinclair-Phoenix aerosol photometer, Linear Model JM-3000-AL. C, Sinclair-Phoenix Console Model JM-3000-FL10. *Courtesy Phoenix Precision Instrument Co.*

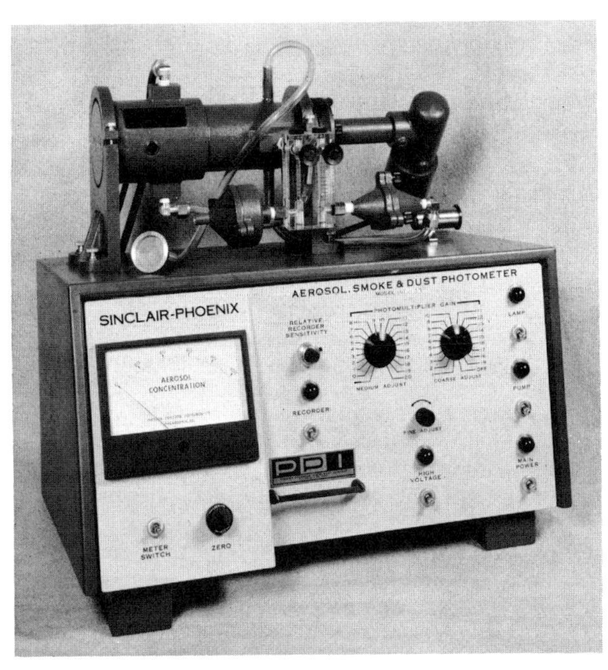

light that may be scattered. Stray light from the boundaries of the sensor cell is minimized by covering the internal surfaces of the cell with a baked-on coating that is optically black. An effective light trap collects virtually all the light from the projection beam, and glare-stops are positioned so that unwanted stray light does not enter the light-collection system.[16]

The active parts of the optical system are shown in Figure 9-42. Zinky continues his discussion of the Royco aerosol photometer as follows:

The moving air stream is brilliantly illuminated by the lamp and projection-lens system. Light from the aerosol scattered at 90 degrees to the projection axis enters a collection-lens system and a slit that is focused on the photocathode of a type 1P21 photomultiplier tube. The output current from the photomultiplier tube is directly proportional to the luminous intensity of the scattered light over a useful dynamic range of 10,000 to 1. The output current from the photomultiplier tube goes through the various electronic circuits to the panel meter and recorder outputs.

A purge system is incorporated to give the operator

[16] Reference *29*, pp. 2 and 3.

a quick check between the response of the aerosol under test, and a well filtered sample of the same air. It is also very useful for quickly air-flushing the cell when comparisons between aerosols of widely varying contamination must be made. The airflow and purge system has a carbon-vane pump mounted inside the instrument to provide an air flow of about 8 liters per minute through the optical sensor. Long life for the pump is assured by an input filter that prevents aerosol particles from entering the pump and causing misalignment of the vanes. To avoid possible contamination of the surrounding atmosphere with carbon particles abraded from the pump vanes, the output of the pump is again filtered.

The aerosol input enters the cell through a 3/16 inch i-d tube. When the purge valve is rotated, this aerosol-input tube is closed by an air-tight rotary valve so that the flow pump draws air into the cell only through the purge filter. The purge filter is a membrane type with a pore size of 100 millimicrons. Thus, the cell is rapidly flushed by a large volume of filtered air. Normally, no more than 10 seconds is required to purge the cell of the most dense aerosol. When the purge valve is opened and normal air flow is restored,

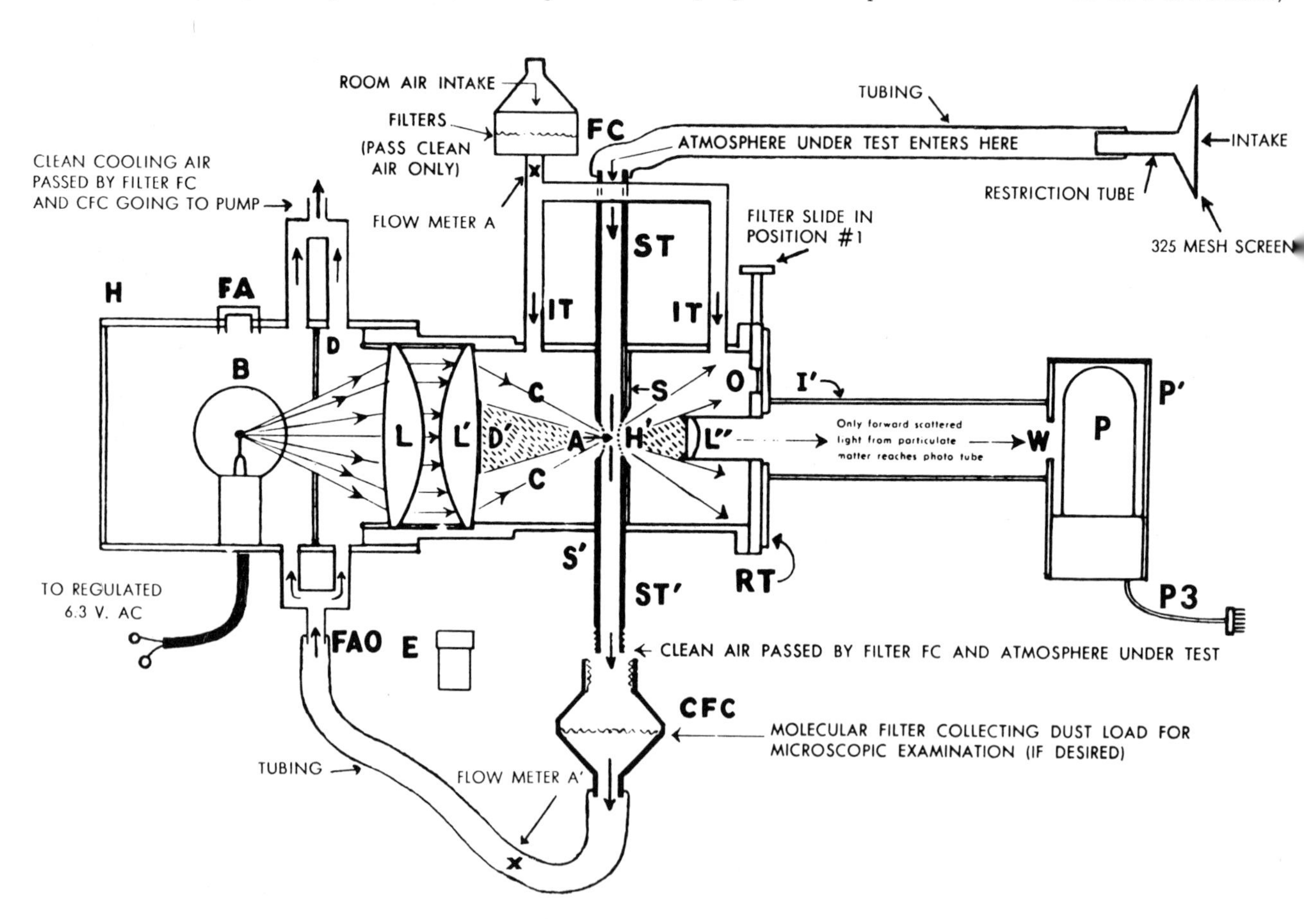

FIGURE 9-40. Basic diagram of the Phoenix-Sinclair photometer. *H*, sealed light source housing. *B*, lamp. *D*, feathered-edge diaphragm. *L* and *L'*, condenser lens. *D'*, diaphragm stop producing converging cone of darkness. *IT*, filtered-air inlets. *FC*, optical system protector filter and carrier. *E*, removable eyepiece which replaces photomultiplier tube for visual observation of smoke particles; also used for alignment. *CFC*, mass collector filter carrier. *A*, stray-light limiting diaphragm. *FA*, filament alignment window. *C*, converging cone of light. *ST*, smoke inlet tube. *ST'*, smoke and filtered-air outlet tube. *H'*, diverging cone of darkness. *S*, stray-light diaphragm. *O*, optical calibration filters. *L''*, scattered-light collecting lens. *I'*, light trap tube. *W*, photomultiplier tube diaphragm. *P*, photomultiplier tube. *P'*, shielded photomultiplier tube housing. *S'*, sealed optical housing. *P3*, cable to logarithmic amplifier. *FAO*, lamp cooling air inlet; *RT*, rotatable light trap tube flange. *Courtesy Phoenix Precision Instrument Co.*

the pressure differential across the 100 millimicron purge filter is insufficient to cause an appreciable air flow into the cell.

A calibrator provides a fixed reference signal for sensitivity adjustment of the instrument to compensate for variations in either lamp intensity (which may occur due to aging of the lamp) or photomultiplier-tube sensitivity. The calibrator consists of a probe that is inserted into the light path by depressing a front-panel button. The sensitivity of the optical sensor can be adjusted with a front-panel knob that controls the gain of the photomultiplier tube by varying the high-voltage bias. The calibration control is adjusted to a calibration point marked on the panel meter. The photomultiplier tube, power supplies, and electronic amplifiers may be serviced in the field without destroying the factory calibration provided by this probe.

The electronic circuitry is provided in two plug-in modules to perform three functions:

1) Four stable voltages are provided to operate the electronic circuitry so that readings of the instrument are independent of variations in power-line voltage from 105 to 125 volts, and are also independent of internal load changes in the instrument itself.

2) An averaging amplifier gives a time-weighted average of the intensity of the light scattered from the airstream over a period of 0.1 seconds, so that the panel meter indicates the additive effects of large particles that would otherwise pass through the sensor too quickly to allow the meter to respond, due to its inertia.

3) A logarithmic amplifier supplies the front-panel meter with a current proportional to the logarithm of the output current from the phototube so that a continuous range of intensities may be indicated on a single meter scale.

The meter scale is marked with pure numbers and is titled *Relative Concentration.* In fact, the instrument measures relative concentration provided that the aerosol maintains a constant size spectrum. A variation of 10,000 to one in scattered-light intensity is presented on a single scale with provision for expansion

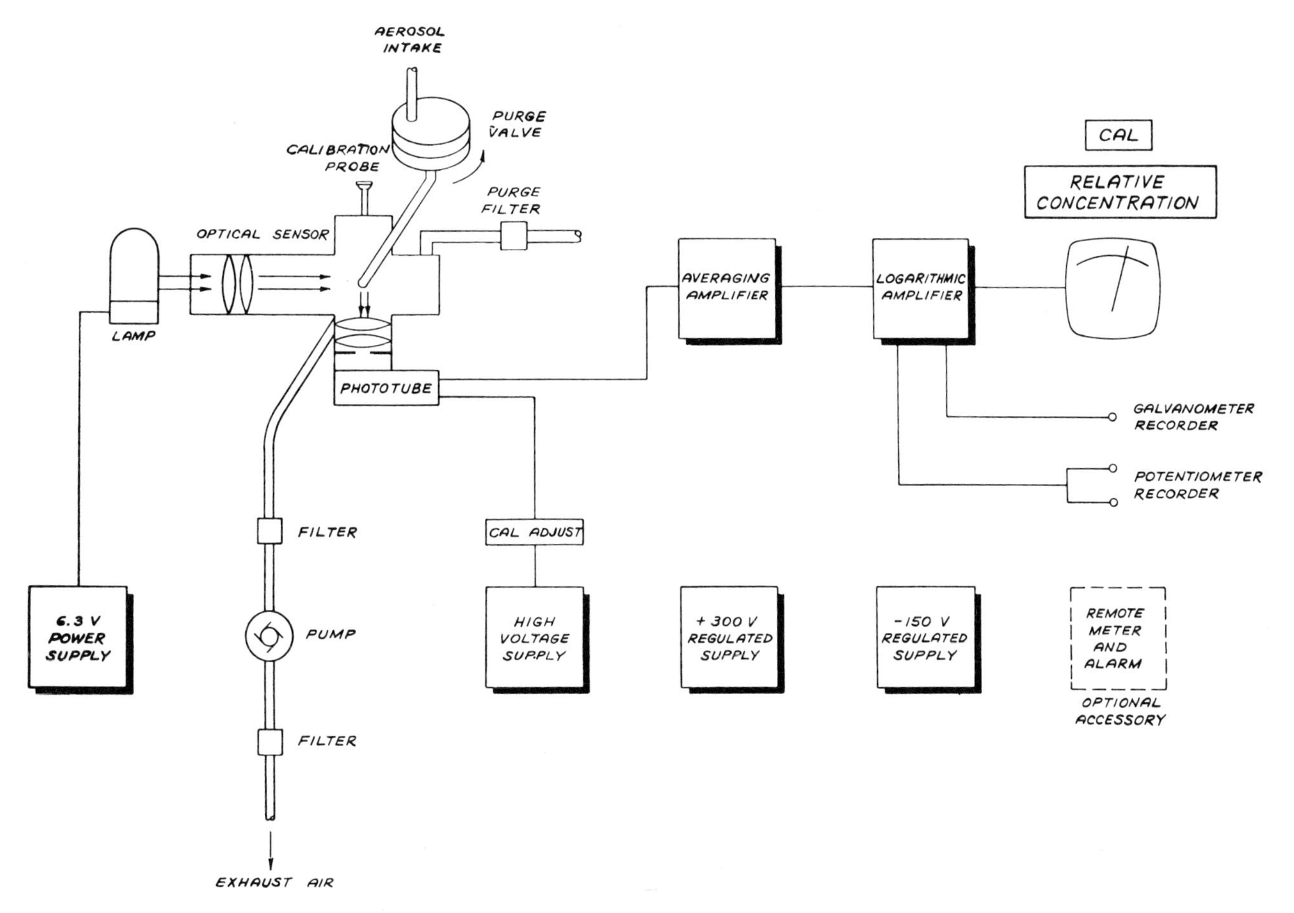

FIGURE 9-41. Block diagram of Model 230 photometer (29).

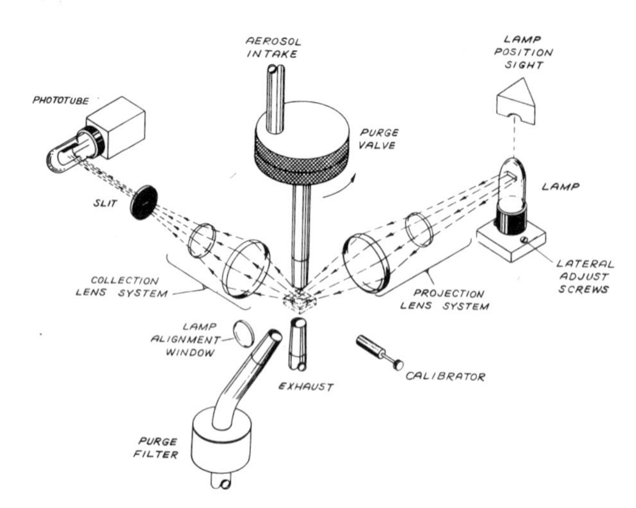

FIGURE 9-42. Optical system for Royco Model 230 photometer(*29*).

of the lower third of the scale for ease in reading the concentration in ultra-clean areas. A recorder output for galvanometer or potentiometer strip-chart recorders is provided. A remote indicator and alarm for the Model 230 aerosol photometer is available to enable plant engineers and quality-assurance people to monitor remotely the operating contamination levels in clean rooms.[17]

Figure 9-43 shows the complete instrument. A brief qualitative outline of some of the physical phenomena involved and their relationship is useful to a better understanding of the operation of a light-scattering photometer.

Light, an electromagnetic phenomenon, differs from radio waves and heat only in its frequency of vibration. The classical problem of interaction of a plane electromagnetic wave with a sphere was solved by Mie(*17*) and Debye(*30*). The most accessible treatment is by Stratton(*31*). A given sphere scatters light as though it has different cross-sectional areas for different wavelengths of light. The scattering area coefficient, *K*, is the factor by which the geometric cross-sectional area of a sphere must be multiplied to give the effective cross-sectional area (i.e., effective in intercepting light).

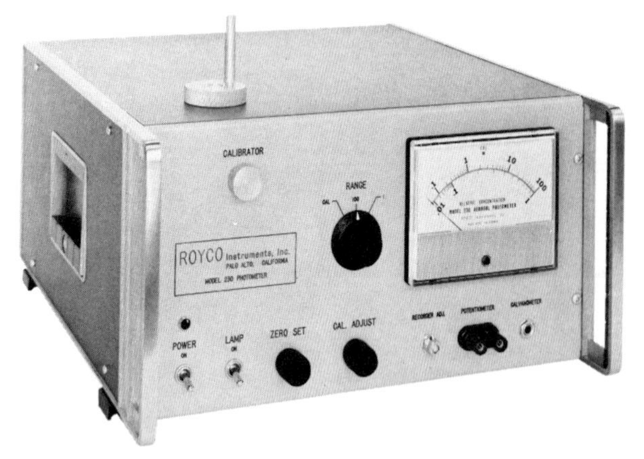

FIGURE 9-43. Royco Model 230 aerosol photometer. *Courtesy Royco Instruments, Inc.*

[17] *Ibid.*, pp. 3-6.

Figure 9-44 gives the scattering area coefficient, *K*, as a function of α for spheres having an index of refraction equal to that of water (1.33). In order to decrease the number of variables plotted, the variable α is defined as

$$\alpha = \frac{2\pi R}{\lambda} \tag{9-9}$$

where λ is the wavelength of light, and *R* is the radius of the sphere. The value α is equal to the number of times one wavelength of light will fit onto the circumference of a particle. To state this another way, α is the circumference in terms of the wavelength of light used.

The curve shown in Figure 9-44 applies only for materials having an index of refraction of 1.33. The shape of the curve is different for materials having other indices of refraction(*32*). The reradiation of

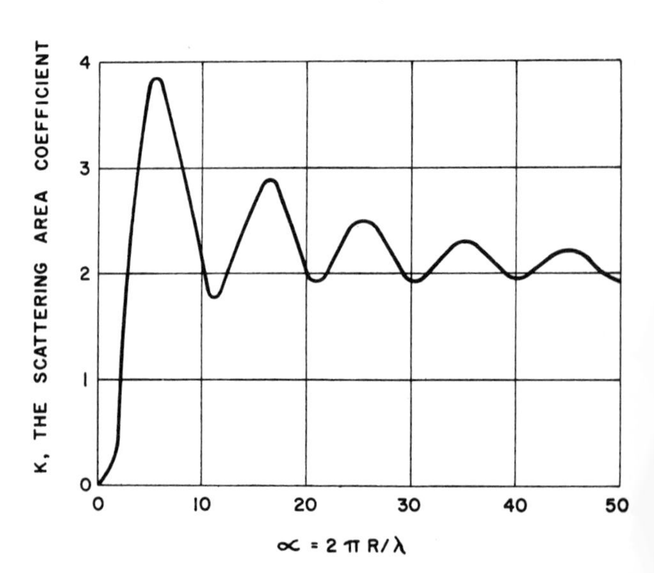

FIGURE 9-44. Scattering area coefficient, *K*, as a function of the particle radius and wavelength(*29*).

scattered light from a particle is not necessarily equal in all directions. As particles grow larger with respect to the wavelength of the incident light, they scatter light more in the forward direction of the incident beam(*33*).

In discussing the light scattering from particles, Zinky writes:

> From the foregoing it is apparent that the amount of light scattered from particles in an aerosol is a function of the particle radius, composition of the particle, the wavelength of the light, and the number of particles. Also, for a given mass-loading of an aerosol, and a given frequency of light, there is an optimum size of particle for which the total amount of light scattered is a maximum. Thus, for example, 1,000 particles that are 0.5 micron in radius would scatter more light than the same weight of water in the form of a single 5-micron drop, or the same amount of water reduced to molecular dimensions by vaporization. These considerations guide design of smoke-screen generators to make effective use of the screen material.
>
> In practical instrumental measurement of suspended aerosols, one must accept a heterogeneity of particle sizes and particle composition. Light of any specific frequency may be used in a photometer, but white light is advantageous partly because it is easily generated but chiefly because the directional scattering effects of the composite frequency spectrum can be averaged out by collecting the scattered light over a wide spherical optical angle(*34*).
>
> Particles of the same radius, but of different materials will not produce exactly equal scattering, but within the range of materials usually encountered, this is not a sensitive function.
>
> An instrument of this light-scattering type, such as Royco Model 200 Particle Counter, can respond to a single 0.3-micron particle through pulse-counting techniques(*35*). This Photometer is responsive to an average level equal to 100,000 particles of 0.3 micron size, per cubic foot. It is thus capable of monitoring all but the most tightly controlled clean-room areas.[18]

Standardization of Photometers

Many techniques to standardize photometers have been and are currently being used. Photometers have been calibrated in micrograms per liter by the expedient of collecting a sample of the particulate matter from the aerosol on a filter and weighing the sample. Although this procedure is simple in theory, it is difficult in practice because the sample weight must be determined with an analytical balance of extreme accuracy. Such a technique is not applicable where the aerosol contains an appreciable amount of volatile fluid particles. This is because such particles will be evaporated by the large volume of air that is passed through the filter.

[18] *Ibid.*, pp. 7-8.

The use of a heavy gas such as Freon 12 as an index of instrument sensitivity is a simple and satisfactory standardization technique. Freon 12 is packaged in small aerosol cans, is relatively inexpensive, and is easy to obtain.

An elegant way to calibrate a photometer is with an aerosol generator monitored by a particle counter to produce a monodisperse aerosol of known concentration. With this technique, both size and spectrum concentration of the test aerosol are known. Zinky reports:

> A laboratory method for determining the response of the photometer involves use of a linear amplifier to indicate the pulse height of a single particle in very clean aerosol as it passes the sensor. It is then very easy to compute the response to any concentrated aerosol made up of the same particles.
>
> The Royco Model 230 is supplied with a chart showing the response of the instrument to concentrations of particles of various sizes determined by the laboratory-calibration method. Such data makes possible the use of the photometer for monitoring aerosol generators and particulate clouds, and determining approximate concentration of monodisperse aerosols from the chart and the photometer reading.[19]

As stated previously, the chief utility of an aerosol photometer is its ability to respond to changes in conditions, and to give consistent, equal responses to unchanged conditions.

When an aerosol photometer is calibrated in terms of total mass loading of aerosol, readings will be proportional to mass providing there is no change in particle size distribution or composition. At a fixed aerosol mass loading, the photometer will reveal a change in particle size distribution.

The environmental conditions, equipment, and actions of people determine the amount, kind, and size distribution of particulate matter suspended in an atmosphere. Increased air velocity will entrain larger particles. Calm air will permit particles to settle. Increased personnel activity will always increase airborne particulate matter, because people stir up and shed copious numbers of particles.

[19] *Ibid.*, p. 9.

Changes in equipment performance also produce changes in mass loading of aerosols.

A photometer can be used to test the dioctyl phthalate (DOP) smoke penetration of high-efficiency particulate air filters. It can be used for production testing of all kinds of filters and has the advantage that it can be easily purged after making upstream measurement on a highly concentrated aerosol.

In order to detect damage to HEPA filters due to shipping or subsequent handling, an incoming inspection can be made by the purchaser with a DOP aerosol generator, a photometer, and a filter test jig incorporating a suitable fan. Photometer readings taken both upstream and downstream will indicate filter penetration directly.

After a filter is installed in the filter bank, the installation may be checked by means of a sniffer tube, attached to a photometer, to scan the filter bank for leaks. A photometer can detect any filters that are clamped incorrectly in the bank or can detect any filters that may be porous or detached from their frames(*36*).

A photometer can be used inside a clean room to monitor the level of contamination at a given point. It can also measure the cleanup time after contamination has occurred and indicate the relative filter efficiency. A portable photometer can be moved around to different locations to determine what areas of the room are less contaminated than others. It can be used to determine whether particles are being generated within the room by leaking furnaces, vacuum pumps, faulty production equipment, etc. The air in a clean work station may be tested to ensure that its enclosure and filter system provide substantially lower contamination levels than other unconfined areas of the clean room. A photometer can also perform a useful function by demonstrating to workers any activities that cause the contamination levels to rise.

Comparison of Data[20]

As an example of a comparison of dust count data obtained from different measuring methods, consider the study made by C. Marsh of Sandia Corporation. As part of this study, two light-scattering techniques were compared—a forward-angle light-scattering photometer (Sinclair-Phoenix aerosol smoke and dust photometer) and a particle counter (Royco Model PC-200A)—using the light scattered from individual particles.

Table 9-8 tabulates dust counts taken in four different locations with different airborne dust loadings. Samples with the different methods were not taken simultaneously but were taken over a period of several months by different personnel with varying techniques. The procedure was the same in all cases, and the sampling position was approximately the same in each location for each sample. The four areas sampled remained relatively constant throughout the recorded period; that is, the type of activity

[20] Abstracted from reference *37*.

TABLE 9–8

DUST COUNT DATA OBTAINED FROM FOUR ROOMS WITH TWO DIFFERENT MONITORING METHODS (37)

Room or Area		*Particle Counter PPCF 0.5*	*Photometer Relative Dust Level*
		580,000	0.45
		614,000	0.44
Clean Room A		612,000	0.42
		607,000	0.45
	Average	603,000	0.44
		120,000	—
Clean Room B		118,000	—
		130,000	—
	Average	123,000	—
		270,000	0.10
Clean Room C		310,000	0.10
		290,000	0.12
	Average	290,000	0.11
		2,150,000	2.4
Uncontrolled lab area		2,500,000	2.1
		2,170,000	2.2
		2,440,000	2.1
	Average	2,315,000	2.2

and the general room conditions contributing to the airborne dust level were closely controlled. The time at which the counts were made was also approximately the same for all four methods.

The data indicate that the dust count in a room is stable for a room with established operations. The scattering methods demonstrated excellent repeatability within the same room. Note that all variations recorded are well within the normal changes in any atmosphere. The maximum variation with the particle counter was 5.5% in clean room A. Notice that the four areas can be compared quite easily when data from light-scattering methods are used.

Because the two light-scattering methods were highly repeatable and correlated well with each other, the data from the two methods were quantitatively compared. The two instruments yield different types of data, however. The particle counter gives particles per volume in discrete size ranges, whereas the photometer reads the relative intensity of the light scattered by the volume of particles present in the instrument at any instant. The photometer readings were converted to particles per cubic foot by assuming an average partial distribution.

Both instruments appear to have some definite advantages. The photometer draws a much larger sample than does the particle counter and has a much better response to fast transients in dust levels. The particle counter gives direct information about particle concentration versus size and is sensitive to much lower concentration than is the photometer. An analysis of the data obtained from the particle counter revealed that the particle distribution curves from all amospheres sampled defined an average curve with little deviation from one atmosphere to another.

By sampling the same atmosphere simultaneously with both the particle counter and the photometer, the curve in Figure 9-45 was obtained. Points on the curve were obtained by sampling a number of different atmospheres with different dust levels and by sampling a single atmosphere of varying concentration. The varying concentration was provided by a Sandia clean room (*38*) in which the two instruments were set up while the clean air supply was operating. This gave a near zero reading on both

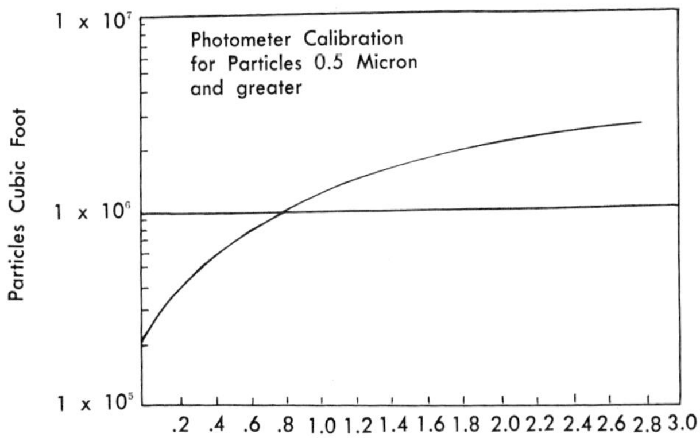

FIGURE 9-45. Photometer calibration for particles 0.5 micron and greater (*37*).

instruments. The air supply to the room was turned off, and the room contamination was allowed to build up slowly. By applying the curve in Figure 9-45, the photometer reading can be converted to particles per cubic foot, if a normal particle distribution is assumed.

Figure 9-46 is a comparison of the dust count taken by the particle counter and the photometer in a clean room over a one-day working period. The photometer readings were converted to particles per cubic foot by employing Figure 9-45. Excellent correlation was obtained. Marsh states (*37*) that, when the particle concentration falls below 1×10^5, the photometer goes to zero.

A significant difference between the response time of the particle counter and the photometer was noted when they were exposed to rapid changing airborne dust concentrations. The photometer responded rapidly to quick changes in dust concentration, whereas the particle counter exhibited some

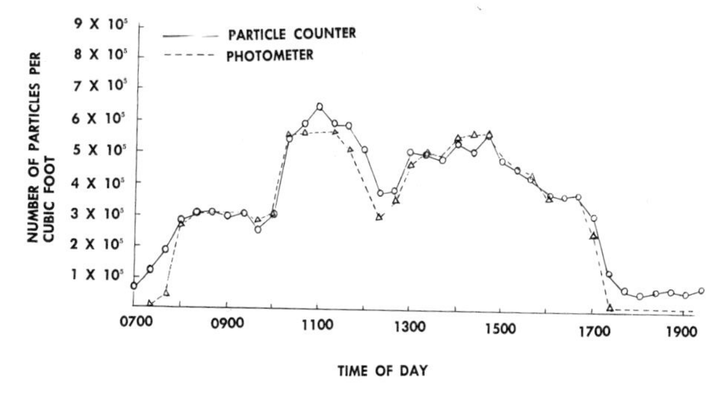

FIGURE 9-46. Comparison of particle counter data with calibrated photometer reading (*37*).

time lag, particularly while going from a high concentration to a low one. This results primarily from particles collecting on the inner surfaces of the air-handling and optical system and then being re-entrained in the air stream. Figure 9-47 shows the response of the two instruments to rapidly changing dust concentrations. The two instruments follow quite closely at increasing levels but differ greatly at decreasing levels.

Phototape Sampler

Another type of airborne contaminant monitoring device is the Gelman automatic phototape sampler-recorder (Figure 9-48). This device records the light intensity of a ½-inch-diameter spot on a 1-inch-wide filter tape through which an air sample has been drawn. This device will indicate the level of airborne contamination. Fifteen-minute to 2-hour samples may be taken automatically with this device by presetting the timer. This device must be calibrated against either a manual counting technique such as the ASTM F25-63T method, or an automatic digital counting device such as the Royco counter, in order that the values recorded be meaningful. By such procedures, this instrument can be calibrated in particles per cubic foot. It should be

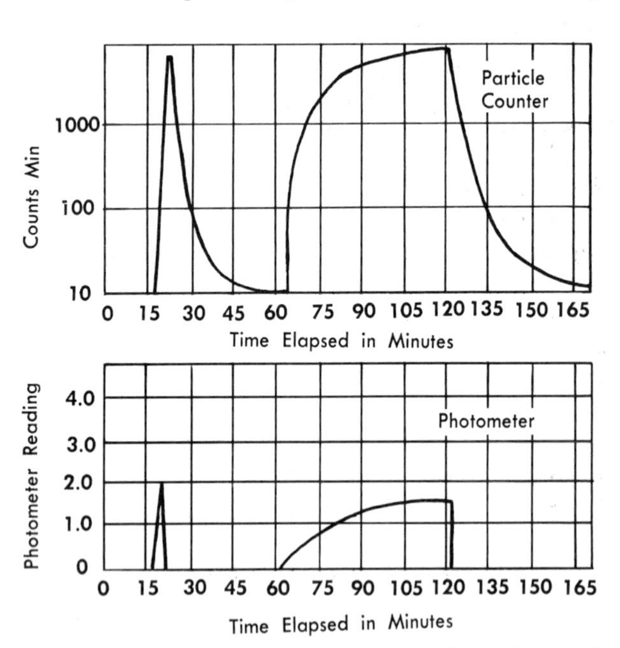

FIGURE 9-47. Comparison of response time of particle counter and photometer(37).

FIGURE 9-48. Gelman automatic phototape sampler-recorder. *Courtesy Gelman Instrument Co.*

noted that this type of device has poor sensitivity to contamination levels of less than 100,000 particles per cubic foot larger than 0.5 micron in size.

High-Intensity Light

One of the most effective devices to locate airborne and settled particulate matter visually is a high-intensity light beam. In a darkened room, such a light beam will cause high reflectance from micron-size particles not normally visible to the naked eye. A dust monitor of this type is qualitative in nature. It will readily show the source of airborne contaminants, however. It will also quickly identify poor work areas. This device is an invaluable tool for those charged with monitoring clean rooms. It should be noted that a high-intensity microscope light can perform a similar function on smaller scale.

Other Methods

Other methods of air monitoring are electrostatic precipitation, thermal precipitation, impaction, and weight analysis.

Electrostatic Precipitation

In this method, an electrical charge is placed on the dust particles in the sample by drawing the particles through a high-potential field. The charged particles are then collected on a metal plate of opposite polarity and viewed by incident light. With this method, a large sample may be taken in a short time. The main disadvantages are the high-voltage requirements and the limitations of incident lighting.

Thermal Precipitation

Particles are passed between two closely spaced hot and cold surfaces and caused to collect on the cold plate. The big disadvantage of this method is a very low collection rate and low efficiency, except for very small particles.

Impaction

In this method, the sample is forced through a small orifice or slit at near-sonic velocity and onto a surface at a right angle to the air stream. The force of the impaction and the sudden direction change of the air stream separates the particles from the air stream and collects them on the flat surface where they can be retained by a tacky material or by electrostatic forces. The principal problems associated with this method are that a single orifice is effective for only a limited particle range, and the forces involved tend to break up and change the nature of much of the material.

Weight Analysis

Any of the collection methods discussed in connection with the microscopic counting may also be used to collect dust samples for evaluation by means of an analytical balance. This method will give only quantitative data, and there is a considerable time lag in obtaining data. Also, it is quite insensitive to very low dust concentration. For a quick gross contamination indication, this method can be profitably used.

No one instrument or method is capable at present of furnishing all the information necessary to obtain an accurate picture of the room and provide a sufficiently rapid warning of a sudden or short-time condition when the room goes out of control. A complete monitoring set at the present time might include an automatic level indicating device for continuous and instantaneous information and a procedure for collecting samples for microscopic analysis to obtain qualitative information.

Fluid Sampling Procedures[21]

Unless adequate attention is given to proper sampling techniques, no amount of refinement of measurement procedures will provide valid, reproducible results when counting by microscopy.

Sampling errors fall into several major categories. Sampling equipment, containers, analytical apparatus, and filters must be clean if subsequent measurements are to be a valid index of the fluid system being tested rather than of extraneous or background contamination.

Adequacy of samples depends on both the level of contamination of the system being measured and the type of measurement being employed. In general, sufficient material must be sampled so that the collected contaminant will be clearly measurable at dangerous levels of contamination. Thus 100 ml would represent an adequate sample from a high-performance hydraulic system of which the contamination was measured by microscopy (particle counting); 1 to 5 gallons would be a proper sample for turbine fuel to be measured gravimetrically (weight of contaminant); and a minimum of 10 cubic feet would be needed for measurement of the air in a super-clean room.

To be meaningful and reproducible, samples should, so far as possible, be representative of the entire fluid system under test when the system is operating normally. Samples from the bottom (or top) of a hydraulic sump will not fairly represent contamination in fluid power lines. Samples of more viscous fluids should be taken from areas of high turbulence where particles are mixed throughout the fluid cross section. When it is necessary to sample a static system, where the contents of the system cannot be thoroughly mixed, a multilevel sample should be taken.

Some types of sampling valves, such as gasketed globe valves, are natural particle generators and must be avoided. Valves with small orifices (needle valves) which tend to act as filters are also to be avoided. Ball valves, plug valves, and quick-release valves are among the acceptable types for sampling purposes.

In certain circumstances, notably in determining

[21] Abstracted from a Millipore Filter Corporation brochure.

contamination levels on surfaces, it is impossible to remove the contaminant quantitatively for filtration through a filter. In these instances, it is extremely important to follow the identical sampling (flushing) regimen, each and every time, for any given component or system. The analytical results from such sampling will not indicate the total extent of surface contamination but will yield meaningful and reproducible data on relative contamination levels from one component to another.

Whenever possible, all fluid sampling should be done on a full-flow basis with all the fluid stream passing through the filter in a closed filter holder. The type and size of holder should be selected for flow required and allowable pressure drop.

Fluid Filtering Procedure[21]

1. Using forceps, remove disk from container; rinse grid-marked surface with filtered petroleum ether; place grid-marked side up on Pyrex filter holder base (Figure 9-49).
2. Lock funnel to base with spring clamp.
3. Pour *entire contents* of sample bottle into funnel.
4. Rinse sample bottle with filtered solvent and add contents to funnel.
5. Apply vacuum to filter flask. *When filtration is approximately half complete*, release vacuum.
6. While some liquid still remains in funnel, use filtered solvent to carefully rinse funnel walls.
7. Apply vacuum and pull remainder of fluid through filter disk. *Do not subsequently rinse funnel walls or filter surface* (to avoid disturbing the even distribution of particles on the filter surface). Release vacuum.
8. Open filter holder; using forceps, immediately place filter in clean plastic disposable Petri dish identified with sample number.

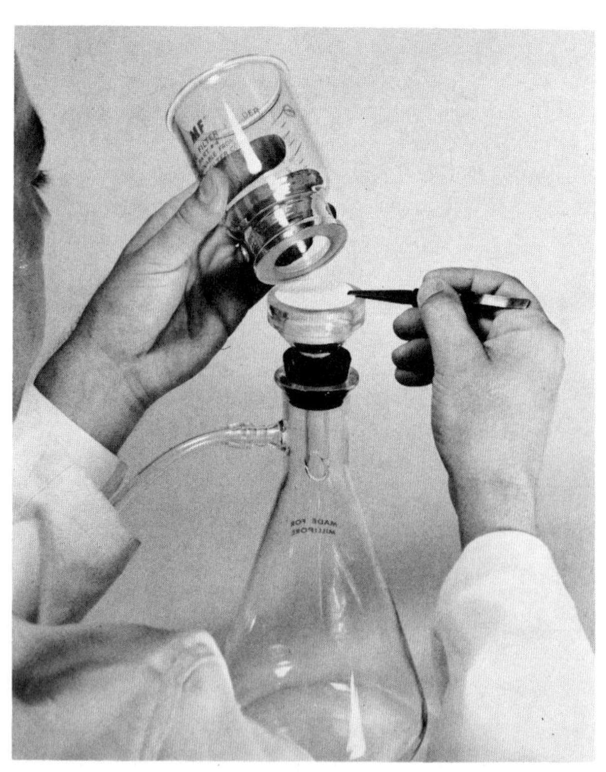

FIGURE 9-49. Millipore filter on base of filter holder. *Courtesy Millipore Filter Corp.*

Counting Procedure[21]

1. Install a measuring eyepiece disk in the eyepiece assembly of the microscope (either lens if a binocular microscope); place a stage micrometer on the microscope stage (Figure 9-50).
2. Adjust the microscope illuminator intensity and position for maximum definition of the stage micrometer scale as viewed through the microscope.
3. Calibrate the measuring eyepiece for each magnification to be used (Figure 9-51). Post chart near microscope for all future work.

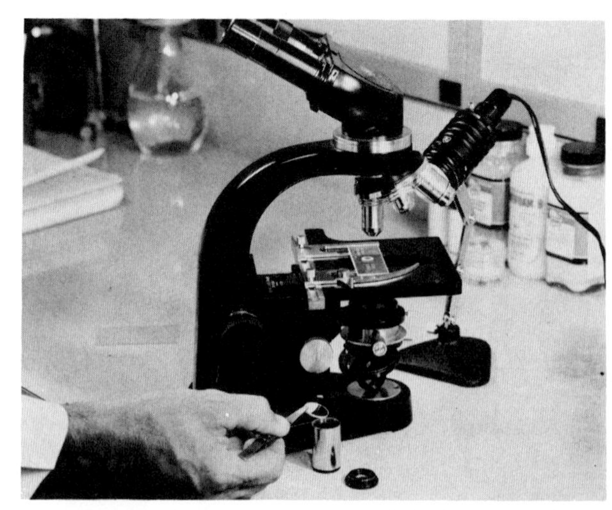

FIGURE 9-50. Stage micrometer slide is mounted on microscope stage, and measuring eyepiece is placed in one of microscope eyepieces. *Courtesy Millipore Filter Corp.*

4. (Transmitted light microscopy only) With forceps, gently float filter on film of immersion oil in cover of plastic Petri dish. Draw filter over rim of cover to remove excess oil from bottom of filter.

5. Place filter on 2 by 3-inch glass slide on microscope stage (light greasing of slide is desirable in reflected-light work to hold filter flat and in place).

6. Move microscope stage so that particles on filter appear to pass under the measuring eyepiece. Count the number of particles in designated size ranges in a sufficient number of randomly selected fields so that the *number of particles counted times the number of fields is equal to or greater than 500.* A field may be any designated area, but it is most commonly the width of a grid square subtended by the length or a portion of the length of the measuring eyepiece scale (Figure 9-52). Particles should always be sized by their longest dimensions. Fibers (particles larger than 100 microns with a ratio of length to width greater than 10 : 1) are usually listed separately.

7. When counting a relatively small number of particles at low magnification, it is usually best to count the entire filtering surface.

8. When less than the entire filter surface is counted, it will be necessary to multiply the number of particles actually counted by a statistical calibration factor to represent the number of particles which would have been counted had the entire filter surface been scanned.

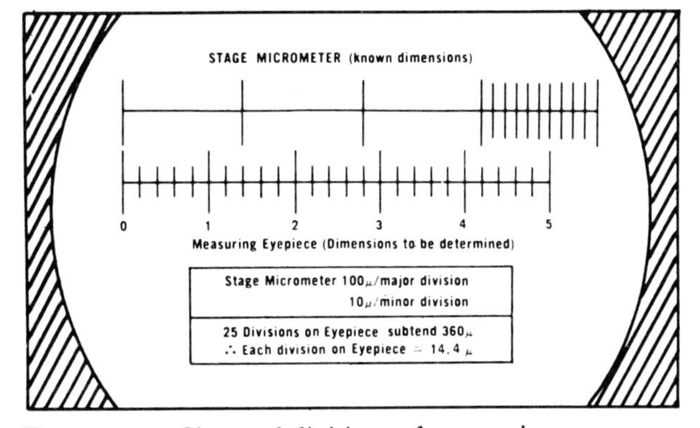

FIGURE 9-51. Since subdivisions of stage micrometer are known (top), divisions of measuring eyepiece (bottom) may be sized from it and will remain constant at that magnification. *Courtesy Millipore Filter Corp.*

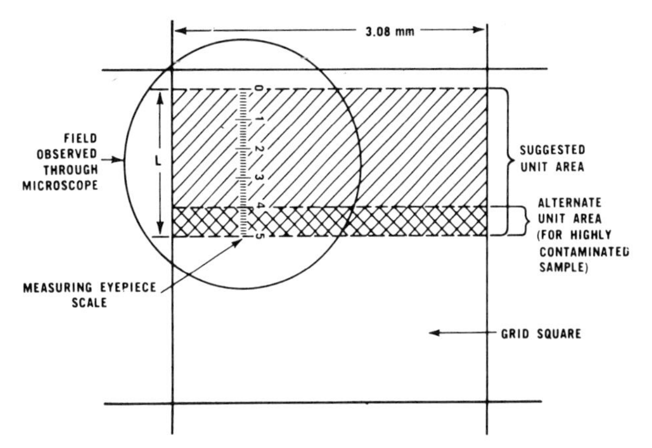

FIGURE 9-52. With Millipore filter on stage, movement of stage makes particles appear to pass divisions on measuring eyepiece. *Courtesy Millipore Filter Corp.*

Example for a Millipore filter:

$$\text{Factor} = \frac{960}{3.08LN} \quad (9\text{-}10)$$

where 960 = effective filtering area of Millipore filter disk, in square millimeters.

3.08 = width of filter grid square, in millimeters.

L = length of unit area, in millimeters.

N = number of unit areas counted.

Any variation of this counting procedure that shows equivalent results is acceptable. Many companies scan one or two diameters of a filter rather than select random squares. The use of Porton, Whipple, or other eyepieces poses both problems and advantages to be considered in any specific case.

Microfiltration—Fluid Cleaning[21]

Many electronic devices require levels of cleanliness during manufacture obtainable only with microfiltration. Distilled deionized water used for rinsing semiconductor components, for example, must be filtered to remove all traces of resins and other particulate matter carried over from deionizing columns (Figure 9-53). This treatment can result in water of nearly 18-megohm purity for washing junction surfaces, thus helping to assure that the device will operate in its solid-state ideal. This same high-purity water is desirable for phosphor "cushion water" in producing screens on cathode-ray tubes for use in radar systems. This filtration can

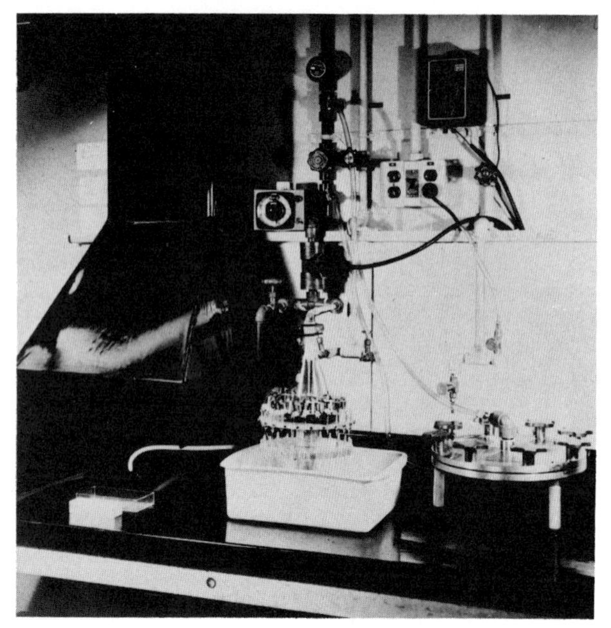

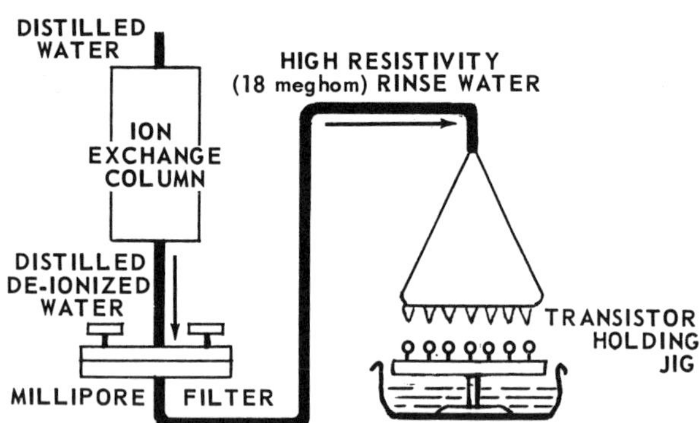

FIGURE 9-53. Millipore microfiltration removes all insoluble impurities and resins carried over from deionizing columns in transistor rinse water and helps to assure ideal solid-state function. *Courtesy Millipore Filter Corp.*

also be used in conjunction with deionizing and deoxygenating equipment for purifying cooling liquids in recirculating loops of high-energy transmitters.

Cleaning and rinsing fluids used in ultrasonic systems must be freed of all particulate matter to perform effectively in cleaning critical devices. For this reason, Millipore microfiltration is employed for cleaning the fluids not only as they are placed into the tanks, but also on a recirculating basis during the cleaning process. In this way, particles that free themselves from the surface of the device are carried away to the filter, and super-clean fluid is returned to the tank for reuse. Proper system design draws fluid for filteration from several depths within the tank to assure against a laminar build-up of contaminants of higher or lower density than that of the fluid.

A new concept of system and fluid cleaning has evolved from the use of membrane filters in portable fill/flush/bleed stands for missile and aircraft hydraulic control systems (Figure 9-54). Fluid is drawn from a vented bottom outlet sump and pumped at operating pressure through the entire control system while controls are actuated under simulated flight conditions. Contaminants are picked

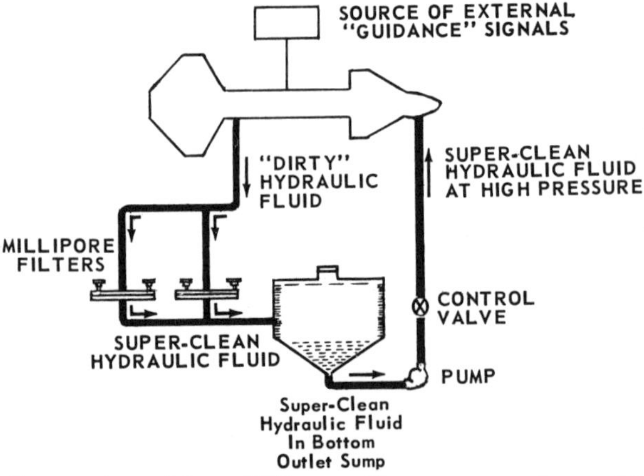

FIGURE 9-54. Two Millipore filters are used on this portable fill/flush/bleed unit for ground-to-air missile hydraulic fluids. *Courtesy Kidde & Co., Inc.*

up from the system by the fluid and carried out at low pressure to the filters where they are trapped quantitatively. The fluid that passes through the filter is returned to the sump in super-clean condition for recirculation through the system. This type of arrangement makes obsolete an old hydraulic principle which utilized the sump as a settling tank for contaminants, since no contaminant is returned to the sump. Pump suction is drawn from the sump bottom, and the entire system becomes cleaner and cleaner as operating time increases.

Microfiltration plays a vital part in manufacturing and assembling such devices as miniature bearings, missile hydraulic valves and actuators, and gyroscopes which are built to mechanical tolerances of remarkable precision. Throughout all stages of fabrication, Millipore filters are used to clean the solvents, lubricants, gases, damping fluids, and flushing fluids that come into the contact with the device (Figure 9-55). Without these super-clean fluids and extreme care in machining and assembling operations, these mechanisms will not function properly. Microfiltration removes from fluids all contaminating particles larger than the pore size. In practice, filters with 0.45-micron pore size ratings are the finest grades generally employed, although microfiltration to 10 millimicrons is possible. For optimum effectiveness, the filter should be installed in the system as close as possible to the point of fluid use.

Microfiltration has become perhaps the most widely employed method for cleaning reagents, solvents, and gases for use in instruments and analytical methods. Although these fluids are normally of high chemical purity, they often contain particulate matter which is harmful to such techniques as spectrophotometry, flame photometry, mass spectrography, light-scattering, and particle size-distribution analyses. In practice, particle-free reagents should be prepared by filtration at point of use to avoid danger of recontamination from handling and storage.

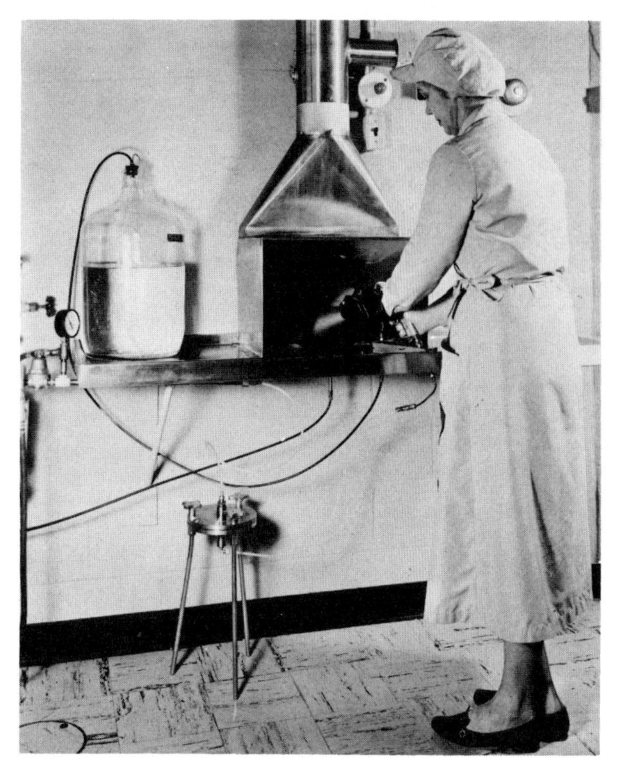

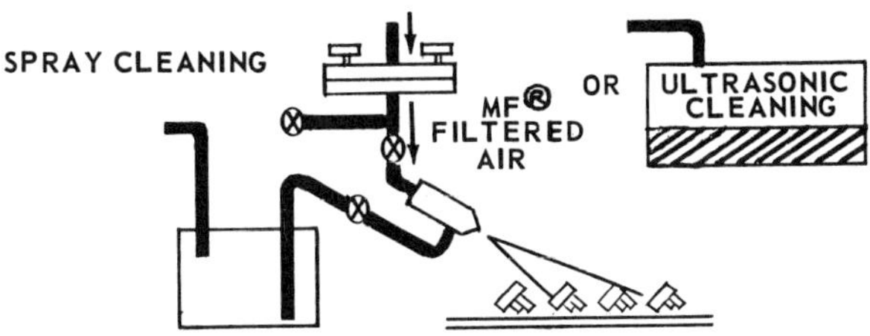

FIGURE 9-55. Microfiltration with Millipore filters provides super-clean solvents for spray cleaning of critical miniature bearings. Bearing lubricants must also be Millipore-filtered to help assure reliable operation. *Courtesy Miniature Precision Bearings, Inc.*

Silting Index[22]

Liquid monitoring devices are in many cases similar to air monitoring devices except that the monitored fluid is no longer low-viscosity air but high-viscosity liquid. Membrane filters as previously discussed under air monitoring lend themselves to fluid monitoring also. Similar manual counting techniques using a 100× microscope may be employed. Of particular note in manual fluid monitoring has been the development of silting index apparatus and procedures. This procedure can be considered a manual analog counting method, whereby relative amounts of contaminants may be compared.

The use of silting index apparatus(*39*) is ex-

[22] Abstracted from reference *25*.

tremely simple. It may be used in the laboratory or taken to an operating field site. It requires no electrical power or laboratory support and can be learned in minutes. One of the typical applications for this equipment is in the checking of aircraft and missile hydraulic systems. In these systems micron and submicron contamination is a major problem in the operation of close-tolerance pumps and servomechanisms. The silting index serves to monitor and evaluate these systems. It has been shown that the silting index of a fluid can predict the final failure rates of high-tolerance servo valves. Another use of this procedure is in testing solid-state and cathode-ray tube wash waters. Present deionizers are highly effective in removing dissolved salts from wash waters; however, solid contaminants can pass through such systems and damage the critical faces of the devices. The silting index can effectively monitor these wash waters and pinpoint trouble in the line through each state of water treatment.

The principle of operation of silting index apparatus can be stated quite briefly. When liquid is passed at uniform high pressure through a membrane filter of 0.8-micron porosity, all particles entrained in the fluid larger than the filter pore size will be retained on the filter surface. Very large particles will form a loose, open, flowing cake, but particles 5 microns and smaller, and stable gels, will tend to block the filter openings and reduce the rate of flow in a mathematically predictable and easily measured manner. Thus, the silting index apparatus is a device that permits the filtration of a contaminated liquid sample through a known filter area at constant pressure so that decay due to filter clogging may be recorded as a function of time.

Figure 9-56 shows a Millipore silting index kit with all components displayed. Figure 9-57 shows a setup of this appartus. It should be noted that this test must never be run in direct sunlight or close to heat sources which may change temperature and possibly affect the viscosity of the fluid during the test.

The following explanation of the theory of operation of silting indices will serve to further clarify this subject.

The flow of a contaminated liquid through a membrane filter can be described by the following equation:

$$Q = \frac{dV}{dt} = \left(\frac{\Delta PA}{\eta}\right)\left(\frac{1}{r_f + r_c}\right) \quad (9\text{-}11)$$

where Q = volume flow rate.
V = volume, in cubic centimeters.
t = time, in seconds.
ΔP = pressure drop, in dynes per square centimeter.
A = filter surface area, in square centimeters.
η = viscosity, in dyne-seconds per square centimeter.

Here r_f refers to the resistance per area of flow through the membrane. For a particular pore size membrane, this is a constant. The term r_c refers to the flow resistance offered by the solid and gelatinous contaminants deposited on the membrane surface. During the course of filtration, the value r_c will increase. The absolute value of r_c is dependent on a number of things—contaminant particle size, particle shape, compressibility, concentration, etc. For a given contaminant, the term can be expressed as follows:

$$r_c = \frac{V}{A}(S) \quad (9\text{-}12)$$

The term S is the silting index of the contaminated fluid. It characterizes the tendency of a given sample to clog a filter.

Rewriting equation (9-10), we have

$$\frac{dt}{dV} = \frac{\eta}{\Delta PA}\left(r_f + \frac{A}{V}S\right) \quad (9\text{-}13)$$

By integration, we have

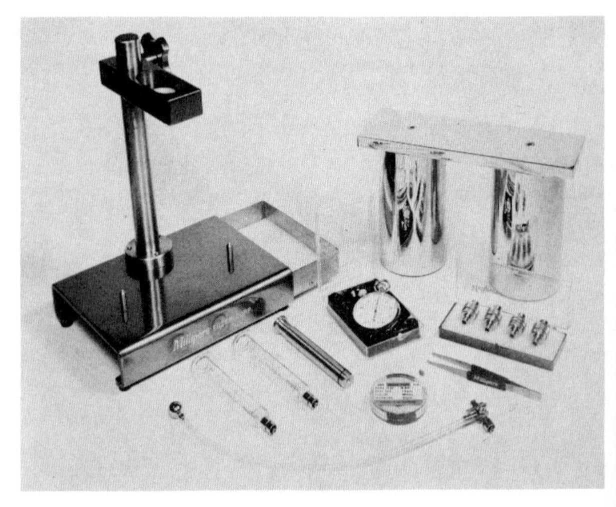

FIGURE 9-56. Millipore silting index kit with all components displayed. *Courtesy Millipore Filter Corp.*

FIGURE 9-57. Millipore silting index kit assembled and operating. *Courtesy Millipore Filter Corp.*

$$\int_0^t dt = \frac{\eta}{\Delta PA} \int_0^v \left(r_f + \frac{V}{A} S \right) dV \qquad (9\text{-}14)$$

$$t = \frac{\eta}{\Delta PA} \left(r_f V + \frac{V^2}{2A} S \right) \qquad (9\text{-}15)$$

$$\frac{t}{V} = \frac{\eta r_f}{\Delta PA} + \frac{\eta S V}{2 \Delta P A^2} \qquad (9\text{-}16)$$

Note that equation (9-16) is linear in the functions of t/V and V. Filtration data of contaminated fluids, if plotted by these coordinates, should yield straight lines.

Now, it is the silting characteristic, S, that is of concern. If a perfectly clean fluid is passed through a filter, the flow rate remains constant. The quantity t/V, the total time elapsed per total volume filtered, must then remain constant. Equation (9-16) would then be

$$\frac{t}{V} = \text{Constant} = \frac{\eta}{\Delta PA} (r_f + 0) \qquad (9\text{-}17)$$

The quantity S then is logically enough equal to zero for a clean fluid. If, on the other hand, S is some finite positive number, the value of t/V will increase as more fluid is passed through the filter. The flow rate correspondingly decreases. The quantity S then is zero for a clean fluid, and some positive number for a dirty fluid. The dirtier the fluid, the higher is the value of S.

It is desired to derive an equation for S in terms of only t and V. One could then perform standard tests on any fluid that would give a value of S independent of all the other parameters of equation (9-16). By applying a method of simultaneous equations to equation (9-16), some of these parameters may be eliminated. Specific values V_1, V_2, and V_3 are more or less arbitrarily selected with their corresponding values t_1, t_2, and t_3. Volumes here chosen are such that $V_3 = 2V_2$:

$$\frac{t_3}{V_3} \left(\frac{2 \Delta PA}{\eta} \right) = 2 r_f + \frac{S V_3}{A} \qquad (9\text{-}18)$$

$$\frac{t_2}{V_2} \left(\frac{2 \Delta PA}{\eta} \right) = 2 r_f + \frac{S V_2}{A} \qquad (9\text{-}19)$$

Subtracting and rearranging, we have

$$S = \frac{2 \Delta P A^2}{\eta} \left(\frac{\frac{t_3}{V_3} - \frac{t_2}{V_2}}{V_3 - V_2} \right) \qquad (9\text{-}20)$$

Equation (9-20) has somewhat more utility, but it still requires measurements such as viscosity and test pressure. Reasonably, the way to eliminate the needs for these measurements would be to compare the filtration of a contaminated fluid to what the filtration would be if the fluid were absolutely clean. From equation (9-11), the performance of a clean fluid can be written:

$$\frac{dV}{dt} = \frac{\Delta PA}{\eta r_f} = \text{Constant} = \frac{\Delta V}{\Delta t} = \frac{V_1}{t_1} \qquad (9\text{-}21)$$

Now, during the initial stage of filtration of a contaminated fluid, r_f is numerically much larger than r_c. Thus the contaminated fluid initially tends to filter just as uncontaminated fluid. If, then, we pick a relatively small value of V_1 during the course of contaminated fluid filtration, the resulting value of V_1/t_1 will be quite close to that expected from an uncontaminated fluid. Applying this ratio of V^1/t^1 to equation (9-20), we have

$$S \frac{t_1}{V_1} = \frac{2 \Delta P A^2}{\eta} \left(\frac{\frac{t_3}{V_3} - \frac{t_2}{V_2}}{V_3 - V_2} \right) \frac{\eta r_f}{\Delta PA} \qquad (9\text{-}22)$$

Rearranging equation (9-20), we have finally

$$S = \left(\frac{t_3 - 2t_2}{t_1}\right)\frac{Ar_fV_1}{(V_2)^2} \qquad (9\text{-}23)$$

Equation (9-21) is a complete equation for the determination of the contamination level of a fluid. By fixing the type filter, filter size, and sample size, equation (9-23) reduces to a comparison of times multiplied by a dimensional constant. (*Note:* r_f can be shown to be a constant involving the thickness and pore diameter of a filter.) It is independent of viscosity characteristics of a fluid and other external variables such as pressure and temperature. By appropriate design of the apparatus, this constant becomes the integer one, and thus

$$S = \left(\frac{t_3 - 2t_2}{t_1}\right) \qquad (9\text{-}24)$$

Note that from equation (9-24) the results of tests must be expressed in terms of the silting head used to conduct the tests. Further, each test should be run three times for each fluid sample and the resulting silting indices averaged for an over-all silting index. For detailed procedure, see SAE Aerospace Recommended Practice 788, "Procedure for the Determination of the Silting Index of a Fluid."

As has been discussed previously, the techniques of microparticle investigations are still being developed. Some areas are more defined than others. Techniques for the identification and counting of microparticles developed prior to March 1, 1960, were not generally accepted or widely documented. On that date, however, the Society of Automotive Engineers issued the first procedure which made for industry-wide comparisons of quantitative analyses of hydraulic fluid microparticles. This procedure was Aerospace Recommended Practice 598 (ARP 598); although it did add standardization, it is frequently modified by contamination investigators to meet more closely the needs of their particular work!

Automatic Fluid Counters

Automatic particle-counting devices for contamination control in fluid media are being developed. Currently there are several counters that will monitor and count particulate matter in fluids; however, these and other devices have not yet been developed to function in large fluid volumes such as aerofuel filling operations. For this a unit is needed that will perform a twofold purpose of monitoring and bypassing fuel containing particulate matter of predetermined objectionable size and number.

A direct-reading instrument, presently being evaluated in the missile program at Grumman, is the Grumman Aircraft-Sperry Products device*(40)*, which is based on ultrasonic principles. This device appears to have the best potential as an in-line control for continuous-flow fluid volumes. The instrument consists of three principal circuits, a basic pulse echo unit redesigned for high sensitivity and repetition rate, a search crystal, a multichannel detector and discriminator, and an electronic counter. A more complete description is available in a Grumman presentation, "An Ultrasonic Method to Detect, Count, and Measure Particle Size of Contamination in Fluids" (August 1960). These data were presented before the Third Pacific Area National Meeting of the American Society for Testing and Material, October 12, 1959.

The Coulter counter was developed for blood cell and other biological counting where it has merit in limited fluid volumes. (See Figures 9-58 and 9-59.) The Coulter counter is based on an electrical conductivity principle. Particle count and measurement are reflected in changes of resistance measurable as a function of particle size and number.

The Coulter counter employs a unique method

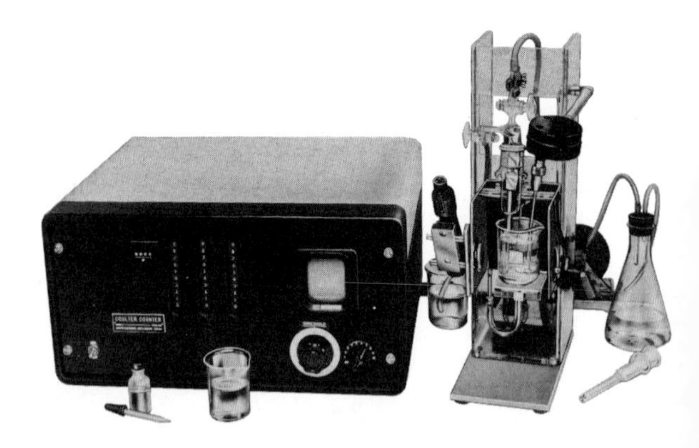

FIGURE 9-58. Coulter counter electronic unit model A and sample stand. *Courtesy Coulter Electronics, Inc.*

(see Figure 9-60) to determine the number and size of particles suspended in an electrically conductive liquid. The suspension flows through a small aperture having an immersed electrode on either side, with particle concentration such that the particles traverse the aperture substantially one at a time.

Each particle passage displaces electrolyte within the aperture, momentarily changing the resistance between the electrodes and producing a voltage pulse of magnitude proportional to particle *volume*. The resultant series of pulses is electronically amplified, scaled, and counted.

The voltage pulses are displayed on the oscilloscope screen as a pattern of vertical "spikes." The pulse pattern serves as a guide for measurement and as a monitor of instrument performance. The pulses are also fed to a threshold circuit having an adjustable screen-out voltage level, and those pulses that reach or exceed this level are counted. Threshold level is indicated on the screen by a brightening of pulse segments above the threshold level.

The electrolyte in the aperture forms the principal resistance between the electrodes. The resistance change due to particle passage is

$$\Delta R = \left(\frac{\rho_0 v}{A^2}\right)\left(\frac{1}{\dfrac{1}{1-\rho_0/\rho} - \dfrac{a}{xA}}\right) \qquad (9\text{-}25)$$

FIGURE 9-59. Coulter counter Model C multiple channel with up to twelve simultaneous size level readout. *Courtesy Coulter Electronics, Inc.*

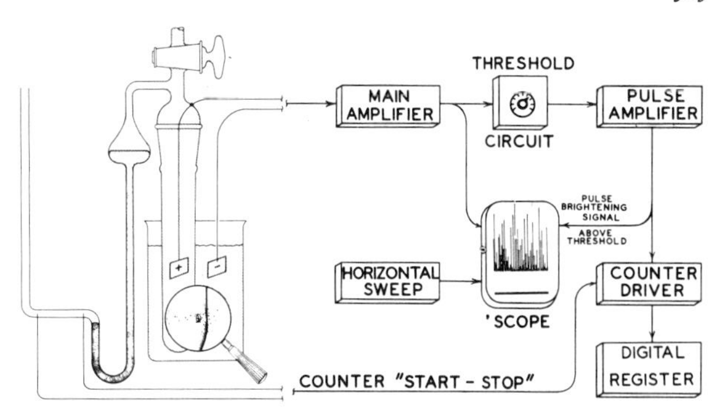

FIGURE 9-60. Coulter counter schematic.

where ρ_0 = electrolyte resistivity.
A = aperture area normal to axis.
v, ρ, a = particle volume, effective resistivity, and area normal to aperture axis.
x = particle dimension ratio.

$$\frac{1}{d} = \frac{\text{length parallel to aperture axis}}{\text{diameter of equivalent sphere.}}$$

Thus, for given aperture size and electrolyte, response is primarily proportional to particle volume. Minor "side effects" are readily avoided or may be suitably reduced by correction.

When the stopcock is opened, a controlled external vacuum initiates flow from the beaker through the aperture, and unbalances the mercury manometer. Closing the stopcock then isolates the system from the external vacuum, and the siphoning action of the rebalancing manometer continues the sample flow. The advancing mercury column activates the counter via start and stop probes, providing a count of the relative number of particles above a given size in a fixed volume of suspension (e.g., 0.5 ml).

The stopcock is opened, the counter reset, and a fresh volume drawn for each count. A series of counts from the sample beaker at various threshold settings provides direct data for plotting particle volume versus cumulative frequency.

Depending on the nature of the sample, measurement factors generally fall in the following ranges:

Aperture size: Two to three or more times the diameter of the largest particles in the sample (standard sizes, 30, 50, 70, 100, 140, 200, 280, 400, and 560 microns).

Beaker volume: 50 to 400 ml, to suit quantity needed for analysis.

Particle concentration: 1,000,000 to 1,000 per

milliliter and lower (0.0001 to 10 mg/ml, varying with size range and density of particles).

Electrolyte resistivity: 10 to 1000 ohm-cm (1% salt water at about 55 ohm-cm is frequently used).

Agitation during measurement: As required to maintain uniform suspension.

Dispersing agents: As required.

The calibration factor for the Coulter counter is constant for given aperture size, electrolyte resistivity, and amplifier gain setting. It is used for conversion of threshold settings to particle volumes, or of their cube roots to equivalent spherical diameters.

Calibration is accomplished by observing the threshold reading for monosized particles of known diameter (adjusting the threshold level to the peaks of the single-height pulses on the oscilloscope screen). Calibration is also made by integrating the distribution curve obtained for a suspension having a known volume per cent of particles.

Instrument design provides direct internal means for checking scale zero and linearity. Effects of extraneous factors on size distribution are readily detected.

Raw counts are adjusted for coincident particle passage via known probability factors, and threshold settings are multiplied by the calibration factor. This provides direct data for plotting particle volume versus relative count above stated size (cumulative frequency). (See Figure 9-61.)

Log-log plotting is desirable, since the ranges of count and particle volume are large. Also, this type of distribution curve is increasingly sensitive toward the size extremes of a given system.

For some applications, size distributions are expressed on a weight basis. The direct frequency data are easily converted for plotting particle diameter versus weight per cent above stated size (cumulative weight). (See Figure 9-62.)

The Casella counter is another counter best used on limited fluid volumes. It is an electronic unit utilizing a wide-tract scanning principle, developed for and used by the British Coal Utilization Research Association. The specimen to be examined is dispersed upon a standard optical slide. This, in turn, is placed upon an oscillating stage where a photocathode measures the light flux quantitatively interpreted by an automatic circuit. Leaflet 872, "Automatic Particle Counter and Sizer," is available from Cooke Troughton and Sims, Inc., 91 Waite Street, Malden 48, Massachusetts.

The HIAC automatic particle counter available from High Accuracy Products Corporation utilizes a light-intensity principle. Automatic counters register the number and a discriminator measures the

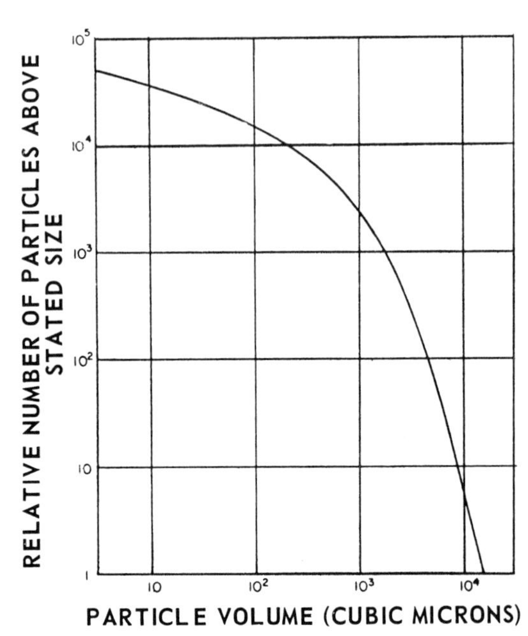

FIGURE 9-61. Particle volume versus relative count above stated size (cumulative frequency).

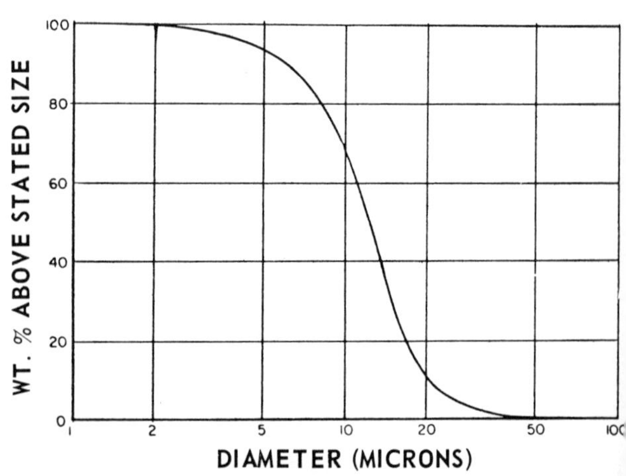

FIGURE 9-62. Particle diameter versus weight per cent above stated size (cumulative weight).

TABLE 9–9

PRINCIPAL METHODS AND EQUIPMENT FOR AIRBORNE CONTAMINANT MONITORING (2)

Method	Principle	Type	Comments	Instruments	Remarks
Light scattering	Light scattered by particles passed through a high-intensity light beam is detected and converted to electrical pulses by a photomultiplier tube.		Produces the least physical effect on the particles themselves and has high sensitivity. Particle range from 0.1 to 30 microns.	(a) Royco counter	Particles from 0.32 to 10 microns are sized and counted in fifteen different size channels. Channels are individually scanned.
(*a*) Particle counters	Pulses corresponding to individual particles are electronically separated, sized, and counted.	Instaneous particle counting and sizing.	Excellent for analytical work where size and concentration versus instantaneous event is desired. No qualitative data can be obtained.	Fromer counter	All particles over a predetermined size are counted and totaled. Instrument is portable.
(*b*) Level indicators	Pulses from photomultiplier are integrated to indicate an average level.	Continuous instantaneous dust level.	Less expensive than (*a*). Dust-level fluctuation versus time easily obtained. Ideal for continuous monitoring use.	(b) Sinclair-Phoenix Scietronic Royco 230 Monitron	Instrument utilizes forward scattering for maximum sensitivity. Instrument utilizes 90° scattering. Instrument utilizes two light beams, one for counting and one for continuous calibration.
Volume displacement	Particles suspended in an electrolyte are drawn through a small aperture. An individual particle displaces its own volume of fluid, producing a resultant electrical pulse proportional to the particle size.	Instantaneous particle counting and sizing.	Gives true particle volume measurement. Some types of particles will be dissolved or altered when suspended in solution. Unsuitable for continuous monitoring of particle range from 0.7 to 200 microns.	Coulter counter	All particles over a predetermined size are counted and totaled.
Microscopic	Collected dust is counted and analyzed by optical microscope.		Provides the best qualitative information for source identification. Requires trained operator and careful technique.	Any high-quality microscope may be used. Counting is made simpler and less tedious by using a projection-type microscope.	
(*a*) Settling collection	Dust is allowed to settle out on some collecting and counting surface.	Continuous sample, cumulative.	Sees only settled-out dust. Requires long sample time with time lag in obtaining results.	None	
(*b*) Filtration collection	Dust is strained from air sample by a membrane filter.	Grab sample, cumulative.	Provides a quick sample. Produces excellent quantitative and qualitative data. Monitors particles 5 microns and larger.	Millipore filter equipment Gelman instruments	Filters, holders, pumps, and associated equipment are available. Filters may be viewed with incident light or rendered transparent by different liquids.
(*c*) Impaction collection	Dust-laden air is forced through a small aperture at near-sonic velocity. By placing a collecting surface in the air path, the dust is separated out by enertial forces and caused to adhere on the collecting surface.	Grab sample, cumulative.	Provides quick sample. Method is most sensitive to one particular size range, depending on orifice. Matter may be altered by forces involved.	Sartorius Conimeter Bausch & Lomb dust counter* Casella cascade impactor MSA impingers	Instrument contains impactor and counting microscope. Device takes very small sample and has poor sensitivity. Same. Instruments provide a series of slits for maximum sensitivity over total size range.
(*d*) Electrostatic precipitation collection	Dust charged in a high-potential field is collected on metal surface of opposite polarity.	Grab sample, cumulative	Requires short sample time. Particles must be collected on metal surface. Requires high volrages (10 kv and over).	MSA electrostatic sampler	Dust is collected on the inside of a metal tube.
(*e*) Thermal precipitation	Dust passed between hot and cold surface is caused to collect on cold surface for counting.	Continuous sample	Very low collection rate and low efficiency for large particles.	MSA thermal precipitator	Collection rate, 7.0 ml/min. Efficiency drops sharply for particles above 5 microns.
Weight analysis	Dust collected by any of microscopic methods (*a*) through (*e*) above is weighed analytically.	Grab sample or long-period sample, depending on collection method used.	Provides no qualitative data. Insensitive to low concentrations. Suitable for gross contamination measuring only.	Any suitable analytical balance	

* Instrument no longer available.

size range of contaminant particles in a test chamber.

In future investigations, the electron microscope will become more valuable in studying and sizing contaminants in the 0.001 to 10-micron range. Procedures for microscopic studies of particles smaller than 5 microns have not yet been formulated as a detailed method by such societies as ASTM or SAE. Operational malfunctions from silt (small particles) is becoming more frequent, especially since filters are effectively removing particles larger than 15 microns.

The Baird-Atomic direct reader spectrograph has been applied with considerable success to the railroad and truck field. Investigations of contamination of lubricating oil have minimized out-of-service time and have avoided costly failures by giving prompt attention to potential trouble spots.

Summary of Methods

Table 9-9 is a summary of the principal methods and equipment used in airborne contaminant monitoring. It is not intended to be an all-encompassing list; however, it does point out the more widely acceptable methods.

Monitoring Questionnaire

The following clean room monitoring questionnaire, prepared by Sandia Corporation, will provide a useful tool to those operating or inspecting a clean room. The answers to the questions in this list will indicate whether the clean room is really intended to be a clean room or just one in name only.

CLEAN ROOM MONITORING QUESTIONNAIRE

General

1. How does the user classify the area? (grey room, clean room, super-clean room, etc.)
2. Has a dust monitoring program been established?
3. Is the program a well-established procedure or a hit-and-miss operation?
4. Who is responsible for the monitoring program?
5. To whom, and how, are the results reported? (graphs, data sheets, verbal, etc.)
6. How are the results fed back into the control of the room?
7. Have maximum limits been set up to indicate an out-of-control condition?
8. What authority or plans have been established for action on the data obtained?

Instrumentation or Procedure

9. Is a single instrument or method used, or a combination of more than one method?
10. Do the results obtained refer strictly to particle number or concentration, or is an attempt made to identify the particle source?
11. Is a commercial instrument used? Name, Manufacturer.
    a) Is is continuously operating? In what form is the data read out?
    b) Is it a periodic sampling device? In what form is the data read out?
    c) How often is the sample taken?
    d) Is the sample taken in a single location or in several locations? Where?
    e) What is the range of the particles counted?
    f) How, and how often, is the method calibrated?
12. Is the monitoring method a sampling plan using microscopic analysis?
    a) How are the samples obtained? (filtration, settling, impaction, etc.)
    b) What is the sampling period? (start time, stop time)
    c) How does the sampling schedule correlate with the work and cleaning schedule?
    d) What is the sample size?
    e) How often are the samples taken?
    f) How many samples are taken at a time?
    g) What is the location in the room of the sample(s)?
    h) What type of microscope is used? What power?
    i) What grade of personnel is used?
    j) What is the range of particles counted?
    k) How is the data reported?

Recorder

13. Are permanent records kept? How?
14. What use is made of them?
15. What degree of confidence, in general, does the user place in the results of the monitoring program?
16. What is the average particle count in the room?

Clean Room Certification *(41–43)*

In the following presentation, the clean room environment will be compared to a precision measurement instrument which must be calibrated. The comparison to be drawn is that clean rooms are not just rooms but precision tools of production. Various techniques of performing certification will also be discussed.

At this point a simile should be made. It is widely accepted that Aerospace and precision-type equipment require the use of calibrated instrumentation to ensure proper manufacture. In most cases, this equipment requires a controlled environment during critical assembly work in addition to calibrated instrumentation. This environmental control which is provided by clean rooms and which is held to specific tolerances is necessary to protect the equipment in question from damaging contamination, temperature, or humidity. As such, the clean room can very definitely be considered a tool that is required for the work being performed. Just as the calibrated instrumentation mentioned above would not be used if they were out of calibration, the clean room should not be used if the operating conditions do not meet the established standards. To ensure the validity of instrumentation, periodic calibration is required. Similarly the clean room will require periodic certification to ensure that the operational standards are met.

Factors Bearing on Problem

When one brainstorms the problem of clean room certification, a number of factors bearing on the problem will come to light. Some of these factors can be stated as follows:

1. No room contamination, temperature, or humidity mapping is currently performed. Little particular knowledge of environmental conditions of areas within the clean room is known.

2. Contamination levels within a clean room fluctuate much more rapidly than temperature and humidity values. Airborne contaminants are the most difficult to control and monitor.

3. Airborne contaminants cannot be regulated through the air-handling system by feedback from automatic controls as can temperature and humidity. Airborne contaminants are a function of clean room operations, personnel, and filter system.

4. All clean rooms have a maximum operating contamination level, above which reliability of products produced in such an environment will be uncertain.

5. Products within the clean room can have various requirements as to the level of contamination control required.

6. A product line may be established many ways within a clean room. This may put clean operations next to dirty operations or clean operations in a highly contaminated area of the room.

7. In order to make a rational judgment as to whether a work station within a clean room is sufficient for a particular operation, it is necessary to know exactly the environmental values at that particular work station.

8. Currently, many electrical and mechanical devices require calibration or certification so that at any time a definite dimension or value can be relied on.

9. A clean room provides definite environmental values. If these values vary, it is the same as a calibrated device that varies and cannot be relied on.

10. In order that a work station within a clean room provide the environmental values necessary, it should be thoroughly investigated on a periodic basis. This will allow the managers of the facilities to take corrective action should the environment about the work station become inadequate.

11. To perform such an evaluation of each work station within a clean room, and then document this information in a random manner, would be a mistake. It appears that this information should be formalized for reference use. Each work station gathered together as a whole will allow a clean room to be certified.

12. Since clean rooms are subject to the outside environment through the air-handling unit, conditions within the room will be subject to this change. Each month brings a different weather pattern and airborne contaminant make-up. Therefore, some form of certification should take place on a monthly basis to ensure that any such change is not affecting the operations within the clean room.

13. It is important that a base reference be used in a certification program. Initial certification in which a thorough mapping of the clean room is performed will be necessary.

Having stated the above factors, what observation can be made? One statement is again re-enforced. The clean room, which a decade ago was an area that provided clean working space, has evolved into a facility that in actuality is a precision tool of production. This change has been the result of product sophistication, miniaturization, and increased reliability. To date the product has been classified to be manufactured or overhauled in a clean room having definite environmental values and tolerances. Investigations of various clean rooms, however, show that the environmental values within these clean rooms very from point to point. The U. S. Air Force Technical Order 00-25-203 establishes a sampling plan to be used in monitoring clean rooms. This is sufficient for everyday operation of the clean room. It will not, however, feed back to the managers of these clean rooms sufficient information to make decisions regarding correction of faults in the environmental control system, or possible shutdown of the room. It appears that a well-defined monitoring program or certification of all work stations is necessary. Without such a program, a work station within a clean room can and many times does operate outside its operating criteria.

Types of Certification

Having essentially portrayed and established the need for clean room work station certification, what type of certification should be performed? Certification of clean rooms should take two forms —design certification and operational certification. Design certification should be performed on completion of construction of the facility and installation of equipment into the facility. This design certification is made to test and qualify the environmental control system of the room. It should test each work station in the clean room. It should be made with the environmental control system and normal clean room production equipment operating. Only personnel necessary to perform the certification tests should be present in the room at this time.

Operational certification should be of two types —prime and secondary. Prime certification should be performed yearly, whereas secondary certification should be performed on a periodic basis. This period is to be determined by the climatic conditions existing in the locale. It is suggested that this period be monthly. Although a program of certification is enacted, this does not do away with the requirement of monitoring the clean room during operational hours. Operational certification is to be used as a tool for the managers of such facilities. Prime certification should test and evaluate each work station in the clean room under everyday working conditions. Secondary certification should test and evaluate a percentage of work stations in the clean room under everyday working conditions. The minimum number of samples taken during secondary certification should be statistically representative of the environmental conditions.

Certification Equipment

Various types of equipment can be used to monitor environmental values during the certification of a clean room and are listed below:

Certification of Contamination Levels:

1. Manual air-sampling equipment only.
2. Digital light-scattering equipment.
3. A combination of digital light-scattering and manual air-sampling equipment.
4. Manual air-sampling equipment and level indicator.
5. Digital light-scattering equipment and level indicator.

Certification of Temperature:

1. Thermometers.
2. Thermocouples and thermometer.

Certification of Humidity:

1. Wet-bulb and dry-bulb thermometers.
2. Automatic humidity sensor.

Certification of Pressure:

1. Manometer.
2. Pressure gauge.
3. Automatic pressure recorder.

Certification of Light Level:

1. Light-intensity gauge.

Certification Procedure (See Note page 314)

The first procedure is to analyze the room layout to determine a central location in the personnel flow path of the room. This point is marked X in sample clean room work station layouts 1, 2, and 3. (See Figures 9-63, 9-64, and 9-65.) Notice that point X is located approximately equidistant from the farthest work stations.

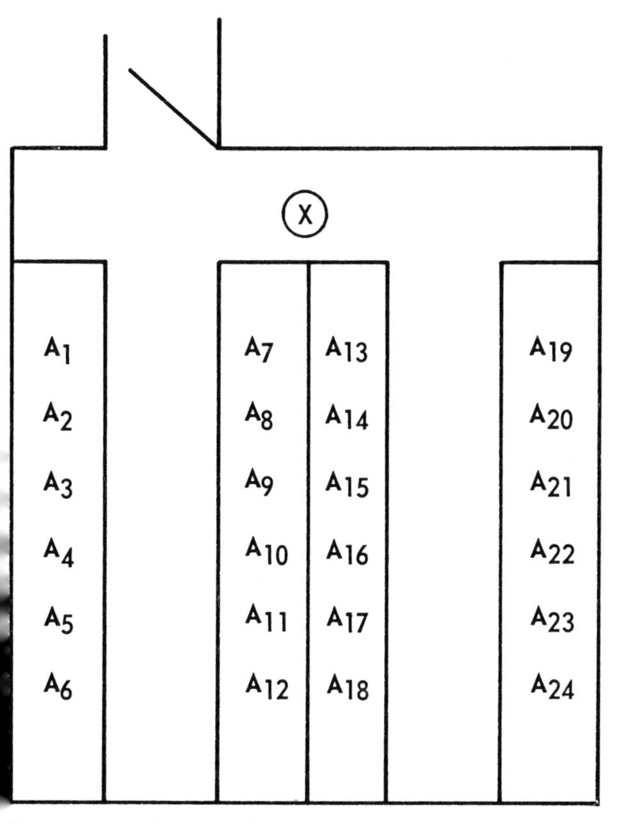

FIGURE 9-63. Sample clean room work station layout 1.

Using layout 1, monitor point X. Next monitor points A_6, A_5, A_4, A_3, A_2, and A_1, in succession or as close together as possible. Next monitor point X again, and then work stations A_7, A_8, A_9, A_{10}, A_{11}, A_{12}, point X, A_{18}, A_{17}, A_{16}, A_{15}, A_{14}, A_{13}, point X, A_{19}, A_{20}, A_{21}, A_{22}, A_{23}, A_{24}, and point X. (The ideal case for monitoring this room is monitoring all work stations during the same period of time.)

Experience has shown that point X should be monitored at least every 20 minutes. Ideally point X should be monitored continuously. If two pieces of equipment are used and point X is monitored continuously, a monitoring program of A_1, A_2, A_3, A_4, A_5, A_6, A_{12}, A_{11}, A_{10}, A_9, A_8, A_7, A_{13}, A_{14}, A_{15}, A_{16}, A_{17}, A_{18}, A_{24}, A_{23}, A_{22}, A_{21}, A_{20}, and A_{19} is recommended. The intent of the monitoring program is to have the least movement of monitoring equipment and most continuous station-to-station monitoring plan possible. In such plans where the minimum amount of monitoring equipment is used, movement must be minimized, time between successive points minimized, and the relationship of environmental values between work stations maximized. To state it another way, the intent of the monitoring program is to approach instantaneous monitoring of all work stations. The compromises that must be accepted because of limited amount of monitoring equipment dictate that the work stations should be monitored in the shortest period of time and in such a manner that adjoining work stations may be related to each other to the maximum extent possible.

With layout 2 as another example in which only one piece of monitoring equipment is used, the monitoring plan should be point X, A_3, A_2, A_1, A_7, A_8, A_9, point X, A_{10}, A_{11}, A_{12}, A_6, A_5, A_4, point X, A_{21}, A_{20}, A_{19}, A_{13}, A_{14}, A_{15}, point X, A_{21}, A_{20}, A_{19}, A_{13}, A_{14}, A_{15}, point X, A_{16}, A_{17}, A_{18}, A_{24}, A_{23}, A_{22}, and point X.

If two pieces of equipment are used so that point X is monitored continuously, the following plan is recommended: A_{10}, A_{11}, A_{12}, A_6, A_5, A_4, A_3, A_2, A_1,

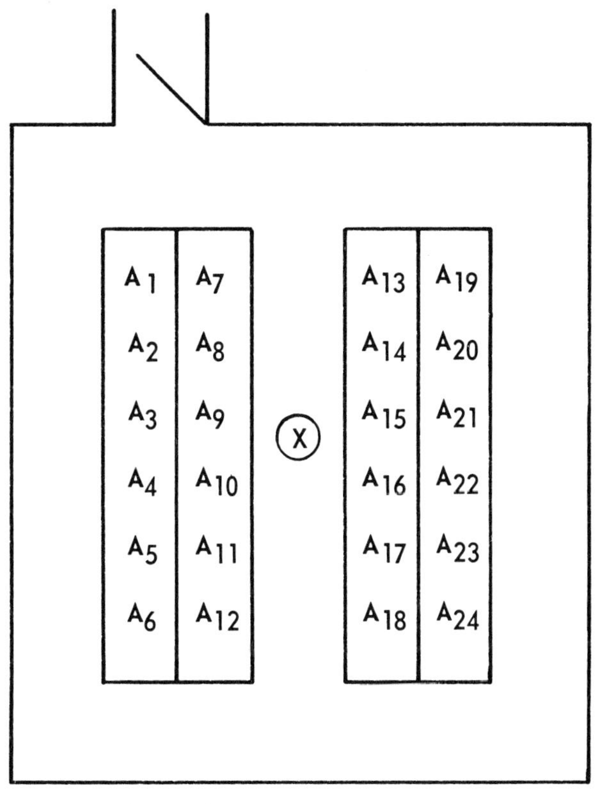

FIGURE 9-64. Sample clean room work station layout 2.

A_7, A_8, A_9, A_{16}, A_{17}, A_{18}, A_{24}, A_{23}, A_{22}, A_{21}, A_{20}, A_{19}, A_{13}, A_{14}, and A_{15}.

In layout 3, if one piece of equipment is used, the following plan is recommended: point X, A_{12}, A_{11}, A_{10}, A_9, A_7, A_8, point X, A_5, A_4, A_3, A_2, A_1, A_6, point X, A_{13}, A_{14}, A_{15}, A_{16}, A_{18}, A_{17}, point X, A_{20}, A_{21}, A_{22}, A_{23}, A_{24}, A_{19}, point X.

If two pieces of equipment are used, the following plan is recommended: A_1, A_2, A_3, A_4, A_5, A_{20}, A_{21}, A_{22}, A_{23}, A_{24}, A_{16}, A_{15}, A_{14}, A_{13}, A_{12}, A_{11}, A_{10}, A_9, A_6, A_7, A_8, A_{17}, A_{18}, and A_{19}.

During certification program point X should be monitored during the entire daily work shift. These data will indicate the room fluctuations in the environmental values. These data should be plotted versus time as shown in Figure 9-66.

Design and Prime Operational Certification

The following is a brief outline of a mathematical test that can be used in the certification of contamination levels. Figure 9-63 shows a floor plan of a typical clean room having twenty-four work stations. These work stations are labeled A_1 through A_{24}. Figure 9-67 is a tabulation of representative contamination levels which might be recorded in a relatively short period of time. When automatic particle counting equipment is used, the shortest time cycle that will give reliable data is recommended. When manual sampling is used, only one sample at each work station need be obtained. This sample should be read several times, however, in order to establish a reliable average operating contamination level at the work station sampled.

The following calculations on the obtained data are recommended:

1. After monitoring all work stations, find the average of the readings and use this average as X_i, where X_i = particles per cubic foot of the *i*th station.

2. Compute the mean particles per cubic foot. This can be accomplished by summing all the averages found in "1" and dividing by the total number of stations.

$$\overline{X} = \frac{\Sigma_i X_i}{N} \qquad (9\text{-}26)$$

where $\overline{X}$ = mean particles per cubic foot, and N = total number of stations.

3. Compute the standard deviation, which is the square foot of the average of the squared deviations from the mean.

$$\sigma = \sqrt{\frac{\Sigma_i (X_i - \overline{X})^2}{N}} \qquad (9\text{-}27)$$

where σ = standard deviation.

4. Calculate Z, which is the number of standard deviation units between the mean and maximum allowable contamination value. For this example let the room be an Air Force standard clean room or Class 100,000 having a maximum allowable value of 100,000 particles/ft³, 0.5 micron or larger.

$$Z = \frac{100{,}000 - \overline{X}}{\sigma} \qquad (9\text{-}28)$$

5. Turn to a table of cumulative probabilities of the normal probability distribution (*44, 45*) (areas under the normal curve from $-\infty$ to Z). On this table locate the Z value obtained in (9-28) and read off p, the probability that a normally distributed value of X will be equal to or less than 100,000 particles/ft³.

6. Calculate P, the probability that all stations in the clean room contain 100,000 particles/ft³ or less.

$$P = (p)^N \qquad (9\text{-}29)$$

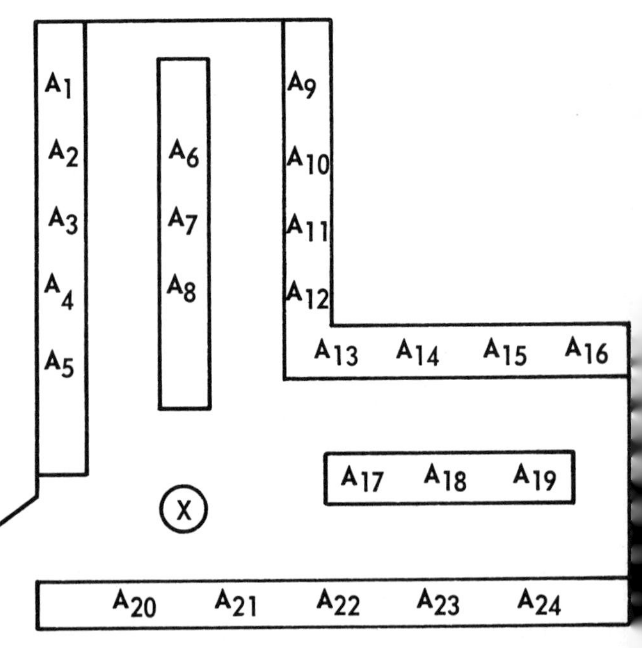

FIGURE 9-65. Sample clean room work station layout 3

The use of logarithms is helpful in performing this calculation.

7. If P is 0.95 or higher, the room passes certification. If P is less than 0.95, the room fails certification, and corrective action must be taken to decrease the particle count in the room. When P is 0.95, a 95% confidence that all work stations in room are operating at an airborne contaminant value less than 100,000 particles/ft³, 0.5 micron and larger, is established.

An Example of Prime Certification

Figure 9-67 is a mathematical model of a standard clean room containing twenty-four work stations. Shown on each work station are three readings of particles per cubic foot, 0.5 micron and larger. The average of these three readings is also shown. The problem is to determine whether or not this room passes prime certification (when $P \geqq 0.95$).

$$\overline{X} = \frac{\Sigma_i X_i}{N} = \frac{X_1 + X_2 + \cdots + X_N}{N} = \frac{90{,}000 + 85{,}000 + \cdots + 70{,}000}{24} = 54{,}600 \qquad (9\text{-}30)$$

$$\sigma = \sqrt{\frac{\Sigma_i (X_i - \overline{X})^2}{N}} = \sqrt{\frac{(90{,}000 - 54{,}600)^2 + \cdots + (70{,}000 - 54{,}600)^2}{24}} = 17{,}700 \qquad (9\text{-}31)$$

$$Z = \frac{100{,}000 - \overline{X}}{\sigma} = \frac{100{,}000 - 54{,}600}{17{,}700} = 2.56 \qquad (9\text{-}32)$$

From cumulative probabilities of the normal probability distribution curve, $p = 0.9948$.

$$P = (p)^N = (0.9948)^{24} = 0.8826 \qquad (9\text{-}33)$$

Conclusion: The room fails certification, since $P = 0.8826$, which is less than 0.95. These calculations state that there is only an 88.26% confidence that all work stations in the room are operating at an air-

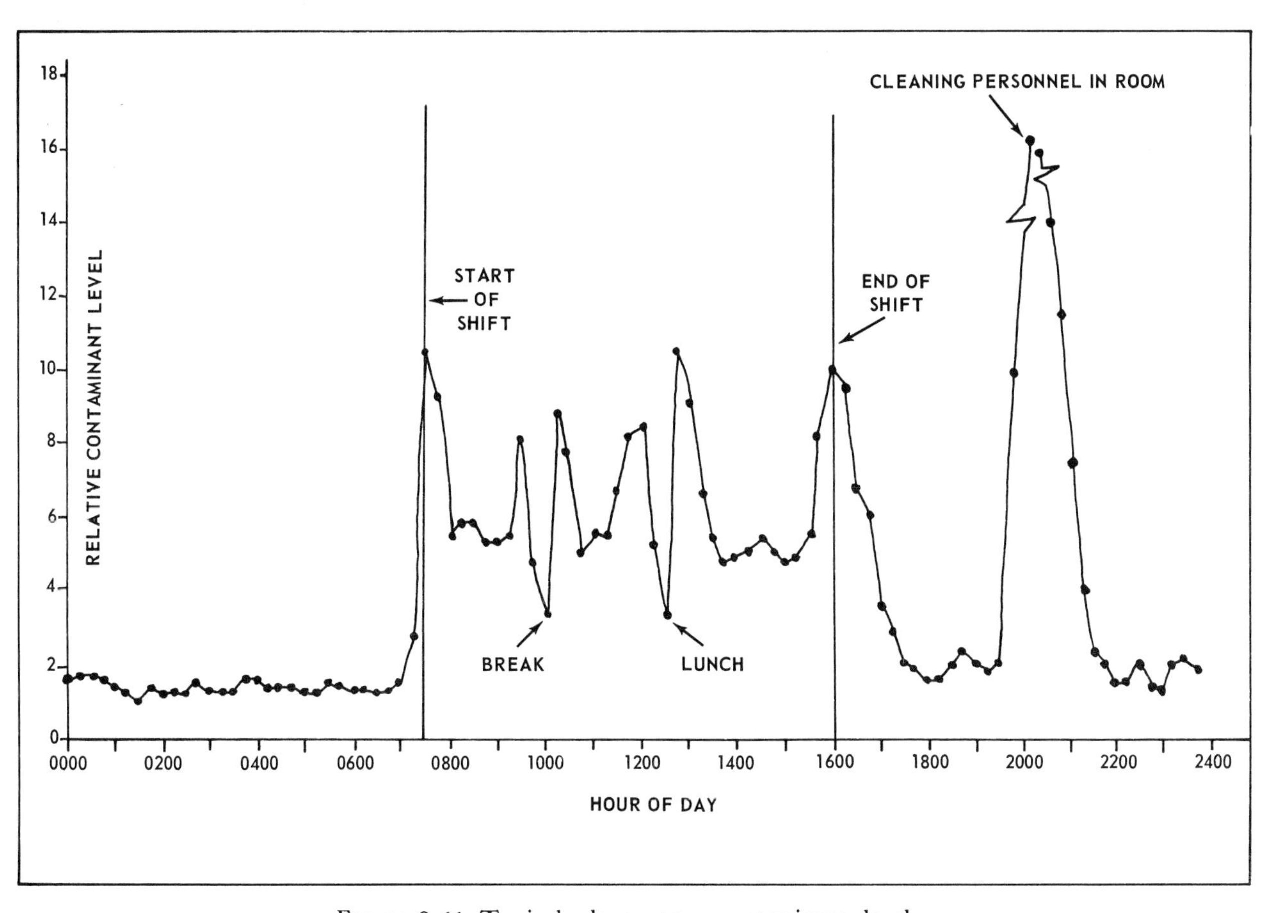

FIGURE 9-66. Typical clean room contaminant levels.

borne contaminant value less than 100,000 particles/ft^3, 0.5 micron and larger.

Now analyze the same room, but assume that A_1 and A_2 do not exist or are not in use.

$$\overline{X} = \frac{X_3 + X_4 + \cdots + X_{24}}{N} =$$

$$\frac{70{,}000 + 50{,}000 + \cdots + 70{,}000}{22} = 51{,}600 \quad (9\text{-}34)$$

$$\sigma = \sqrt{\frac{(70{,}000 - 51{,}600)^2 + \cdots + (70{,}000 - 51{,}600)^2}{22}} = 15{,}300 \quad (9\text{-}35)$$

$$Z = \frac{100{,}000 - 51{,}600}{15{,}300} = 3.16 \quad (9\text{-}36)$$

From cumulative probabilities of the normal probability distribution curve, $p = 0.9992$.

$$P = (p)^N = (0.9992)^{22} = 0.9824 \quad (9\text{-}37)$$

Conclusion: This room passes certification, since the confidence factor is 98.24%.

Note: In this example, $A_2 = A_7$ in contamination level. It is recommended in this case that work be stopped at both work stations until corrections to the contamination level can be made.

Secondary Operational Certification

1. Secondary certification should be performed once per month after prime certification. From a random sample of at least one-third of the work stations in the clean room, obtain three readings. Find the average of these three readings, and use this average as X_i, where X_i = particles per cubic foot of the *i*th work station.

2. Compute the mean particles per cubic foot of the sample. This can be accomplished by summing all the averages found in "1" and dividing by the total number of stations sampled.

$$\overline{X} = \frac{\Sigma_i X_i}{n} \quad (9\text{-}38)$$

where X = mean particles per cubic foot of the sample, and

n = total number of stations sampled.

3. Compute σ, the standard deviation of the sample.

$$\sigma = \sqrt{\frac{\Sigma^i (X^i - \overline{X})_2}{n}} \quad (9\text{-}39)$$

4. Calculate Z for the sample, which is the num-

<table>
<tr><td>A1
95,000
90,000
85,000
X1 = 90,000</td><td>A7
90,000
85,000
80,000
X7 = 85,000</td><td>A13
75,000
70,000
65,000
X13 = 70,000</td><td>A19
40,000
50,000
60,000 } Readings
X19 = 50,000 } Average of Readings</td></tr>
<tr><td>A2
90,000
85,000
80,000
X2 = 85,000</td><td>A8
75,000
70,000
65,000
X8 = 70,000</td><td>A14
20,000
30,000
40,000
X14 = 30,000</td><td>A20
40,000
50,000
60,000
X20 = 50,000</td></tr>
<tr><td>A3
75,000
70,000
65,000
X3 = 70,000</td><td>A9
20,000
30,000
40,000
X9 = 30,000</td><td>A15
20,000
30,000
40,000
X15 = 30,000</td><td>A21
40,000
50,000
60,000
X21 = 50,000</td></tr>
<tr><td>A4
40,000
50,000
60,000
X4 = 50,000</td><td>A10
40,000
50,000
60,000
X10 = 50,000</td><td>A16
40,000
50,000
60,000
X16 = 50,000</td><td>A22
75,000
70,000
65,000
X22 = 70,000</td></tr>
<tr><td>A5
40,000
50,000
60,000
X5 = 50,000</td><td>A11
20,000
30,000
40,000
X11 = 30,000</td><td>A17
20,000
30,000
40,000
X17 = 30,000</td><td>A23
40,000
50,000
60,000
X23 = 50,000</td></tr>
<tr><td>A6
40,000
50,000
60,000
X6 = 50,000</td><td>A12
40,000
50,000
60,000
X12 = 50,000</td><td>A18
40,000
50,000
60,000
X18 = 50,000</td><td>A24
75,000
70,000
65,000
X24 = 70,000</td></tr>
</table>

All values particles/ft^3 > 0.5 μ

FIGURE 9-67. Tabulation of sample contamination level readings.

ber of standard deviation units between the mean of the sample and 100,000.

$$Z = \frac{100,000 - X}{\sigma} \quad (9\text{-}40)$$

5. From the table of cumulative probabilities of the normal probability distribution *(44)* locate the Z valve found in (9-40) and read off p, the probability that a normally distributed value of X will be equal to or less than 100,000.

6. Calculate P, the probability that all stations in the clean room contain 100,000 particles/ft^3 or less.

$$P = (p)^N \quad (9\text{-}41)$$

where

N = the total number of work stations in the room.

7. If P is 0.95 or higher, the room passes secondary certification. If P is less than 0.95, the room fails secondary certification, and the following action must be taken:

a. Sample all work stations in the room.

b. Discontinue operations at all work stations containing more than 100,000 particles/ft^3, 0.5 micron and larger, and other higher value work stations which prevent the confidence factor from being equal to or greater than 95%.

c. Determine the causes of the high contamination level, and rectify the deficiencies.

d. Monitor daily each work station that sampled over 100,000 particles/ft^3, 0.5 micron and larger, until the count drops below 70,000. Then resume normal operations at the station.

An example of Secondary Certification

Perform secondary certification of the clean room shown in Figure 9-67. From a table of random numbers, our sample will contain A_{16}, A_7, A_{23}, A_{12}, A_{15}, A_2, A_{11}, and A_{20}.

$$\bar{X} = \frac{50,000 + 85,000 + \cdots + 50,000}{8} = 53,750 \quad (9\text{-}42)$$

$$= \sqrt{\frac{(50,000 - 53,750)^2 + \cdots + (50,000 - 53,750)^2}{8}} = 19,800 \quad (9\text{-}43)$$

$$Z = \frac{100,000 - 53,750}{19,800} = 2.34 \quad (9\text{-}44)$$

$$p = 0.9904$$

$$P = (0.9904)^{24} = 0.793 \quad (9\text{-}45)$$

Conclusion: This room fails secondary certification, since 0.793 is less than 0.95.

The examples given above are worked for contamination values; however, the mathematics works equally well for calculations regarding temperature and humidity.

Certification Organizations

The question now arises, "Who should perform certification of clean rooms?" It is apparent that the answer to this question is a function of who will ultimately receive the product being produced in the clean room, and what are its reliability requirements. It also is a function of what claims are made by the clean room operator about the merits of the clean room and how these claims influence the user of the products produced in the clean room. If the products are produced in the clean room but will be used internally within the organization, the responsibility for certifying the clean room appears to fall on the shoulders of the quality control group. If the products are procured by an independent agency which only specifies reliability requirements of the product, the certifying responsibility is again an internal quality control problem. If, however, the products are procured under a specification which defines the manufacturing environment, then the service of an independent certifying organization is required. This certifying organization must have experience in monitoring and monitoring equipment. Since such an organization is actually performing a type of audit, it must not have a conflict of interest present in its structure.

From the foregoing discussion, it appears that a new service industry handling matters pertaining to clean room certification is needed. The above listed procedures, techniques, and mathematics embody a state-of-the-art clean room certification program. To operators and managers, this certification program can be an effective and potent tool for management control of clean rooms.

Note on Certification Procedure

The preceding certification procedure was developed by the clean room engineering group at Olmsted AFB, Pa. It is a first attempt at developing a technique which will meet the certification requirements. Since its release, some questions have been raised concerning the statistical methodology used. The authors' intent was that the statistical sample be representative of each work station in the clean room. They felt that if there were areas in a clean room which did not meet acceptable levels, these areas would be of no consequence as long as they were not in the area of a work station. This is essentially correct, but this idea led to the use of statistics which may not correctly estimate the level of contamination of the work station areas.

The room certification appears to contain a number of problems which are brought about by statistically biasing room certification by the number of work stations present. When two independent rooms are considered with equal individual work station contamination levels, the room with the greater number of stations will have a lower probability of passing certification. At the time of the writing of this book, a more suitable statistical procedure was being developed. The preceding certification procedure is included here to illustrate the type of methodology needed, the idea behind certification, and the type of results desired.

The new procedure will be similar, but will treat each station independently. This will be accomplished by obtaining a number of samples at each work station and statistically analyzing each work station independently. These samples will be analyzed in a manner similar to that previously used, to determine the probability that the work station is operating at or below a specified contamination level. If this probability is 95% or greater, the station is satisfactory. The room is certified only if every work station in the room passes the above test.

REFERENCES

1. *U.S. Air Force Technical Order 00-25-203, Standards and Guidelines for the Design and Operation of Clean Rooms and Clean Work Stations,* Office of Technical Services, Department of Commerce, Washington, D. C., July 1963.

2. Marsh, R. C., and Whitfield, W. J. *Dust Monitoring in Clean Rooms.* SCTM 131-61(25). Albuquerque, N. Mex.: Sandia Corp., 1961.

3. Austin, 1/Lt. Philip R. *Proposed Air Force Standard Clean Room.* Western Regional Symposium of the American Association for Contamination Control, Los Angeles, Calif., February 1963.

4. Whitfield, W. J., and Marsh, R. C. *Dust Monitoring by the Dry Slide Settling Technique.* SCTM 87-61(25). Albuquerque, N. Mex.: Sandia Corp., 1961.

5. May, K. R. "The Cascade Impactor; 'An Instrument for Sampling Coarse Aerosols'." *Journal of Scientific Instruments,* Vol. 22, pp. 187-195 (October 1945).

6. Sonkin, L. S. "Application of the Cascade Impactor to Studies of Bacterial Aerosols." *Journal of Hygiene,* Vol. 51, pp. 319-342 (May 1962).

7. Wolf, H. W., Decker, H. M., *et al. Sampling Microbiological Aerosols.* Publication H, Monograph No. 60, Library of Congress No. 59-60091. U.S. Government Printing Office, Washington, D. C., April 1959.

8. Austin, 1/Lt. Philip R. *Basic Requirement for Automatic Monitoring.* Automatic Airborne Monitoring Symposium. Bethpage, N.Y.: Grumman Aircraft Engineering Corp., June 1963.

9. Austin, 1/Lt. Philip R. *Size Distribution Relationships for Airborne Particulate Matter.* Report 17.0002.-04.01. Olmsted AFB, Pa.: MAMES, April 1963.

10. Austin, 1/Lt. Philip R. *Size Distribution Relationships for Airborne Particulate Matter.* Report 17.0003.04.02 Olmsted AFB, Pa.: MAMES, July 1963.

11. Timmerman, S. W., and Austin, 1/Lt. P. R. *Investigation of Cross-Flow Clean Room Characteristics.* Report 17.0006.16.03 Olmsted AFB, Pa.: MAMES, October 1963.

12. Cadle, R. D. *Particle Size Determination.* New York-London: Interscience, 1955.

13. Green, H. L., and Lane, W. R. *Particulate Clouds Dusts, Smokes and Mists.* New York, N.Y.: Van Nostrand, 1955.

14. Heywood, H. *The Scope of Particle Size Analysis and Standardization.* Symposium on Particle Size Analysis London: Institution of Chemical Engineers, February 1947.

15. Magill, P. L., Holden, F. R., and Ackley, C. *Air Pollution Handbook.* New York, N.Y.: McGraw-Hill 1955.

16. Schadt, C., and Cadle, R. D. "Critical Comparison of Efficiencies of Commonly Used Aerosol Sampling Devices." *Analytical Chemistry,* Vol. 29, p. 864 (1957).

17. Mie, F. "Beitrage zur Optik Truber Medien, Speziel Kolloidaler Mellalbsungen." *Annalen der Physik,* serie 4, Vol. 25, pp. 377-445 (1908).

18. DEBYE, P. *Mathematische Annalen,* Vol. 67, p. 540 (1909).

19. DEBYE, P. *Annalen der Physik,* Vol. 30, p. 57 (1909).

20. GUCKER, F. T., O'KONSKI, C. T., PICKARD, H. B., and PITTS. "A Photoelectric Counter for Colloidal Particles." *Journal of the American Chemical Society,* Vol. 69, p. 2422 (1947).

21. GUCKER, F. T., and ROSE, D. G. *British Journal of Applied Physics,* Vol. 5, Suppl. 3, S138 (1954).

22. FISHER, M. A., KATZ, S., LIEBERMAN, A., and ALEXANDER, N. E., "The Aerosoloscope; An Instrument for the Automatic Counting and Sizing of Aerosol Particles." *Proceedings of the Third National Air Pollution Symposium.* Menlo Park, Calif.: Stanford Research Institute, 1955.

23. GUCKER, F. T. JR., and O'KONSKI, C. T., "An Improved Photoelectric Counter for Colloidal Particles Suitable for Size Distribution Studies." *Journal of Colloid Science,* Vol. 4, p. 541 (1949).

24. KATZ, S., FISHER, M. A., and LIEBERMAN, A. "Automatic Measurement of Aerosol Particles." *Proceedings of the 42d Midyear Meeting.* Chicago, Ill.: CSMA, May 1956.

25. PILCHER, J. M. *How Clean Is the Room.* 69th Annual Meeting, American Society of Heating, Refrigeration, and Airconditioning Engineers, Miami, Fla., June 1962.

26. LIEBERMAN, A. *Comparison of Techniques for Analysis of Aerosols.* 1st National Convention of the American Association for Contamination Control, San Francisco, Calif., May 1962.

27. MAGILL, PAUL L. "For Your White Room . . . An Automated Way to Count Fine Particles." *Air Engineering,* Vol. 4, No. 10, p. 31 (October 1962).

28. DUTCH, P. H. *White Room Monitoring.* Western Regional Symposium of the American Association for Contamination Control, Los Angeles, Calif., February 1963.

29. ZINKY, W. R. *A New General Purpose Aerosol Photometer.* 56th Annual Meeting of Air Pollution Control Association, Chicago, Ill., 1963.

30. DEBYE, P. "Der Lichtdruck auf Kugeln von Beliebiegem Material." *Annalen der Physik,* Series 4, Vol. 30, pp. 57-61 (1909).

31. STRATTON, J. A. *Electromagnetic Theory.* New York, N.Y. McGraw-Hill, 1941.

32. "Tables of Scattering Functions for Spherical Particles." *Applied Mathematics,* Series No. 4. Washington, D. C.: National Bureau of Standards, 1949.

33. VAN DE HULST, H. D. *Light Scattering by Small Particles,* p. 404. New York, N.Y.: Wiley, 1957.

34. GUCKER, F. T., and ROSE, D. G. "The Response Curves of Aerosol Particle Counters." *Proceedings of the Third National Air Pollution Symposium,* pp. 120-130. Menlo Park, Calif.: Stanford Research Institute, 1955.

35. ZINKY, W. R., "A New Tool for Air Pollution Control: The Aerosol Particle Counter." *Journal of the Air Pollution Control Association,* December 1962.

36. LINDEKIN, C. L. "Selection, Installation and Maintenance of White Room Filters." *Air Engineering,* Vol. 5, No. 2, p. 20 (February 1963).

37. MARSH, C. *A Comparison of Dust Count Data Obtained from Different Measuring Devices.* 4th Pacific Area Meeting, American Society for Testing and Materials, October 1962.

38. WHITFIELD, W. J. "A New Approach to Clean Room Design," *Proceedings of the Illuminating Engineering Society,* 1962.

39. *Silting Index Apparatus, Principles and Operating Instructions.* Bedford, Mass.: Millipore Filter Corp., 1962.

40. RILLINGS, K. W., and WILLIAMSEN, C. T. *Micro Particle Contamination of Aero Fluid Control Systems.* Project AD-13-08-60-0. Bethpage, N.Y.: Grumman Aircraft Engineering Corp., 1960.

41. AUSTIN, 1/Lt. P. R., *Clean Room Certification.* American Association of Contamination Control Mid-Atlantic Chapter Meeting, Cross Keys Hotel, Rahway, N. J., March 17, 1964.

42. AUSTIN, 1/Lt. P. R., and LEVOSKY, B. W. *Clean Room Certification,* Report 17.0012.04.04. Olmsted AFB, Pa.: MAMES, April 3, 1964.

43. AUSTIN, 1/Lt. P. R., *The Need for Clean Room Certification.* American Association for Contamination Control, Technical Sessions, Los Angeles, Calif., May 1964.

44. MOOD, A. M. *Introduction to the Theory of Statistics,* p. 423. New York: McGraw-Hill, 1950.

45. DUNCAN, A. J. *Quality Control and Industrial Statistics,* rev. ed., p. 869, Table A2. Homewood, Illinois: Richard D. Irwin, 1959.

Chapter 10. *Garments*

Man-Made Textile Fibers

It is a well-established fact that clean room products can be readily contaminated by particulate matter emitted from clothing of personnel. Therefore, special protective clothing has been designed for clean room employees. This clothing is usually fabricated from man-made textile fibers. In the following presentation, the physical and chemical properties of ten man-made fibers will be discussed. These fibers are acetate, acrylic, modacrylic, nylon, nytril, olefin, polyester, rayon, saran, and spandex. For comparison, the natural fibers—cotton, flax, silk, and wool—will also be considered.

A brief summary of the microscopic appearance of textile fibers appears in Table 10-1. The characteristics of the fibers listed in this table are divided into longitudinal appearance and cross-sectional shape as they would appear when a specimen of the fiber is mounted[1] on a slide and examined at 250 to 500×.

During the course of operating a clean room, there will be instances when, for some unexplained reason, a higher rate of rejects may occur than is normally accepted. Questions as to why this is happening will be asked, and an answer to the problem sought. Past experiences have shown that fibers contribute greatly to this problem. As an aid to those who have had little exposure to textile fibers and their identification, Tables 10-1 through 10-8 are presented *(1)*. Tables 10-2 through 10-8 contain a brief test procedure.

Photomicrographs *(1)* of man-made textile fibers are shown in Figure 10-1.

[1] Procedures for mounting and examining specimens of fibers are given in ASTM Test Method D276-60T.

Identification of Other Fibers

A number of natural and man-made fibers were not included in the identification tests and are not listed in Table 10-1 through 10-8. They were omitted because identification procedures for many of them are well known.

The cellulose and protein-base natural fibers omitted from the tables can be identified by microscopic tests and by other methods discussed in the handbook "ASTM Standards on Textile Materials" as well as in the books entitled "Identification of Textile Fibres"[2] and "The Identification of Textile Materials."[3]

Teflon[4] and glass fibers can be distinguished from all other fibers by the following characteristics:

1. High specific gravity: Specify gravity for Teflon is 2.3; for glass, 2.6.

2. High resistance to chemical degradation: Neither of these fibers is dissolved by any of the chemicals listed in the general solubility table (Table 10-8). Teflon and glass can be distinguished from each other by the fact that glass dissolves in hydrofluoric acid. Teflon is not soluble in this acid.

3. High resistance to heat degradation: Neither of these fibers is appreciably degraded by exposure for 1 hour to air at 550°F.

Identification of Fibers

Having discussed man-made fibers in detail, it would be appropriate to show how a fiber is identi-

[2] Fourth edition published in 1958 by the Textile Institute of Manchester, England.

[3] Written by Bruno Luniak, and published in 1953 by Pitman Publishing Corporation of New York City.

[4] DuPont's registered trademark for its fluorocarbon fiber.

TABLE 10–1

MICROSCOPIC APPEARANCE OF TEXTILE FIBERS (1)

		Fibers	*Longitudinal Appearance*	*Cross-Sectional Shape*	*Group**
Man-Made:	Acetate	ACELE†, "Arnel"	Distinct lengthwise striations; no cross-markings	Irregular shape with crenulated or serrated outline	I
	Acrylic	"Acrilan" regular and Type 16, "Courtelle," "Creslan," "Zefran"	Rod-like with smooth surface and profile	Round or nearly round (includes bean shape)	II
		"Dralon," ORLON† regular	Broad and often indistinct lengthwise striation; no cross markings	Dog-bone	III
		ORLON SAYELLE‡	Lengthwise striations; no cross-markings	Irregular mushroom or acorn	IV
	Modacrylic	"Dynel"	Lengthwise striations; no cross-markings	Irregular worm- or ribbon-like	V
		"Verel" regular	Broad and often indistinct lengthwise striation; no cross-markings	Dog-bone	III
	Nylon	Nylon 6, nylon 6-6 regular	Rod-like with smooth surface and profile	Round or nearly round	II
		Certain types of nylon 6-6 (e. g., ANTRON§ and DUPONT 501)	Broad, sometimes indistinct lengthwise striations; no cross-markings	Trilobal	VI
	Nytril	"Darvan"	Distinct lengthwise striations; no cross-markings	Irregular shape with crenulated or serrated outline	I
	Olefin	Polyethylene, polypropylene	Rod-like with smooth surface and profile	Round or nearly round	II
	Polyester	DACRON† regular and Type 64, "Fortre," "Kodel," "Terylene," "Toray-Tetoron," "Vycron"	Rod-like with smooth surface and profile	Round or nearly round	II
		DACRON Type 62	Broad, sometimes indistinct lengthwise striations; no cross-markings	Trilobal	VI
	Rayon	"Corval," "Fortisan," "Topel," viscose regular	Distinct lengthwise striations; no cross-markings	Irregular shape with crenulated or serrated outline	I
		Cuprammonium, Fabelta Z-54	Rod-like with smooth surface and profile	Round or nearly round	II
	Saran	Saran	Rod-like with smooth surface and profile	Round or nearly round	II
	Spandex	LYCRA†	Broad, often indistinct lengthwise striation; no cross-markings‖	Dog-bone	III
		"Vyrene"	Dark; very large; no cross-markings	Irregular shape; very large size	VII
Natural:	Cotton	Mercerized and not mercerized	Ribbon-like; convolutions sometimes change direction; no significant lengthwise striations	Tubular shape with tubes usually collapsed and irregular in size	VIII
	Flax	Bleached	Bamboo-like; pronounced cross-marking nodes and fissures; no significant lengthwise striations	Tubular shape with tubes often collapsed and very irregular in size as well as shape	IX
	Silk	Boiled-off	Smooth surface and profile, but may contain nodes; no significant lengthwise striations	Mostly triangular with point of triangle usually rounded off; irregular in size and shape	X
	Wool	Cashmere, mohair, and regular (Merino)	Rough surface; cross-markings due to surface scales; medulla sometimes apparent in coarse grades	Round or nearly round	XI

* *The fibers that could be present in each group are as follows:*

Group I	Acetate, nytril, rayon	Group IV	Acrylic	Group VIII	Cotton
Group II	Acrylic, nylon, olefin, polyester, rayon, saran	Group V	Modacrylic	Group IX	Flax
Group III	Acrylic, modacrylic, spandex	Group VI	Nylon, polyester	Group X	Silk
		Group VII	Spandex	Group XI	Wool

One method of distinguishing the fibers within a group containing more than one fiber is by solubility:

In Group I: Acetate fibers are soluble in glacial acetic acid at 100°F, but nytril and rayon fibers are not soluble.
Rayon fibers are soluble in concentrated (37 to 38%) hydrochloric acid at 75°F, but nytril fibers are not soluble.

In Group II: Nylon fibers are soluble in 20% hydrochloric acid (density = 1.096) at 75°F, but acrylic, olefin, polyester, rayon, and saran fibers are not soluble.
Rayon fibers are soluble in concentrated (37 to 38%) hydrochloric acid at 75°F, but acrylic, olefin, polyester, and saran fibers are not soluble.
Saran fibers are soluble in dioxane-1,4 at 200°F, but acrylic, olefin, and polyester fibers are not soluble.
Olefin fibers are soluble in boiling *meta*-xylene but acrylic and polyester fibers are not soluble.
Acrylic fibers are soluble in boiling 70% ammonium thiocyanate, but polyester fibers are not soluble.

In Group III: Acrylic fibers are soluble in boiling 70% ammonium thiocyanate, but modacrylic and spandex fibers are not soluble.
Modacrylic fibers are soluble in butyrolactone at 75°F, but spandex fibers are not soluble.

In Group VI: Nylon fibers are soluble in 20% hydrochloric acid (density = 1.096) at 75°F, but polyester fibers are not soluble.

† DuPont's registered trademark.
‡ DuPont's registered trademark for its bicomponent acrylic fiber.
§ DuPont's registered trademark for its trilobal multifilament nylon yarn.
‖ This fiber is supplied by the producer as a multifilament yarn with the individual filaments joined together to form a monofilament yarn.

fied by its physical appearance. By using the accompanying diagram[5] and establishing the physical characteristics of an unknown fiber, the majority of fibers may be identified fairly readily. Of course, it must be noted that this technique is suggested for those who wish to know generally, without great expense, the identification of the fiber.

[5] *Applications Data Manual—70*, "Microchemical and Instrumental Analysis," p. 12, Millipore Filter Corporation.

Requirements[6]

The minimum clean room clothing required in a conventional clean room should be smocks, caps,

[6] Abstracted from reference 2, pp. 4-5 and 4-6.

TABLE 10–2

REACTION OF TEXTILE FIBERS TO HEAT AND FLAME (1)

Test Procedure: A specimen of the fiber is moved toward a small flame, and the reaction of the fiber to heat is observed. One end of the specimen is then pushed directly into the flame to determine the burning characteristics of the fiber. After removal from the flame, the fiber's burning characteristics are again observed, and the burning odor is noted. (The burning odor can be compared with that of known fibers.) The specimen is then allowed to cool, and the characteristics of the ash are checked.

Groups of fibers, short lengths of yarn, or small pieces of fabric can be used as test specimens unless the product to be tested contains a combination of yarns or a blend of fibers. In such cases, individual fibers selected from the textile material with the aid of a magnifying glass may be used.

Caution: This test should be made with care to prevent burning of the fingers and to avoid inhaling excessive amounts of smoke from the burning sample.

Fibers		*Typical Behavior of Fiber Specimen:* *When Approaching Flame*	*When in Flame*	*After Removal of Flame*	*Typical Ash Characteristics*
Man-Made:	Acetate	Fuses away from flame	Burns with melting	Continues to burn with melting	Leaves brittle, black, irregular-shaped bead
	Acrylic	Fuses away from flame	Burns with melting	Continues to burn with melting	Leaves hard, brittle, black, irregular-shaped bead
	Modacrylic	Fuses away from flame	Burns very slowly with melting	Self-extinguishing	Leaves hard, black irreggular-shaped bead
	Nylon	Fuses and shrinks away from flame	Burns slowly with melting	Usually self-extinguishing	Leaves hard, tough, gray, round bead
	Nytril	Fuses away from flame	Burns slowly with melting	Continues to burn with melting	Leaves hard, black, irregular-shaped bead
	Olefin	Fuses, shrinks, and curls away from flame	Burns with melting	Continues to burn with melting	Leaves hard, tough, tan, round bead
	Polyester	Fuses and shrinks away from flame	Burns slowly with melting	Usually self-extinguishing	Leaves hard, tough, black, round bead
	Rayon	Does *not* fuse or shrink away from flame	Burns *without* melting	Continues to burn *without* melting	Does *not* leave knob or bead
	Saran	Fuses and shrinks away from flame	Burns very slowly with melting	Self-extinguishing	Leaves hard, black, irregular-shaped bead
	Spandex	Fuses but does *not* shrink away from flame	Burns with melting	Continues to burn with melting	Leaves soft, fluffy, black ash
Natural:	Cotton	Does *not* fuse or shrink away from flame	Burns *without* melting	Continues to burn *without* melting	Does *not* leave knob or bead
	Flax	Does *not* fuse or shrink away from flame	Burns *without* melting	Continues to burn *without* melting	Does *not* leave knob or bead
	Silk	Fuses and curls away from flame	Burns slowly with some melting	Burns very slowly; sometimes self-extinguishing	Leaves soft, fluffy, black ash
	Wool	Fuses and curls away from flame	Burns slowly with some melting	Burns very slowly; sometimes self-extinguishing	Leaves soft, fluffy, black ash

and clean room shoes or shoe covers (see Figures 10-2, 10-3, and 10-4). Laminar-flow clean rooms may require only caps.

The fabric of smocks and caps should be of a synthetic type that is nonflammable, exhibits limited-linting properties, has a weave and fiber that will not allow fuzzing, has a very low or no electrostatic generating property, and has the ability to discharge electrostatic build-up rapidly. The fabric must be able to be cleaned so that it exhibits limited-linting properties after cleaning. For clean rooms with static problems, materials exhibiting low static properties should be chosen. Colored garments can be worn for purpose of identification.

Smocks should be of simple design, with no pockets and with as few seams as possible. Seams should leave no open end of fabric which might become frayed and give off lint or loose strands. Whenever possible, an extra top stitch should be taken to minimize fraying at hidden cut edges of the fabric. Seams should be double-stitched with synthetic thread of the same fiber as the garment

TABLE 10–3

CHEMICAL SOLUBILITY OF TEXTILE FIBERS

Test Procedure: A specimen is placed first in one and then in another of the liquids according to the numerical sequence shown below. (The liquid-to-specimen weight ratio should be at least 100:–1.) In each liquid, the specimen is stirred periodically for 5 minutes, and the effect of the liquid on the specimen is carefully noted. Special illumination may be required to observe the results of the test.

Small clumps of fibers, short lengths of yarn, or small pieces of fabric can be used as test specimens; however, if there is any doubt about the results, individual fibers should be tested. Such fibers must be carefully selected from the textile material to assure that specimens of each fiber present are tested. Selection of the individual fibers can be facilitated by use of a magnifying glass or microscope.

Effect of Liquid: I = Fiber insoluble. P = Fiber partly soluble or partly disintegrated. S = Fiber soluble or completely disintegrated.

Caution: These are hazardous liquids and should be handled with care. Chemical laboratory exhaust hoods, gloves, aprons, and goggles should be used for fiber solubility work.

Chemical Agent	*Concentration*† (*% by weight*)	*Density* (*at 75° F*)	*Temperature* (*°F*)	*Acetate*	*Nylon*	*Silk and Wool*	*Olefin and Saran*	*Acrylic*	*Modacrylic and Nytril*	*Spandex*	*Cotton, Flax, Rayon*	*Polyester*
1. Acetic acid, glacial	—	—	75	S*	I	I	I	I	I	I	I	I
2. Hydrochloric acid	20	1.096	75	I	S	I	I	I	I	I	I	I
3. Sodium hypochlorite solution (pH 11)	(5% avail.) (chlorine)	—	75	I	I	S**	I	I	I	I	I	I
4. Xylene (*meta-*)	—	—	282††	I	I	I	S***	I	I	I	I	I
5. Ammonium thiocyanate	70	—	266††	I	I	I	I	S	I	I	I	I
6. Butyrolactone	—	—	75	S	I	I	I	I	S§	I	I	I
7. Dimethyl formamide	—	—	200	S	I	I	I & S	S	S	S	I	I
8. Sulfuric acid	75	1.665	75	S	S	S & I	I	S & I	I	P	S§§	I
9. Cresol (*meta-*)	—	—	200	S	S	I	I	I	P	P	I	S

† If not otherwise specified, the concentration was approximately 100%. Where lower levels of concentration are specified, water was used as the diluent.

†† At the boil.

* Vigorous agitation may be required to dissolve triacetate fibers in the specified time. A more rapid dissolution can be accomplished at a temperature of 100°F.

** Silk and wool fibers can be separated by dissolving the silk in concentrated (37 to 38%) hydrochloric acid at 75°F. Wool fibers are not soluble.

*** Olefin and saran fibers can be separated by dissolving the saran in dioxane-1,4 at 200°F. Olefin fibers are not soluble.

§ Modacrylic and nytril fibers can be separated by dissolving the nytril in 60% nitric acid (density = 1.362) at 75°F. Modacrylic fibers are not soluble.

§§ Rayon fibers can be separated from cotton and flax fibers by dissolving the rayon in concentrated (37 to 38%) hydrochloric acid at 75°F. Cotton and flax fibers are not soluble. Cotton and flax can be distinguished by their longitudinal appearance when observed with a microscope.

fabric threads; otherwise a thread of continuous-filament synthetic material should be used. Adjustable neck bands and cuffs are preferred over collars and loose sleeves for smocks. The adjustable neck bands and cuffs should provide a snug fit when worn.

The cap should be of the style worn in hospital operating rooms. It should fit snugly around the head, covering the hair so as not to allow hair and dandruff to fall in the clean room area.

Additional clean room clothing such as coveralls, hoods, and gloves may be required, depending on the type of operation being performed. (See Figures 10-2 through 10-7.) Facilities dealing with cleaning and handling of missile components such as liquid oxygen (LOX) tubing, large parts, and built-up missile assemblies will normally require personnel to be completely covered with clean room garments. In such facilities, clean room coveralls, caps or hoods, and shoe covers or shoes should be worn. If clean room conditions can be met without the wearing of coveralls, this approach should

TABLE 10–4

SPECIFIC GRAVITY OF TEXTILE FIBERS

Test Procedure: A single-filament or single-fiber specimen is placed in a series of specially prepared liquids of known specific gravity. If the specific gravity of the fiber is greater than that of the liquid, the specimen will sink in the liquid; conversely, if the specific gravity of the fiber is lower, the specimen will float. (The fiber's surface must be free of air bubbles since they can affect the results of the test.)

A suitable series of liquids for this test may be prepared by mixing, in various proportions, carbon tetrachloride (specific gravity of 1.60 at room temperature) with xylene (specific gravity of 0.87 at room temperature). Before using any of the liquids for fiber identification, their specific gravity should be checked with a calibrated hydrometer.

		Fibers	*Specific Gravity*
Man-Made:	Acetate	Secondary (ACELE*) and triacetate ("Arnel")	1.32
	Acrylic	All (including ORLON* and ORLON SAYELLE**)	1.14 to 1.19
	Modacrylic	"Dynel"	1.30
		"Verel"	1.36
	Nylon	Nylon 6 and nylon 6-6 (including ANTRON*** and DU PONT Type 501)	1.14
	Nytril	"Darvan"	1.18
	Olefin	Polyethylene and polypropylene	0.92
	Polyester	DACRON,* "Fortrel," "Terylene," "Toray-Tetoron"	1.38
		"Kodel"	1.22
		"Vycron"	1.37
	Rayon	All	1.52
	Saran	All	1.70
	Spandex	LYCRA*	1.21
		"Vyrene"	1.35
Natural:	Cotton	All (including mercerized and not mercerized)	1.52
	Flax	Bleached	1.52
	Silk	Boiled-off	1.25
	Wool	Cashmere, mohair, and regular (Merino)	1.32

* DuPont's registered trademark.
** DuPont's registered trademark for its bicomponent acrylic fiber.
*** DuPont's registered trademark for its trilobal multifilament nylon yarn.
† These are average values; hence, individual determinations on the same fiber specimen may produce values that vary by as much as 0.02.

be taken, since the worker will be less restricted in his movements. Normally, if small items are being overhauled within clean work stations and transfer units are used in conjunction with the clean work station, only minimum clean room clothing will be needed.

Coveralls should be made available in enough sizes, with adjustable neck bands and cuffs, for maximum comfort. Coveralls should have a full-length zipper with flap front. A metal snap is preferred for the final fastening of the neck band. If coveralls are used with shoe covers, the coveralls should fit inside the shoe cover. Coveralls to be used with clean room shoes should be designed so that the pants legs meet and slightly overlap the shoes.

Hoods should match the coverall in fabric and color, except in specific instances where a different color is desired for identification. The hood should fit snugly inside the coverall to provide complete coverage of the personnel and to eliminate any

TABLE 10–5

MELTING POINT OF TEXTILE FIBERS (*1*)

Test Procedure: A single-filament or single-fiber specimen, inserted between 19-mm micro-cover glasses, is placed on a calibrated Fisher-Johns melting point apparatus†. The specimen is observed with a magnifying glass while the fiber temperature is raised. (The temperature may be raised as quickly as possible to about 15°C below the anticipated melting point; thereafter, the rate of temperature rise should be limited to 3° or 4° per minute.) The melting point is that temperature at which flow of the fiber is first observed when a slight downward pressure is exerted on the upper cover glass.

		Fibers	*Melting Point* (°C)	(°F)
Man-Made:	Acetate	Secondary (ACELE*)	260	500
		Triacetate ("Arnel")	288	550
	Acrylic	All (including ORLON* and ORLON SAYELLE**)	Indeterminate	
	Modacrylic	"Dynel"	188††	371††
		"Verel"	210††	410††
	Nylon	Nylon 6	213	415
		Nylon 6-6 (including ANTRON*** and Du PONT Type 501)	250	482
	Nytril	"Darvan"	218††	424††
	Olefin	Polyethylene	135	275
		Polypropylene	170	338
	Polyester	DACRON,* "Fortrel," "Terylene," "Toray-Tetoron"	250	482
		"Kodel"	282	540
		"Vycron"	232	450
	Rayon	All	Indeterminate	
	Saran	All	168	335
	Spandex	LYCRA,* "Vyrene"	230††	446††
Natural:	Cotton	All (including mercerized and not mercerized)	Indeterminate	
	Flax	Bleached	Indeterminate	
	Silk	Boiled-off	Indeterminate	
	Wool	Cashmere, mohair, regular (Merino)	Indeterminate	

* DuPont's registered trademark.
** DuPont's registered trademark for its bicomponent acrylic fiber.
*** DuPont's registered trademark for its trilobal multifilament nylon yarn.
† Product of Fisher Scientific Company, Pittsburgh, Pa.
†† Approximate value. Fiber softens at a somewhat lower temperature, and reproducible melting point values are difficult to obtain.

danger of contamination. All hair should be confined under the hood.

Covers to be worn over employees' street shoes must be high enough to cover and hold the trouser or coverall pants legs and should have a reinforced sole. A nonslipping sole is recommended to prevent personnel from slipping and falling on smooth surfaces. Because of its durability and economical features, nylon is recommended for boots. To provide proper fit and comfort and to achieve optimum cleanliness, covers should have both snaps and ties.

If desired, an extra pair of personal shoes that are simply designed, comfortable, and washable, and exhibit limited-linting properties can be used exclusively for wear in the clean room. These shoes should be furnished to employees as part of the

TABLE 10–6

MOISTURE REGAIN OF TEXTILE FIBERS (*1*)

Test Procedure: A carefully selected specimen of the fiber to be tested† is placed in an uncovered, tared, weighing can and dried in an oven at 220°F. for 2 hours. A tared cover is placed on the can which is then removed from the oven, allowed to cool in a desiccator, and weighed to determine the dry net weight of the specimen. The dried specimen is then conditioned in the uncovered can at 70°F., 65% RH, for 24 hours, recovered, and reweighed to determine the conditioned net weight of the specimen. The moisture regain of the fiber is calculated from the following formula.

$$\text{Moisture regain } (\%) = \frac{\text{Net weight of conditioned specimen} - \text{Net weight of dried specimen}}{\text{Net weight of dried specimen}} \times 100$$

		Fibers	*Moisture Regain†† AT 70°F, 65% RH (%)*
Man-Made:	Acetate	Secondary (ACELE*)	6
		Triacetate ("Arnel")	4
	Acrylic	All (including ORLON* and ORLON SAYELLE**)	1.5 to 2.5
	Modacrylic	"Dynel"	0.4
		"Verel"	—
	Nylon	Nylon 6 and nylon 6-6 (including ANTRON*** and DUPONT Type 501)	4–5
	Nytril	"Darvan"	2–3
	Olefin	Polyethylene, polypropylene	None
	Polyester	All (including DACRON*)	0.2 to 0.8
	Rayon	All	11–14
	Saran	All	None
	Spandex	LYCRA*	1.3
		"Vyrene"	—
Natural:	Cotton	All (including mercerized and not mercerized)	7–11
	Flax	Bleached	8
	Silk	Boiled-off	10–11
	Wool	Cashmere, mohair, and regular (Merino)	About 15

* DuPont's registered trademark.

** DuPont's registered trademark for its bicomponent acrylic fiber.

*** DuPont's registered trademark for its trilobal multifiament nylon.

† In general, this test is not suitable for yarns spun from a blend of fibers, or for fabrics made from such yarns.

†† These are actual regains and in many cases are different from commercial regains. The latter are the accepted values for determining the commercial weight of fibers, and for calculating the fiber content of textile products for labelling purposes.

clean room clothing requirement, as an alternative for shoe covers.

Hand coverings should be used when finger or hand contact will contaminate the product. Such coverings should be comfortable and should enable the user to maintain a delicate finger touch. If plastic is necessary for the "touch" portions of the glove, the remainder of the glove should be made of fabric that will allow "breathing" and thus prevent overheating of the hands.

When not in use, clean room garments should not be allowed to come in contact with any possible contaminant. Garments should be kept on individual hangers.

Clothing worn in clean room areas should be changed according to a locally established schedule determined by experience. Three sets of clothing per clean room employee are recommended: one set in use, one set in the laundry, and one set for emergency use. Disrobing prior to donning of clean room garments is not recommended.

All personnel working in clean rooms should be allotted enough time to change, put their clean room clothing away, and don topcoats, raincoats, rubbers, etc.

Visitors should not be permitted to enter clean rooms without observing appropriate clean room discipline.

Personal clothes that tend to produce a great deal of lint, such as angora or fur-blend sweaters, linty stockings, or any other lint-producing garment, should not be worn in clean rooms.

Fabrics

As previously discussed, many types of synthetic or man-made fibers are offered under a variety of

TABLE 10–7

REFRACTIVE INDEX OF TEXTILE FIBERS (*1*)

Test Procedure: A single-filament or single-fiber specimen, immersed in a suitable liquid and illuminated by polarized light vibrating parallel or perpendicular to the axis of the fiber, is examined with a microscope; the "Becke line" method is used to determine the refractive index.

		Refractive Index		
		Direction of Light Relative to Fiber Axis		*Birefringence*
Fibers		*Vibrating Parallel* $n \parallel$	*Vibrating Perpendicular* $n \perp$	($n \parallel$ *minus* $n \perp$) Δn
Man-Made:	Acetate	1.47–1.48	1.47–1.48	Less than 0.01
	Acrylic	1.50–1.53	1.50–1.53	Little or none
	Modacrylic	About 1.54	About 1.53	Less than 0.01
	Nylon	1.57–1.59	1.51–1.53	0.06
	Nytril	About 1.48	About 1.48	Little or none
	Olefin	About 1.56	About 1.51	0.05
	Polyester (except "Kodel")	1.71–1.73	1.53–1.54	0.18
	"Kodel"	—	—	—
	Rayon	1.54–1.56	1.51–1.53	0.03
	Saran	1.61	1.61	Little or none
	Spandex	—	—	—
Natural:	Cotton	1.56–1.59	1.52–1.54	0.05
	Flax	1.58–1.60	1.52–1.53	0.06
	Silk	1.59	1.54	0.05
	Wool	1.56	1.55	0.01

TABLE 10–8 A GENERAL TABLE OF SOLUBILITY FOR THE QUALITATIVE ANALYSIS OF TEXTILE FIBERS (1)

Test Procedure: A specimen is placed in the appropriate liquid and is stirred periodically for 5 minutes. (The liquid-to-specimen weight ratio should be at least 100:1.) The effect of the liquid on each specimen is carefully noted. Special illumination may be required to observe the results of the test.

Effect of Liquid: I = Fiber insoluble. P = Fiber partly soluble or partly disintegrated.

Caution: These are hazardous liquids and should be handled with care. Chemical laboratory exhaust hoods, gloves, aprons, and goggles should be used for fiber solubility work.

Small clumps of fibers, short lengths of yarn, or small pieces of fabric can be used as test specimens; however, if there is any doubt about the results, individual fibers should be tested. Such fibers must be carefully selected from the textile material to assure that specimens of each fiber present are tested. Selection of the individual fibers can be facilitated by use of a microscope.

S = Fiber soluble or completely disintegrated.

Chemical Agent	Concentration† (% by weight)	Density (at 75°F)	Temperature (°F)	Acetate: Secondary ("Acele"*)	Acetate: Triacetate ("Arnel")	Acrylic: "Acrilan" regular, "Acrilan" Type 16, "Courtelle", "Dralon", Orlon* regular, Orlon Sayelle**, "Zefran"	Acrylic: "Creslan"	Modacrylic: "Dynel"	Modacrylic: "Verel" regular	Nylon: Nylon 6	Nylon: Antron***, Nylon 6-6 regular & DuPont Type 501	Nytril: "Darvan"	Olefin: Polyethylene	Olefin: Polypropylene	Polyester: Dacron* regular, Dacron Type 62, Dacron Type 64, "Fortrel", "Terylene", "Toray-Tetoron"	Polyester: "Kodel"	Polyester: "Vycron"	Rayon: "Corval", Cuprammonium, Fabelta Z-54, "Fortisan", "Topel", Viscose regular	Saran	Spandex: Lycra*	Spandex: "Vyrene"	Cotton and Flax: Mercerized and not mercerized, Bleached	Silk: Boiled-off	Wool: Cashmere, Mohair, Regular (Merino)
Acetic acid, glacial	—	—	75	S	S	I	I	I	I	I	I	I	I	I	I	I	I	I	I	I	I	I	I	I
Acetic acid, glacial	—	—	200	S	S	I	I	I	I	S	P	I	I	I	I	I	I	I	I	I	—	I	I	I
Acetic acid, glacial	—	—	244††	S	S	I	I	I	I	S	S	I	I	I	I	—	—	I	I	—	—	I	I	I
Acetone	—	—	75	S	P	I	I	P	I	I	I	I	I	I	I	I	I	I	I	I	I	I	I	I
Acetone	—	—	133††	S	S	I	I	S	S	I	I	P	I	I	I	I	I	I	I	I	I	I	I	I
Acetone	65	—	75	S	I	I	I	I	I	I	I	I	I	I	I	I	I	I	I	I	I	I	I	I
Acetonitrile	—	—	75	S	I	I	I	I	S	I	I	I	I	I	I	I	I	I	I	I	—	I	I	I
Acetonitrile	—	—	180††	S	—	I	I	S	S	I	I	S	—	—	I	I	I	I	I	I	—	I	I	I
Ammonium thiocyanate	70	—	200	I	I	S§	S	I	I	I	I	I	I	I	I	I	I	I	I	I	I	I	I	I
Ammonium thiocyanate	70	—	266††	I	I	S	S	I	I	I	I	I	I	I	I	I	I	I	I	I	I	I	I	I
Benzyl alcohol	—	—	200	S	I	I	I	I	I	I	I	I	—	—	I	I	I	I	I	I	—	I	I	I
Butyrolactone	—	—	75	S	S	I	I	S	S	I	I	S	I	I	I	I	I	I	I	I	I	I	I	I
Butyrolactone	—	—	200	S	S	S	S	S	S	I	I	S	I	I	I	I	I	I	I	I	I	I	I	I
Carbon tetrachloride	—	—	170††	I	I	I	I	I	I	I	I	I	S	P	I	I	I	I	I	I	I	I	I	I
Chloroform	—	—	75	I	S	I	I	I	I	I	I	I	—	I	I	I	I	I	I	I	—	I	I	I
Cresol (meta-)	—	—	75	S	S	I	I	I	I	S	S	I	I	I	I	I	I	I	I	I	I	I	I	I
Cresol (meta-)	—	—	200	S	S	I	I	P	I	S	S	P	I	I	S	S	S	I	I	P	—	I	I	I
Cresol (meta-)	—	—	396††	S	S	I	I	P	S	S	S	S	—	—	S	S	S	I	S	—	—	I	I	S
Cyclohexanone	—	—	75	I	I	I	I	P	I	I	I	I	I	I	I	I	I	I	S	I	—	I	I	I
Cyclohexanone	—	—	200	S	S	I	I	S	S	I	I	S	I	—	I	I	I	I	S	I	—	I	I	I
Cyclohexanone	—	—	313††	S	S	I	I	S	S	I	I	S	S	S	P	—	S	I	S	S	S	I	I	I
Dimethyl acetamide	—	—	75	S	S	I§§	P	S	S	I	I	S	—	—	I	I	I	I	—	I	—	I	I	I
Dimethyl formamide	—	—	75	S	S	P§	S	S	S	I	I	S	I	I	I	I	I	I	P	I	—	I	I	I
Dimethyl formamide	—	—	200	S	S	S	S	S	S	I	I	S	I	I	I	I	I	I	S	S	S	I	I	I
Dimethyl formamide	—	—	307††	S	S	S	S	S	S	—	I	S	—	—	S	I	S	I	S	S	S	I	I	I
Dimethyl sulfoxide	—	—	75	S	S	P	S	S	S	I	I	S	—	—	I	I	I	I	I	I	—	I	I	I
Dioxane-1, 4	—	—	75	S	S	I	I	I	I	I	I	I	I	I	I	I	I	I	P	I	—	I	I	I
Dioxane-1, 4	—	—	200	S	S	I	I	P	P	I	I	I	I	I	I	I	I	I	S	I	—	I	I	I
Ethylene carbonate	—	—	200	S	I	S	S	S	P	I	I	S	—	—	I	I	I	I	I	I	I	I	I	I
Formic acid	85	—	75	S	S	I	I	I	I	S	S	I	I	I	I	I	I	I	I	I	—	I	I	I
Hydrochloric acid	37 to 38	—	75	S	P	I	I	I	I	S	S	I	I	I	I	I	I	S	I	I	I	I	S	I
Hydrochloric acid	20	1.096	75	I	I	I	I	I	I	S	S	I	I	I	I	I	I	I	I	I	I	I	I	I
Hydrochloric acid	15½	1.073	75	I	I	I	I	I	I	S	I	I	I	I	I	I	I	I	I	I	I	I	I	I
Monochlorobenzene	—	—	269††	P	I	I	I	P	I	I	I	I	S	S	I	I	P	I	S	I	I	I	I	I
Nitric acid	70	1.407	75	S	S	S	S	I	—	S	S	S	I	I	I	I	I	I	I	P	—	I	P	P
Nitric acid	60	1.362	75	S	P	S	S	I	I	S	S	S	I	I	I	I	I	I	I	P	S	I	P	I
Pyridine	—	—	200	S	S	I	I	S	S	—	—	I	—	—	I	I	I	I	S	I	—	I	I	I
Sodium hydroxide	40	—	At boil	P	P	I	I	I	I	I	I	—	I	I	S	P	S	I	I	P	—	I	S	S
Sodium hydroxide	5	—	At boil	P	P	I	I	I	I	I	I	I	I	I	I	I	I	I	I	I	I	I	S	S
Sodium hypochlorite solution (pH 11)	(3.6 or 5.0% avail. chlorine)	—	75	I	I	I	I	I	I	I	I	I	I	I	I	I	I	I	I	I	I	I	S	S
Sulfuric acid	75	1.665	75	S	S	—	S	I	I	S	S	I	I	I	I	I	I	S	I	P	P	S	S	I
Sulfuric acid	69	1.595	75	S	S	I	I	I	I	S	S	I	I	I	I	I	I	S	I	P	—	S	S	I
Sulfuric acid	40	1.300	75	I	I	I	I	I	I	S	S	I	I	I	I	I	I	I	I	I	I	I	I	I
Xylene (meta-)	—	—	200	I	I	I	I	I	I	I	I	I	P	P	I	I	I	I	P	I	I	I	I	I
Xylene (meta-)	—	—	282††	I	I	I	I	I	I	I	I	I	S	S	I	I	I	I	S	I	I	I	I	I

The data in the above table should be used only for fiber identification tests, since their suitability for quantitative analysis tests was not determined in every case.

† If not otherwise specified, the concentration was approximately 100%. Where lower levels of concentration are specified, water was used as the diluent.

†† At the boil.

§ "Zefran" insoluble.

§§ "Courtelle" and "Dralon" partly soluble.

* DuPont's registered trademark.

** DuPont's registered trademark for its bicomponent acrylic fiber.

*** DuPont's registered trademark for its trilobal multifilament nylon yarn.

brand names. This discussion deals only with those fibers most commonly used in clean room uniforms. These fibers are nylon, polyester, rayon, and blends of these fibers. Although the majority of clean room garments are woven of the above-mentioned fibers, garments made from other fibers may be needed in a particular operation because of the solvency effect a chemical will have on the garment.

For easy classification, fabrics of synthetic fibers can be divided into two groups—those made with filament yarns, and those made with spun yarns. All fabrics of 100% nylon, 100% Dacron polyester, or blends of polyester and rayon are made from filament yarns of monofilament fiber. A monofilament fiber is a continuous strand that might be compared to a long wire. The fabrics woven of these filaments exhibit good limited-linting properties.

Nylon is the generic name for a synthetic hydrophobic fiber. Nylon fabrics are commonly available in a plain weave (taffeta) or in a seersucker weave (which, if properly set, is a permanent finish). Like all synthetics, its strength and opacity depend on the size and weight of the yarns. In comparable sizes and weights, nylon is the strongest of the synthetics. As shown in Table 10-2, nylon melts rather than flames when exposed to fire. It is moisture-resistant, stain-resistant, and wrinkle-resistant. It does retain static charges. In itself, it produces very little lint.

Nylon is ideally suited for garments where acid and static are not major factors. Its extreme durability and ease of laundering make it quite economical. Nylon is also used where opacity is not a major factor, although this factor can be compensated for by the selection of colored nylon or a sufficiently heavy yarn.

Nylon makes uniforms that are crisp and firm. They have a silk-like luster, are very durable, and are stain-resistant. That does not mean they will not get stained, but very few things will penetrate nylon to such an extent that it cannot be removed. Nylon is one of the most washable fabrics known. It washes easily and is extremely quick-drying, because it absorbs only about 4 to 5% moisture. (Cotton absorbs 25% moisture.) Nylon requires, at most, a light pressing. It is extremely stable. Shrinkage and stretching of properly finished goods is no longer a problem with continuous-filament nylon.

Dacron is DuPont's trade name for a polyester fiber. Dacron fabrics are more opaque than nylon fabrics of comparable strength and weight, but, like nylon, the strength and opacity will vary, depending on various types of garment construction. Dacron is different from nylon, in both physical and chemical senses, to a far greater degree than is suspected from their appearance. Dacron has definite advantages over nylon. It is crisp, but softer, drapes more smoothly, has a finer feel. It has a better initial whiteness and retains that whiteness if washed properly.

Dacron is one of the most wrinkle-resistant fabrics known. No matter how it is wrinkled, it will regain its original shape unless subjected to excessive heat. Dacron is a heat-sensitive fiber. If subjected to excessive heat, it stays in the position it had when the heat was applied. This means permanent wrinkles.

Both Dacron and nylon are heat-set at about 400° to 420°F. The heat stabilizes the fabric. As a result the fabric will not shrink unless subjected to temperatures higher than 400°F. The fiber melts at 480°F, but at any temperature up to 420°F fabric distortion will be less than 1%.

As shown in Table 10-2, Dacron polyester melts rather than flames when exposed to fire. It is moisture-resistant and highly wrinkle- and stain-resistant. This filament produces very little lint. It is extremely static-retentive, however. Dacron should be used instead of nylon when a high acid resistance is essential for the garments. Appearance is also an important reason for the selection of uniforms of Dacron over other synthetics. When opacity is desired, Dacron is preferred over nylon of comparable weight, construction, and color. Dacron is less absorbent than nylon, absorbing approximately 0.2 to 0.8% moisture. It is the fiber to use when a garment with quick-dry properties is desired.

When uniforms with low static electricity properties are desired, a blend of continuous-filament yarns is recommended. An example of a plied blend of two continuous filaments is Dacron polyester and Cordura, which is DuPont's trademark for high-tenacity rayon. This blend is called Dacura.

Dacura retains the low-linting characteristics of

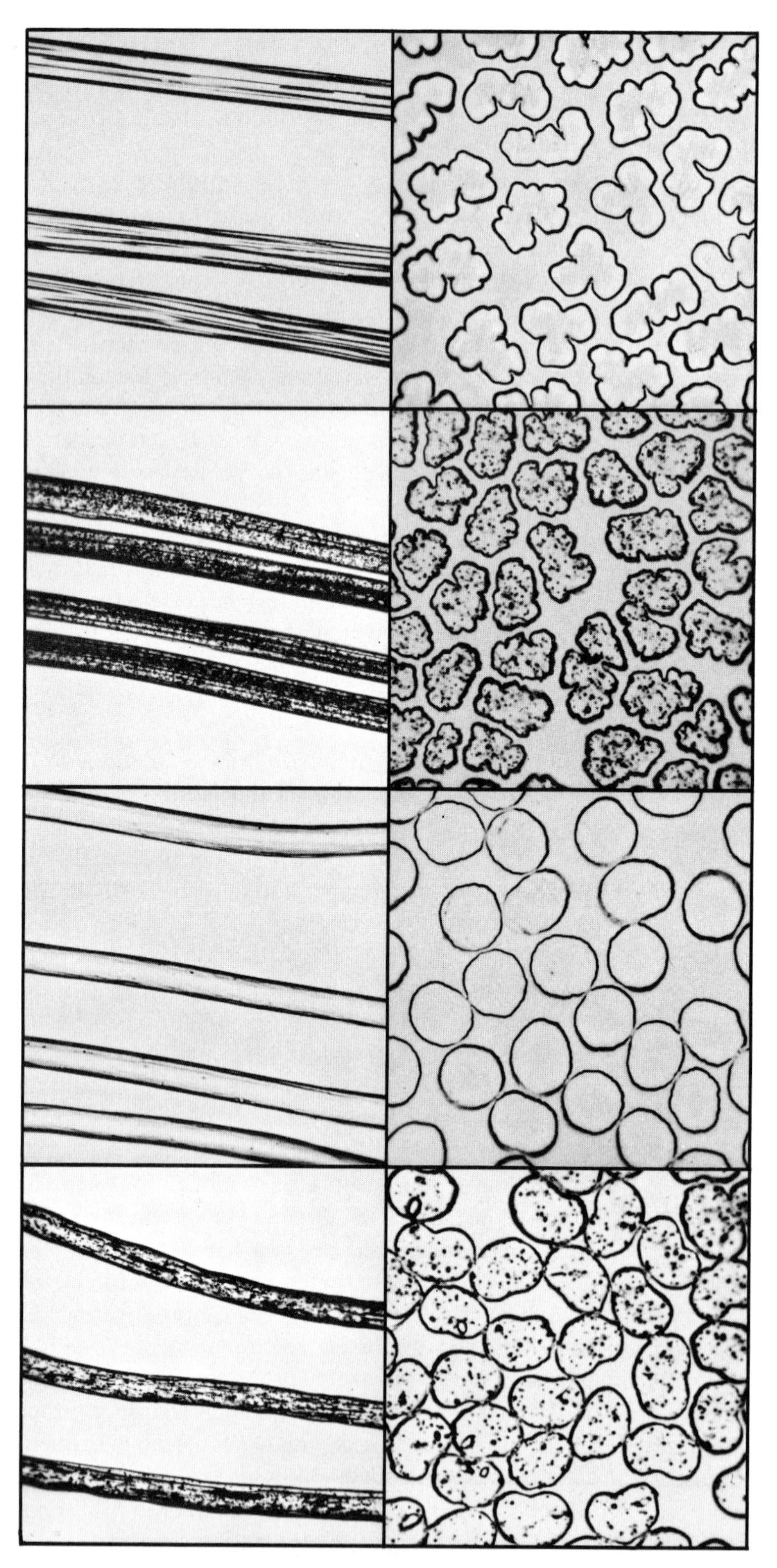

ACETATE FIBERS

ACELE* (secondary acetate)

3.8 denier per filament
bright luster

"Arnel" (triacetate)

2.5 denier per filament
dull luster

ACRYLIC FIBERS

"Acrilan" regular

3.0 denier per filament
bright luster

"Acrilan" Type 16

3.0 denier per filament
semidull luster

FIGURE 10-1. Photomicrographs of man-made textile fibers. Longitudinal view at 250×. Cross-sectional view at 500×. *Courtesy E. I. DuPont De Nemours & Co., Inc.*

**Du Pont's registered trademark for its acetate fiber*

ACRYLIC FIBERS (cont'd.)

"Courtelle"

3.0 denier per filament
semidull luster

"Creslan"

3.0 denier per filament
semidull luster

"Dralon"

2.3 denier per filament
semidull luster

ORLON* regular

3.0 denier per filament
semidull luster

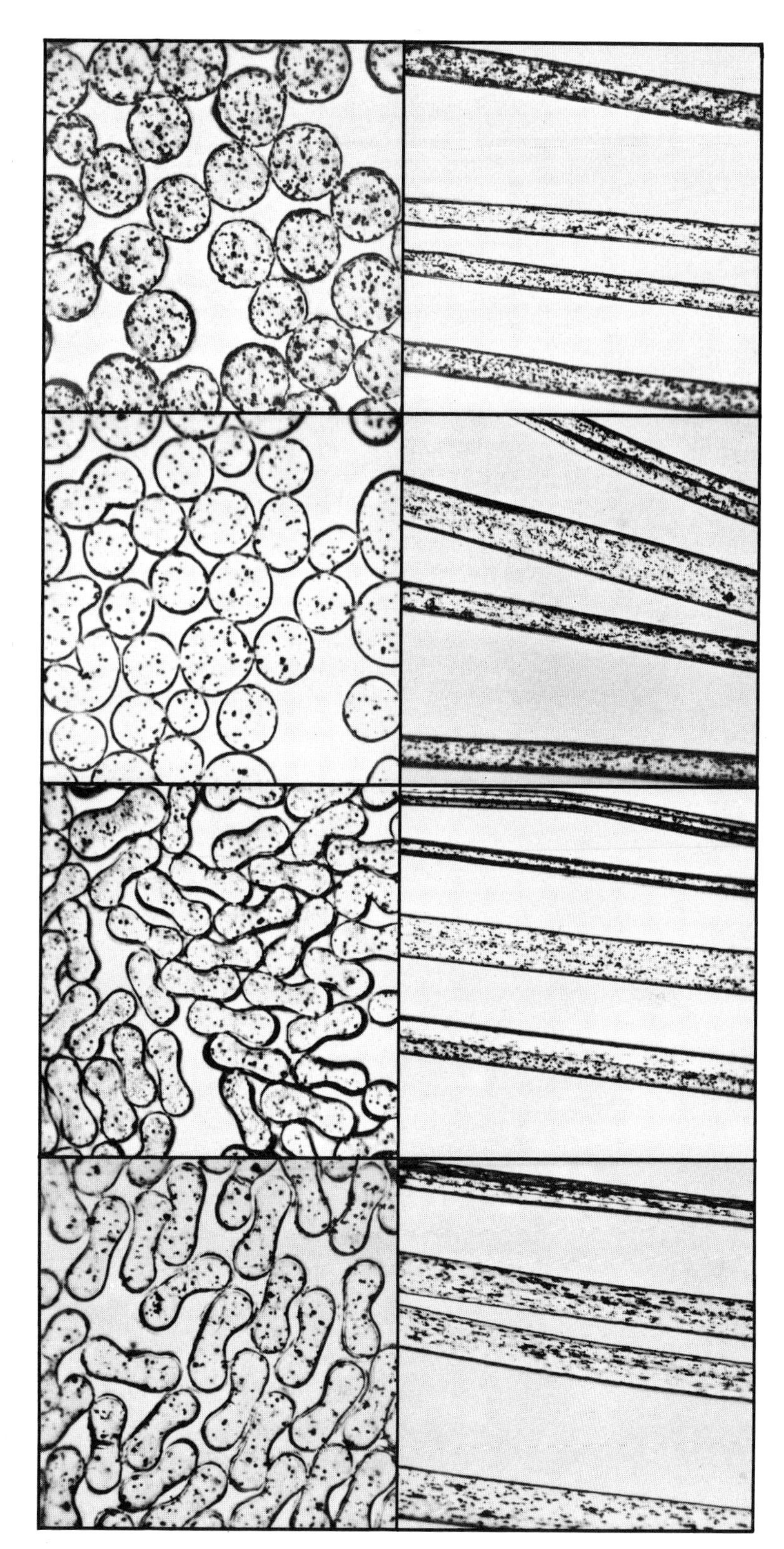

FIGURE 10-1. Photomicrographs of man-made textile fibers. Longitudinal view at 250×. Cross-sectional view at 500×. *Courtesy E. I. DuPont De Nemours & Co., Inc.*

**Du Pont's registered trademark for its acrylic fiber*

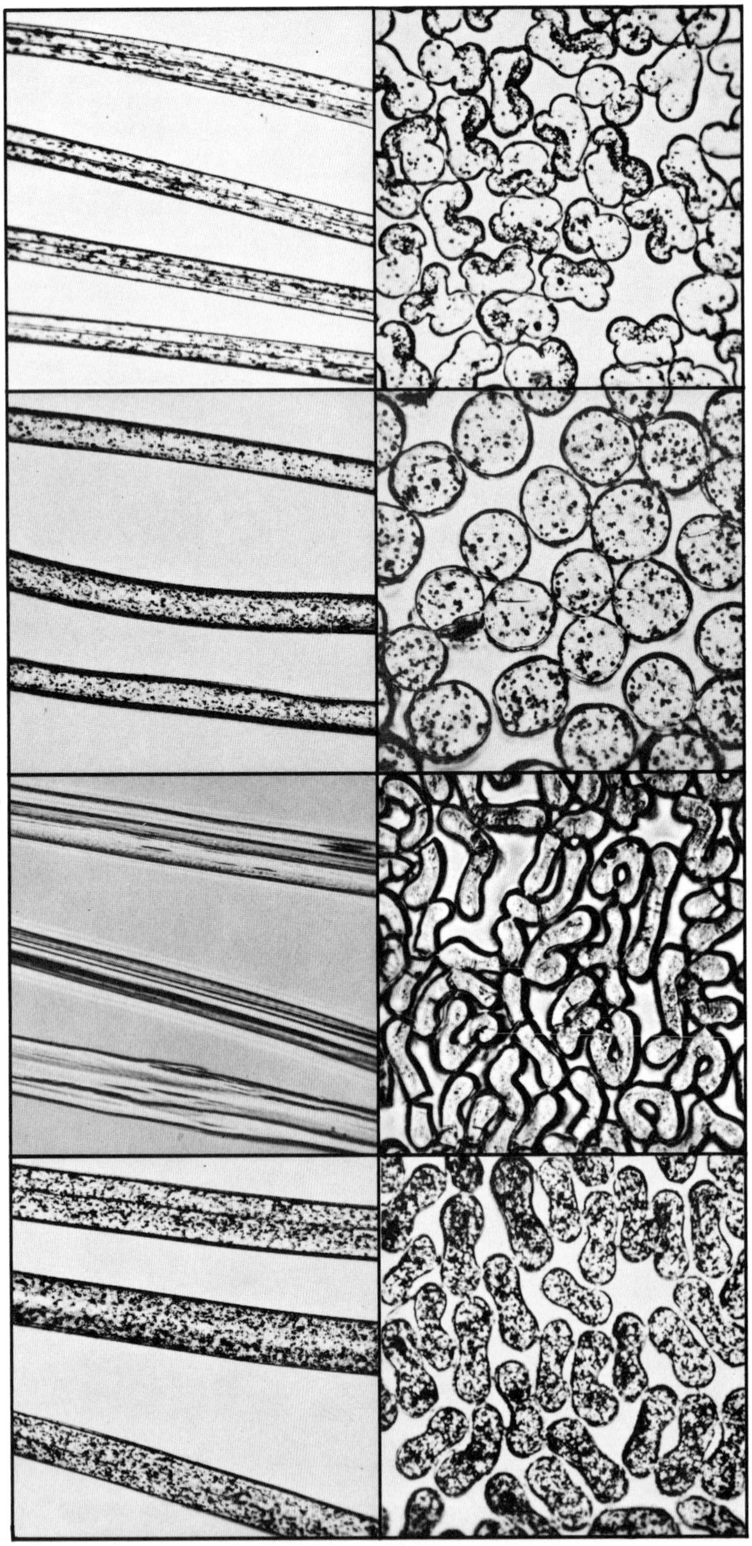

ACRYLIC FIBERS (cont'd.)

Orlon Sayelle*

3.0 denier per filament
semidull luster

"Zefran"

3.0 denier per filament
semidull luster

MODACRYLIC FIBERS

"Dynel"

3.0 denier per filament
natural luster

"Verel" regular

3.0 denier per filament
dull luster

Figure 10-1. Photomicrographs of man-made textile fibers. Longitudinal view at 250×. Cross-sectional view at 500×. *Courtesy E. I. DuPont De Nemours & Co., Inc.*

* *Du Pont's registered trademark for its bi-component acrylic fiber*

Dacron, with the added benefit that it has very low static properties, similar to those of ordinary cotton cloth. Comfort is added by the softness and drape imparted by the rayon. It also has good opacity. Its resistance to acids and caustics is good, since it is approximately 75% Dacron. It flames slightly and then melts when exposed to fire.

Spun yarns are made from relatively short lengths of fibers. In the case of uniform fabrics, these short synthetic fiber lengths are mixed with other fibers, such as rayon or cotton, to create blends. There are two types of blends—intimate blends and com-

NYLON FIBERS

Antron*

15 denier per filament
bright luster

Nylon 6

3.1 denier per filament
semidull luster

Nylon 6-6 regular

3.1 denier per filament
semidull luster

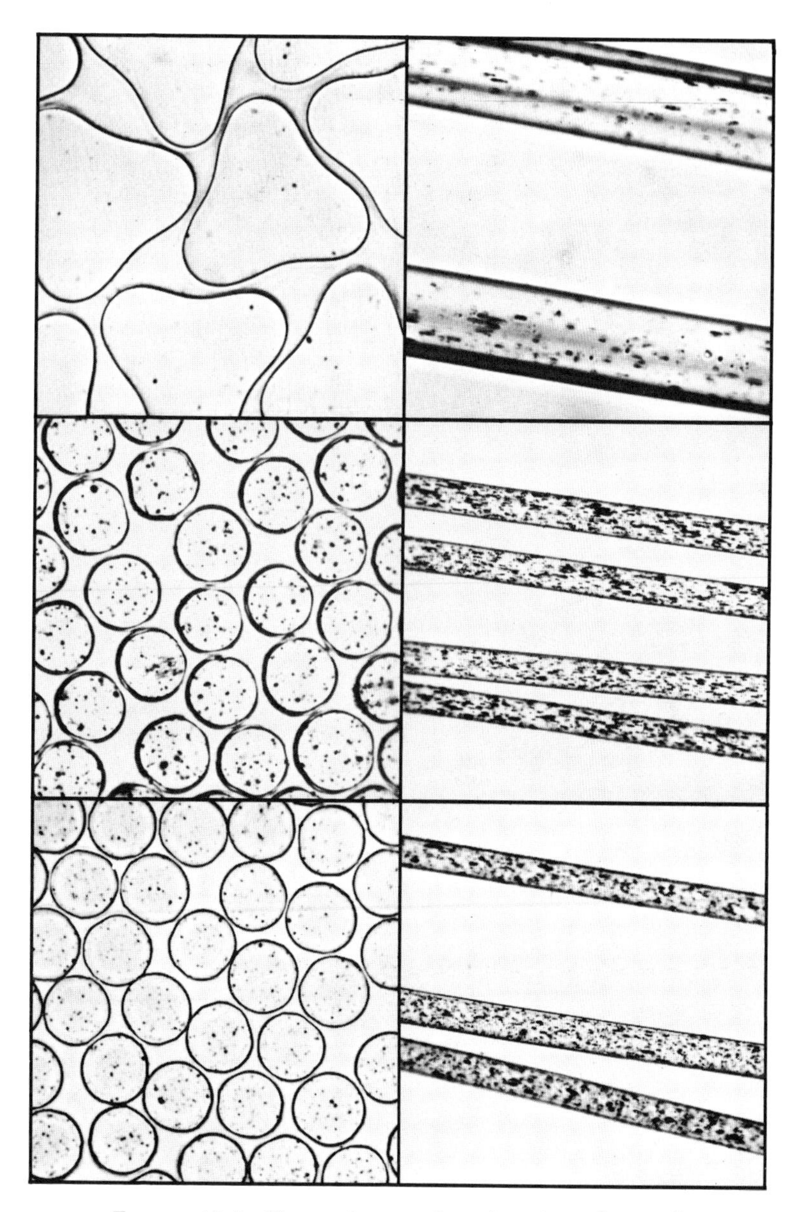

Figure 10-1. Photomicrographs of man-made textile fibers. Longitudinal view at 250×. Cross-sectional view at 500 ×. *Courtesy E. I. DuPont De Nemours & Co., Inc.*

**Du Pont's registered trademark for its trilobal multifilament nylon 6-6 yarn*

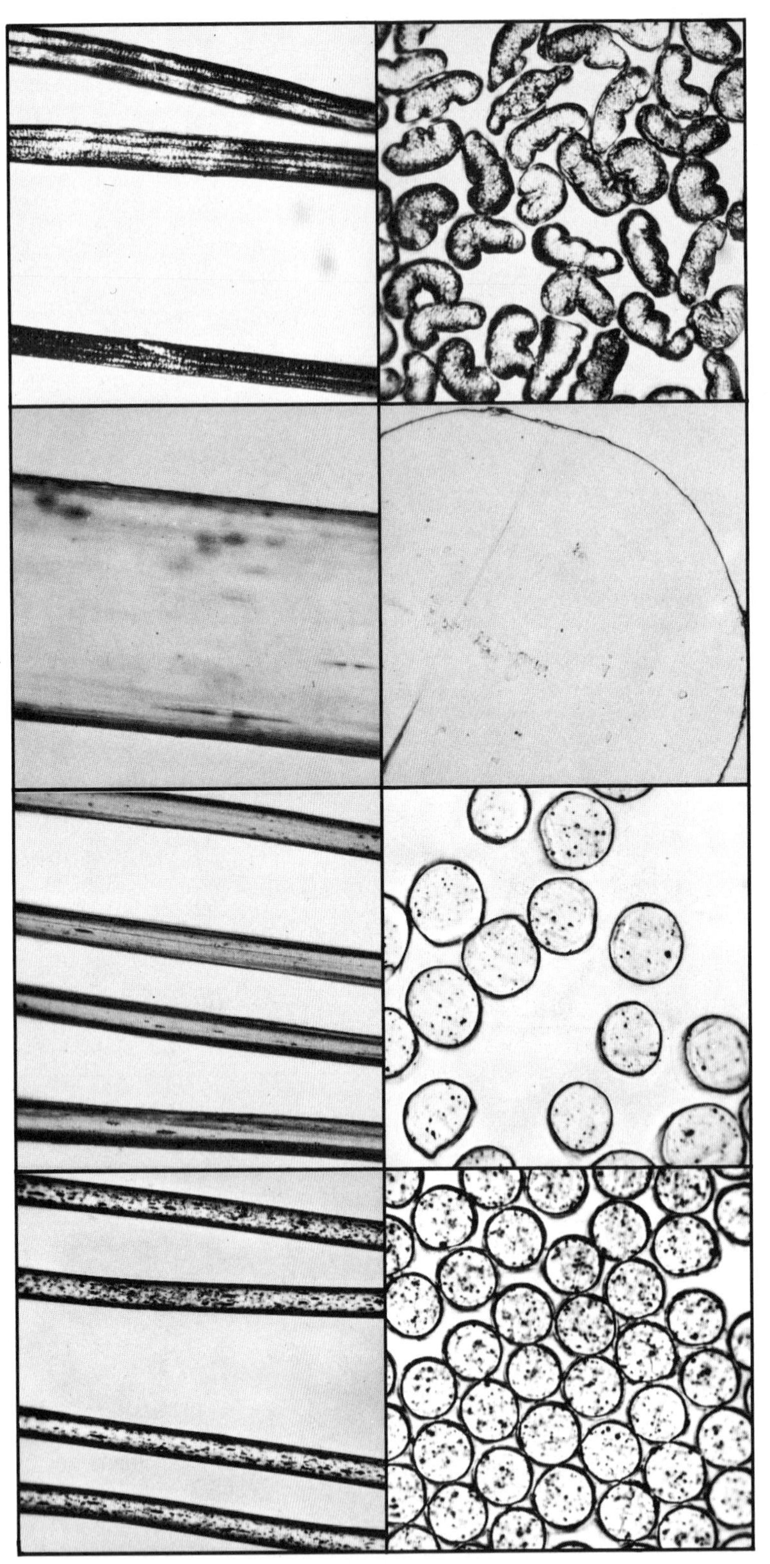

NYTRIL FIBER

"Darvan"

2.0 denier per filament
dull luster

OLEFIN FIBERS

Polyethylene

90* denier per filament
natural luster

Polypropylene

3.0 denier per filament
natural luster

POLYESTER FIBERS

DACRON regular**

3.0 denier per filament
semidull luster

FIGURE 10-1. Photomicrographs of man-made textile fibers. Longitudinal view at 250×. Cross-sectional view at 500×. *Courtesy E. I. DuPont De Nemours & Co., Inc.*

**4 to 5 mil (diameter) monofilament yarn*
***Du Pont's registered trademark for its polyester fiber*

POLYESTER FIBERS (cont'd.)

Dacron* Type 62

1.4 denier per filament
semidull luster

Dacron Type 64

3.0 denier per filament
semidull luster

"Kodel"

2.3 denier per filament
semidull luster

"Terylene"

2.3 denier per filament
bright luster

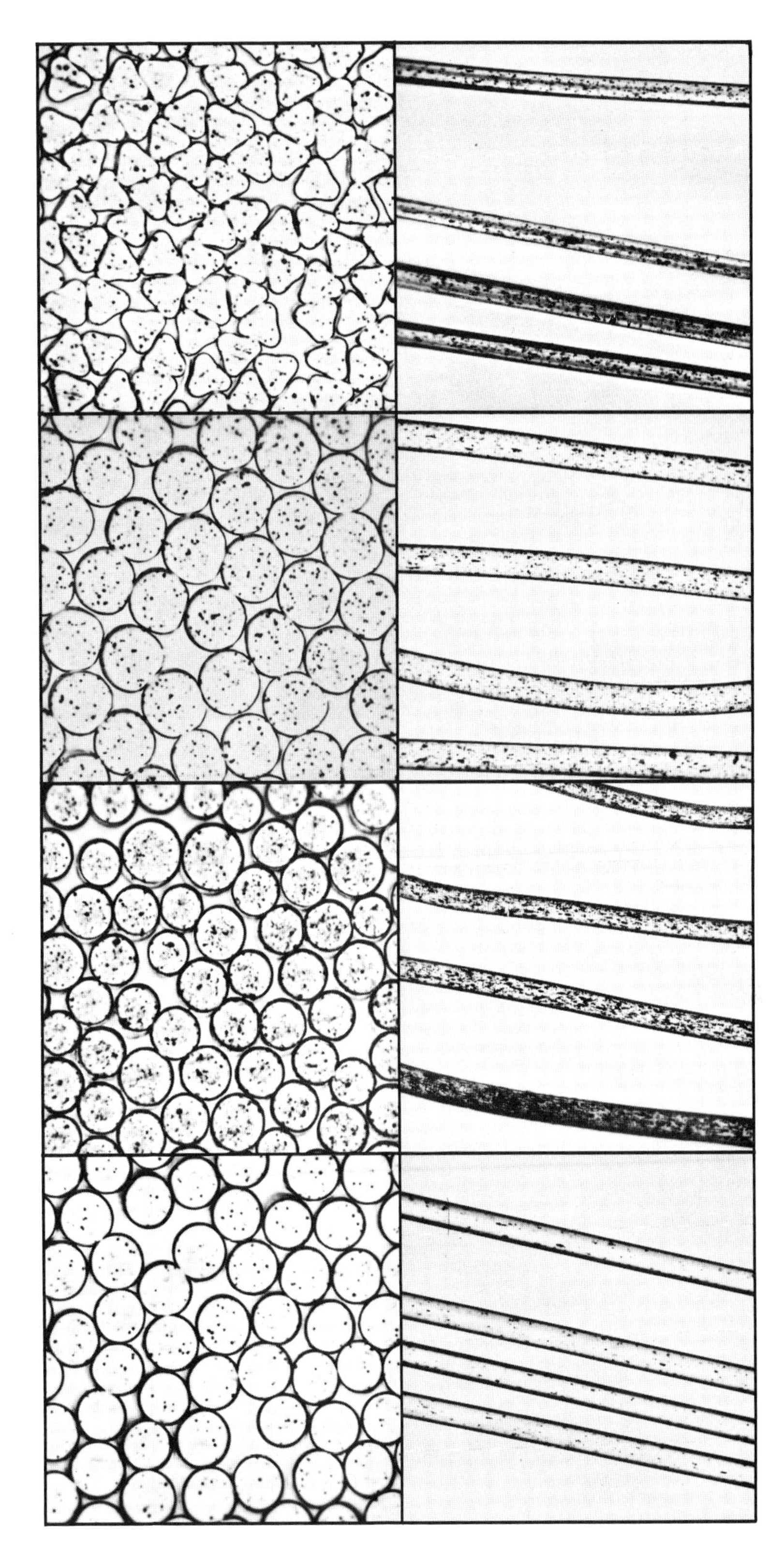

Figure 10-1. Photomicrographs of man-made textile fibers. Longitudinal view at 250×. Cross-sectional view at 500×. *Courtesy E. I. DuPont De Nemours & Co., Inc.*

**Du Pont's registered trademark for its polyester fiber*

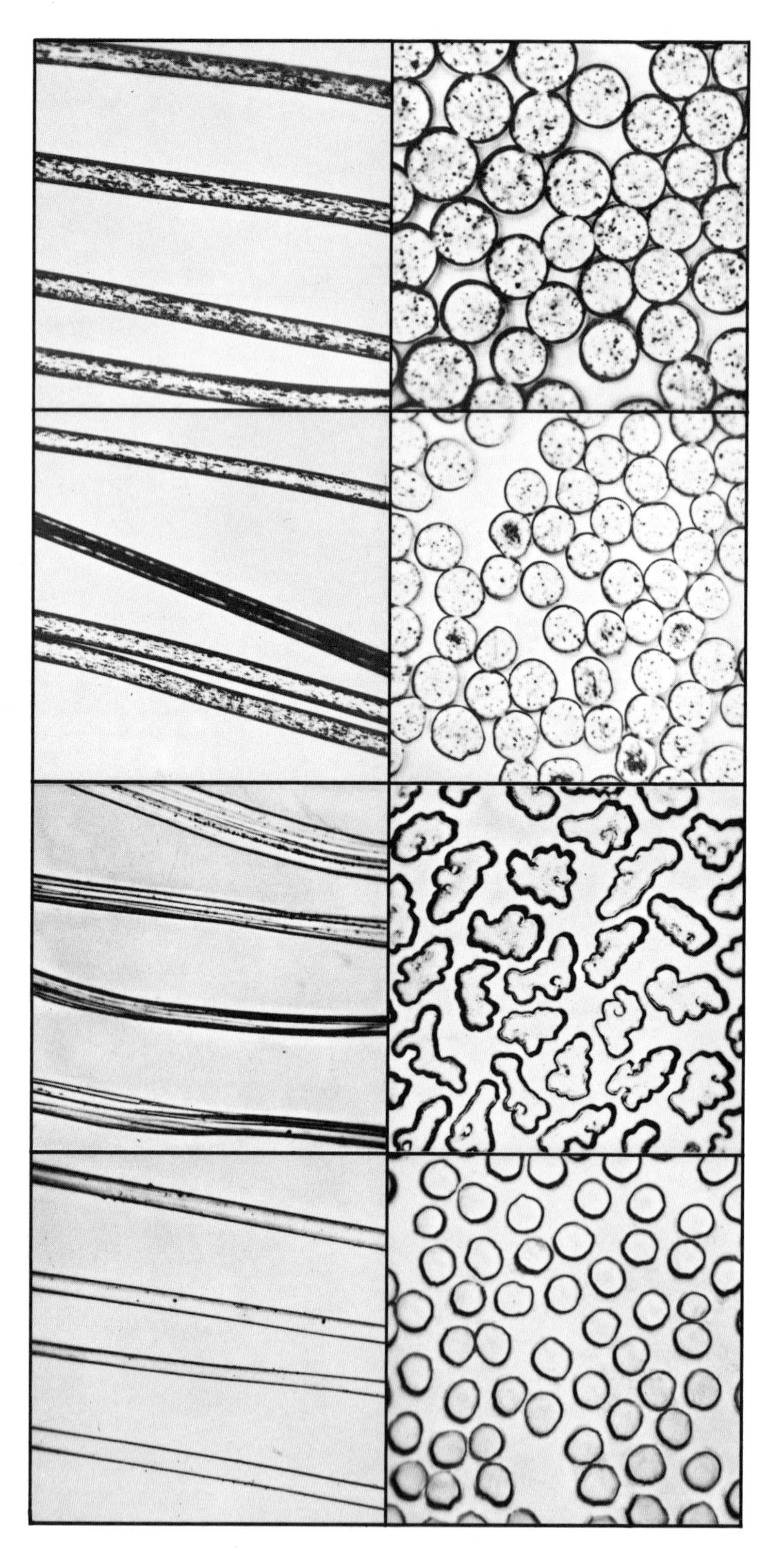

FIGURE 10-1. Photomicrographs of man-made textile fibers. Longitudinal view at 250×. Cross-sectional view at 500×. *Courtesy E. I. DuPont De Nemours & Co., Inc.*

POLYESTER FIBERS (cont'd.)

"Toray-Tetoron"

3.0 denier per filament
semidull luster

"Vycron"

1.5 denier per filament
semidull luster

RAYON FIBERS

"Corval"

3.0 denier per filament
bright luster

Cuprammonium

1.3 denier per filament
bright luster

Fabelta Z-54

1.5 denier per filament
semidull luster

"Fortisan"

0.8 denier per filament
natural luster

"Topel"

1.5 denier per filament
bright luster

Viscose regular

3.8 denier per filament
bright luster

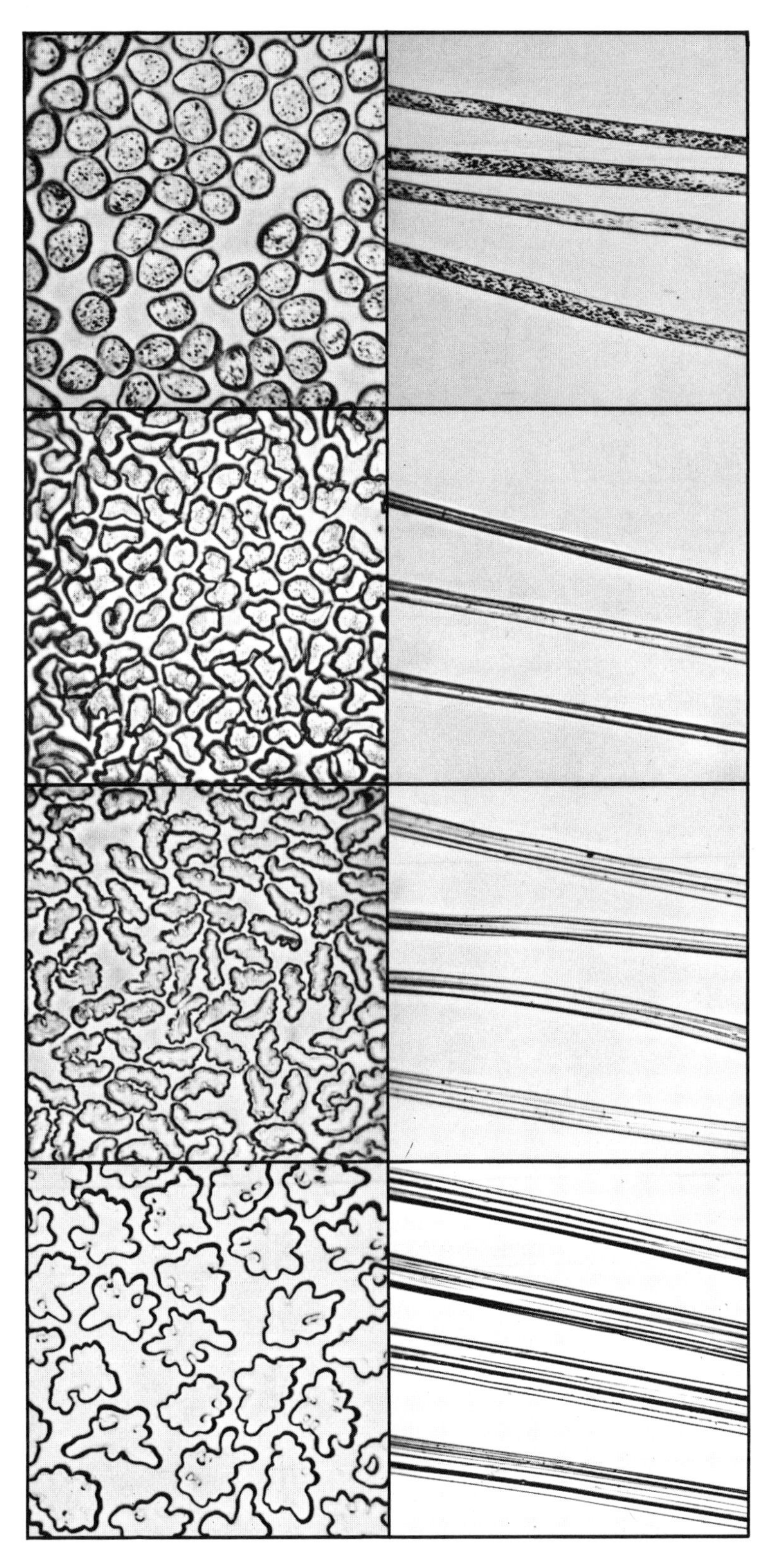

FIGURE 10-1. Photomicrographs of man-made textile fibers. Longitudinal view at 250×. Cross-sectional view at 500×. *Courtesy E. I. DuPont De Nemours & Co., Inc.*

bination blends. These blended fabrics have many of the same properties as filament yarn fabrics, except that they will produce more lint.

Dacron and rayon make what is probably the most compatible intimate blend there is, although Dacron and cotton are excellent. In this process, 65% Dacron and 35% rayon are mixed and blended until they are completely homogenized. This blend is then twisted and stretched as it is pulled out and the yarn is spun. The fibers become parallel to each

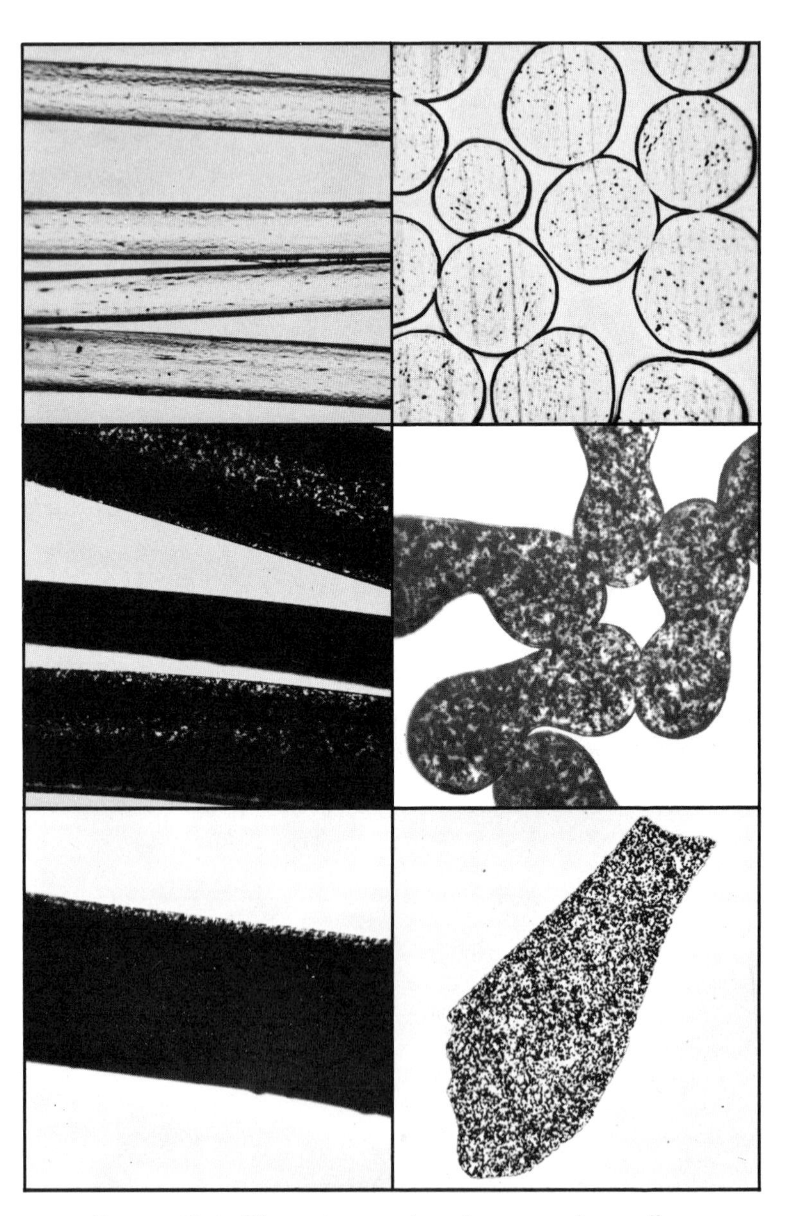

SARAN FIBER

Saran

16 denier per filament
natural luster

SPANDEX FIBERS

Lycra*

12 denier per filament
dull luster

"Vyrene"**

250 denier per filament
dull luster

Figure 10-1. Photomicrographs of man-made textile fibers. Longitudinal view at 250×. Cross-sectional view at 500×. *Courtesy E. I. DuPont De Nemours & Co., Inc.*

**Du Pont's registered trademark for its spandex fiber*
***Magnifications for "Vyrene" were as follows: Cross-sectional view 200X; Longitudinal view 100X*

COTTON FIBERS

Cotton, mercerized

1.5* denier per filament
natural luster

Cotton, not mercerized

1.5* denier per filament
natural luster

FLAX FIBER

Flax, bleached

3.0* denier per filament
natural luster

SILK FIBER

Silk, boiled-off

1.2* denier per filament
natural luster

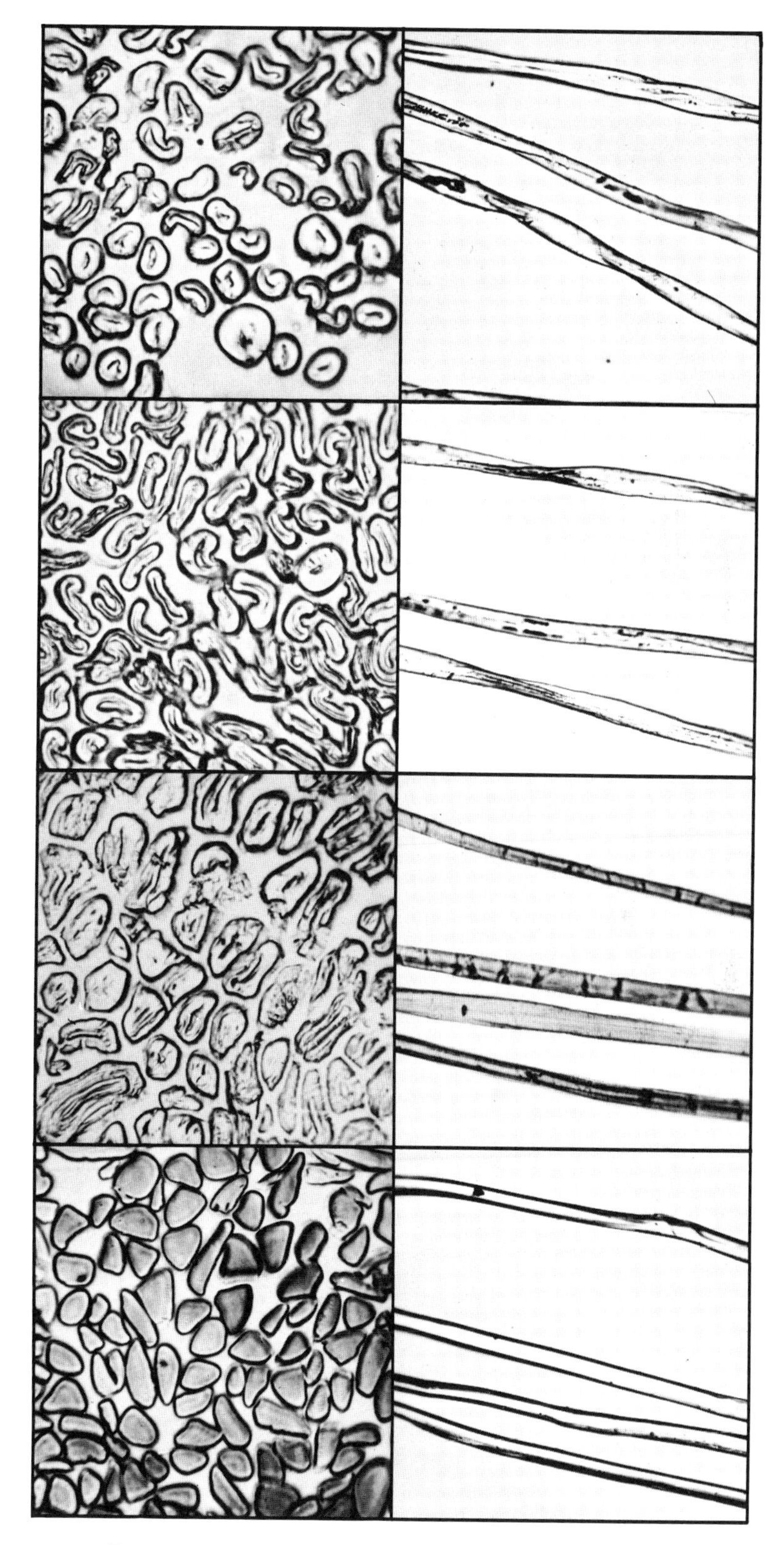

*Approximate average denier per filament

FIGURE 10-1. Photomicrographs of man-made textile fibers. Longitudinal view at 250×. Cross-sectional view at 500×. *Courtesy E. I. DuPont De Nemours & Co., Inc.*

other and twist around each other so many times that the yarn is extremely strong, and every inch of the yarn is 65% Dacron and 35% rayon.

A combination blend differs from an intimate blend in the weave. Across a smooth continuous filament of 100% Dacron is woven a blended yarn of 65% Dacron and 35% cotton. This means that the over-all percentage of Dacron is approximately 80%. As the percentage of Dacron increases, so do the durability, launderability, and wrinkle-resistance of the material.

Blending nylon and Dacron with other low-static

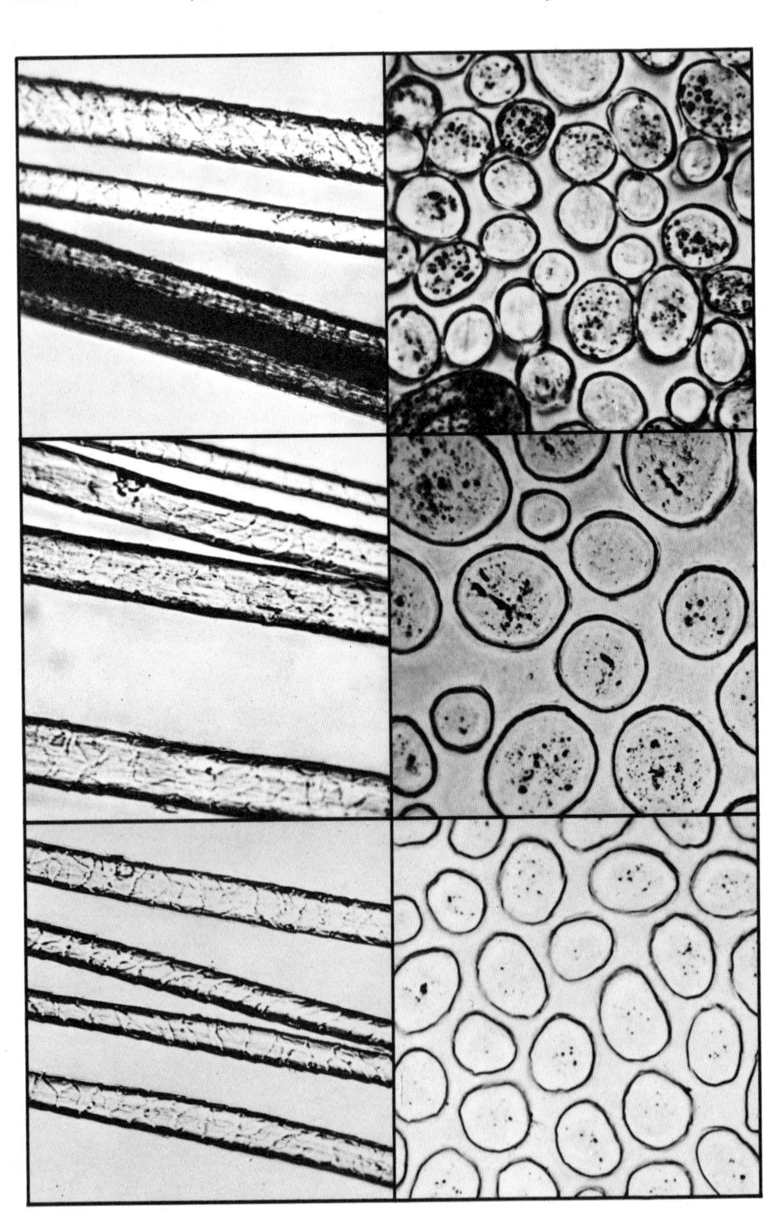

FIGURE 10-1. Photomicrographs of man-made textile fibers. Longitudinal view at 250×. Cross-sectional view at 500×. *Courtesy E. I. DuPont De Nemours & Co., Inc.*

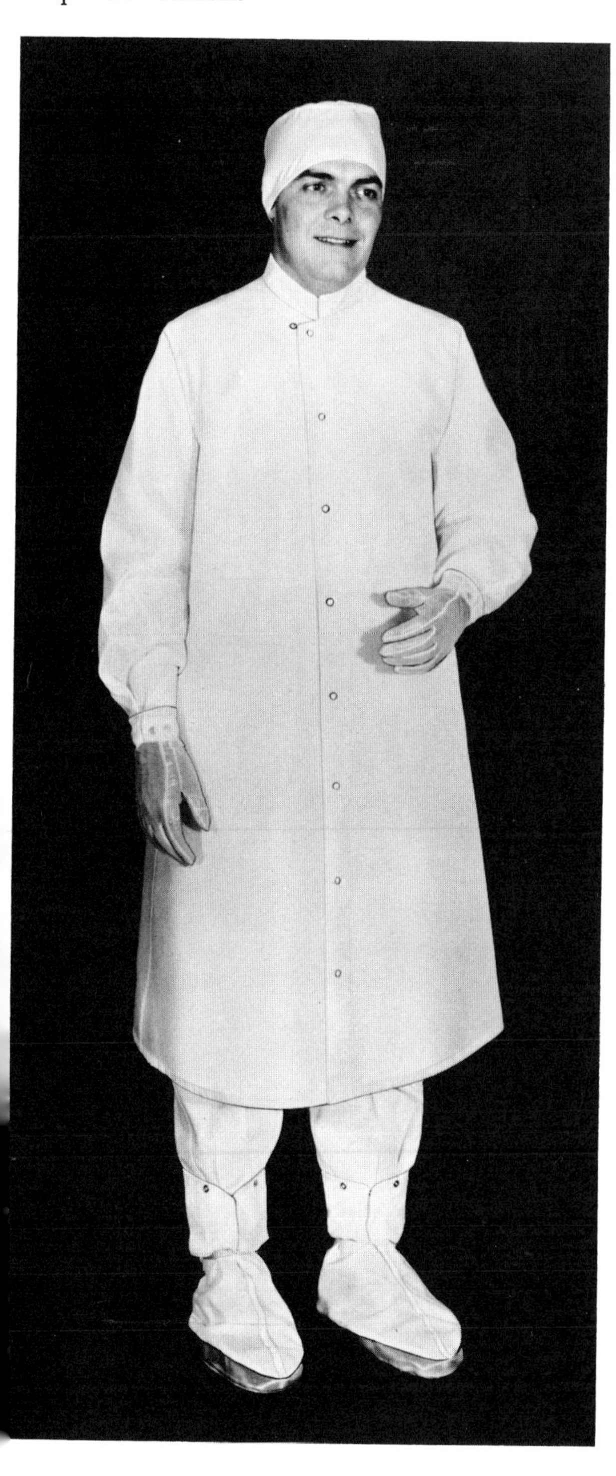

FIGURE 10-2. Clean room clothing. *Courtesy Angelica Uniform Co.*

fibers (cotton, rayon or wool) reduces the static problem. There are no permanent finishes that will eliminate static from 100% Dacron or nylon fabrics. To date, the best finish is guaranteed up to fifty washings. Even this guarantee is subject to severe limitations with regard to laundering pro-

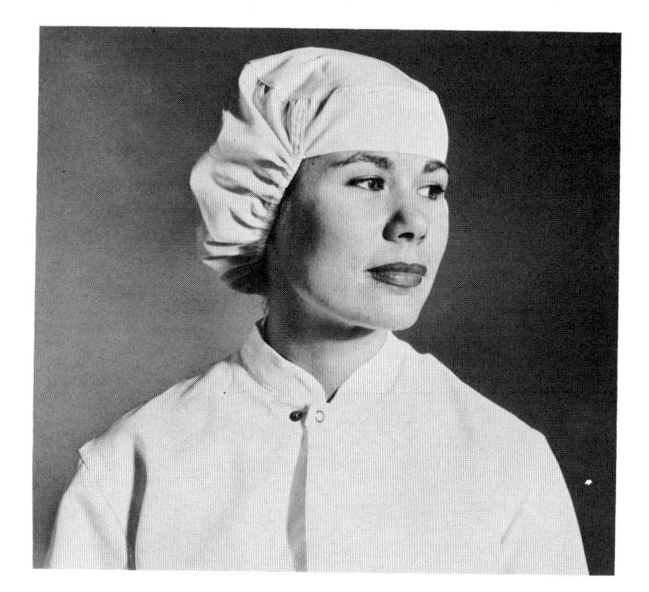

FIGURE 10-3. Clean room head-covering capable of handling long hair styles. *Courtesy Angelica Uniform Co.*

FIGURE 10-4. Clean room contoured hood. *Courtesy Angelica Uniform Co.*

FIGURE 10-5. The proper sequential procedure for donning this clean room clothing is hood, suit, booties, and then gloves. *Courtesy Angelica Uniform Co.*

cedures. The Onyx Chemical Corporation which registered the Astonized[7] finish states that an Astonized garment should not be laundered in the presence of a chemical bleaching agent of the oxidizing type, such as hypochlorite, perborate, or peroxide. Such agents have a tendency to remove the antistatic protection from the garments. There are also other antistatic agents such as Avitex NA or

[7] An antistatic garment process.

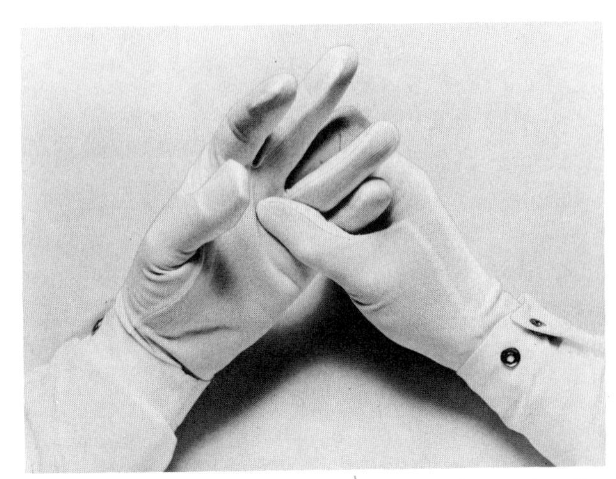

FIGURE 10-6. Nylon stretch gloves. *Courtesy Angelica Uniform Co.*

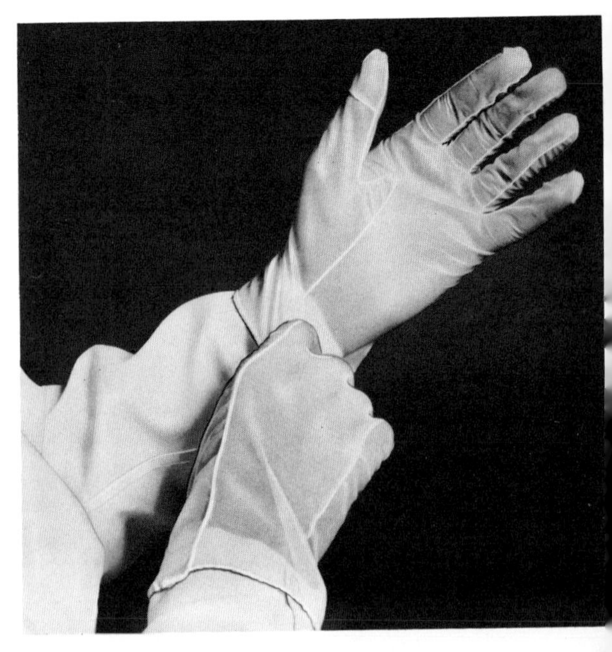

FIGURE 10-7. Nylon gloves. *Courtesy Angelica Uniform Co.*

Avitex R which must be added to the rinse during each washing. These agents aid in reducing the likelihood of large static charge buildup during wearing.

Two types of stitches are used for seams in synthetic uniforms—serged stitch and double-needle stitch. Serged stitching is used on the inner side of the uniform and then trimmed. No stitching appears on the outer side of the garment. Despite its strength, a serged stitch may pull away in areas such as pockets. This results in raw edges and lint. Serged stitching can be used for garments that do not give total coverage, when maximum lint control is not essential. A practical comparison is the difference between coveralls and smocks.

In double-needle stitching, seams are overlapped and stitched with dual needles. Raw edges are eliminated. This stitching prevents exposed raw edges in such areas as belt loops and where pockets are attached to the garment. Double stitching prevents fraying and pulling loose. This type of stitching can result in higher costs, depending on the type of garment and the construction desired; however, it will result in a garment that is less likely to produce profuse linting. Normally, a double-needle stitch is used in employee uniforms for clean rooms.

Although it presents many difficulties in the manufacturing process, synthetic thread is less lint-producing than highly mercerized cotton thread. It is recommended that all clean room garments for wear in contamination-sensitive areas be stitched with filament synthetic thread.

Laundering

In washing synthetic garments, it is important that certain restrictions be followed: (1) Wash in water not over 160°F for white and not over 140°F for colors. (2) End the wash cycle with a cold rinse. (3) Never leave synthetic garments piled up hot, in either a wash-wheel, an extractor, or a tumbler.

The following general washing formula is suggested for white garments of Dacron and blends of Dacron and cotton or rayon: Maintain heavy suds. Use water of low hardness value (not more than two grains per gallon for best results). Wash at 140° to 160°F, using built soap and alkali. Use a multiple-suds type of washing procedure, with at least three suds operations. A bleach operation at 140° to 160°F, using 2 quarts of 1% available chlorine bleach per 100 pounds of load, is recommended. With a hydrogen peroxide bleach, 1 pint of 3% concentration per 100 pounds of load is recommended.

At least three rinses of a minimum of 2 minutes' duration should follow the bleaching. If three rinses are used, the first should be water at the temperature of the bleach, the second mixed hot and cold water, or a split rinse, and the final rinse should be cold. A sour operation to bring the final bath to pH of 5.0 is necessary if alkali is used in suds.

Like all other laundry items, the formula used depends on soil conditions. If there are no grease stains, either animal or mineral, and only light soil, the following formula is being successfully used: Wash, for 5 minutes or more, using low temperature water (110° to 120°F) with a high water level in the wheel. Best results can be obtained by washing the garments of synthetic fibers alone. Use a synthetic detergent such as Colgate-Palmolive Arctic Syntex HD, Proctor and Gamble Orvus Extra Granules, or Swift and Co. Solar Flake.

Use three rinses with a high water level in each. The first should be at the temperature of the wash water, the second should be a split rinse, and the third, a cold water rinse. Do not use a sour rinse on the garments. Use of synthetic detergents will avoid high alkalinity and the necessity to sour to neutralize this alkalinity.

As far as wash ingredients are concerned, there are undoubtedly many good products. A nonprecipitating type of sequestering agent such as Versene, Sequestrene, or Calgon may be used. A heavy-duty synthetic detergent such as Orvus Hytemp Granules, Sterox S.E., or Arctic Syntex HD may also be used successfully with alkali as needed.

One successful laundry washes 30 pounds of Dacron dresses in a 50-pound wash-wheel, using 8 ounces of Talb TST-09 and ½ cup of Kohnstamm 1179. Their formula for washing is 10 minutes suds, rinse, 5 minutes carry-over suds, and then three 3-minute rinses—the last two in cold water.

Synthetics can be dried by drip-drying, tumble drying, or steam air finisher. If space and proper air filtration and circulation are available, synthetics can be removed from the wash-wheel after the final rinse and allowed to drip-dry. These garments will be essentially free of wrinkles. Extraction is not to be performed with this method.

Synthetic uniforms should be tumbled at a temperature of 150°F. The drying time will vary with materials—100% nylon and 100% Dacron will usually be dry and essentially wrinkle-free in 15 minutes. Dacron–rayon (65%–35%) may take 20 to 25 minutes, depending on the type of extraction. Dacron–cotton (65%–35%) can be dried wrinkle-free in about 20 minutes. Consequently, a control must be available on the drier for the temperature setting.

Wrinkles are effectively removed from nylon fabrics at 130°F, and from Dacron fabrics at 150°F. Tumble drying at appreciably higher temperatures (160° to 210°F) introduces many wrinkles. Since no serious wrinkling is introduced with any of these fibers until the temperature exceeds 160°F, it appears that the optimum temperature for wrinkle removal by tumble drying is 150°F. The operating temperatures discussed above were measured in the exhaust duct of the dryer. After drying, the actual temperatures reached by the fabrics in the drying were 20° to 30° higher than the exhaust air temperatures noted.

Good tumbling action is necessary for wrinkle removal. The drier should have a maximum load capacity of 50% of its total weight; that is, a 100-pound drier can take 50 pounds of clothes, dry weight. To avoid the wrinkling that occurs if the fabrics are allowed to stand under pressure while hot, the blower and tumbling action must continue for 5 to 10 minutes after the heating current is shut off. This permits the clothes to be cooled while they are still being tumbled. Garments should be removed immediately after tumbling action stops.

It should be noted that creases or pleats that have been properly ironed into these fabrics will persist throughout repeated washing and tumble-drying cycles. Tumbling in a drier at a proper temperature is effective in removing wrinkles from dry garments.

Companies laundering synthetic dresses believe that the best job can be obtained by using a dry cleaner's steam air finisher. In this method, extraction is necessary after removal from the final rinse. For extraction, a centrifugal extractor is used. If the extractor runs at 1220 rpm or more, the garments should be in it for no more than 2 minutes; at 750 rpm, approximately 3 or 4 minutes. Less extraction is required for lightweight garments than for the heavier types. It is estimated that one operator using three air finishers can turn out three times as many finished garments as one operator on a cotton press operation.

A laundry facility using clean room techniques to water-wash clean room garments is owned and operated by Coyne Industrial Laundries, Syracuse, New York. This facility consists of two clean rooms, a drying tunnel, and two small personnel preparation rooms. Soiled garments enter the process clean room through the air lock shown in Figure 10-8 and are emptied into the tub for transporting to the washer.

In Figure 10-9 the garments are shown being placed into the industrial washer. A water extractor has been placed in a separate enclosure in order to isolate it from the room. Figure 10-10 shows a garment being prepared for placement on the overhead conveyor in the drying tunnel. This tunnel is approximately 4 feet wide and runs the length of both the process and the packaging clean rooms.

Figure 10-11 shows the packaging clean room where the garments are inspected, folded, and packaged in polyethylene bags. Notice through the door window in this picture an empty hanger on the conveyor in the drying tunnel. Figure 10-12 shows a close-up of the bag sealing operation. This unit is foot-operated.

Another example of clean room techniques being employed in the water washing of clean room garments is shown in Figures 10-13 through 10-15. This facility is operated by Ultra-Clean Uniform Service, Inc., Waterbury, Connecticut. Figure 10-13 shows soiled clean room garments being loaded into the washer in the receiving area. Figure 10-14 shows these garments being removed into the clean room through a second door after washing. Figure 10-15 shows the packaging operation employed by Ultra-Clean Uniform Service.

This room is finished in white epoxy resin. The room air-conditioning system is equipped with HEPA filters. Air enters the room through ceiling diffusers.

Dry Cleaning

Dry-cleaning equipment should be designed to continually refilter and/or distill the dry-cleaning solvent. Filtration systems will vary from unit to unit, depending on the solvents used; however, a processed garment should pass specified tests. One such test for checking the contamination level of a garment is presented later in this discussion.

Tests on dry-cleaning solvents to be used on clean room garments indicate that a very high percentage of filtration of particles 0.5 micron and larger in size is necessary. Improper filtration of dry-cleaning solvents or insufficient rinsing of particular solvents used to remove local spots may result in yellowing or discoloration, or in a decrease in garment brightness. Care must be used to avoid these results.

One company that is successfully using a solvent process on clean room garments is the Prudential Overall Supply in Los Angeles, California. Figure

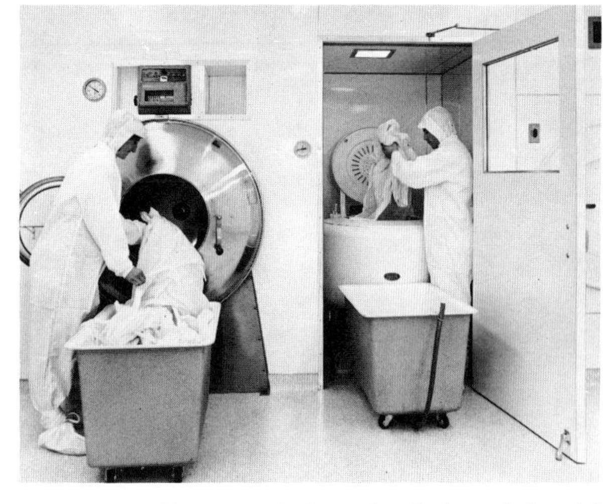

FIGURE 10-9. Garments being placed into industrial washer and being removed from extractor. *Courtesy Coyne Industrial Laundries, Inc.*

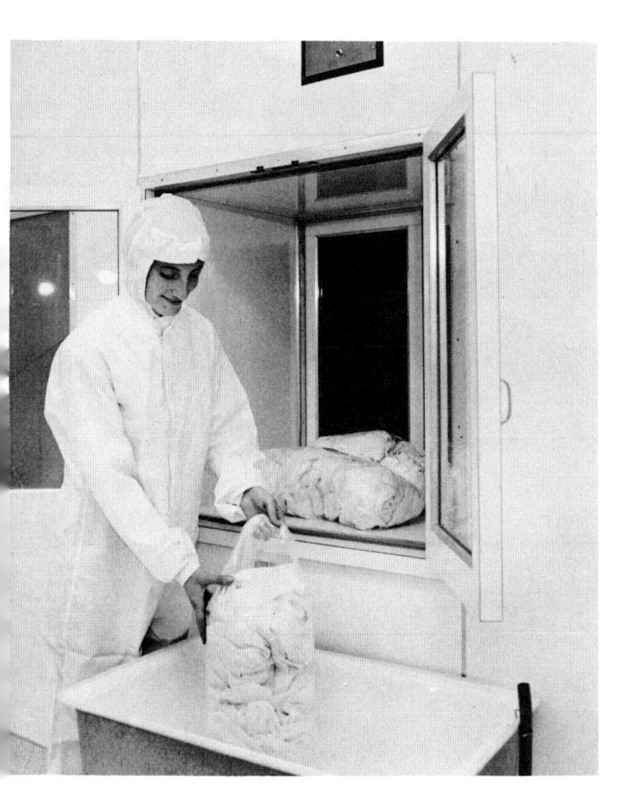

FIGURE 10-8. Soiled garments entering clean room through air lock and then being emptied into tub. *Courtesy Coyne Industrial Laundries, Inc.*

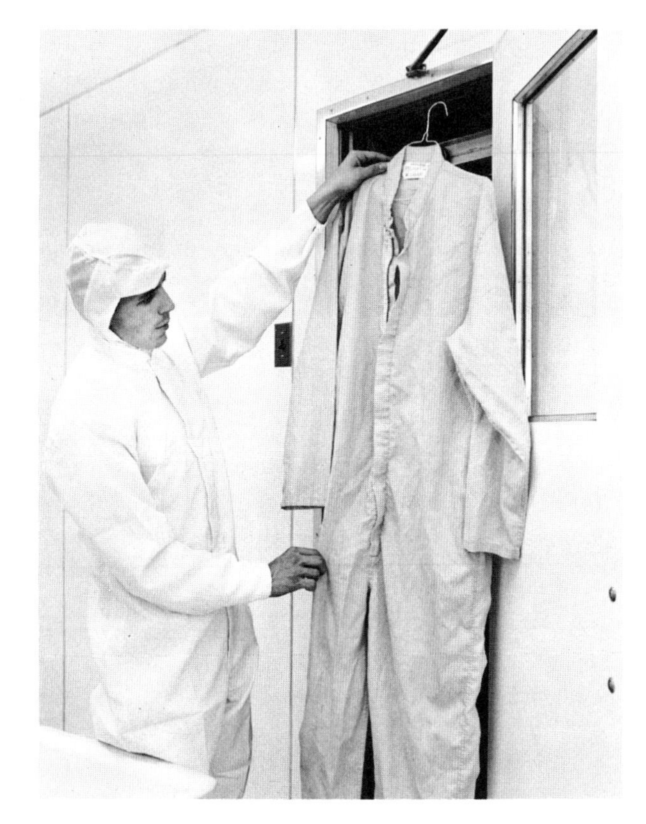

FIGURE 10-10. Garments being prepared for drying in conveyorized drying tunnel shown behind garment. *Courtesy Coyne Industrial Laundries, Inc.*

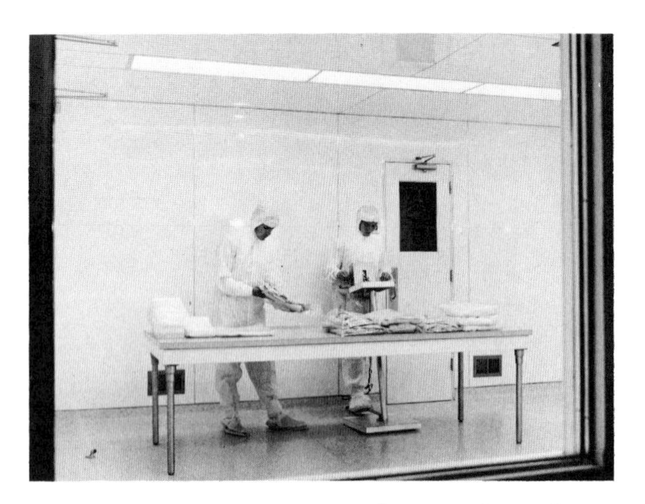

FIGURE 10-11. Packaging room of Coyne. Door shown in picture opens into conveyorized drying tunnel. *Courtesy Coyne Industrial Laundries, Inc.*

10-16 shows the rear-view plumbing of the Spencer dry-cleaning machine employed by Prudential. This machine is completely automated and provides for self-purification of fluids and air. Air filtration on this unit could be increased by use of filters of higher efficiency.

The front of the Spencer unit forms one wall of the processing room, as shown in Figure 10-17. Garments, stored in plastic bag, are received through an air lock in presorted load-lot quantities. The garments are taken from the air lock and loaded directly into the machine. After loading of the garments, the face of the machine, the floor, and the operator are vacuumed. On completion of the decontamination cycle, the garments are loaded into polyethylene bags to await inspection and packaging. Typical macro-inspection, packaging, and bag-sealing operations are shown in Figure 10-18. Micro-inspection of garments is shown in Figure 10-19. A random 5% sampling of each load is made with a Millipore filter disk. Each garment can also be checked under ultraviolet light for hydrocarbon contamination.

Prudential reports that the immersion phase of the solvent processing cycle is conducted with the solvent temperature at less than 90°F. The solvent recovery or drying cycle is conducted at less than 120°F. The processing time for a lot of fifty gar-

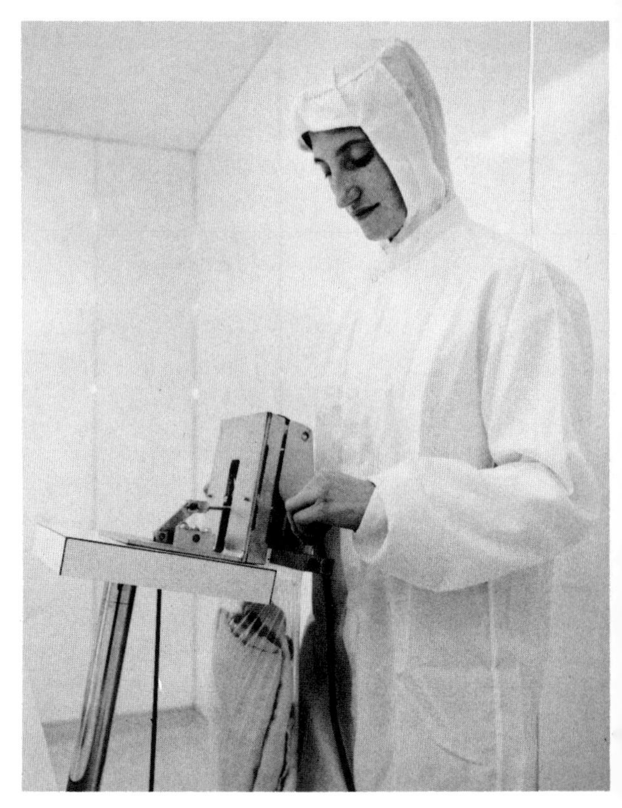

FIGURE 10-12. Bag-sealing operation at Coyne. *Courtesy Coyne Industrial Laundries, Inc.*

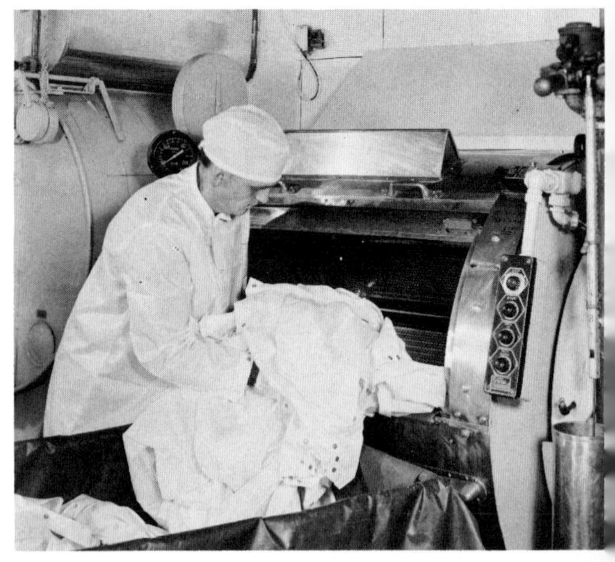

FIGURE 10-13. Soiled garments being loaded into washer from receiving area. *Courtesy Ultra-Clean Uniform Service, Inc.*

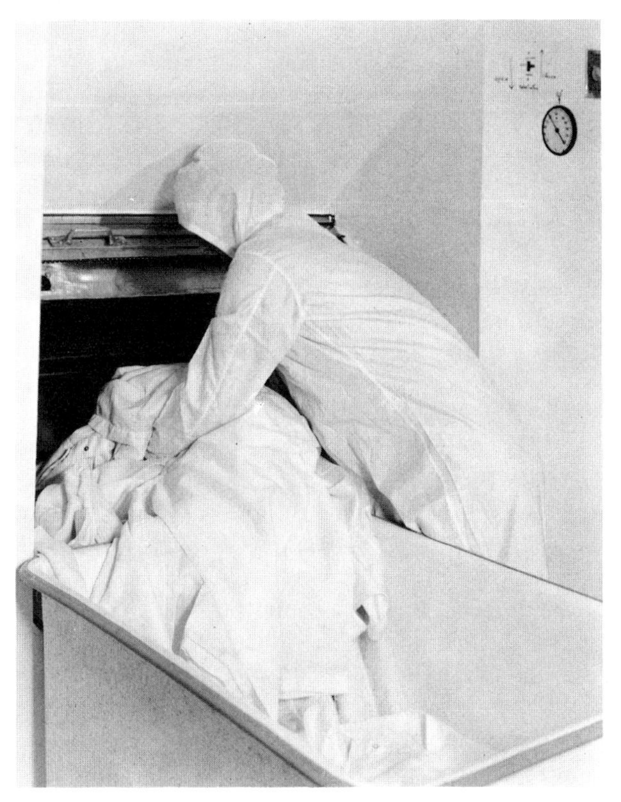

FIGURE 10-14. Washed garments being removed inside clean room. *Courtesy Ultra-Clean Uniform Service, Inc.*

ments is approximately 30 minutes. The effect of the solvent process on the durability of materials is significant. One of the tests conducted in Prudential's facility gave the following results as reported by Textile Testing Institute of Los Angeles:

Dacron herringbone material (as used in coveralls):

1. Tensile strength of monitor: warp 219 pounds, filling 306 pounds.
2. Tensile strength retention after 144 processing cycles: warp 183 pounds, filling 264 pounds; or warp 84%, filling 86%.
3. Comparison of whiteness retention after 144 processing cycles: 101% retention.

Particulate Contents

The quality control organization should make random checks of newly cleaned garments to ensure that they meet requirements of limited linting. A limited-linting test should consist in a sampling plan similar to that given here. A garment is considered to exhibit limited-linting properties if it has less than 1500 particles per square foot per cubic foot of air drawn through the membrane filter. The limited-linting test is applicable to other fabrics and materials which shed and lint particulate matter.

Manual Garment-Sampling Method

A "Manual Method for Determining Particulate Contents of Garments Worn by Clean Room Per-

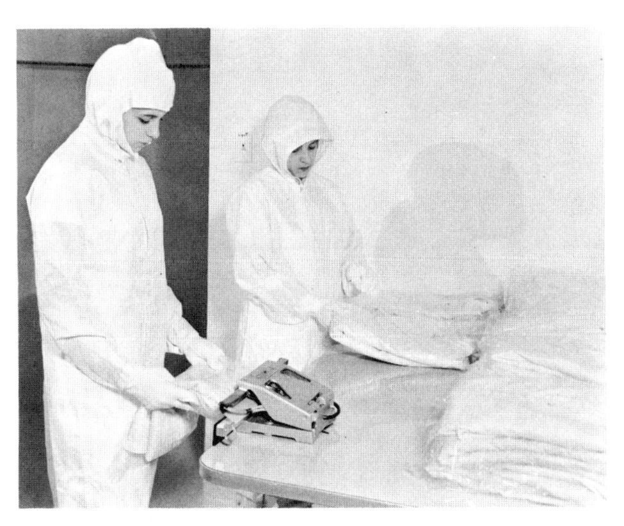

FIGURE 10-15. Packaging operation on clean room garments. *Courtesy Ultra-Clean Uniform Service, Inc.*

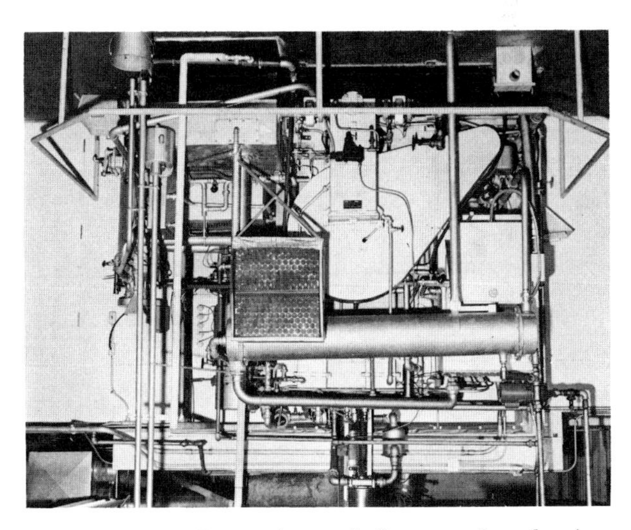

FIGURE 10-16. Rear view of Spencer dry-cleaning machine installed at Prudential Overall Supply. *Courtesy Prudential Overall Supply.*

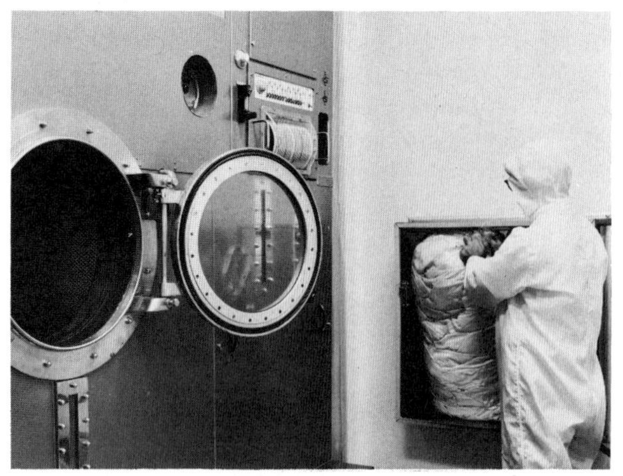

FIGURE 10-17. Front on Spencer dry-cleaning unit. Soiled garments enter room in plastic bags through air lock. *Courtesy Prudential Overall Supply*

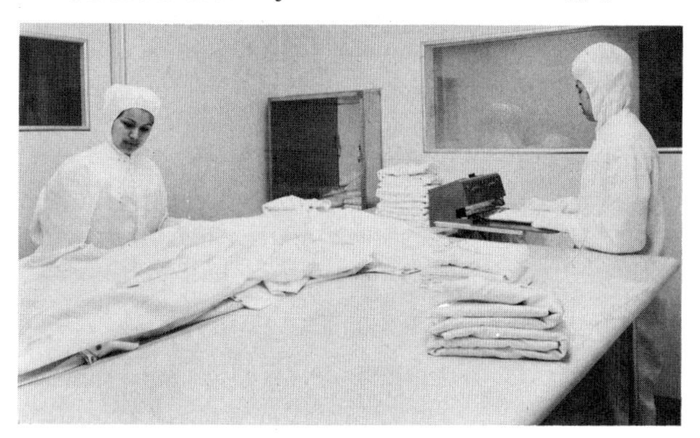

FIGURE 10-18. Marco-inspection, packaging, and bag sealing of cleaned garments. *Courtesy Prudential Overall Supply*

sonnel" has been established by Air Force Technical Order 00-25-203.[8] This method should be used for determining the relative cleanliness level of clean room garments. It may also be used to determine if a fabric exhibits limited-linting characteristics.

The equipment recommended for this test is a vacuum sampling device used in conjunction with a membrane filter, as discussed previously. Membrane filters should have a pore size of 0.8 micron or less, be of such color (black, blue, green) as to contrast with the particles to be collected, and be inscribed with grid lines. The counting equipment is the same as that used for airborne contamination monitoring.

The garment to be tested must be sampled in an area having a contamination level equal to or less than that of an Air Force standard clean room. The sample should not be removed from the sealed plastic package until the test is ready to be performed. Care must be taken to ensure minimum handling of the sample after its removal from the sealed bag.

The sampling apparatus should be thoroughly cleaned before the experiment is performed. The vacuum pump is turned on, and filtered air is passed through the fabric at an adjusted rate of 14 liters per minute for 30 seconds. Ten different areas in the same garment (coveralls or smock) should be sampled (see Figure 10-20). More samples may be required for garments with very low contamination levels. Increasing the volume of air or sampling time does not necessarily increase results, as 75% of all particles will be withdrawn in 30 seconds with a flow rate of 14 liters per minute. At least four areas per shoe cover and hood will be sampled. The experience to date has demonstrated that the front of the garment and areas along any seams will have a higher contamination level. Figure 10-20 indicates points to be sampled for standardization. Figure 10-21 shows one application of this technique.

A background count should be run on a new filter from the same box from which the sample filter was obtained. This background count should be subtracted from the sample count. For best results, the background count should be established

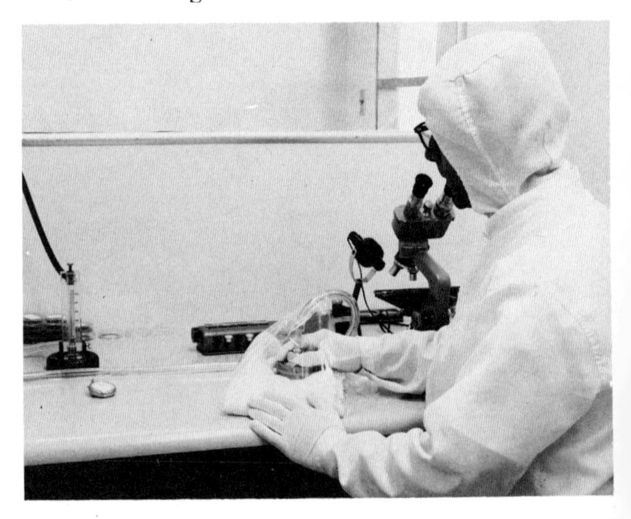

FIGURE 10-19. Micro-inspection of garments. *Courtesy Prudential Overall Supply*

[8] Reference 2, Appendix V.

for the exact filter used for testing purposes. If the background count is 10% of the estimated sample count, a larger sample volume must be established. It is not advisable to count more than 50% of the filter surface. The counting procedure will be the same as the method outlined in Chapter 9. Particles will be tabulated in two groups: (1) particles of which the major dimension exceeds 5 microns; (2) fibers. Particles should be identified, if possible, to help determine the source of contamination. Results are to be reported as particles per square foot rather than the standard particles per cubic foot.

To determine the contamination value, the total number of paricles greater than 5 microns is calculated in accordance with the formula

$$P_t = N_t \times \frac{E}{n \times A_f} \tag{10-1}$$

where P_t = the total number of particles greater than 5 microns on the filter.
N_t = the total number of particles counted in n unit areas.
n = the number of unit areas counted.
A_f = the unit area, in square millimeters.
E = the effective total filter area, in square millimeters.

This value P_t represents the total number of particles collected from ten areas of the garment ($10 \times E$ is the effective total sample area, in square millimeters); $10E$ is multiplied by 0.0000107 square foot per square millimeter to convert the effective total sampling area to square feet. The resultant is divided into P_t:

$$\text{Particles/ft}^2 = \frac{P_t}{10E \times 0.0000107}$$

This figure is divided by the total volume of air used to collect the particles on the membrane filter (2.5 cubic feet). This will be the value if ten 30-second samples were collected (14 liters/minute × ½ minute × 10 samples × .03531 cubic foot/liter = 2.5 cubic feet). For other sample sizes, the correct value will have to be calculated. The final answer (P_g) is now expressed in particles per square foot per cubic foot of air:

$$P_g = \frac{P_t \text{ (particles)}}{10E \text{ (mm}^2) \times 0.0000107 \text{ (ft}^2/\text{mm}^2) \times 2.5 \text{ ft}^3} \tag{10-2}$$

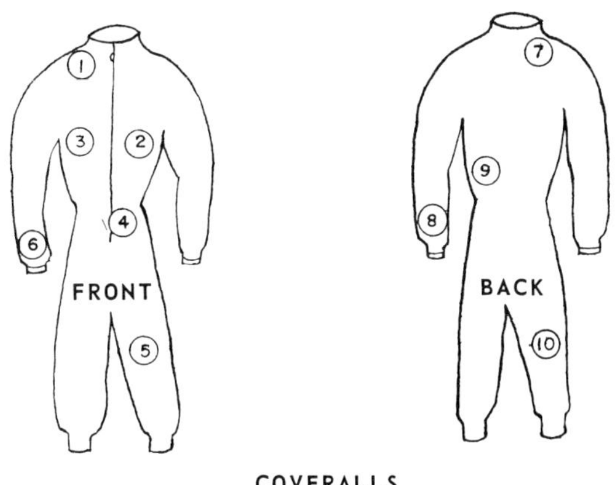

NOTE: WHEN SAMPLING A SMOCK, THE BOTTOM OF THE GARMENT IS SUBSTITUTED FOR THE COVERALL LEGS #5 and #10.

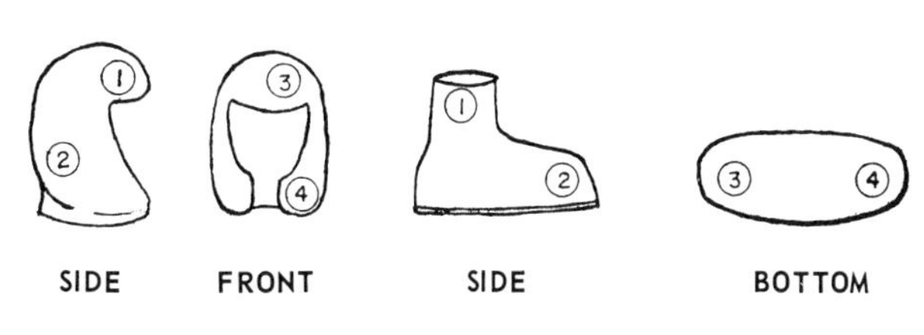

FIGURE 10-20. Points of garment to be sampled. *U.S. Air Force Technical Order 00-25-203*

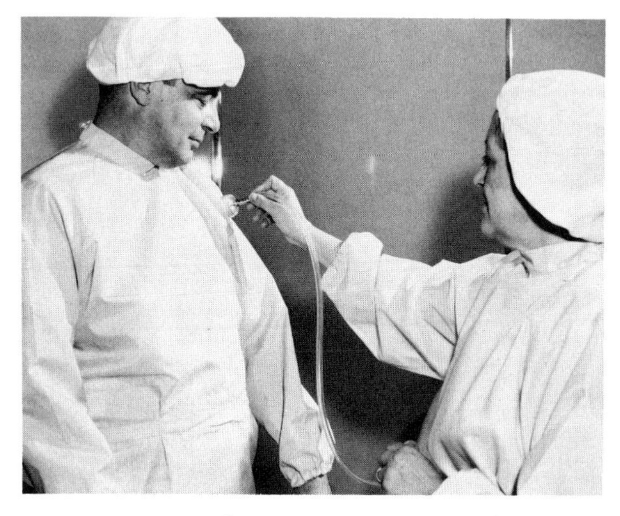

FIGURE 10-21. Application of manual sampling technique to garment monitoring. *Courtesy Millipore Filter Corp.*

Example: P_t = 100 particles collected on effective total filter area from ten areas sampled by passing 2.5 cubic feet of air through a clean room garment.

$$P_g = \frac{100}{10(960) \times 0.0000107 \times 2.5}$$

$$P_g = 389 \text{ particles/ft}^2/\text{ft}^3$$

A method for determining the particulate contents of garments using automatic equipment has been documented in NAVAER 01-1A-503 *(3)*. The equipment to be used is shown in Figures 10-22 and 10-23. The step-by-step procedure to be followed while performing the garment inspection is outlined in Figure 10-24.

Garment Contamination[9]

One of the functions of dust-control practice is to find sources of airborne contaminants and eliminate these sources from areas under consideration. Many such sources are readily recognized; motors with exposed carbon brushes; hot-air driers with exposed elements; belts and pulleys that become frayed and worn. These sources of contamination are easily recognized because of the character of particles they produce; remedial action is obvious. Some other sources of airborne contamination are not so easily found, nor is the method of eliminating the source so readily discernible.

Routine sampling of airborne "dust" from many areas reveals the particulate matter to be nearly identical in composition. Samples taken from Autonetics Compton, Downey, Ball Road, and La Palma facilities in Anaheim, Calif., show the same composition. Further, it makes no major difference whether the samples are collected inside or outside the controlled-environment areas, although in closely controlled areas small amounts of some contaminants peculiar to the manufacturing practices of the area are found.

In tests made by Autonetics, Division of North American Aviation Corporation, samples of the particulates were collected on Millipore membrane filters, 0.47-micron pore size, contained in an open filter holder. Vacuum was supplied by a constant-flow pump. A flowmeter in the system allowed ac-

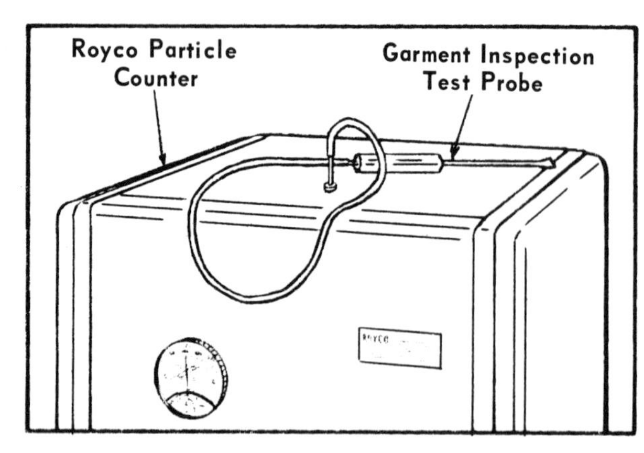

FIGURE 10-22. Particle counter with garment inspection accessories. *NAVAER 01-1A-503*

[9] Abstracted from reference *4*.

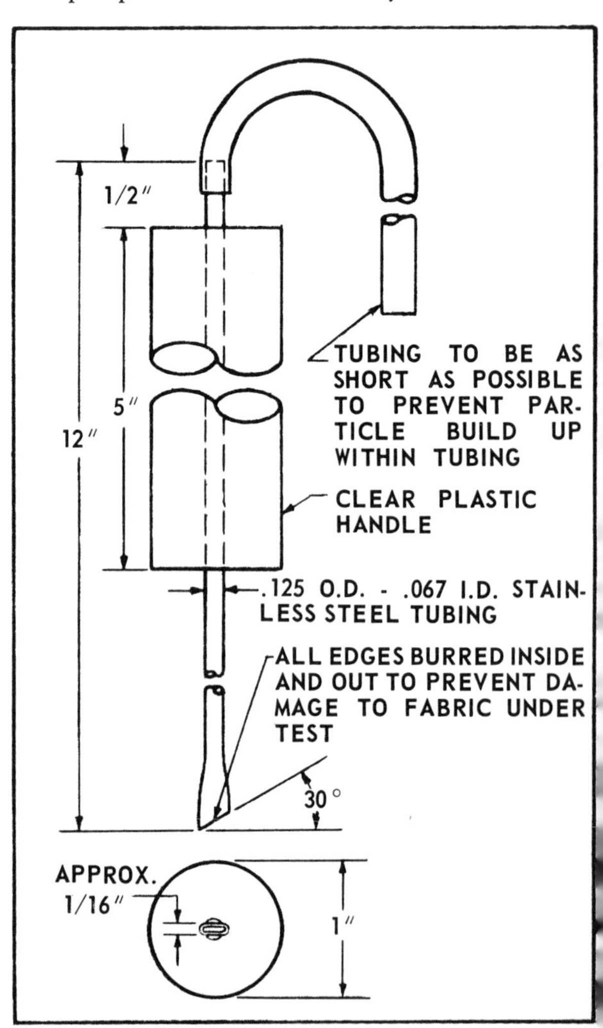

FIGURE 10-23. Garment inspection test probe. *NAVAER 01-1A-503*

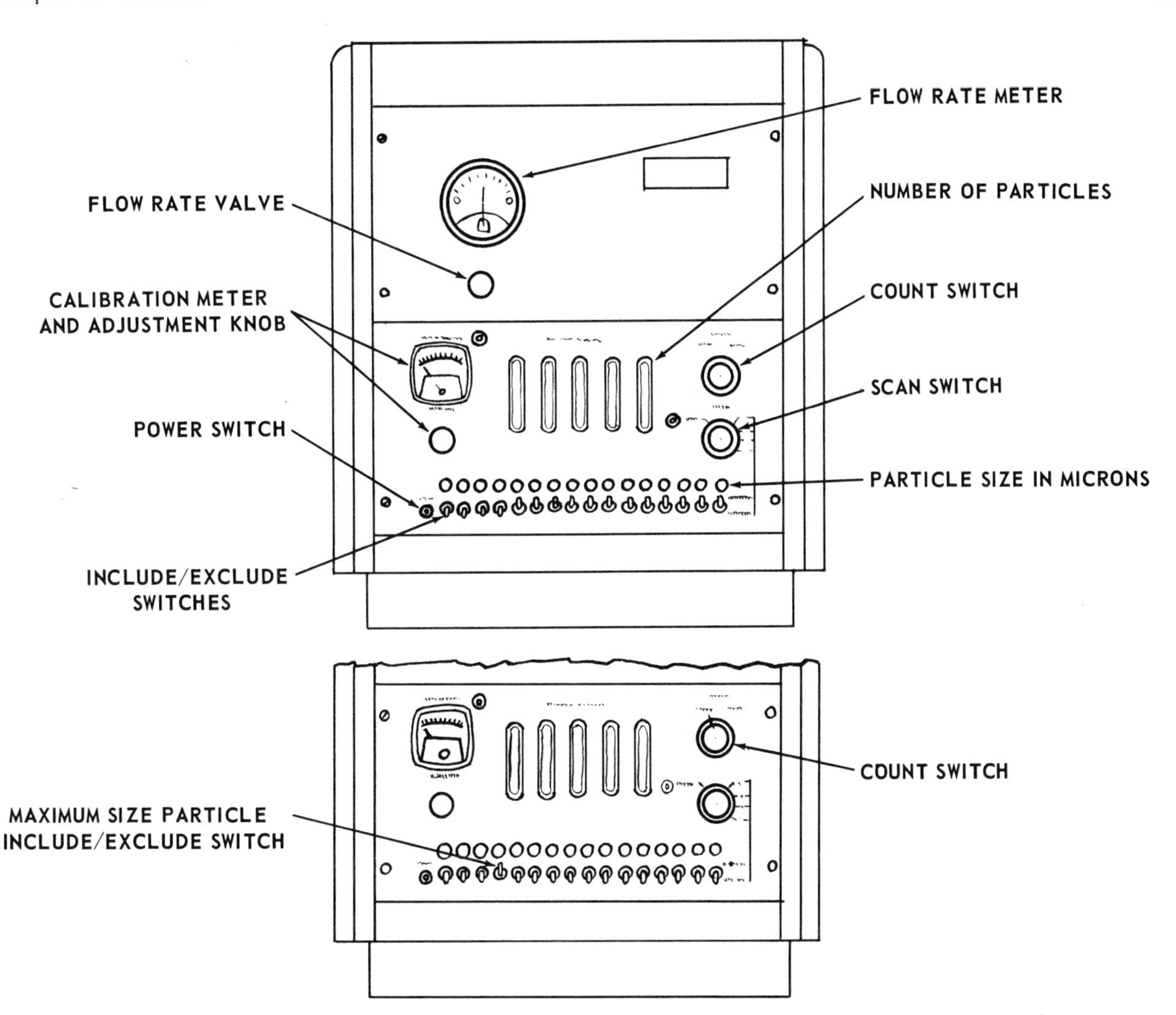

FIGURE 10-24. Particle Counter Set-Up For Garment Inspection. *NAVAER 01-1A-503*

Step 1: (*a*) Program the INCLUDE/EXCLUDE toggle switches to cover particles one step above or larger than the maximum allowed particle size limit. (*b*) Purge the garment probe by placing a 0.3-micron filter over the probe tip and varying air flow rate between 0 and 200 cc/min until clean. (*c*) Insert the purge pick-up probe (Figure 10-23) directly into the sealed garment bag by puncturing the pliofilm bag. (*d*) Place COUNT switch to TOTAL. (*e*) Place SCAN switch at *3 minutes* position and allow the unit to complete the scan cycle before starting test. (This will assure a complete 3-minute test period.) (*f*) Sweep the garment with the probe tip for the entire three minute test period. There should be no count on the display unit after this part of the test. *Note:* Particular attention should be given to difficult-to-clean seam area.

Step 2: (*a*) Rotate COUNT switch to SINGLE count position. (*b*) Program INCLUDE/EXCLUDE toggle switch for the maximum allowable particle size only. All other switches shall be in the EXCLUDE position. (*c*) Allow the unit to complete scan cycle before starting count. (*d*) Repeat the sweep operation of the garment as in Step 1, paragraph *f*. (*e*) Single count totals shall be no greater than the maximum allowable count range as specified by any laundry contract.

Step 3: Any single count that exceeds the preset level shall be cause for rejection.

curate measurement of air volume. Samples from the air were taken for a 10-minute period at the rate of about 15.5 liters per minute. Samples taken from clothing were obtained by vacuuming the subject, using the open filter holder, for 1 minute. Samples taken from garments not being worn were taken for 3-minute periods with the sampler being moved over 1 square yard of the upper half of the garment. Samples were taken from clean new smocks, the clean room after the smock test, smock room, subject A wearing smock, subject A clothes, subject B wearing smock, subject B clothes, subject C clothes, subject D clothes, and outside air.

All samples were examined microscopically and chemically. Gross examination showed that samples taken from clothing and from people wearing smocks yield the greatest quantity of dirt. The clothing samples contained a large volume of fibers of all varieties.

Allison(*4*) states that the particulate matter consisted of colored and translucent particles and, occasionally, metal particles. All samples appeared to have the same type of particulates. Distributions are indicated in Table 10-9. Spectrographic analyses are indicated in Table 10-10.

Microchemical analysis indicated the presence of aluminum, calcium, and magnesium silicates with traces of iron and copper. Unsuccessful attempts were made to find some of the other elements found in the spectrographic analysis. Several samples were submitted to an outside laboratory for particle identification. Petrographic analysis confirmed the presence of two forms of aluminum silicate as the major contaminant in all samples—kaolenite and hallyocite, which are of volcanic origin. These analyses show that nearly all airborne contaminants (dust) within these areas are of the same material. Impurities in these minerals include iron and copper. The titanium found by spectrographic analysis probably came from the fibers in the sample. Titanium dioxide is used as a dulling agent by most fiber manufacturers. It is probable that the other elements found on the clothing samples resulted from washing residues and were present in amounts much too small to be picked up by presently applicable microchemical techniques.

The fact that the same material was present in all the samples, varying only in concentration, with the greatest concentration being on clothing, supports the hypothesis that clothing is the greatest contributor to airborne contamination within dust-controlled areas. To verify this hypothesis, average daily dust counts of each of seven rooms were tabulated. These average counts showed a general tendency for the dust count to rise as the work week progressed. Figure 10-25 illustrates the effect that results from changing the outer protective garment being used in the dust-controlled environment. The averages for the day preceding the change of garments are tabulated along with the average counts for the day on which the garments were changed. Also the average counts for the day before personnel were vacuumed are indicated along with the average counts for the day after vacuuming. It is to be noted that in the first three series Friday was the day before the garments were changed, and Monday was indicated as the day after the garments were changed. The last four series show Monday as the day before and Tuesday as the day after the garment change or vacuuming. The results show that in most cases changing to clean garments produced a decrease of about 50% or more in the average daily dust count. Vacuuming personnel instead of changing garments also resulted in a decrease in the average daily dust count.

Allison(*4*) describes another study conducted to demonstrate the direct relationship between dust

TABLE 10–9

TYPES OF PARTICULATE MATTER (*4*)

(Values given in per cent)

Source	*Colored**	*Translucent*	*Metal*
Clothing	39	60	1.0
Personnel wearing smocks	43	55	2.0
Smocks	38	61.5	0.5
Air in controlled-environmental area	35	64	1.0
Air in locker room	33	66.5	0.5
Air in other locations	34	65.4	0.6
Air at Guard Gate 4	35	64	1.0

* Colored particles are differentiated from translucent particles only by the fact that they contain colors other than white.

counts and the ability of protective garments worn over street clothes to absorb and retain contaminants. Samples were taken from protective garments worn in an area where complete coverage (coveralls, hoods, booties) is used. The mass of contaminants found on the garments was plotted against the dust count (5 microns and above). The protective garments were sampled on a random basis. The controls consisted of samples taken from the garments as received from the laundry. Three samples were taken from an area of about 1 square yard from the upper torso of the personnel. The sampling procedure as previously mentioned was used. The samples were weighed on a Cahn gram electrobalance, and the weights in milligrams were compared to the average dust count. The data, presented in Figure 10-26, indicate that street clothes are the major contributing source of contamination to the clean room. The outer protective garments act like a sponge, becoming saturated after 24 hours of use. After this time, they no longer serve their purpose. After they have absorbed about 5.5 mg of dirt, they no longer restrict the amount of dirt escaping into the air.

A change from a multifabric garment to a monofabric garment was made. (See Figure 10-27.) It is apparent that the change in the type of garment has prolonged the usage time of garments for Autonetics and has brought about a better control within the dust-controlled area.

TABLE 10–10

SPECTOGRAPHIC ANALYSIS (4)

Element	*Clothing*	*Personnel Wearing Smocks*	*Air inside Dust-Controlled Area*	*Air inside Locker Room*	*Air from Lobby Area outside Dust-Controlled Area*	*Air by Guard Gate 4*	*Air by Guard Gate 4*
Boron	X	X					
Silicon	XH*	XH	X	X	X	X	X
Phosphorus	X	X					
Manganese	X	X	X	X	X	X	X
Iron	XH	X	X	X	XH	X	X
Gold	T*				X		
Magnesium	XH	X	X	X	XH	X	X
Lead	X	X	X	X	X	XT	X
Chromium	X	X	X	X	X	XT	X
Tin	X	X			X		
Nickel	X	X	X		X		XT
Aluminum	XH	XH	X	XH	XH	X	X
Copper	X	X	X	X	X	X	X
Silver	X	X	X	X	X	X	
Zinc	X	X					
Sodium	XH	XH		X	X		X
Titanium	X	X	X	X	X		X
Cadmium	X	X			X		
Calcium	X	X	X	X	X	X	X

* H=high; T=trace.

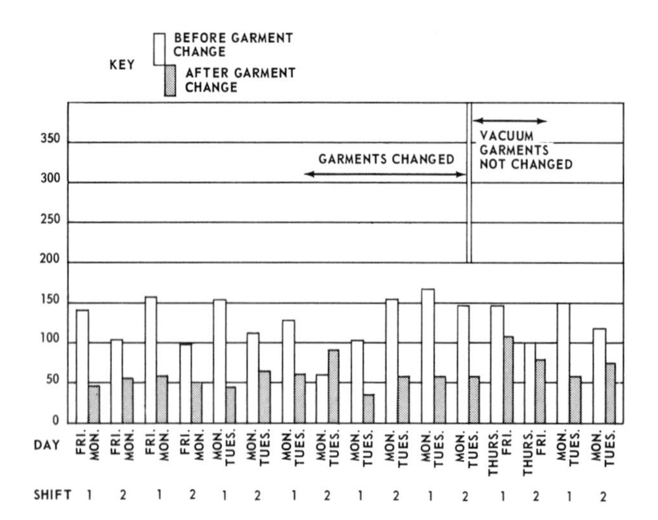

FIGURE 10-25. Effects of garment change on dust control. *Journal of the American Association for Contamination Control*

Measuring and Predicting the Generation of Static Electricity *(5)*

The generation of static electricity on clean room garments can pose serious problems. Personnel shocks, possible explosions, variation of delicate electrical instruments, etc., can all take place. Therefore, it is important to realize that all garments generate static charges to one degree or another. By understanding how these charges are generated on garments, better facility design should be possible. It should be noted that much more experimental work in this area is needed. The following discussion will concern work*(5)* performed by the Quartermaster Research and Engineering Center, Natick, Massachusetts. This work will give an insight into the static electricity problem.

Static Electricity[10]

Static electricity has long been recognized as a fire and explosion hazard in industrial processes. Hospital operating-room explosions traceable to the accumulation of static electricty on nonconducting surfaces, such as rubber or fabric sheetings, have become increasingly conspicuous in recent years, both in this country and abroad. In discussing static electricity, a clear definition of the terminology is important. The basic mathematical relationships are as follows:

1. Static electricity*(6)* connotes the phenomena of attraction and repulsion observed between electrically charged bodies from the effects of "dynamic electricity" which is utilized in the generation of power or energy when it passed through a system.

2. If an object exerts an electrical force on another object, it is said to be charged. The force exerted is dependent on the amount of the charge; that is, a static charge *(Q)* is considered an amount or quantity of electricity. If a body is electrically neutral, the resultant charge is zero. The unit of static charge, the coulomb, corresponds to a charge of 6.25×10^{18} electrons(7).

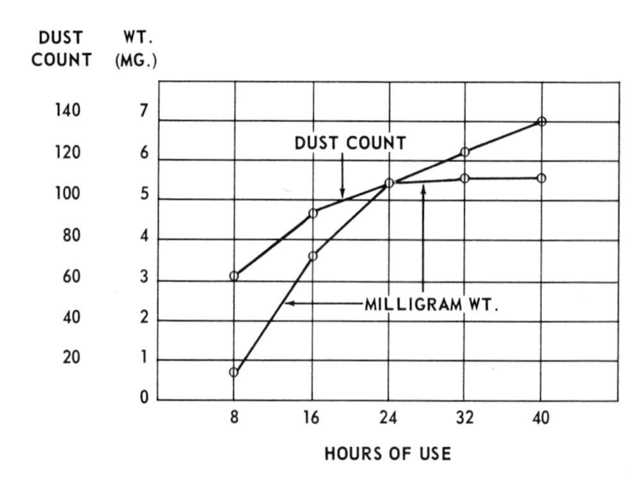

FIGURE 10-26. Relation of dust count and garment contamination. *Journal of the American Association for Contamination Control*

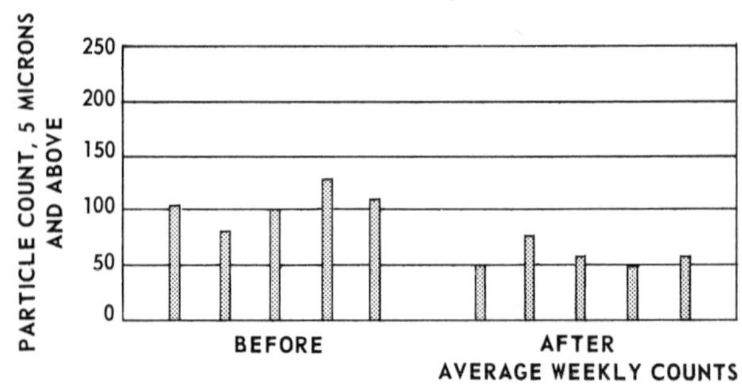

FIGURE 10-27. Effect of changing type of garment. *Journal of the American Association for Contamination Control*

[10] Abstracted from reference *5*, pp. 1-4.

3. When an electrical force is applied to a body, the body tends to move in the direction of the force. If the body is free and moves in the direction of the force, it loses potential energy. If, instead, the body moves against the force, work must be done to overcome it, and the body gains potential energy. An electrostatic unit of potential difference exists between two points A and B when 1 erg of work must be expended to move 1 stat-coulomb of positive charge from B to A against the electric field created by a positively charged body A. The potential (V) is therefore a measure of the electrical forces which are present in a given situation. There is a definite distinction between charge and potential. It is important to avoid confusing these two quantities: charge, which measures the excess or deficiency of electrons, and potential, which measures the possibility of work being done if a charge is available to do it. In approximate analogy between electricity and water, electric charge corresponds to the quantity of water, and potential corresponds to the pressure which forces the water to flow.

4. When a charge on a conductor is increased, the strength of the force field surrounding it increases in direct proportion to the charge. It follows from the previous definitions that the potential (V) of the conductor is proportional to the charge on it (Q):

$$\frac{Q}{V} = C \qquad (10\text{-}3)$$

where C (by definition, the capacitance) is the constant for any given conductor. If a given charge is accumulated on a body of small capacitance, the potential of this small capacitance could be considerably higher than that observed when the identical charge is placed on a body of larger capacitance.

5. In general, a *conductor* is a medium through or on which electricity can pass. A *nonconductor*, or insulator, is a medium that prevents or reduces the flow of electricity. There is no sharp distinction, however, between conductors and insulators; it is only a matter of degree. Under ordinary conditions, there is no perfect conductor and no perfect insulator; instead, materials can be rated from good conductors to very poor conductors or from poor insulators to very good insulators.

6. The energy which is releasable from a charged conductor through the formation of a spark can be calculated from the equation

$$W \text{ (energy)} = \tfrac{1}{2}\, CV^2 \qquad (10\text{-}4)$$

where C is the capacitance, and V is the potential.

7. Static propensity is a qualitative measure of the tendency of a material to accumulate an electrostatic charge.

Basic Theory

Crugnola and Robinson state:

When two materials are placed in contact with one another, electrons pass from one material to the other without the addition of energy. The direction of transfer of the electrons depends upon the relative positions of the energy levels of the surface electrons. There are vacant or unoccupied energy levels on both surfaces; these are referred to as "holes." Electrons seek the lowest available energy level. Certain electrons of one surface have or occupy energy levels higher than on unoccupied levels on the second surface; and so, seeking the lowest available level, the electrons leave one surface for the other. As a result, one surface collects a surplus of electrons and will be negatively charged; the second will be deficient in electrons and will become positive. As long as the surfaces remain in contact with each other or in close proximity, the opposite charges bind each other, and the external system remains neutral.

When the surfaces are separated, the work which is done against the binding forces establishes a potential gradient between the surfaces. This potential difference acts to reestablish electrical equilibrium. How effectively this is accomplished depends on the conductivity of surfaces involved. If both surfaces are good conductors (or rather, poor insulators), the transferred electrons and resultant holes have mobility. Thus the potential gradient is effective in discharging the surfaces at points where the surfaces separate. If, on the other hand, both surfaces are good insulators, then the mobility of electrons and holes is restricted and the potential difference is not effective in discharging the surfaces. If one surface is a good insulator, the charges on the poor insulator do have mobility. However, a complete discharge still does not take place because those charges on the good insulator cannot flow freely and hence the recombination of electrons and holes is not possible.

When a charge exists on a material, the extent of possible hazard depends upon the specific situation and a spark may occur. (8) If gasoline fumes or other flammable substances are at hand, the amount of energy released by the formation of the spark must be at least equal to the ignition or excitation energy required to detonate the hazardous substance. A spark is a release of the energy from the charged system, and this is calculated as shown previously from the equation, $W = \frac{1}{2} CV^2$.[11]

Clothed Man

As a practical application of the theory, a man may be considered a charged conductor. His capacitance has been estimated at 200 micromicrofarads *(9)*.

Since little documented work is available regarding static charges on clean room garments, qualitative observations on tests made with synthetic fiber garments will be made.

Consider for the first situation *(5)* an individual insulated from ground, wearing a wool shirt and a nylon armor vest over it. These materials in contact result in a transfer of charge such that the wool becomes positively charged and the nylon negatively charged. With the fabric layers in contact or in close proximity, the system (man, shirt, and vest) is neutral; that is, there is an electrical balance so that no charge is apparent on the man. Negative charges on the nylon are offset or bound by the positive charges on the wool. If the outer garment, the nylon armor vest, is removed, the lack of conductivity of these materials prevents the flow of the charges that would restore electrical neutrality. The result is that the individual is left with a high positive charge.

In this case, the positive charges on the wool are no longer bound by the negative charges on the nylon. Since electrical neutrality must be maintained, the charges on the wool now attract negative charges to the skin immediately beneath the shirt. Because (by intentional experimental design) the man is insulated from ground, the redistribution of body charges alters his potential with respect to ground, leaving him with a high positive charge which, in turn, will produce a spark if any part of his body should approach a conductor.

The release of the spark brings the man and his shirt into electrical balance. Nevertheless, if the man subsequently removes the wool shirt, the body is left with uncompensated charges, and a second spark can be released on contact with a grounded conductor. The first spark enabled the body to take up electrons to neutralize the positive charge in the shirt; subsequent removal of the shirt leaves the body with an excess of negative charges. The electrons which moved to the body in the first spark now leave it on a second spark.

Writing of another experiment, Crugnola and Robinson state:

> The second experimental situation uses the same ensemble, but the man is grounded. The same distribution of charges is produced on the wool and nylon but now when the nylon vest is removed, the unbalance of charges on the body is neutralized by electrons immediately taken up from ground, and the man's potential is unaltered. Under such conditions, no spark can take place. When the shirt is removed, the flow of electrons is immediately to ground. Thus again no spark can be realized.
>
> In practice, we are concerned most often with something between the two extreme situations discussed above. The degree of insulation between the man and ground is usually neither infinite nor zero. Much depends on his footwear and on the nature of the surface upon which he stands or on whatever separates his body from ground.[12]

The consequences of the release of a spark depend on the specific situation in which the individual finds himself. If no hazardous substance is present, the only result of a spark is discomfort to the individual. If a hazardous substance is present, the extent of the hazard depends on the amount and rate of release of energy which is contained by the charged system and the amount of energy required to initiate the hazardous reaction.

Hazardous Electrical "Ceiling" for Clothed Man

In order to explore the problem of static in clothing systems from the standpoint of the possible hazard incurred, the Quartermaster Corps contracted for a study at the National Bureau of Standards *(10)*. As part of this study, an investigation was made of the energy required to initiate various explosive reactions. These are listed in Table 10-11. Also listed is the potential to which an individual ($C = 200 \times 10^{-12}$ farad) would have to be charged in order to contain this specific energy. It is seen that any clothing system that produces a potential on the man exceeding 2650 volts is capable of igniting gasoline–air mixtures as well as all the

[11] Reference *5*, pp. 3, 4.

[12] Reference *5*, p. 5.

TABLE 10–11

ENERGIES AND CORRESPONDING POTENTIALS IN AN INDIVIDUAL NECESSARY FOR IGNITION (5)

	Ignition energy (millijoules)	*Corresponding Potential Necessary for Ignition (volts)*
Methane	0.5	2150
Gasoline	0.8	2650
Ether (diethyl)	0.2	1350
Cyclopropane	0.2	1350
Benzene	0.5	2150
Acetone	0.6	2350
Copper acetylide	0.002	150
Lead azide	0.04	650

other compositions listed. A potential of 650 volts is theoretically capable of igniting certain militarily important primer materials, such as lead azide.

National Bureau of Standards Studies

The data on ignition energies appearing in Table 10-11 supply a basis of reference by which the nature and extent of the static electricity problem may be assessed. The program at the National Bureau of Standards was extended to the measurement of the voltages generated on the individual by manipulating components of his ensemble. This study included fabrics of nylon, wool, cotton, saponified acetate, and a wool–nylon blend. The measurements were made at 75°F and at relative humidities of 65%, 35%, and 20%. The experimental design was similar to the first condition utilized in the application of one of the theoretical situations previously discussed—that is, the man insulated from ground. The conclusions of this study, as reported in the Quartermaster Report (5), may be summarized as follows:

1. *Effect of Removing Garments.* No significant voltages were obtained unless one of the garment layers was removed.
2. *Effect of Humidity.* The following tabulation summarizes the results at various humidities: (The temperature was 75°F in each situation)

65%RH: None of the garment combinations produced potentials required for the detonation of the most active of the materials studied by the National Bureau of Standards.

35%RH: Garment combinations containing nylon and wool, nylon and cotton, and nylon and wool-nylon, produced potentials in excess of 2650 volts (this represents the potential required for the more active materials).

20%RH: The garment combinations listed above (for 35%RH test) caused higher potentials; also, high potentials were obtained with a wool and cotton combination.

Below 20%RH: High voltages were produced on the man, even with cotton (normally not a troublesome fiber). The voltages so produced are of a degree considered dangerous for the group of primers and other materials studies by the National Bureau of Standards.[13]

Quartermaster Laboratory Study, at 84°F (5)

Studies by the Quartermaster Laboratory, Natick, Massachusetts, reveal that the magnitude of the resulting generated voltage between man and ground is dependent on whatever separates the individual from ground. In order to obtain a quantitative example of this, measurements were made with the test subjects standing alternately on ½-inch plywood (a relatively poor insulating material) and on ½-inch Lucite (a good insulating material). The purpose was to illustrate the manner in which the voltages obtained are related to the degree of insulation afforded by the test subject's footware and the material on which he is standing. These observations were made in the Quartermaster laboratory at ambient conditions (84°F and 13% relative humidity).

The following data(*5*) show the variation of potential (in volts) with degree of platform insulation (½-inch Lucite or ½-inch plywood) for subjects A and B:

After removing:	*Lucite*		*Plywood*	
	A	*B*	*A*	*B*
1. Mittens and inserts	233	400	0	0
2. Jacket and liner	1833	2000	333	567
3. Vest	1600	4033	500	1133

It is obvious that the voltages registered and consequently the hazard is markedly affected by the degree of insulation involved between the subject and the ground.

[13] Reference 5, p. 8.

It will be noticed that the higher voltages were generally obtained by test subject B. In order to determine if this was due to differences in clothing or to differences between individuals (that is, one being more susceptible to these phenomena than another), a series of observations were made in which the test subjects exchanged vests, jackets, and shirts. The following tabulation*(5)* gives the variation of potential (in volts) according to particular garments:

After removing:	*As Worn in Tests*		*Vest and Jacket Exchanged*		*Shirt only Exchanged*	
	A	*B*	*A*	*B*	*A*	*B*
1. Mittens and inserts	733	400	700	600	500	200
2. Jacket and liner	1833	2000	1200	2000	1300	1000
3. Vest	1600	4033	1100	3100	3500	1300

The results obtained indicate that, at least in part, the differences were due to clothing, in particular to the wool–nylon shirt. Tests subsequent to these, however, have also shown that one individual may be more liable to these effects than another.

By rationalizing the significance of the data just presented, in terms of actual wear conditions, Crugnola and Robinson concluded that:

(1) Static charges in excess of those which could initiate certain hazardous reactions in militarily significant materials are generated in clothing systems.

(2) The hazard does not exist except as layers of clothing are separated upon removing clothing components. As long as the components remain on the individual, the system is neutral because positive and negative charges, although possibly separated, are in sufficient proximity to each other to be within the normal field of neutral influence and, therefore, equalize each other.

(3) Only elements of the clothing ensemble in direct contact with each other need to be made conductive. Thus, in a system which involves an outer layer fabric, an insulating layer, and a lining in which the lining contacts a clothing element of dissimilar characteristics, only the lining needs to be treated.

(4) Underwear may not require treatment due to the high regain obtainable from body moisture.

(5) Footwear must be conductive.

(6) The outer layer of the ensemble would not normally require treatment to increase its conductivity; however, because of the danger of frictional contact between the clothed man and other surfaces (leather or plastic seats, vehicles, drums, etc.) the outer layer should be treated in those ensembles which are worn where hazards are likely to occur.[14]

Evaluation of Antistatic Finishes

To minimize the hazard and discomfort caused by the electrification of fabric, the chemical industry has developed a series of compounds known as "antistats." The basic property imparted by these finishes to a fabric is an increase in fabric surface conductivity. This higher conductivity enables the transferred charges to move more freely across the fabric surface and to dissipate to the under clothing layers.

As a basis of establishing the level of effectiveness, industry's practices in this regard have been accepted. Industry considers any material having a surface resistivity, in log R units, not exceeding 11.0 to have good characteristics. A fair rating is given to any material that does not exceed 12.5 log units, and any material exceeding 13.1 log units is considered unsatisfactory. In reality, the establishment of a value of 11.0 represents the acceptance of cotton fabrics as a frame of reference for static propensity. Cotton fabrics present no serious problems with respect to static generation, although static development on cotton fabrics becomes possible under certain conditions.

The antistatic agents which are the subject of Table 10-12 are identified as follows: (1) Aqueous dispersion of a polymeric cationic material. (2) An organic ester. (3) A cationic polymeric material. (4) Polyvinyl pyrrolidone derivative. (5) Conductive carbon applied from alcohol dispersion—concentration on fabric, 1%. (6) Conductive carbon applied from an aqueous dispersion—concentration on fabric, 1%.

The table summarizes the findings of the National Bureau of Standards for four fabrics of different fiber composition which had been treated with six different antistatic agents. There results are expressed in terms of the log of resistivity per square unit of surface.

It should be pointed out that the contaminant-producing properties of antistatic agents with regard to clean rooms are not well defined. Before such agents are used, their possible effect on clean room

[14] *Ibid.*, pp. 11-12.

operation such as adding contaminants should be investigated.

Clothing Experience

Figure 10-28 demonstrates the clothing required by Litton in the manufacture of radar tubes. C. V. Freeman states that "Super-Clean Klystrons" are produced in this Facility.

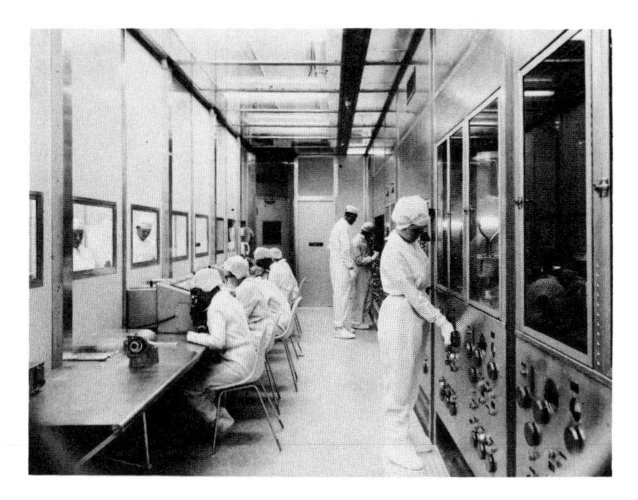

FIGURE 10-28. Litton clean room used in the production of Klystron tubes. *Courtesy Air Engineering*

Norden (*11*) has run the gamut of materials in uniforms and has traced many problems to the various rayon mixtures. The point of highest wear in a uniform is the sleeve, and the sleeve is the cloth closest to the assembly or part on which work is being performed. Norden further reports that, after fighting the lint battle for some time, the firm has found that pure Dacron does an almost perfect job. Little of the discomfort or static charge problem that the firm was warned against has been experienced, probably because a tight control is maintained on temperature and humidity, at what is a comfortable range for wearing Dacron.

Norden also has supplied its clean room personnel with shoes to be worn only in the clean room. Norden reports that, after one year of use, the shoes look as if they were just delivered from the factory.

TABLE 10–12

SURFACE RESISTIVITY (LOG R/UNITS²) OF FOUR FABRICS WITH SIX ANTISTATIC FINISHES AT VARIOUS TEMPERATURES AND RELATIVE HUMIDITIES (5)

Antistatic Agent	*2% RH −4°F*	*2% RH 32°F*	*70% RH 32°F*	*50% RH 75°F*	*2% RH 122°F*
a. Cotton, 6-ounce oxford					
Untreated	17	15.5	10.0	10.3	14.5
1	17	15.3	9.7	9.8	13.8
2	17	14.0	9.3	9.5	11.8
3	17	15.3	10.0	10.3	14.5
4	17	15.5	9.0	10.0	14.3
5	17	15.5	10.0	10.0	14.3
6	17	15.5	10.0	10.0	14.3
b. Wool, 16-ounce serge					
Untreated	17	15.7	12.5	12.3	16.0
1	17	15.7	11.0	11.0	14.3
2	10.88	12.9	10.3	10.0	10.6
3	17	15.8	11.3	11.6	15.0
4	17	15.7	12.6	12.3	15.8
5	17	15.8	12.3	11.8	15.9
6	17	15.8	12.3	12.0	17.0
c. Nylon, 3-ounce oxford					
Untreated	17	15.7	13.0	14.3	14.9
1	17	15.3	8.9	9.7	12.8
2	10.9	12.6	9.9	10.0	10.5
3	17	15.6	11.5	12.3	14.0
4	17	15.5	10.9	13.0	13.8
5	17	15.7	14.3	14.3	14.8
6	17	15.5	12.3	13.6	13.9
d. Nylon, 14-ounce duck					
Untreated	17	15.8	13.5	13.9	15.3
1	17	15.3	8.0	8.9	12.6
2	11.9	13.0	9.6	10.0	10.5
3	17	15.3	11.6	11.9	13.8
4	17	13.8	9.9	9.9	11.3
5	17	15.3	13.7	14.0	14.6
6	17	15.8	13.6	13.7	14.9

REFERENCES

1. *Identification of Fibers in Textile Materials.* Bulletin X156. Wilmington, Del.: E.I. DuPont De Nemours & Co., December 1961.

2. *U.S. Air Force Technical Order 00-25-203, Standards and Guideline for the Design and Operation of Clean Rooms and Clean Work Stations.* Office of Technical Services, Department of Commerce, Washington, D. C., July 1963.

3. *NAVAER 01-1A-503.* Section XII Revision. North Island Naval Air Station, Calif., April 1962.

4. Allison, F. M. "Control of Airborne Particulate Contamination." *Journal of the American Association for Contamination Control,* Vol. II, No. 2, February (1962).

5. Grugnola, A. M., and Robinson, H. M. *Measuring and Predicting the Generation of Static Electricity in Military Clothing.* Textile Series Report 110. Natick, Mass.: Headquarters Quartermaster Research and Engineering Command, U.S. Army, September 1959.

6. Silsbee, F. B. *Static Electricity.* National Bureau of Standards Circular C438. Department of Commerce, Washington, D. C., 1942.

7. Cusick, G. E., and Hearle, J. W. S. "Electrical Resistance of Synthetic and Cellulose Acetate Fibres." *Journal of the Textile Institute,* Vol. 46, T699 (1955).

8. Adams, N. K. *The Physics and Chemistry of Surfaces.* London: University Press, 1941.

9. Schiefer, H. F., and Hermach, F. L. *Static Electricity Generated in Fibrous Materials.* National Bureau of Standards Report 4158. Department of Commerce, Washington, D. C., June 1955.

10. *Static Electricity Generated in Fibrous Materials.* National Bureau of Standards Report 4752. Department of Commerce, Washington, D. C., June 1956.

11. Levenson, Howard. "Clean Room Rules at Norden Division, United Aircraft Corp." *Journal of the American Association for Contamination Control,* Vol. II, No. 8 (August 1963).

Chapter 11. *Parts Cleaning*

Introduction[1]

Manufacturing may involve casting, stamping, rolling, molding, and machining operations, and it may use materials that are metallic, plastic, or a combination. Contaminants introduced during manufacturing operations include casting inclusions and carry-over from previous manufacturing operations. Generally this kind of contamination consists of fairly large, easily distinguishable inhomogeneities. Contaminants produced during manufacture are not too serious if they can be removed during the subsequent normal cleaning process. Standard cleaning processes are usually effective for removal of all materials that are not physically or chemically well bonded to the submaterial. Personnel responsible for removal of these contaminants must be well versed in these skills.

It is often necessary to clean individual components during the assembly process. It is sometimes difficult, however, to realize that the cleaning process itself can be a source of contamination. Any cleaning process involves transfer of dirt from a higher concentration to a lower one. Little emphasis need be placed on the fact that the higher concentration is on the part and the lower one is in the cleaning fluid, and not vice versa. Contamination can occur during cleaning as a result of transfer in either a dry stage or a wet stage. Dry transfer usually occurs when very large numbers of particles are removed by wiping the component with an absorbent material that deposits fibers on the surface, or it may be that the absorbent cannot break the bond between the contaminant and the surface itself. Wiping action can cause electrical charging of the surface, and any particles in the air that are oppositely charged will be attracted to the surface at a very great rate. Wet cleaning exposes the contaminated surface to a clean fluid which wets the particles and the surfaces. Agitation removes the particles from the surface, the contaminated fluid is removed from the surface, and the surface is then dried. The mechanism used in this cleaning process often results in partially or improperly cleaned surfaces. Differences in energy distribution in the cleaning tank where ultrasonic cleaners are used, careless handling during vapor-degreasing processes, and increased probability of sticking when a wet object is exposed to a dirty air stream all result in contamination of a supposedly clean device. This phase of the problem is connected not with the source of contamination but with the removal of previously acquired contaminants.

[1] Abstracted from reference *1*, pp. 20 and 21.

Cleaning Methods

Decontaminating by Sonic Energy[2]

Sonic energy is in its infancy when compared to other methods of decontamination now employed by the clean room industry. Its acceptance as a practical production tool dates back a little more than 5 years, yet it had its beginnings as early as 1900 when Pierre Curie discovered the piezoelectric effect. Curie found that voltages impressed across certain crystalline materials caused them to vibrate. The long period of incubation (practically 55 years) during which this source of energy grew from a scientific curiosity to a practical tool was due to the lack of effective electrical generating

[2] Abstracted from reference *2*, p. 29.

equipment that could perform at the required frequencies and necessary power levels. In a sonic energy cleaning system, vibrations (sound waves) are radiated into a liquid. When these vibrations exceed 15,000 cps, they are termed ultrasonic.

A sonic system is composed of two basic parts: (1) a generator, and (2) a transducer. The function of the generator is to supply electrical energy to the transducer. The electrical energy provided must be at the resonant frequency of the transducer. The generator may be either electronic or rotary. The electrical energy supplied by the generator is converted by the transducer into mechanical energy in the form of vibrations. It can be considered the heart of the sonic system. Transducers fall into two classes—piezoelectric and magnetostrictive. A piezoelectric transducer is composed of a natural crystal such as quartz or a specially produced ceramic such as barium titanate which will emit sonic vibrations under the influence of an impressed voltage. The magnetostrictive transducer is composed of a magnetostrictive metal such as cobalt, nickle, or iron. A magnetostrictive metal is one that undergoes dimensional change when subjected to a magnetic field. When the magnetic field is relieved, the metal returns to its natural dimensions. In a magnetostrictive sonic system, the transducer can then be vibrated through dimensional changes by introducing an interrupted or alternating magnetic field.

The sonic energy application that is used will dictate the choice of a transducer. Crystal or ceramic transducers are usually chosen for low-power applications. When driven at high power for extended periods of time, these tranducers undergo natural degradation. Magnetostrictive transducers are used where power applications are needed for extended periods of time without loss in efficiency.

The sound waves produced by either piezoelectric or magnetostrictive transducers are utilized in gas, liquid, or solid media. The application of sound as a power tool is very limited in a gaseous medium, owing to the attenuating effects that a gas has on sound waves. Therefore, those applications that can be considered as practical industrial tools are currently those in which sound is transmitted into a liquid or solid.

In decontamination of parts associated with a fluid system, many types of mechanical energy, of which sonic energy is one, may prove satisfactory. The most important effect that sonic energy or a sound wave has on an activated cleaning solution is cavitation of the liquid medium. Bulate writes:

> Cavitation in this sense may be defined as the formation and collapse of small voids or bubbles within a liquid. Technically, it occurs when gas or vapor filled cavities form in a liquid as a result of the high negative pressure of an intense sound wave. Better understanding can be had of this phenomenon by visualizing a container of water at room temperature and normal atmospheric conditions. If an intense sound wave is sent into the liquid, three important phases occur: (1) The degassing phase: voids or bubbles present in the liquid which are large enough to be visible to the naked eye are energized by the sound wave. They coalesce, become buoyant and quickly rise out of the solution. This phase is important because large gaseous bubbles in the liquid act as sound absorbers and actually impede insonation. (2) The pulsing phase: this phase occurs when gaseous bubbles 40 microns or less in diameter are caught by the compressional forces of the sound wave. They are alternately effected by compression and rarifaction at the frequency of the sonic vibration and will thus pulsate several thousand times per second. This rapid pulsation creates a scrubbing action within the liquid. If a contaminated part is immersed in this liquid, the scrubbing action will strive to separate the contaminant from the part. (3) The collapse phase: the most important phase in the sonic activation of the liquid occurs when its compressional forces act upon vapor filled cavities or bubbles which are 40 microns or less in diameter. Instead of pulsating as the gaseous bubbles did, these collapse, leaving a void in the liquid. The liquid surrounding the voids, driven by hydrostatic and atmospheric pressure, rushes to fill the opening in the fluid and tremendous pressures are generated at the locus of the collapsing bubble. When a contaminated part is immersed in cavitating liquid, contamination will be pulled from the part by the suction or vacuuming force of these imploding bubbles.[3]

The above-mentioned physical action is the basis for sonic energy cleaning. A further enhancement is gained by the fact that these decontaminating forces are carried by a sound wave and can, therefore, occur wherever the sound wave penetrates, thus facilitating the cleaning of parts that have complicated geometric configurations such as channels, blind holes, and capillary tubes. A further advantage of this system is its ability to engage the contaminated surface at a molecular level, which

[3] Reference 2, p. 29.

cannot be done by ordinary mechanical systems, owing to fluid boundary-layer effects. It is also important to note that any chemical advantage added to the cleaning solution, such as solvency, surface tension lowering, acid or alkaline energy, and ionization, is enhanced by sonic activation by virtue of its ability to maintain a high concentration gradient of the chemical at the surface of the part being processed. The incorporation of all these advantages into a specific cleaning system must be based on careful consideration of production capabilities and economic feasibility.

Acid Methods[4]

As an example of acid cleaning methods, Chaikin*(3)* used the following cleaning procedure to prepare palladium for his laboratory studies of contact resistance due to surface contamination. Tabe ¼ by ½ by 0.01 inch were etched in aqua regia for 15 seconds, rinsed in 1 : 1 HCl, and dipped in distilled water. This was followed by 15 minutes in sulfuric-chromic acid cleaning solution at 80°C. After four rinses in double-distilled water, the tabs were rinsed for 1 hour in running double-distilled water. Finally, they were dried in a desiccator containing magnesium perchlorate.

Solvent Methods[5]

Schetky*(4)* reports that the two most effective solvent cleaning systems are (1) nital[6] and solvent cleaning, and (2) ultrasonic cleaning with graded solvent. Nital cleaning is more effective where extreme cleanliness is required. In cases where the slight etching produced by nital is unsuitable, however, the second process is effective. Schetky uses polarized light to determine cleanliness. Surface particles show up as bright white or colored points of light. Ordinary dust will glow to a certain degree under polarized light, but abrasive residues from finishing are either transparent or translucent and have two distinct indexes of refraction. The cleaning proceduces recommended by Schetky are as follows:

1. *Nital Cleaning*
   a. Clean finished parts ultrasonically in xylene; dry with filtered compressed air.
   b. Scrub parts with a solution of 1% nitric acid in methanol. Optical lens tissue makes a suitable scrub rag.
   c. Rinse in methanol. Neutralize any residual acid by rinsing in sodium bicarbonate solution.
   d. Repeat step *a*.
   e. Dip in half-and-half methanol–acetone bath to remove residual moisture.
   f. Protect clean parts with VPI paper, a moisture barrier fluid like Aquasorb, or the actual service lubricant.
2. *Ultransonic Cleaning with Graded Solvents*
   a. Clean ultrasonically for 5 minutes in xylene; dry with filtered compressed air.
   b. Repeat using Freon 113.
   c. Repeat using methanol.
   d. Repeat using xylene.
   e. Repeat using methanol.
   f. Dip in half-and-half methanol–acetone bath to remove residual moisture.
   g. Protect by VPI paper, Aquasorb, or service lubricant.

Biondi*(6)* reports that the life and reliability of many electronic devices now appear to be more dependent on contaminating influences of impurities associated with the materials of construction than on the inherent behavior of the materials themselves. Undesirable contaminants have been divided into five groups: (1) physical contaminants such as dust, lint, and small metal fragments; (2) ionic contaminants, which are generally water-soluble acid or plating residues; (3) contaminants, principally mineral greases and oils, that are soluble in solvents other than water; (4) chemically active contaminants, such as polar inorganic materials, oxides, sulfides, and (5) gaseous contaminants that may be absorbed, or generated within the device. Physical contaminants have three principal effects on electronic components. First, some particles are large enough to bridge the close spacings and provide leakage paths between parts. Second, many particles decompose to yield gaseous or other end products the presence of which is deleterious. Finally,

[4] Abstracted from reference *5*, p. 15.
[5] *Ibid.*, pp. 15–18.
[6] Dilute nitric acid solution in alcohol.

the large surface areas of fine particles offer sites for the sorption of unwanted gases and chemicals.

Biondi(*6*) found that acetate gloves used to reduce fingerprint contamination are a source of lint and dust. Monofilament nylon gloves with the palm coated with a continuous thin film of plastic which is impervious to perspiration and transfer of body oils and skin scales are now used. Polarized light is used to inspect parts for lint and fibers.

A multistage cleaning cycle is used to remove contaminants. Loosely held physical contaminants are removed in an ultrasonic bath of hot water and a wetting agent. Ionic contaminants are removed in a countercurrent extractor with deionized water. The presence of contaminating organic film is detected by spraying fine water droplets onto the test specimen and observing the tendency of the droplets to coalesce and form a thin uniform film. Parts passing this test have organic films of less than a tenth of a molecular layer. It was found that tightly held organic films are not removed by trichlorethylene degreasing, vacuum firing, hydrogen firing, or acid etching. The only effective means to remove these films is to alter or split the organic molecules by exposure to oxidizing conditions such as heating in air at 400°C, by boiling in a 3% solution of hydrogen peroxide, or by exposure to an oxidizing acid. The resultant oxidized film can be removed if need be by chemical action or reduction in a hydrogen atmosphere.

Cleaning of Electro-Mechanical Devices[7]

In the sophisticated componentry of today's technology, very small amounts of a contaminant can cause failure. Clean air and work areas are essential to effective contamination control, but they provide only a partial solution to the over-all problem. When electromechanical devices are being considered, the major reasons for cleaning can be listed as follows: (1) To achieve low and stable contact electrical resistance. (2) To control insulation resistance. (3) To prevent mechanical interference. (4) To achieve low or reproducible friction characteristics.[8] (5) To enhance adherence of films. (6) To eliminate corrosive residues.[8]

All these objectives are of concern, but achieving low contact electrical resistance and good adherence of films are probably most important. Note that in two of the reasons—achieving low friction and eliminating corrosive agents–cleaning can aggravate as well as help. For example, development prototypes with contaminant films acting as lubricants may work well. Later, production units made and assembled under strict cleanliness procedures may gall or corrode. Or, if the design contains crevices that are difficult to rinse, a corrosive cleaning agent may be trapped and contribute to corrosion, instead of preventing it. Care must be taken during development to avoid such pitfalls.

Some of the important factors in achieving cleanliness which must be considered and which are a function of the design of the device, its manufacture, and the personnel assembling it can be listed as follows:

1. *Design*
   - *a.* Geometry (the avoidance of crevices that could trap contaminants)
   - *b.* Materials selection (the avoidance of materials that outgas to produce contaminants)
   - *c.* Process definition (the use of welding instead of soldering where possible in order to avoid flux contamination)
2. *Manufacture*
   - *a.* Environment (sufficient cleanliness about work stations)
   - *b.* Fabrication methods (selection of those methods that produce the least amount of contamination)
   - *c.* Cleaning methods (those that are compatible with environment)
   - *d.* Cleanliness verification tests (selection of tests that will give a high confidence factor)
3. *People*
   - *a.* Personal actions and habits (elimination of those detrimental to the product)
   - *b.* Technical know-how

The major types of contaminants detrimental to electromechanical devices are:

1. Discrete particles (airborne, processing debris, wear products, debris generated by personnel and clothing, etc.).
2. Organic films and residues (cutting oils, machine lubricants, parting compounds, mold release, cleaning agent residues, process materials, out-

[7] Abstracted from reference 7, pp. 25–32.

[8] Cleaning can aggravate as well as help.

gassed products, contact "polymer" material, solder flux, fingerprints, etc.).
3. Inorganic films and residues (tooling smears, process materials, plating residues, corrosion products, cleaning agent residues, fingerprints, etc.).

It should be mentioned at this point that there is considerable confusion in the literature as to when to call a particular type of contamination a film or particulate matter. Because of this confusion, some people say that the majority of electrical contact contamination problems are the result of particulate matter and others say that they are the result of films. Yet indications are both groups may be talking about the same thing.

Some methods of cleaning in common use are listed in Table 11-1.

It is important to remember that no one cleaning method or cleanliness verification test is universal. Each is specific, and, because of this, it is necessary to know the probable types of contaminants before defining an effective cleaning method. Also, the degree of cleanliness required depends on the function of the part.

As an example of techniques currently being employed, Bild*(7)* states that Sandia Corporation has been concerned primarily with two general approaches to cleaning. One approach is typified by cleaning of parts for high-reliability long-life vacuum tubes, and it involves a very rigorous cleaning schedule and strong cleaning agents. To illustrate how rigorous these cleaning schedules are, one typical tube assembly being manufactured for Sandia has 54 parts. A total of 153 operations are required to put these 54 parts together; 41 of the 153 assembly operations, or approximately 28%, are cleaning operations. The particular supplier of this equipment is very knowledgeable in contamination control and has worked out cleaning operations that include vapor blasting to remove gross particulate matter, oxide films, solvents, and detergents; oxidation-reduction reagents to remove organic matter; and ultrahigh-purity water for rinsing. Ultrasonic agitation of the liquids is utilized. Also, numerous other types of cleaning such as acid cleaning, alkaline cleaning, and vacuum firing are sometimes used. In vacuum tube cleaning processes, extreme cleanliness is necessary for high reliability and long life. Parts and subassemblies are relatively simple in shape, without capillary crevices, and no plastic parts are involved. Thus severe, rigorous methods can be used.

TABLE 11–1

CLEANING METHODS (7)

Type	*Cleaning Material*	*Techniques*
Chemical	Etchant, solvent, detergent	Immersion, spray, vapor
Agitated chemical	Solvent, detergent	Ultrasonics, mechanical agitation
Mechanical	Abrasive	Scrubbing, tumbling, blasting
Electrical	—	Glow discharge, electropolish
Thermal	—	Vacuum heating (electron beam, induction, resistance)

Bild further reports:

> A second approach to cleaning, with which Sandia [Corporation] is concerned, is quite different and it constitutes the majority of our problems. This approach involves the cleaning of parts, subassemblies, and complete assemblies of components made of a variety of materials including metals and plastics. These assemblies often contain large numbers of parts and usually include many crevices and capillary traps from which strong cleaning agents cannot always be thoroughly rinsed. Typical of such components are timing and switching devices with wheels, gears, rotary and stationary printed circuit boards, electrical contacts, and bearings requiring low and controlled friction. Because of the large amount of handling during assembly, it is necessary, in addition to part cleaning, to also clean subassemblies and complete assemblies before sealing of the containers. Epoxy staking operations, adhesive bonding and sealing, soldering, and other assembly operations further complicate the picture. The variety of materials, plus the crevices and capillary traps, prohibit the use of strong cleaning agents such as can be used on simpler piece parts. Therefore, compromise procedures utilizing relatively mild solvents and detergents are used, followed by extensive rinsing and low temperature vacuum bake. Ultrasonic agitation of the cleaning liquids, at a relatively high energy level, is used to penetrate the assembly. The problem is aggravated in cases where the assembly or fixturing is relatively massive in that much of the ultrasonic energy is damped and absorbed. Also, there is a limit as to how high an energy level can be used or some of the more fragile parts will be damaged. Ex-

treme care must be taken in design of cleaning fixtures. Thus everything about the cleaning operation becomes a compromise. All this says that more attention must be paid to processing and handling operations with the purpose of *preventing* contamination.

A typical cleaning procedure for the type of subassembly or final assembly just described consists of five steps. The first four steps are: (1) trichloroethylene solvent, (2) a nonionic detergent, (3) distilled or deionized water, and (4) high purity isopropyl alcohol. Between each of these first four steps, the assembly is blown dry with dry filtered nitrogen. Particular care is taken to see that the nitrogen is clean to avoid recontamination. The fifth and last step is usually a low temperature bakeout.

There is no single solvent capable of removing all types of contaminants without being so reactive as to damage parts being cleaned. Therefore, the choice of solvent is always a compromise. Trichloroethylene cannot always be used because it will attack some plastics and insulation materials. With most plastics, no problem is encountered with trichlor unless the plastics are incompletely cured. Acid and alkaline solvents, though very effective on some parts, can, of course, not be used in the type of component assembly just described. The rather mild cleaning procedure just outlined has been found to be effective and "safe" for most of these applications. The types of solvents and cleaning schedules vary with the particular manufacturing line and assembly sequence and with the particular contaminant removal problem. Two of the most commonly used solvents at Sandia are trichloroethylene and isopropyl alcohol. It is important that these solvents be pure so as not to leave deposits, and it is important that trichloroethylene be chemically stabilized to eliminate free HCl. Also, regardless of the solvents used, parts should normally be heated in a vacuum to remove final traces of solvent because it is difficult to remove even relatively volatile solvents from capillary-like enclosures by any other method.[9]

The detergents most commonly used by Sandia Corporation are of the nonionic type and have, in general, done a satisfactory job. Recently, Alconox, an ionic detergent, has been compared with Igepal, which is one of the nonionic detergents, and has proved superior in removal of certain specific contaminants. This comparison was made in preparing substrates for vacuum deposition of metallic films. Further evaluation of this ionic detergent is continuing. The effectiveness of Alconox will be mentioned again during the discussion of verification tests.

One other example of a cleaning method used on Sandia products of high storage life will be mentioned, namely, the preparing of metal surfaces for painting. A typical cleaning procedure may include the following steps: (1) wipe off gross contamination with a dry cloth, (2) abrade the surface with sandpaper, (3) rinse with water while wiping with clean cloths, (4) wash with abrasive powder cleaner and wet cloth, (5) rinse, (6) clean with chemical solvent, (7) rinse with water, and (8) dry with filtered compressed air.

These abbreviated descriptions of cleaning processes are illustrative of a few methods and are by no means complete. For example, a detail procedure for electrical contacts may cover several pages, spelling out such items as the required environment, personnel washup and clothing, handling procedures, fixtures, cleaning equipment, purity of materials used, sequence, times, ultrasonic frequency, orientation of parts in cleaning bath, temperatures, and storage instructions. Also, the cleaning procedure may vary with the type of part being cleaned; for example, electrical contacts, O-rings, plastic parts, metal parts, assemblies involving many crevices and capillary paths, parts coated with dry film lubricants, and printed circuit boards—all require individual consideration.

Verification[10]

After cleaning of the parts or assemblies, the next problem is to verify their cleanliness. Verification methods can be direct, such as visual and water-break methods; semidirect, utilizing fluorescent dye or radioactive tracers; or indirect, such as electrical contact resistance or film adherence tests.

In discussing verification of cleaning, Bild writes:

"Among the more common direct tests are the visual, the water-break, the atomizer, and the solvent tests. The visual test is frequently used and its sensitivity can vary from low to relatively high, depending on the knowledge and experience of the observer and the magnification and lighting used. It is also tedious and time-consuming. The water-break and water-atomizer tests depend on visual observation of the contact angle of water droplets and are effective for water repellant contaminants only. The water-break test is performed by immersing the surface to be tested in a container of deionized water and withdrawing it in a vertical position. If the amount of remaining water-repellant con-

[9] Reference 7, p. 27.

[10] Abstracted from reference 7, pp. 28-30.

taminant is a monolayer or less, the water film on the part will be continuous and will remain unbroken for a period of 30 to 60 seconds. The time for the water film to break and draw up into droplets or partially wetted areas is an indication of the amount of water-repellant contaminant present. On grossly contaminated parts, water break occurs immediately. The atomizer test is similar but more easily interpreted and more sensitive and can detect traces of contaminant or fractions of monolayers. In this test, parts are sprayed with water from an atomizer, and where water-repellant contaminants are present, the droplets will not spread and uniformly wet the surface. Since the majority of contaminants are water repellant, the water-break and atomizer tests are very useful. These methods are frequently used in the laboratory to compare efficiency of cleaning methods and are also useful in manufacture to monitor cleaning operations and to test cleanliness of parts having simple shapes. A freshly cleaved mica surface is often used as a reference to check the operation of the test.

Also, a series of go/no-go photographic standards may be used. However, test techniques utilizing visual standards are time consuming and are subject to individual interpretation and require considerable personnel experience. If the contaminant is not water repellant, it will, of course, not be detected by water-break or atomizer tests.

Sandia is presently conducting a study to determine if color photographic standards for water-break and atomizer tests will enable easier interpretation than black and white photographic standards. Initial work has been with printed circuit boards.

Another direct test is the solvent drop test. Choice of the solvent depends on the suspected contaminant, but trichloroethylene serves for the majority of contaminants with which we are concerned. Following is the technique as developed at Sandia. First, to make sure that the solvent itself is not contaminated, a drop of it is placed on a clean glass slide and allowed to evaporate. If the solvent is pure and the slide clean, no stain or a barely perceptible stain will result. Next, a drop of solvent is placed on the surface of the part being tested. After a few seconds, the drop is stirred by and then picked up by a capillary tube and transferred to the glass slide. If the surface of the part contained significant soluble contaminants, these contaminants will dissolve in the solvent and concentrate in the periphery of the drop and a pronounced ring-shaped stain will show on evaporation. The technique is also often applied "in place" on the surface of the part being tested. Sensitivity of this test is similar to that of the water break. Again visual interpretation is required, which is a disadvantage in identification of contaminants since the solvent drop containing the contaminant can be easily transferred for infrared analysis. In addition to the direct verification tests just mentioned, there are numerous other less commonly used direct techniques, all of which are specific to various types of contaminants.

Two of the *semidirect* methods involve purposely contaminating the parts prior to cleaning with tracer components such as fluorescent dyes or "tagged" radioactive atoms. It is hoped that if the tracer contaminants are removed, other contaminants will also be removed. The fluorescent dye technique is less sensitive than the water break and also requires visual interpretation. The radioactive tracer technique is more sensitive than the water break and is capable of quantitative go/no-go interpretation. But it has drawbacks from the expense and health hazard standpoints, as well as from the fact that it is not a direct test. In addition to being of some value as a semidirect verification test, the radioactive tracer technique is a good tool for comparing the efficiency of various cleaning methods for specific contaminants. Another example of a semidirect method is the cleaning agent that is electrically conducting, thus permitting monitoring of the rinse water to a certain quantitative low value of conductivity. (General Electric has done considerable work in this area.) The use of an ionic detergent such as Alconox is an example.[11]

A recent study by Dr. B. T. Kenna, of Sandia Corporation, involved the use of radioactive tracers to evaluate the efficiency of various cleaning methods, including use of Alconox, for removing specific contaminants. The radioactively tagged contaminants used were a hydrochloric acid solution of iron-59 stearate, an aqueous solution of diethanolamine, silicone oil, and an aqueous solution of urea plus lactic acid. (The urea plus lactic acid material is actually artificial fingerprint per Military Specification C-1507.) The substrates studied were glass, alumina, sapphire, and Kovar.

Table 11-2 shows comparative results for Igepal and Alconox detergents in removing diethanolamine contaminant from a sapphire substrate. Distilled water alone is shown as a control. After cleaning with Igepal or Alconox, distilled water was used for thorough rinsing. Sodium-22-tagged Alconox was used to check the removal of the Alconox detergent during rinsing. The Igepal was not tagged. Note the comparison of final counts per minute for the control part washed with distilled water only and those cleaned with Igepal and Alconox. The counts show that Alconox was more effective for this particular contaminant. You will recall that Alconox is ionic, permitting a production line test

[11] Reference 7, pp. 28 and 29.

on conductivity of the rinse water. Alconox also proved more effective than Igepal for the iron stearate and artificial fingerprint-tagged contaminants previously mentioned. To illustrate again, however, that no one cleaner will do all jobs well, neither Igepal nor Alconox was effective in removing the tagged silicone oil. The examples just mentioned are a small part of a fairly extensive cleaning evaluation study, but they illustrate how radioactive tracer techniques can be used to evaluate cleaning methods.

Two examples of indirect verification tests for cleanliness are the measurement of contact electrical resistance and the measurement of adherence of paints or metal films. Such tests can serve to prevent bad parts from going into stock, but finding out at this late stage that cleaning was inadequate can result in a lot of expensive rejects.

TABLE 11–2

COMPARATIVE REMOVAL OF DEA FROM SAPPHIRE BY WATER AND CLEANING AGENTS (7)

Cleaning Procedure	*Initial cpm**	*Final cpm†*	*Per cent Remaining‡*
Distilled water	18,709	96	0.51
Igepal	14,915	46	0.31
Alconox	11,689	2	0.02

* Average standard deviation ±123 cpm.
† Average standard deviation ±5.1 cpm.
‡ Average estimated error ±15% of values listed.

An example of detective work that may be required of contamination control personnel is brought out by Sandia Corporation experience.

A certain component, involving a high-voltage application, went into production. Some of the assemblies failed the hi-pot test and others did not. Contamination was suspected. One part of the component assembly was a hat-shaped Kovarglass seal. These were being procured from two different suppliers, and it was soon determined that trouble was occurring only in those components utilizing seals from one particular supplier. A supply of these seals was obtained, and the inner surface of the seal was found to be coated with an organic compound containing sulfur. The contamination on the inner surface was traced to an inhibitor used in a pickling operation of the seal prior to electroplating the outer surface of the Kovar. The answer, of course, was for the supplier to stop using the particular inhibitor. The study did not end there, however, as there were a lot of seals to salvage, and a cleaning method had to be worked out to remove the film. Fortunately, it was a simple piece, so strong methods could be used. Solvents, boiling detergents, acid, and alkaline cleaners were tried without success. The film was extremely stubborn. Finally, a 500° to 600°F bake was tried and was successful. The standard cleaning procedure for the part had utilized only a low temperature bake of 225°F. Fortunately the 500° to 600°F bake could be used in this case without harm, and the parts were salvaged.[12]

Freon as a Cleaning Agent

Demands for the cleaning of ultraprecision devices have made almost any degree of contamination intolerable. The result has been a need for a cleaning solvent with many unique properties as well as an extremely high degree of purity. For example, manufacturers of gyroscopes have been using Freon solvents for cleaning their miniature parts and assemblies. Freon is normally manufactured with a high degree of purity and is available for this type of cleaning. When manufactured for precision cleaning Freon is loaded in special plastic-lined drums in a clean room atmosphere. Since the handling of the solvent exposes it to contamination, both the loading and unloading of the drums are critical.

In addition to its purity, other physical and chemical properties make Freon an excellent cleaning agent. All the compounds of Freon are completely nonflammable, and they have very low toxicity; few solvents exhibit both characteristics. The selectivity of Freon solvents has led to their use in the gyroscope industry. They are good solvents for greases, oils, and many organic materials but do not harm commonly used materials of construction. Thus Freon can be used to flush a completely assembled gyroscope containing many metals, plastics, and elastomers. In addition, Freon is a pure stable chemical compound. It resists degradation and will not need inhibitors to prevent it from breaking down. Another result of Freon's stability is the low solubility of water in the compound. Low surface tension is another attribute, which allows the Freon to penetrate small openings.

[12] *Ibid.*, p. 30.

Ultrasonic cleaning has recently made additional demands on solvents. Optimum cavitation properties are necessary for removing insoluble particulate soils and dispersing them so that they may be removed from the solvent by filtering.

At present, there is no unified quantitative theory to predict the cavitational behavior of liquids(*8*). This behavior is known to depend on temperature, hydrostatic pressure, vapor pressure, surface tension, viscosity, and the presence of desolved gases. Freon has proved to be very satisfactory for use in ultrasonic cleaners.

Evaluating Cleaning Methods

In the field of sonic energy, one of the most difficult areas to evaluate has been the cleaning ability or efficiency of a bath that is under sonic activation. The problem is that no single method is adaptable to measuring the cleanliness of all types of parts(*9*). Further, there is no generally accepted method for cleanliness evaluation.

Some of the methods used are performance tests, visual inspection, gravimetric tests, chemical tests, radioactive tracer tests, wettability tests, and surface contamination tests. Berry(*10*) in the Sandia report SCTM 73A-60(16) discusses cleaning methods and recommends procedures for ultrasonic cleaning. He finds ultrasonic cleaning effective for removing metal dust, epidermal scale, fly ash, airborne dust, and materials soluble in the solvent used. Ultrasonic cleaning is not considered effective against burrs and epoxy adhesives, however.

Harris(*11*) improved ultrasonic cleaning by applying vacuum to the loaded tank prior to starting ultrasonic agitation. This allows air bubbles to be drawn out of blind holes, etc., which otherwise would not be filled with liquid and therefore not reached by ultrasonic agitation. It should be pointed out that the main concern in ultrasonic cleaning is to supply sufficient energy to overcome the forces of adhesion between the substrate and the contaminant(*12*). In this regard, ultrasonic aqueous detergents which allow the rapid removal of dislodged contaminants from the environment of the parts being cleaned will allow maximum sonic energy to the substrate. An effective method is to use a flowing detergent bath to remove the contaminants from the proximity of the parts.

Evaluation of Sonic Energy Cleaning[13]

While discussing the subject of evaluation of sonic energy cleaning, Bulat states:

> The reason for failure in finding a gauging method for the cleaning ability of a sonic cleaning system is basically in the philosophy of the investigators. Most investigators are looking for a single or easily applied evaluation tool. The tool they seek would be analogous to the go-no-go gauge available in the industrial tool room. This is not possible because any single scientific situation is marked by a number of variables which are difficult to predict or reproduce. This does not mean that the quest for a valid means of evaluation should be abandoned. It does dictate that a carefully planned approach embodying several evaluating methods and employing trained personnel will be necessary.
>
> Evaluation methods for sonic cleaning can be divided into two basic categories, (1) those based on acoustical parameters or direct physical activity in the insonated bath, and (2) those based on the cleaning action of the unit.[14]
>
> . . . These methods are measurements of various forms of energy in the bath and not direct measurements of cleaning. The two are not necessarily interrelated closely. To predict cleaning ability on physical energy alone would be a mistake because the energy within the bath may be in a form which is not effective in cleaning. If the measurement of physical activity is correlated with other methods of evaluation, particularly those based on direct cleaning action, it can be of great value in an over-all analysis.[15]

Acoustical Power of Sonic Energy

Acoustical power into the bath can be measured by immersion of a crystal pickup, usually in the form of a hydrophone. Bulat reports:

> A piezoelectric system of this type converts mechanical energy in the bath into electrical energy which can be read directly on a volt meter. Two phases can be checked with a probe of this type, acoustical pressure and cavitation noise. Of the two, cavitation noise would be the most logical to measure because it is considered by most investigators as the prime source of energy for cleaning.
>
> In practice it becomes very difficult to measure the cavitation because it is a high frequency response and has a duration of only a few micro seconds. Low-frequency noises must be filtered out of the system. This is complicated by the fact that the crystal may be driven into resonant vibration at the higher frequencies, thus obliterating results.

---

[13] Abstracted from reference *13*.

[14] Reference *13*, p. 31.

[15] *Ibid.*, p. 32.

If the system is used to measure acoustical pressure, it loses its latitude of measurement because the sound is being measured in a confined volume where it tends to distribute itself equally throughout the bath. Thus all areas in the solution will exhibit fairly close readings even though the cleaning action in the bath is focused or diversified. The acoustical probe can be useful in evaluating a sonic unit over an extended period of time. If a unit begins to degrade or lose its ability to clean, the overall pressure readings can be observed to fall.[16]

Chemical Activity[17]

The rate of chemical reaction can be increased by sonic energy. It is logical to suppose that an increase in the chemical activity of a solution should be directly proportional to the amount of sonic energy it receives. A typical reaction used for this purpose has been the rate of converting iodine salts to free iodine, which can readily be quantitatively detected by simple analytical procedures. This method has not been successful, owing to inability to reproduce results under repeated standard conditions. Extensive control techniques are necessary, since this procedure is also very sensitive to environmental and chemical changes associated with the system.

By introduction of sonic energy into the electrolyte, electrolytic activity can be increased. Cavitation at the surface of the electrodes removes the gases being evolved, thus allowing better contact of the electrolyte with the electrode. The increase in electron flow is readily measured. This is a good method to show increase in activity, but it is limited because a plateau (saturation point) is reached at which increased sonic activity is not marked by increased electrolytic action. This is because maximum disruption of the gases at the electrode can occur before maximum sonic levels are reached.

The electrolytic method is further hampered by two difficult-to-handle variables: (1) the electrolyte characteristics change during the process; and (2) it is difficult to maintain a standard surface area on the electrodes.

Metal immersed in a sonically activated fluid is exposed to cavitation. Cavitation will subject the metal to a series of pressure changes at its surface. These pressure differentials are capable of cold-working the surface. In a thin metal such as aluminum foil, many small perforations will occur within a few seconds (Fig. 11-1). In a solid piece of metal such as lead, a pitting erosion will occur after several minutes of activation (Fig. 11-2). By calculating the weight loss of the sample during the

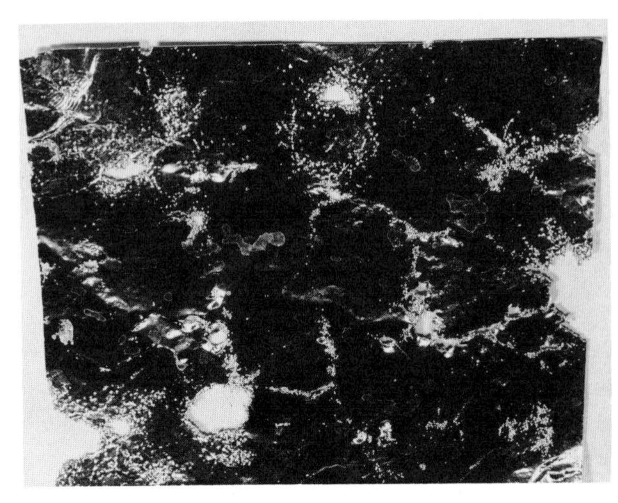

FIGURE 11-1. Aluminum foil eroded by cavitation. *Courtesy Pioneer-Central Div., Bendix Aviation and Air Engineering*

FIGURE 11-2. Lead sheet eroded by cavitation. *Courtesy Pioneer-Central Div., Bendix Aviation and Air Engineering*

[16] *Ibid.*, p. 32.
[17] Abstracted from reference *13*, p. 32.

sonic activation, a clue to the relative amount of sonic energy expended can be obtained. In practice the lead erosion test has not been a good method of evaluation because of poor reproducibility of results under repeated tests. The foil test may be used to determine the distribution pattern of cavitation in a specific cleaning container.

Efficiency measurements are based on the ability of the sonic system to convert electrical energy into mechanical energy and then to deliver this energy into the load (in this case, a cleaning bath). For purposes of measuring cleanliness, one is interested only in the phase wherein the energy is transferred to the load.

By use of an impedance bridge one can obtain an over-all evaluation of energy transfer and thus determine the amount of energy into the load. When the reactance of a vibrating transducer element is plotted against the ac resistance obtained at various input frequencies, a circle is obtained (Fig. 11-3).

In explaining this diagram, Bulat states:

> A circle of this type may be obtained for both an air load and a water load. The relative size of the circles, the circle positions, and the distribution of frequency plot points make possible the analysis of transducer efficiency. This test method is very helpful in the design of sonic systems but is limited in production evaluation by the fact that accurate measurements with the impedance bridge are very difficult to obtain at the higher powers usually associated with cleaning systems.

The accelerometer is a device which may be used to measure excursions of a sonically activated diaphragm and the peak acceleration at which these excursions occur. With this information, plus the mass of the transducer and diaphragm, energy can be computed ($E = \frac{1}{2}MV^2$). This method is complicated by the fact that it is difficult to determine the exact mass of the vibrating system.

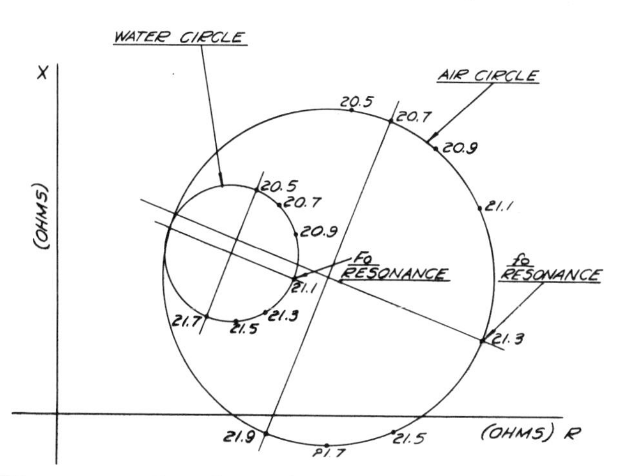

FIGURE 11-3. Impedance circle diagram. *Courtesy Pioneer-Central Div., Bendix Aviation and Air Engineering*

In computing the mass, the transducer and diaphragm must be considered as a single entity. Just which portion of the diaphragm should be included in this entity is made difficult by the variable flexations which it will undergo when sonically activated. Also it is difficult to derive the true mass of the transducer since approximately one-half of its total mass is effective. Most sonic systems have multiple transducers attached to the diaphragm which act to compound the diaphragm flexure problem.

By measuring the amount of heat transferred from the sonic system into the bath during a specified period of activation, the amount of energy expended can be measured (Fig. 11-4). In order to make an estimate of the actual sonic energy expended, the amount of heat transferred to the liquid medium by conduction from the transducer must be determined and compensated for in the final measurement. Strict environmental controls are necessary for accurate measurement but evaluations of relative nature can be easily obtained.

One of the phenomena which occurs when a sound wave is sent into a liquid is that of degassing the larger (visible) bubbles from the liquid. The speed at which degassing occurs is directly related to the amount of energy into the bath. Relative efficiencies can therefore be determined by measuring the time necessary for degassing. The degassing of a solution can be easily determined by capturing the gas evolved in a confined area or by noting the change in sound level as the gas is evolved. As the gas bubbles are driven from the solution, a change in sound level occurs which is audibly detectable. The length of time necessary for this audible change is directly proportional to the cavitation producing capabilities of the system.[18]

Cleaning Ability

This second group of evaluation methods is based solely on the cleaning ability of the sonic system being tested. The methods used are those which would be effective in evaluating any cleaning system whether it uses sonic energy or not. Most of these techniques have been used for many years. Much data has been accrued and many variations have been developed. Most cleaning tests fall into the categories listed. The advantage of this group of evaluation methods is that results can be directly related to cleaning. The disadvantage is that there is no single method which can be used in all situations.[18]

[18] Reference *13*, pp. 33 and 34.

Performance Tests

An excellent way to determine whether a part has been cleaned well enough to operate properly is to subject it to a series of performance tests. A precision ball bearing can be subjected to a standard torque test after cleaning. If the bearing is not clean it will not respond to predetermined torque values. The bearing could also fail the torque test due to mechanical or geometric disconformities, but the fact remains that the improperly cleaned bearing will not pass the performance test. Printed circuits with attached components can be subjected to electrical tests and any contamination present will alter resistance ratings, thus providing a method of evaluation. Unfortunately, many parts are too complicated to be checked against performance economically and others would have to be tested individually for extensive periods of time making the test impractical. The performance test is good for individual empirical tests only. It does not lend itself to an analytical method of evaluation.

Visual inspection can be performed by the unaided eye or with the aid of optical magnification (Fig. 11-5). The contamination can be made more readily detectable by such techniques as the addition of fluorescent dyes or by viewing under ultraviolet light.[19]

Visual Inspection

Visual inspection is probably the most widely used method of cleaning evaluation. It is limited by the fact that only exposed surfaces of the mechanism being cleaned can be evaluated. Integral areas, channels, tapped holes cannot be examined. Some contaminants such as monomolecular films on critical assemblies cannot be detected by visual methods.

In this method a part is weighed before and after cleaning. The weight loss recorded after cleaning is due to the amount of contamination removed by the cleaning procedure. If the part and contamination can be standardized, the gravimetric test may be used as an analytical method of evaluation (Fig. 11-6). The test is limited to small parts. As the weight ratio of contamination to part broadens, accuracy of results drop proportionately. A point is eventually reached

[19] Reference *13*, pp. 33 and 34.

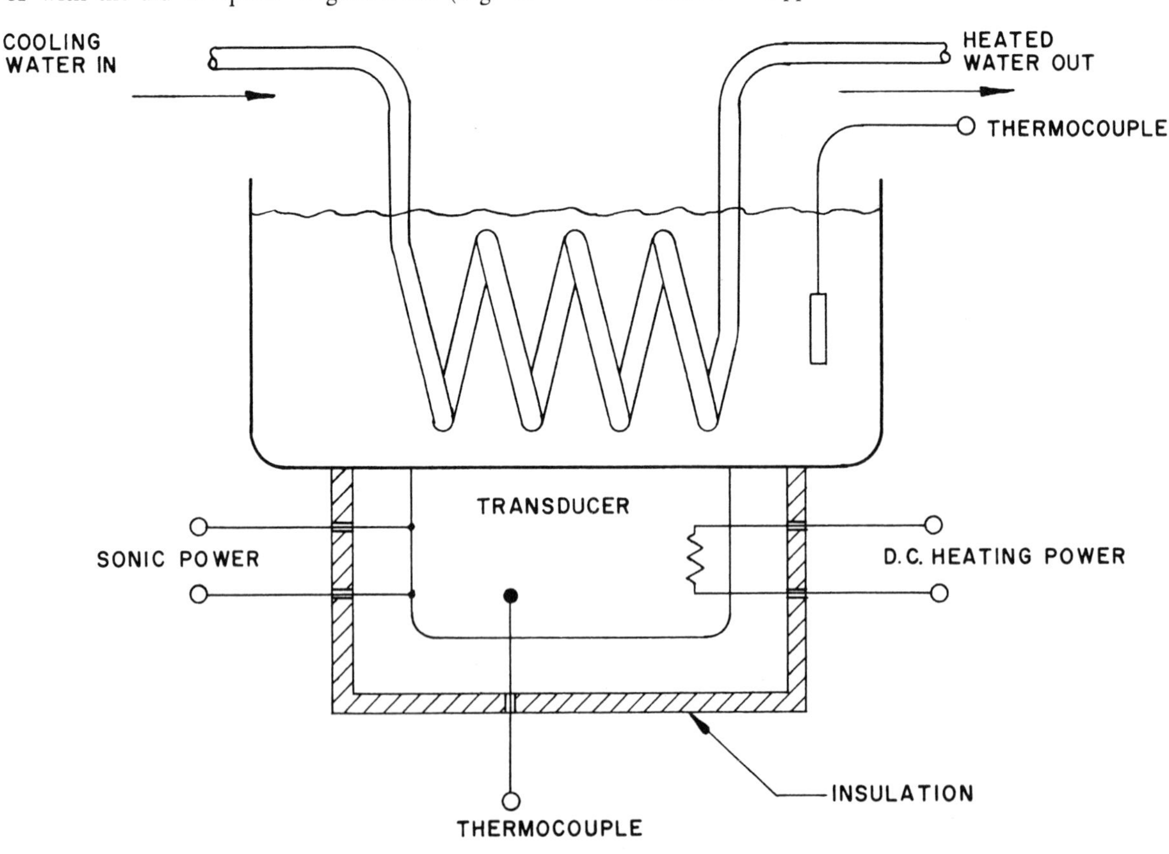

FIGURE 11-4. Schematic diagram of calorimetric test equipment. *Courtesy Pioneer-Central Div., Bendix Aviation and Air Engineering*

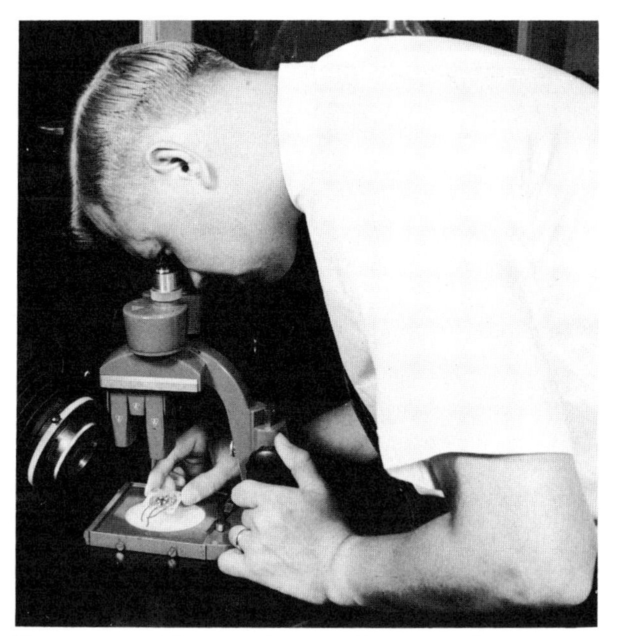

FIGURE 11-5. Microscopic examination of processed part. *Courtesy Pioneer-Central Div., Bendix Aviation and Air Engineering*

where the weight of the part makes the method mechanically impractical.

Many contaminants can be detected by analytical chemical methods which can be both qualitative and quantitative. An example of this is the detection of chloride residues remaining on a part after use of a soldering flux. The chlorides can be detected in submilligram amounts by precipitation techniques using

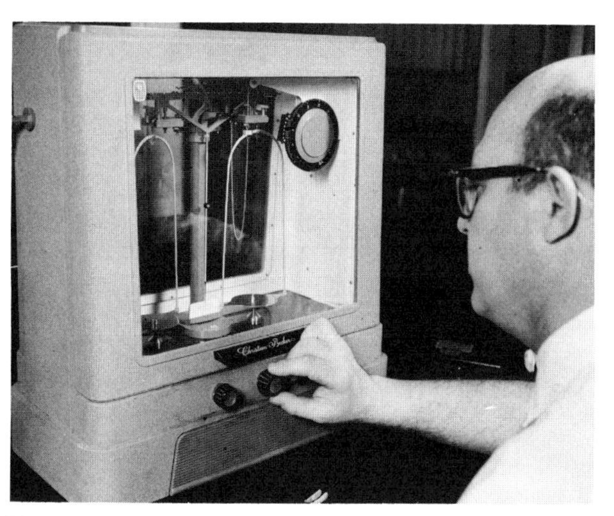

FIGURE 11-6. Detection of soil removal by gravimetric method. *Courtesy Pioneer-Central Div., Bendix Aviation and Air Engineering*

silver nitrate as the precipitating agent. There are several other good analytical tests of a similar nature but all are based on the chemical makeup of a specific contaminant. Inert contaminants and those of heterogeneous composition cannot be evaluated.

In a tracer evaluation the soil is tagged with a radioactive atom (Fig. 11-7). The radioactive count can be measured before and after cleaning and the actual contaminant can be traced throughout the entire processing history. Analytical methods of evaluation can be established. Some of the objections to this system are (1) that the soil being evaluated must be artificially introduced, (2) production conditions must be simulated, and (3) that tracer processes often necessitate high material cost and expenditure of technical personnel.

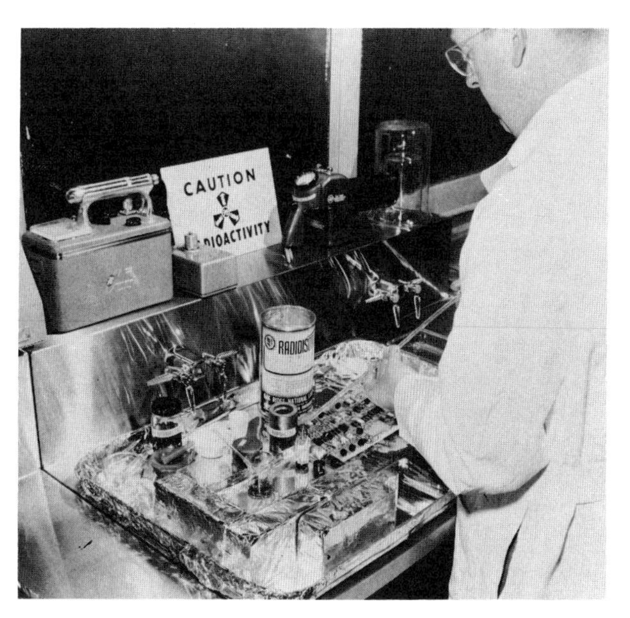

FIGURE 11-7. Soils tagged with radioactive tracers. *Courtesy Pioneer-Central Div., Bendix Aviation and Air Engineering*

This test is best exemplified by the plater's waterbreak test wherein the parts being evaluated are immersed in clean tap water. If the part is not clean, the water film will break into droplets on the surface of the part. There are many varieties of this method, aside from immersion, such as spraying the water with an atomizer or even forming the moisture film by condensation. Refined tests can detect very minute amounts of contamination. Evaluation by wettability is limited to exposed surfaces and is only definitive for organic soil; small amounts of insoluble inorganic material will not be detected, and minute residues of soaps or detergents on the surface will cause false indications.

Wettability

In this method of evaluation a standard contaminant is developed. It is then placed on standard test parts and they are cleaned under controlled conditions. The amount of soil remaining is usually measured visually. A method of this type often used is placing graphite on etched ceramic surfaces. This has the advantage of providing a system which can be reasonably well controlled and is based on the actual cleaning capabilities of the unit or process being tested. Difficulties occur in attaining a standard dirt and devising reproducible methods of attaching the contaminant to the sample to be cleaned.[20]

Sampling from Surfaces

No area of sampling is fraught with greater problems than sampling from surfaces. Essentially, all procedures involve rinsing the item to be sampled with particle-free solvent and recovering and filtering the rinse solvent. The procedure has the collateral advantage of providing an additional and final parts cleaning step.

The recovery of particles in any given instance, and the reproducibility of the test for any given piece, will depend on: (1) The nature of the solvent used. Freon, trichlorethylene, alcohol, water, and many other solvents may be used, but one should avoid switching from one to another. (2) The volume of solvent per square inch of surface. (3) The flow intensity or spray velocity. (4) The intensity of mechanical or ultrasonic agitation (if any) of fluid in contact with surface.

In establishing a test procedure, these factors must be fixed as part of the test criteria. The examples given below are illustrative only. The collected sample fluid may be analyzed by any number of procedures. Particle-count analyses are most often used. Once established, the test procedure must be conducted the *same way each time* for any given device to achieve maximum reproducibility.

Equipment requirements for surface sampling will vary with each specific application. The following list includes those items most commonly used: solvent filtering dispenser, high-pressure filter holder, test filter holder, high-volume filter holder, multiplate filter holder, microtube cartridge filter, Pyrex filter holder, bomb sampling kit, stainless-steel pressure vessels, and sample bottles.

[20] *Ibid.*, p. 35.

Sampling from Rigid Tubing

For short sections, fill tubing approximately half-full of filter solvent. Cap each end and turn end-for-end six times. Decant solvent directly into a clean Pyrex filter holder or into a clean sample bottle for filtration in the laboratory. (See Fig. 11-8.)

For long sections, connect tubing section by means of suitable adapters and clean Tygon hoses to a recirculating source of pressurized filtered solvent. Draw off 100-ml samples of solvent from the end of the tubing section while the solvent is circulating, and submit samples to laboratory for analysis.

When sampling small valves and manifolds, connect the device by means of suitable adapters and clean Tygon hoses to a recirculating source of pressurized filtered solvent. Divert 100-ml samples periodically for analysis into clean sample bottles, directly into a Pyrex filter holder (Fig. 11-9).

When sampling from flexible hoses, fill hose to within 10% of total volume with filtered solvent. Cap ends and flex hose six times at 180° to minimum allowable bend radius along its entire length. Decant solvent into a clean sample bottle, or filter directly in a clean Pyrex filter holder.

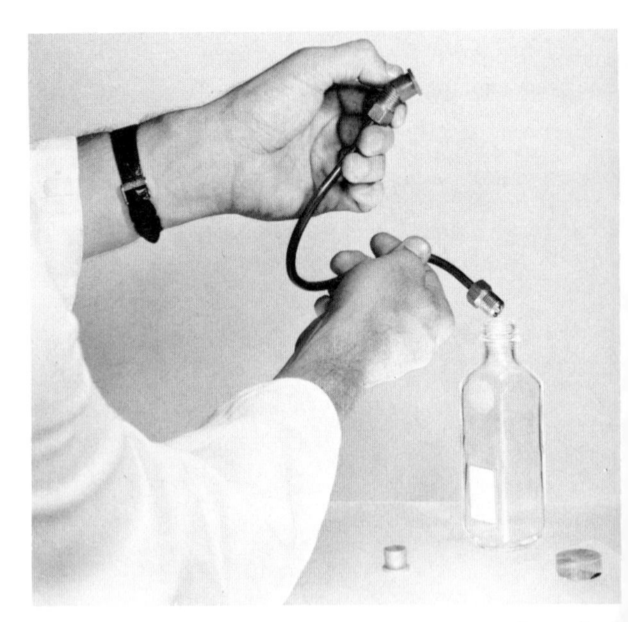

FIGURE 11-8. Test fluid from above is poured out into labeled clean sample bottle for forwarding to the laboratory. *Courtesy Millipore Filter Corp.*

When sampling from large valves and fittings, remove bonnet, cover, etc., and hold the component over a sample container or filter holder funnel for convenient draining. Direct a forceful stream of filtered solvent over the entire inner surface of the component, using particular care on rough surfaces and in crevices. Use approximately 200 ml of solvent per square foot of surface, and collect the solvent volume for analysis. Never use less than 200 ml of flushing solvent, regardless of component size.

When sampling from tanks, direct a forceful stream of particle-free solvent from a pump-driven spray nozzle over the entire inner surface of the tank. Use approximately 1 gallon of solvent per square foot of surface. Collect effluent samples for analysis (approximately 100 ml per 5 gallons of solvent) at evenly spaced intervals.

Cryogenic Sampling

Cryogenic sampling may be approached from two standpoints: sampling "off-line" and sampling "on-line." On-line sampling is more rapid but is sometimes more difficult to accomplish.

When off-line sampling is used, samples drawn in the field are promptly returned to the laboratory in appropriate Dewar-type flasks. A portion by weight or volume is decanted in the laboratory into a clean shallow dish and allowed to evaporate. The particulate fraction may then be rinsed from the dish into a Pyrex filter holder for routine analytical treatment. No special sampling or analytical equipment is required, but a question is raised as to the representativeness of the sample and recovery of residues from the evaporating dish.

Alternatively, the Dewar sample may be poured directly into a Pyrex filter holder. The placement of an absorbent par beneath a membrane filter and prechilling with a few milliliters of fluid is indicated to help reduce temperature of holder and filter simultaneously and prevent damage to the filter disk (Fig. 11-10).

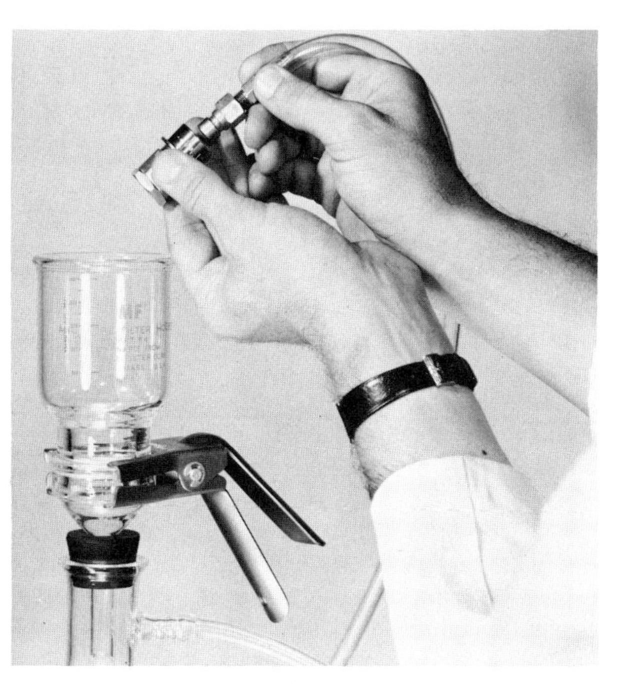

FIGURE 11-9. Quick-release valve being flushed by flow of filtered solvent, in this case directly into Pyrex filter holder. *Courtesy Millipore Filter Corp.*

FIGURE 11-10. The Dewar sample may be filtered directly with an absorbent pad beneath the filter if the filter and holder are first prechilled with a small quantity of fluid. *Courtesy Millipore Filter Corp.*

With a few precautions, cryogenic systems may be sampled on-line with distinct gains in accuracy.

As shown in Fig. 11-11, the high-pressure filter holder is installed in the purge or flow line with appropriate valves and gauges. In extreme cases of sampling from a rapidly moving stream, an isokinetic probe may be required, since the viscosity

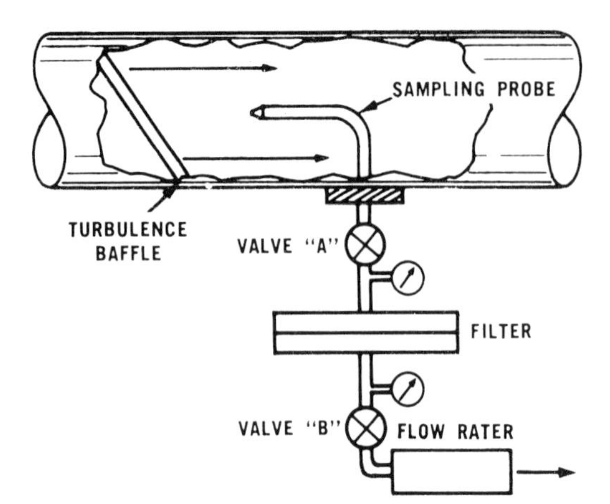

FIGURE 11-11. Baffle, probe, and valving must be considered when only a small volume is sampled from a rapidly moving large stream. *Courtesy Millipore Filter Corp.*

of the fluids will be extremely low. The placement of a turbulence baffle ahead of the sampling point is advantageous where the entire flow is not being sampled. Valve "A" should be cracked slowly to chill the high-pressure holder and until pressure equilibrates across the filter. Pressure differential across the filter and the sampling rate are then controlled by means of valve "B".

Sampling at too-high velocities, where large particles are present, may result in impingement damage to the filter.

Detection of Organic Surface Contaminants[21]

The following discussion categorizes quality test methods used for determining pre-existing organic surface contamination levels and the relative effectiveness of these tests. These tests can be generally listed as (1) visual tests, (2) black-light tests, (3) water-break test, (4) spray test, (5) wipe test, (6) final wash test, (7) conductance and/or capacitance tests, and (8) pressure-sensitive tape test.

Visual tests can be both macroscopic and microscopic. In both, the difficulties are the same: the problems of varying personal interpretation and the lack of satisfactory and reproducible standards tend to put many variables into the analysis. These tests are largely nonquantitative and cannot be used for internal and inaccessible surfaces. Macroscopic visual tests often miss contaminants below 10 to 50 micrograms per square centimeter. Microscopic tests cannot be applied to areas of any appreciable size except at great cost and time.

[21] Abstracted from reference *14*.

Wipe tests are qualitative and not desirable because they are both recontaminating and invalid below approximately 50 micrograms per square centimeter.

The final wash liquid test is valid only for soluble materials. It does not determine the materials remaining on any surface. For small surface areas the wash tests are practically invalid. Usually this technique requires a small laboratory. It is time-consuming, and it has a very large probable error in the quantitative sense, particularly when the acceptable limits of contamination are of the order of 1 to 10 micrograms per square centimeter. The level of hydrocarbon contaminant dissolved in the wash liquid is normally determined by a boil-down gravimetric method—or, more recently, by the absorption in the infrared at 3.5 microns.

Since cleaning procedures almost always use a wash-down method, the use of the wash-down test method also suffers from the problem of not being independent of the cleaning method. What is being tested in this way is the cleaning method, not the cleanliness of the product. An additional disadvantage is that many of the halogenated compounds used in the wash-down test are extremely toxic when used in repetitive applications.

Conductance and/or capacitance tests, when calibrated and used with a highly standardized process, have proved fairly effective. This method does not work well under field conditions, however, nor does it prove dependable with a variety of surface shapes and finishes.

The main hazard of the pressure-sensitive tape test is the problem of recontamination. It is not applicable for very small parts.

Anderson's report(*14*) on work being performed by Space Research Inc. is of particular interest to those persons concerned with the nonvolatile residue contaminant problem as opposed to the particulate contaminant problem. In the area of the nonvolatile residue contaminants, this organization has concentrated primarily on oils and greases normally found in the metal-working trades. During this work, a physical principle was uncovered that offers considerable promise for the general detection of extremely small amounts of surface contaminants. Stated in its simplest form, the principle is this:

The rate of evaporation of a volatile material from a surface is an inverse function of the amount of pre-existing contaminant. $R \backsim 1/C$, where R is the rate of evaporation, and C is the concentration of pre-existing contamination. Measurement of the evaporation rate of a volatile compound is made relatively easy through the use of a suitable radioactive labeled compound and a radiation detector. It was found that when a mildly volatile radioactive labeled compound was applied to a surface significantly more radioactivity was retained by a contaminated surface than by a clean one (see Fig. 11-12). Determination of the rate of evaporation (the slope of the counts-per-unit-time versus elapsed-time curve) gives a measure of the amount of contaminant on the surface: The steeper the slope, the cleaner is the surface.

The slope of the curve is a measure of the amount of pre-existing contaminant at any time during the test. Also, the contaminated surface will exhibit a greater amount of radioactivity than will the corresponding clean surface at any given time.

In discussing the rate of evaporation, Anderson states:

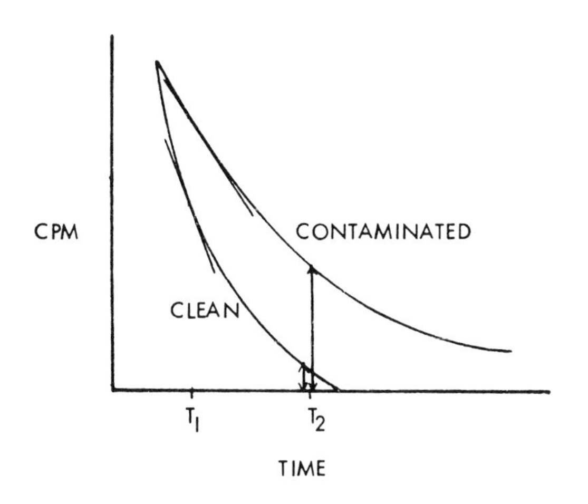

FIGURE 11-12. Evaporation rate from clean and contaminated surfaces. *Courtesy Journal of the American Association for Contamination Control*

The rate of evaporation from a surface depends primarily on the vapor pressure of the radiochemical, on the amount and rate of gas or air passing over the surface, on the probe design, on gas or air and surface temperatures, and . . . on the amount of contamination.

Except for the contamination, the factors are held constant under the conditions employed. For metal and other surfaces so far examined, the rate of evaporation appears to be largely independent of the surface finish.

The actual high sensitivity of this method depends also in part on the specific activity found in the radiochemical—that is, the amount of activity per unit weight. Artificially attainable specific activity for carbon-14 compounds provides the degree of activity which permits detection down to about 0.1 micrograms per square centimeter.

One of the prime considerations of the method is the thin film character of both the contaminant and the radiochemical.

Because thin films permit rapid diffusion into and out of each other, a profound mixing of the radiochemical and contaminant is almost instantaneous, even if the two are not chemically compatible.

This is in reference to the thin film characteristics of layers just a few molecules thick.[22]

For miscible and soluble systems, very rapid mixing and homogeneity are obtained. Even in nonmiscible systems, enough surface mixing and a type of heterogeneity that produces the same effect in at least a few of the surface layers are apparently obtained.

For the purpose of illustration, Figure 11-13 shows the molecules to be orderly and static. Actually, they are disorderly and in constant motion.

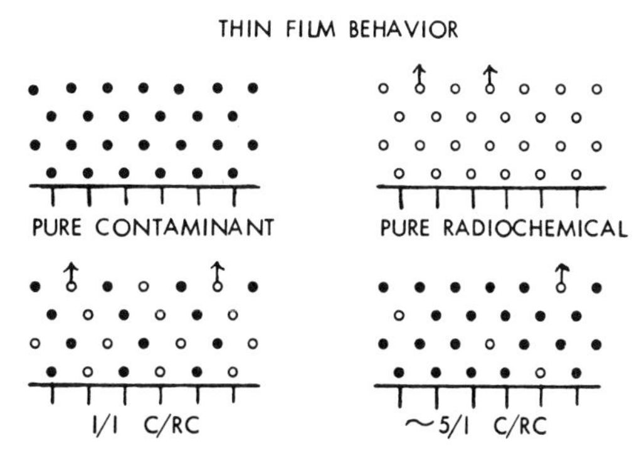

FIGURE 11-13. Thin-film behavior. *Courtesy Journal of the American Association for Contamination Control*

[22] Reference *14*, p. 11.

At any given instant, however, this particular example will be valid. Evaporation under mild air flow is primarily the escape of upper-surface molecules only. Down to the monolayer, the number of surface molecules is constant. At any given time after evaporation has started, the residual activity still detectable over a given surface area will be greater for the contaminated surface than for the clean one.

Because the observed rate of evaporation decreases with time, the sensitivity of the test increases, as can be seen in the accompanying chart.

SENSITIVITY COMPARISON*

Molecules/Unit Area				
C	*RC*	*Mixture*	*Surface*	*C/RC*
100,000	1,000,000	1,100,000	20,000	1/10
100,000	100,000	200,000	20,000	1/1
100,000	10,000	110,000	20,000	10/1
100,000	1,000	101,000	20,000	100/1
100,000	100	100,100	20,000	1000/1

*Courtesy *Journal of the American Association for Contamination Control.*

The nonvolatile contaminant-to-radiochemical ratio and its effect on the rate of evaporation become more critical with decreasing amounts of the radiochemical. Under constant control, the method is self-calibrating. It is suitable for both accessible and inaccessible surfaces. Equipment has been designed by Space Research Inc. to perform both types of tasks.

Accessible surfaces are easier to inspect than inaccessible ones. For accessible surfaces, a probe similar to the one illustrated in Figure 11-14 is used. The output of a ratemeter is plotted on a strip chart recorder to express the rate of evaporation directly. The surface to be examined is sprayed with a premeasured amount of a radiochemical from an aerosol package using a metering valve to deliver the proper amount. The probe is positioned over the sprayed area, and a maximum reading in counts per minute is established. Immediately, a constant flow of air is provided over the surface by an attachment to the probe, and the rate of evaporation is measured by plotting the decreasing amount of detectable activity on the spot being examined. The

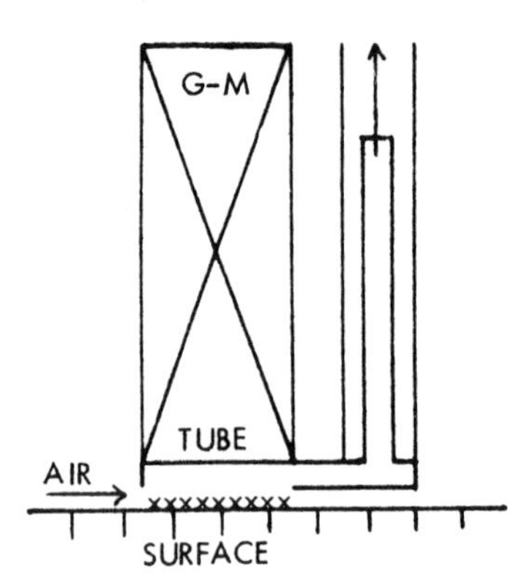

FIGURE 11-14. Inspection of accessible surfaces by means of a probe. *Courtesy Journal of the American Association for Contamination Control*

rate of evaporation is continually measured by plotting the counts per unit time against elapsed time. For accessible surfaces, the probe is set up substantially as shown. On larger components, this accessible surface test is used as a spot check. It can be used, too, as a virtually 100% inspection method for smaller components such as ball bearings, small gyros, and valve seats.

The second type of test is the inspection of inaccessible surfaces. Current evidence indicates that virtually all internal and external surfaces can now be inspected by this method.

Figure 11-15 gives an idea of this second method. To perform the inaccessible surface tests on small components, a container is held at ambient temperature plus 2° (T_2). It is loaded with the cleaned parts and evacuated or purged with dry nitrogen gas. Then, the container is filled with pure dry nitrogen gas which is saturated with respect to a slightly volatile gamma-emitting radiochemical at T_2. The system is permitted to stand for a controlled time, allowing a very small amount of the

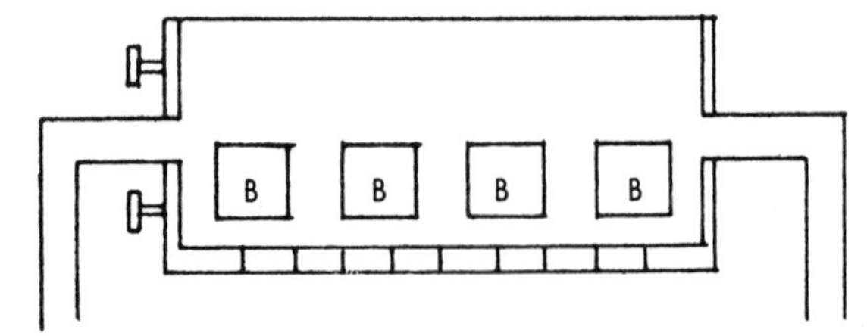

FIGURE 11-15. Inspection of inaccessible surfaces in a container. *Courtesy Journal of the American Association for Contamination Control*

radiochemical to condense uniformly on all surfaces. Then the container is re-evacuated or flushed with dry, pure nitrogen until the radiochemical deposited on the clean parts has evaporated to a previously established level. Finally, the container is examined for the presence and amount of radioactivity—and, therefore, contamination—by measuring the radioactivity through the walls of the container.

With this system, the internal surfaces of entire fuel systems can be inspected. The whole system is heated to T_2 with hit purge gas and then filled with a gas containing the radiochemical as a saturated component. When the system cools down, it is purged with pure gas. Contamination is detected by measuring the external surfaces with the detector.

The following information on the present practices in the verification of cleanliness was the result of a Sandia Corporation report.[23] Some of the cleanliness tests listed have been previously discussed. They are included again in this report. It is felt that this comprehensive listing should remain intact.

Summary

There are many known techniques for detecting contamination or, conversely, for verifying the relative cleanliness of the surface. However, there is no one method that can be used on all materials and for all types of contaminants. Few methods are suitable for production use and each of these is limited in application.

The present general approach to the verification of cleanliness is not easily defined. For highly reliable underseas cable repeater vacuum tubes, for example, parts are tested for cleanliness with the most sensitive techniques. For plating and painting, parts inspection involves observing water break as the part is removed from the last water rinse. Many sensitive components which are environmentally protected by the use of tight case joints, or gaskets, or hermetic sealing, get no more than visual inspection for cleanliness.

There is presently no definition of cleanliness or degree of cleanliness. An absolutely clean part is highly impractical if not impossible. Contamination goes on continually under even the most favorable environments and varies under different environments. There is also the question of how clean the part or functional surface under consideration should be. Vacuum tube components for critical applications require the utmost in cleanliness; electrical contacts have cleanliness requirements dependent on contact pressure, voltage, contact material, and operating conditions. Some precision ball bearings are preferably cleaned only to the point where an oily film remains for protection from rusting and for lubrication before the bearing is grease packed. The point is, that the degree of required cleanliness depends on the application. Overcleaning is unnecessarily expensive; conversely, insufficient cleaning may cause malfunction of the assembled component which obviously cannot be tolerated. To be able to verify that a part is "clean" or that a part is "not clean" is a most indefinite approach. There is a need for a quantitative measurement of cleanliness that can be used during processing and in preparing specifications that define the degree of required cleanliness.

[23] Abstracted from reference *15*.

Background

A contaminant may be defined as any material not called for by the product drawings, or it may be defined as material "out of place" or not necessary. It may or may not be detrimental. It is usually only a problem when it affects the function of a component.

The word "clean" in the term "a clean part" should mean a part with no contaminant on its surfaces. This is not possible, however, so it is used rather loosely to describe a part sufficiently clean to perform properly in its intended application.

Non-wettable (hydrophobic) contaminants consists of oils, fats, waxes, fatty acids and their salts, adsorbed gases, some organic solvents, dusts from the air, graphite, some carbons, and carbon residues.

Wettable (hydrophilic contaminants consist of metal oxides; most passive surfaces; scale; cleaning residues in the form of compounds with the metal, such as silicates and phosphates; and water-soluble acids, bases, and salts, such as alkaline-cleaner residues.

Lint, hair, finger nail polish, epidermal scale, rosin particles, talc, airborne algaes, metallic burrs, and dust, are just a few of the many types of particle contaminants. These are the contaminants that cause malfunction in parts fitted to microtolerances. Most of these contaminants can be detected by microscopic techniques at 4 to 50 magnification. Metallic burrs may be detected with a comparison microscope. Where individual particles are not detrimental, they may, however, conglomerate to sufficient size to cause trouble.

Before examining methods currently used to measure contamination, it might be of considerable help to list some of the most common contaminant sources (Table 11-3) and some of the most common processing faults which lead to contamination (Table 11-4).

Known Test Methods

The following descriptions of different tests for cleanliness are summarized in Table 11-5. As stated previously, there is no single procedure for detecting

TABLE 11–3

COMMON CONTAMINANT SOURCES

1. Silicone oil
2. Lubricants
3. Epoxy adhesives
4. Soldering and brazing fluxes
5. Outgassing
6. Sealing compounds
7. Corrosion products
8. Parting compounds
9. Molded parts
10. Paint coatings
11. Plating
12. Machining and finishing
13. Heat-treat processes
14. Wear particles
15. Component and piece-part storage
16. Processing
17. Handling
18. Ovens or furnaces

all contaminants. Each procedure has limitations; however, some tests are worthy of further consideration.

Visual

Visual inspection is the least sensitive and most commonly used method of inspection. It is effective only for visible contaminant and particulate matter. Invisible films cannot be detected by visual inspection. Magnification, up to 50X, helps to detect very small particulate matter and visible films; however, identification may not be possible.

Tissue Paper

It is claimed that routine estimation of cleanliness is possible by rubbing the cleaned surface with white tissue paper and then observing for grease or soot. Obviously, this technique is limited to visible soil and is a relatively insensitive qualitative test.

Water Break

One of the most commonly used tests for cleanliness is the water-break test. Water-film break is caused by the increase in contact angle that water makes with some water repellent material, generally of an oily or greasy nature (hydrophobic). There is a zero angle of contact with a clean surface or with a hydrophilic contaminant.

The water-break test is most frequently used during the last clean water rinse when the part is observed for water-break as the rinse water drains off. The receding contact angle of the water film with the part becomes visible, if the part is contaminated, when the water drains off the part and the film of water becomes thin enough for the contact angle to show. Any contaminant in the water makes the test less sensitive. Use of deionized water and careful technique may make this test sensitive to a single molecular thickness of contaminant.

Water Spray

The water-break test can be modified by spraying on water instead of dipping the component being tested. Presumably, this technique gives a more sensitive reading; however, this is probably because the water film is thinner.

Atomizer Test

The method of applying water and the preparation of the sample is quite a different process in the atomizer test than it is in the water-break test. The

TABLE 11–4

COMMON PROCESSING FAULTS

The following are common processing faults leading to contamination:

1. Handling or touching parts with bare fingers.
2. Touching inside of clean containers with bare fingers.
3. Using improper wrapping materials.
4. Using uncovered parts containers for storage or transfer.
5. Using dirty parts containers.
6. Using improper parts containers (sealing methods).
7. Using dirty drying ovens.
8. Using improper clothing on operators.
9. Using dust-catching work areas.
10. Using contaminated solvent or overusing cleaning solutions.
11. Misusing ultrasonic cleaning machines.
12. Using improperly distilled solvents.
13. Purchasing solvents in too large quantities.
14. Using the wrong type of solvent containers (allow contamination).
15. Using the wrong solder flux.
16. Over-oiling tools and equipment.
17. Mixing sealing compounds improperly and overusing or misusing.
18. Storing parts in solvent. (The solvent may react to make contaminants left on the part insoluble.)

Table 11–5

SUMMARY OF TEST FOR CLEANLINESS

Test	*Any Soil*	*Hydrophobic Only*	*Laboratory*	*Production*	*Very Sensitive*	*Sensitive*	*Relatively Insensitive*	*Expensive*	*Not Expensive*	*Method of Verification Available: Good Quantitative*	*Method of Verification Available: Visual Qualitative*	*Method of Verification Available: None*	*Limitation*
Visual				X					X			X	Visible soil
Tissue paper				X			X		X			X	
Water break		X		X		X			X			X	Hydrophobic contaminants only
Water spray		X		X		X			X			X	
Atomizer		X		X	X				X		X		
Contact angle		X	X			X			X		X		
Rock Island drop		X	X			X			X		X		
Ring test		X	X			X			X			X	
Kerosine		X	X		X				X			X	
Radioactive tracer	X		X		X			X		X			Laboratory specimens only
Gravimetric	X		X			X			X	X			
Fluorescent dye	X		X				X		X			X	
Ferricyanide paper			X				X					X	Ferrous Parts only
Mear's (Elm's modification)							X					X	
Copper dip	X			X		X			X			X	
Oil spot				X			X		X			X	Grease-Type contaminant
Solvent test	X			X		X			X			X	Limited to solvent used

part surface is completely dried at room temperature before spraying, and therefore shows a pattern determined by the value of the advancing contact angle, which is always larger than the receding angle. In the atomizer test, the water droplets arrive as fine, discrete droplets, and therefore, show less tendency than the relatively heavy water film present in the water-break test to cover and obscure small contaminated areas. However, it is said that considerable experience and training are required for interpretation of the droplet pattern.

When hydrophobic contaminants are absent, the metal will wet continuously. There is no interface contact angle between the water and the metal. When hydrophobic contaminants are present, the water will form a medium to high contact angle with the surface of the metal (the result of not wetting the surface and spreading) and will tend to remain as fine droplets. When there are traces of contaminant, probably a fraction of a monolayer, a transitional pattern, both wetted and non-wetted, appears.

Some of the variables in the atomizer test are:

1. Spray time is 3 to 30 seconds. If spray time is too short, the pattern does not develop. If spray time is too long, too much water will spill over and obscure the pattern. The pattern develops in about 30 to 45 seconds.
2. The spray nozzle-to-part distance is 18 to 24 inches. If the nozzle is held too close to the part, the droplet distribution will be uneven. If this distance is too great, minor air currents may affect the spray.
3. Too low an air pressure will cause a coarse, uneven pattern. Too high an air pressure causes the pattern to develop too rapidly and causes droplet run-off.
4. This test should be performed at room temperature. Temperatures higher than room temperature will cause oil spread and evaporation of tiny droplets on contact with the part or panel.

It is claimed than an oriented layer of fatty acids and oils, even less than one complete layer thick, can cause water droplets to form. Table 11-6 is a quantitative comparison of the sensitivity of the atomizer test compared to the sensitivity of the water-break test.

It is claimed that the extreme sensitivity of the atomizer test requires a test procedure to verify the technique. A freshly cleaved mica surface contains no hydrophobic contaminant. A drop of 0.05 percent fatty acid in acetone is placed in the center of this surface. The acetone evaporates. This will show a contaminated spot in an otherwise clean field. If the field does not test clean, it means that there is contaminant in the equipment. If the spot does not appear, the area has been flooded by too much water, a condition indicative of incorrect operation of the atomizer.

Device components with plane surfaces as small as 0.125 inch in one direction and wires as fine as 0.015 inch in diameter are being examined routinely by the atomizer test methods. As a matter of practicability, these examinations are made at 5X to 40X magnification depending upon the size of the surface being tested. Corrosion-resisting steels and gold cannot be inspected by atomizer testing because a water-break pattern does not show.

Contact Angle

This test involves the measurement of contact angle or angle of incidence of a droplet of water on the test surface. A light beam is directed into the droplet and the angle of the beam reflected from the droplet indicates the contact angle. It is claimed that this technique will detect oil with an accuracy of 0.01 percent. It is effective only on nonwetting or hydrophobic contaminants.

Rock Island Drop

Distilled water droplets are allowed to fall from a given height to the panel surface being tested; then the diameter of the droplet is measured. This test will distinguish between a clean panel and one soiled with a 0.01 percent oil solution. It is not clear just what mini-

TABLE 11–6

QUANTITATIVE COMPARISON OF SENSITIVITY OF TESTS

	Minimum Amount of Soil Detectable			
	Water-Break Test		*Atomizer Test*	
Substance	*Grams per Square Centimeter*	*Molecular Layers*	*Grams per Square Centimeter*	*Molecular Layers*
Stearic acid	1.1×10^{-7}	0.5	0.16×10^{-7}	0.075
Oleic acid	1.5×10^{-7}	1.5	0.18×10^{-7}	0.18
Lard oil	6.7×10^{-7}	5.3	0.67×10^{-7}	0.53
Mineral oil	90×10^{-7}	—	3.0×10^{-7}	—

mum amount of soil can be detected. It is undoubtedly difficult to determine the exact edges of the droplets and there would seem to be some question on what the droplet diameters should be.

Ring Test

In this test, a drop of water is formed on a surface tension tester ring. Then the ring is lowered to touch the test surface. The process of repeatedly touching the test surface is continued until the entire drop of water is transferred. The number of contacts, called B-number, is used as a measure of wettability.

Kerosine Viewing of Water Break

After withdrawing from the water in the water-break test the panel is immediately submerged in a transparent container of kerosine which is lighted from the bottom. Near water breaks are displaced by kerosine. It is claimed that this test is equal in sensitivity to the atomizer test. However, it can only be considered as a special laboratory technique because the kerosine would normally be a contaminant. The test is sensitive only to nonwettable contaminants.

Radioactive Tracer

The latest advance in the detection of soil retained by metal surfaces is the radioactive tracer technique. It is essentially the most sensitive of the quantitative methods now available. However, this technique does not use existing soil. A specific composition of radioactive soil is applied to a test piece. Then the cleaning process under study is applied to the test piece, and the difference between initial count and final count indicates the effectiveness of the cleaning process. The sensitivity of this method has been measured as 2×10^{-7} g/cm^2. In this test, the soiling composition was comprised of the following materials:

Lubricating oil, SAE No. 60	97 percent
Fluorescent Green HW 175 percent	2 percent
N_1 N_1-di-*n*-butyl stearamide	1 percent

The radioactive tracer method is subject to a number of corrections and requires statistical treatment of the data.

The method for calculating the amount of soil remaining is as follows:

$$\frac{\text{Final count}}{\text{Initial count}} \times \frac{\text{mg of initial soil}}{\text{area of pan or test panel}} = \text{soil remaining}$$

It is claimed that the sensitivity of the radioactive tracer test can be pushed back indefinitely by improved technique since the test has no inherent limit of sensitivity.

Gravimetric

This is a method for estimation of the degree of cleanliness by weighing the metal piece being cleaned before and after the cleaning process. This is essentially a laboratory method because the same price must be weighed before and after cleaning. The sensitivity is dependent on the sensitivity of the balance and the size of the piece, but it is usually 5×10^{-5} gm per sq cm with a very sensitive balance.

This method may be varied by weighing the soil. The part or panel is cleaned with solvent and then the solvent is allowed to evaporate or is boiled away. The remaining soil is weighed.

Fluorescent Dye

An oil soluble fluorescent dye is mixed in an oily soil. A measured amount is used to soil a panel. After cleaning, the retained soil is observed under ultraviolet light. It is claimed this method is not sensitive to a 0.1 percent solution of oil in naphtha applied to a panel. Essentially this is a test of cleaning efficiency using a single contaminant. It is therefore, a laboratory technique.

Ferrocyanide Paper

Suitable paper is immersed in a solution of NaCl, $K_3Fe(CN)_6$ and $K_4Fe(CN)_6$ in water and then dried. The paper is then moistened and placed in contact with the metal surface being tested. After removal, the paper is rinsed in clear water. Soiled spots on the metal provide clear areas on the paper. This test is effective only on ferrous metals.

Elm's Modification of the Mear's Test

A solution of 32 ml of hydroxyl (30 percent H_2O_2) in 1 liter of distilled water is used. Single drops of this solution are placed on selected areas and the time required for the first appearance of corrosion spots is measured. Accurate detection of these spots requires proper adjustment of the illumination. This test was insensitive to the oil film left from the application of a 0.5 percent oil in naphtha solution.

Copper Dip

Cleaned and rinsed metal test panels are dipped into an acid copper sulfate solution. This is the same as the application of a copper flash. The continuity and adherence of the copper plate is an indication of the cleanliness. This is applicable only to ferrous metals and requires good judgment by the operator.

Oil-Spot

In the oil-spot test, a drop of solvent dropped and picked up with a pipette is used to degrease an area the size of the drop. This drop of solvent is then observed as it evaporates on ground glass. An evaporation ring gives evidence of oil. The limit of this test is said to be 5×10^{-3} grams per sq cm of soil.

Solvent

Any contaminant that can be removed by a solvent can be detected by this method. The technique consists of repeatedly depositing and picking up a drop of solvent on the contaminated surface. This method of agitation improves the concentration of contaminant in the drop. Some of the many solvents that may be used are acetone, benzine, carbon tetrachloride, anyl acetate, ether, and chloroform. When examining very small contacts, drop size may be controlled by using a capillary dropper.

The solvent drop is observed for contaminant rings as it evaporates. This may be done on a clean glass slide, on a quartz slide, or on the surface from which the contaminant was accumulated. If done on a quartz slide, it may subsequently be used for infra-red analysis.

Being able to use the contaminant deposit for identification is an important advantage in the application of this technique. The infra-red spectrophotomer makes a wavelength spectrum of the minute quantity of contaminant deposited on the quartz slide. The spectrum is an indication of the structure of the material and may be identified by comparison with the spectrum of a known material. For example, if the unknown contaminant is suspected to be an epoxy, a spectrum of epoxy can be compared with the spectrum of the unknown for identification. It may be advisable to first observe the spectrum of the solvent for impurities in the solvent. Allowance is made for these impurities when identifying the contaminant.

Particulate Contaminant

Particulate contaminants may be detected under a microscope but their study is difficult on an opaque surface. According to L. K. Jones, a method developed at Bell Telephone Laboratories has proved effective. In this method, a thin film of polyvinyl chloride is carefully placed between the contacts and a slight pressure is applied. The contacts are heated to about 240°F for a few minutes and then allowed to cool to room temperature. The vinyl sheet is then carefully removed. The particulate contaminants will be embedded in the vinyl sheet. Having the contaminants on the transparent replica enables the microscopist to use any type of illumination he may need, thus removing the guesswork involved in identification on smooth metal surfaces by reflected light. The identification may be made by optical properties, or by selected microchemical tests. The replica technique is usually of little value in the identification of various organic films and some organic particulate contaminants. Some of these contaminants will sublime at a temperature lower than that of the replica exposure temperature.

Process Control

Admittedly, process control is not a cleanliness test; however, it is one of the most widely used methods of verifying cleanliness. Where cleanliness requirements are severe, both close process control and cleanliness tests may be used. Monitoring of cleaning processes should be based on the requirements of specifications. A cleaning process defined by an approved specification is usually a tested process that can be depended upon to provide parts sufficiently clean for the intended application. Furthermore, if a cleaning technique meets an approved specification and contamination is still a problem, the contamination may be introduced somewhere in the assembly line. Verification of cleanliness in this category, therefore, includes observation of the entire component assembly line.

Specifications

Federal

Federal specification TT-C-490 covers Cleaning Methods and Pretreatment of Ferrous Surfaces for Organic Coatings. In the section on tests for removal of soils and corrosion products, the requirement is that "the items, test specimens, or panels, for test purposes after removal from the final rinse, shall be rinsed in running water and the surfaces then examined for discontinuity of the water film (water break). The surface should then be dried and examined visually for rust, corrosion products, and soils. If the water film is discontinuous or the surface shows signs of corrosion products, corrective action shall be taken. Inspection for acceptance shall be stopped until corrective action has been taken. After corrective action, testing shall be continued at least once every hour until the water film maintains its continuity."

ASTM

There are four known ASTM specifications that have required or suggested tests to indicate cleanliness.

ASTM-B183 on Preparing Low Carbon Steel for Electroplating states that there is no completely reliable test to ascertain that the surface of the steel part has been properly prepared other than its behavior under conditions of service. However, this specification does give four "desirable" tests:

1. Before plating the part may be inspected for smut on the surface by wiping it with a clean white cloth, and observing any darkening of the cloth.
2. A water-break test may best be made after pickling or acid dipping since the presence of alkali may mask its appearance.
3. Parts may be inspected under ultraviolet light. Mineral oil film fluoresces brightly under ultraviolet or "black" light.
4. Parts may be removed from the plating solutions and inspected after a few seconds of plating. A surface free from oil and grease will show a uniform color. Patchy areas or wavy dark lines indicate incomplete cleaning.

ASTM-B320 on Preparation of Iron Castings for Electroplating states that "The most reliable test of the effectiveness of the preplating cleaning cycle is the appearance of the plated part and its performance in service. A *none too reliable*, but commonly used, test for the removal of greases and oils is the inspection for water breaks. This is best done after pickling or acid-dipping, as an alkali film may mask a water break. Wiping a part with a clean white cloth just prior to entry into the plating bath will reveal whether or not smut has been removed. An inspection of parts after just a few seconds of plating may reveal either a uniform color, indicating a clean surface, or blotchy areas, indicating incomplete cleaning."

ASTM-A380 on Descaling and Cleaning Stainless Steel Surfaces calls for "visual inspection for evidence of paint, oil, grease, welding slag, heat treating scale, iron rust, or other forms of contamination. Inspection for metallic iron or iron oxide remaining on a stainless steel surface is also done visually within 24 hours after the final acid and water rinse treatments. The inspector looks for rust stains. These stains may be accelerated by intermittent wetting and drying during the 24-hour period. This is considered a practical method for most fabricators but much more sensitive methods are available. However, these are hypersensitive tests that should be used and interpreted only by trained personnel. The tests are designated as: (1) Potassium Ferricyanide—Nitric Acid Solution; (2) Aceto-Acetanilide Solution; and (3) Copper Sulfate."

ASTM-B322 is a general specification on Cleaning Metals Prior to Electroplating. Under a heading *Criteria of Cleanliness*, this specification calls for, "a water break test after a final rinse in clear cool water." This document further emphasizes that some experience is necessary to judge the appearance of a break in the film of water. A dip in clean dilute acid and re-examination is desirable to avoid false water film continuity caused by adsorbed soaps. Other methods, including plating and testing of the plating, should be used occasionally to confirm visual observations. One procedure that is suggested, involves scrubbing with pumice and then comparing the surface produced by this good, "though almost obsolete," method with that produced under production conditions.

New Developments and Research

Coulter Principle

The particles to be measured and counted are suspended in an electrically conductive liquid. The Coulter principle involves forcing this liquid to flow through an aperture with a simultaneous flow of electrical current. Particles passing through the aperture with the electric current cause electrical pulses. Each pulse is proportional in magnitude to the volume of the particle causing it. The pulses are amplified, scaled, and counted to provide direct data for plotting cumulative particle frequency against particle size. The overall particle size ranges from about 0.6 micron to over 200 microns; however, a specific aperture diameter is effective on particles up to 40 to 50 percent of the aperture diameter.

Electron Microscope

In an informative report on contamination of contacts *(Study of Effects and Control of Surface Contaminants on Electrical Materials)* some outstanding results are reported using an electron microscope to detect contamination. This technique requires a replica of the surface to be studied and a method is used which does not disturb or affect contaminants. The surface is coated with a drop of 15 percent solution of polyvinylalcohol (PVA) in water. This viscous liquid has no appreciable solvent action on nonpolar organics. The coating is dried under a 100-watt lamp and is then easily stripped from the surface for study. The coating is placed on a glass slide, replica side up, shadowed in a vacuum evaporator, first with palladium at an angle of 30 degrees from the horizontal, and then with carbon from directly overhead. The shadowed replica is then floated on the surface of warm water with the PVA side down; it dissolves in about 30 minutes. The carbon-plus-palladium film is left floating on the surface of the water. The electron microscope grid (200 mesh, ⅛-inch diameter) is used to lift the replica film out of the water. After drying, the replica, in position on the grid as lifted out of the water, is ready for observation and photographing in the electron microscope.

Probe Instrument

Results were also given in the above referenced report on contact contamination measurement with a specially developed probe instrument. The probe consists of a 2-mil platinum wire which is moved slowly, stopping intermittently, over the specific surface being tested, at a contact force of 8–10 mg. The IR drop at the probe-surface junction (20 mv, 10 μa) is amplified by a standing wave amplifier and recorded. Part of this amplified voltage is used to charge a resistance-capacitance type of integrator. Thus, for each traverse across a specific surface, an integrator value is obtained which is a figure-of-merit reflecting the cleanness of the specific surface. One disadvantage cited in Chaikin's report with regard to the probe contact is that a fluid deposit will not prevent metal-to-metal contact. Another is that probe measurement yields an integrated figure summing the voltage drop across the specific surface, as a function of time, and does not indicate instantaneous resistance during the course of a traverse unless reference is made to the recorder chart and the oscilloscope.

Rate of Evaporation of Suitable Volatile Radioactive Tracers

A new technique for quantitative detection of surface contaminants has been reported by John L. Anderson, Ph. D., Space Research Inc., Orlando, Florida. Pre-existing organic contaminants on a metal surface can be detected by measuring the rate of evaporation of suitable volatile radioactive tracers under controlled conditions. The rate of evaporation is an inverse function of the amount of preexisting contaminant. The tracer is applied in extremely small quantities (less than a microgram per square centimeter) and analysis of the rate of evaporation against standards permits quantitative detection of very small amounts of organic contaminants. Studies are not complete, but the lower limit of detectability may be less than a monomolecular layer.

Research

At the Armour Research Foundation, much work is being done to find a new technique of contamination detection and measurement. The following information has been reported on this work:

In the study of hydrocarbon contamination levels in trichloroethylene cleaning fluids, they are studying ellipsometry at the critical angle for infra-red light. A sample cell consisted of a pair of semicylindrical flint glass shell vials cemented side by side to one face of an equilateral flint glass prism. Glass–liquid interfaces for sample and reference solutions were observed at the critical angle, using a spectroscope equipped with polarizers. The sensitivity of this method has, so far, proved less than that desired. Near infra-red absorption analysis of contaminated trichloroethylene solutions is also being studied with somewhat more successful results than the ellipsometry method. Long-path absorption spectra were recorded on a spectrometer for trichloroethylene and u-dodecane to locate the bands most suitable for the polarimetric analysis. Resolvable bands of these two substances were sufficiently intense to suggest the possibility of direct analysis of trichloroethylene solutions to the required 5 mg/liter. This study is being continued.

Another technique which would develop a method of direct analysis of contaminated surfaces is called "flash photolysis." The method is applicable only to the inside surfaces of LOX tanks or other components of sufficient size that a flash tube with reflector housing and connecting coaxial cable can be placed inside. Average surface contamination or specific surface contamination can be determined. There are variables which require experimental answers before the reliability of this technique can be assessed.

The increased retention of selected test vapors by contaminated metal surfaces is being studied for measurement by both vapor absorption and vapor desorption. Vapor absorption is being measured by gas chromatography. The decreased rate of desorption of test vapors from contaminated metal surfaces has been demonstrated. A vacuum technique is involved. Detection is not sufficiently sensitive, but various avenues are being investigated.

Work is also under way to develop a technique of contaminant film detection by charge injection. Potentials of 500–2000 volts are used. The course of charge decay is monitored by an oscilloscope sweeping at 1 cm/sec. A recorder is connected to the oscilloscope's vertical output and prints once every 2 seconds. Greasy surfaces show decay half-times on the order of 5–10 minutes. Clean surfaces have half-times which can not be detected in the limits of measurement (~0.2 sec). Means are being evaluated for improving the sensitivity.

Studies are also being made on detection of contaminants in compressed gases. Methods involve: (1) the use of a corona discharge, (2) a capacitance procedure, and (3) detection by chromatography with readout on a rapid-scan oscilloscope.

REFERENCES

1. LIEBERMAN, ALVIN. "Cleanliness versus Need." *Conference on Clean Room Specifications.* SCR-652. Office of Technical Services, Department of Commerce, Washington, D. C., May 1963.

2. BULAT, T. J. "Decontaminating Fluid Systems." *Journal of the American Association for Contamination Control,* Vol. II, No. 4, (April 1963).

3. CHAIKIN, S. W., et al. *Review of Scientific Instruments,* Vol. 32, p. 1294 (1961).

4. SCHETKY, L. McD. *Product Engineering,* Vol. 31, p. 51 (August 1960).

5. LIEBERMAN, ALVIN. *Contamination Effects Study.* ARF 3216-5. Chicago, Ill.: Armour Research Foundation, November 1962. Prepared for Sandia Corp., Albuquerque, N. Mex.

6. BIONDI, F. J. *Bell Laboratories Record,* Vol. 36, No. 8, p. 288 (August 1958).

7. BILD, C. F. "Contamination Control–Cleaning and Verification." *Conference on Clean Room Specifications.* SCR-652. Office of Technical Services, Department of Commerce, Washington, D.C., May 1963.

8. DUMONT, L. F. "Cleaning Precision Bearings with 'Freon Solvents'." *Solvent Bulletin FS12.* Wilmington, Del.: E. I. DuPont de Nemours & Company, 1960.

9. BULAT, T. J. *Evaluation of Sonic Energy Cleaning.* Presented at Western Electric Show and Conference, San Francisco, Calif., 1960.

10. BERRY, L. M., et al. *Contact Resistance and the Effect of Materials and Process Variables on Contact Reliability in Switching Devices.* SCTM 73A-60(16). Albuquerque, N. Mex.: Sandia Corp., February 1960.

11. HARRIS, M. A. *Proceedings of the Institute of Mechanical Engineers,* Vol. 172, p. 759 (1958).

12. *STP No. 246*. Symposium on Cleaning of Electronic Device Components and Materials. Philadelphia, Pa.: American Society for Testing and Material, October 1958.

13. BULAT, T. J. "Evaluating Sonic Energy Cleaning." *Air Engineering*, Vol. 4, No. 6, p. 32 (1962).

14. ANDERSON, J. L. "A Practical Technique for Quantitative Detection of Surface Contaminants." *Journal of the American Association for Contamination Control.* Vol. II, No. 6, (June 1963).

15. HOF, G. J. *Present Practices in the Verification of Cleanliness*. SCTM 147-63(25). Albuquerque, N. Mex.: Sandia Corp, September 1963.

Chapter 12. *Clean Work Station Design*

Introduction

Soon after it became apparent that conventional clean rooms could not produce the control necessary for the manufacture of sophisticated components, the "dust-free" hood was developed. (See Figure 12-1.) The purpose of these hoods was to exclude airborne contaminants and thus allow assembling or other operations to be performed in a near dust-free atmosphere. The design of these cabinets in many cases did not consider air-flow patterns inside the hood. Filtered air was forced in at some point through some size opening, and it exited through some other point which was equally unimportant as to size or shape.

The result was that, although these hoods achieved very low contamination levels (depending on the type of filtration), the problem of contamination generated while operations were being performed inside the hood was not solved. Contaminants so generated moved about in the turbulent air and found their way out of the hood only at random intervals. In spite of this, the dust-free hood did allow a degree of cleanliness not attainable in a conventional room.

Some of the better-designed dust-free cabinets were constructed with a "curtain effect" at the hood opening. (See Figure 12-2.) This curtain of air, usually directed down from the top across the slanting hood face, was intended to shield the inside of the hood from outside contaminants. This type of hood produced a better-controlled atmosphere than its counterparts, but it still did not perform satisfactorily in relation to contaminants released inside the hood.

Another design that has achieved superior cleanliness levels is the completely enclosed hood or "glove box." (See Figure 12-3.) Recirculation of the air will yield low contamination levels. This type of design has the definite disadvantage of requiring the operator to work through arm ports, usually with attached gloves. Most of the glove-box type of equipment also did not consider contaminants generated inside the box. Random air currents did not assure that the particles would be captured in any given length of time. Some of the newer, completely enclosed units are designed to produce essentially laminar-flow air patterns in the

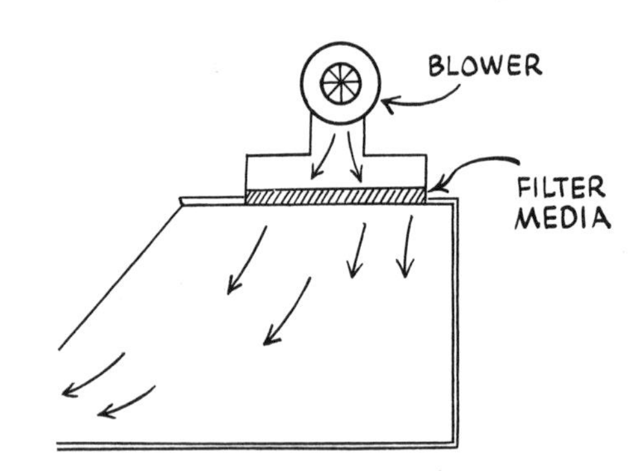

FIGURE 12-1. Bench-mounted dust-free hood.

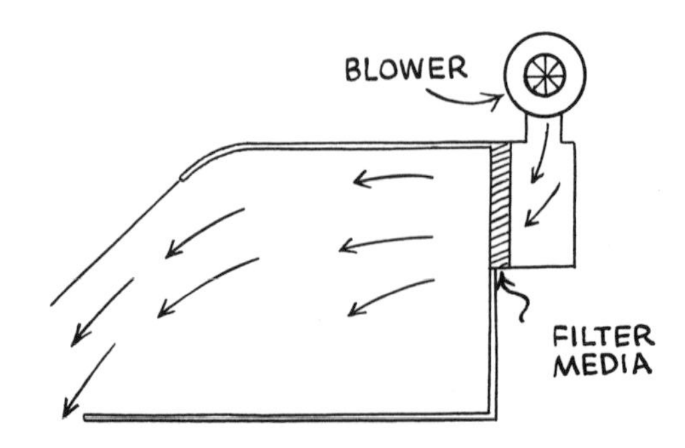

FIGURE 12-2. Bench-mounted curtain-effect hood.

working area. This will allow operation-generated particulate matter to be immediately captured. Some units are also being constructed with flexible polyvinyl chloride coverings which allow a great deal of freedom of movement in spite of the glove ports. Where a need exists for complete segregation of an atmosphere (because of toxicity, expense, etc.), this type of unit should prove very satisfactory.

Clean Work Stations[1]

An outgrowth of the original laminar-flow room developed by Sandia Corporation is the clean bench or clean work station. The clean bench provides a

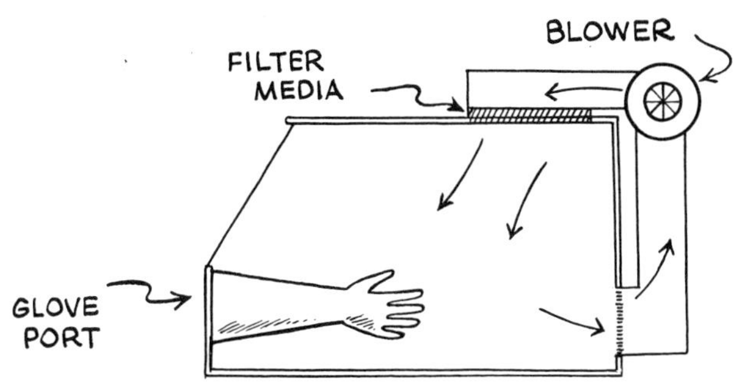

FIGURE 12-3. Bench-mounted glove box with recirculating atmosphere.

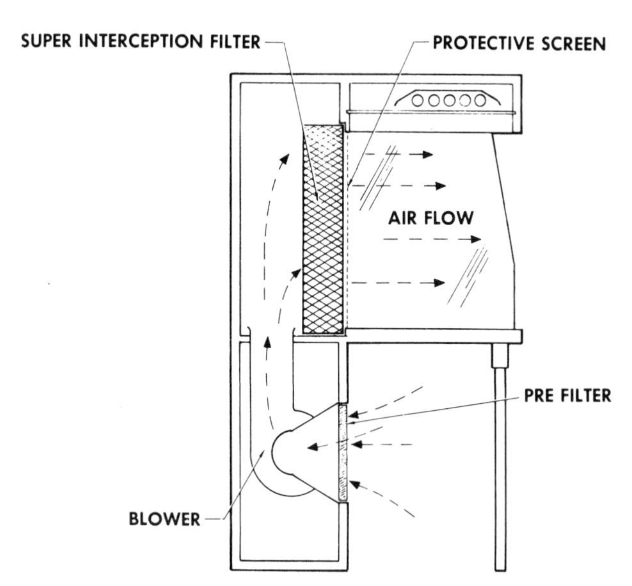

FIGURE 12-4. Cross-sectional view of laminar-flow clean work station. *Courtesy Sandia Corp.*

[1] Parts abstracted from reference *1*.

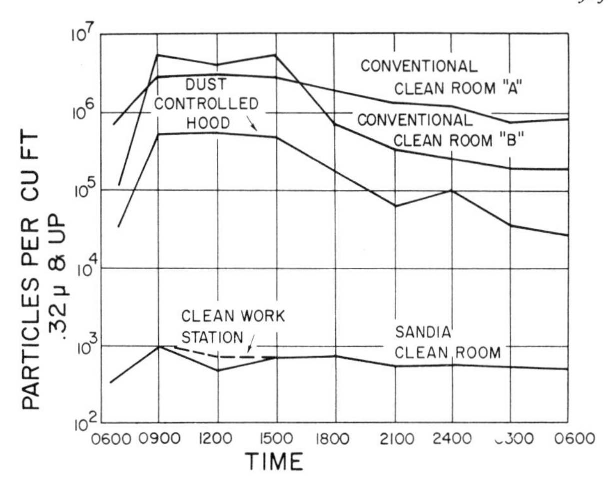

FIGURE 12-5. Dust level chart showing the comparison between the Sandia laminar-flow clean room and a clean work station. *Courtesy Sandia Corp.*

super-clean work area without the expense imposed by the construction of a complete room. Prior to the introduction of the clean work station, a superior cleanliness level was achieved by using dust-controlled hoods. As mentioned above, these hoods had two major disadvantages: (1) they restricted the workers' freedom of movement, and (2) the airflow patterns did not immediately eliminate contamination that might be generated within the unit. The primary function of the air flow was to exclude outside contaminants from the work area. Contaminants, once inside the hood, were not moved out of the work area immediately, but moved about inside the hood at random.

In developing a new dust-controlled hood, the design objectives were directed toward correcting these deficiencies. The new design must not restrict the worker's movement, and it must have a very rapid recovery rate. The rapid recovery rate suggested bathing the work area with clean air. The nonrestricting requirement necessitated an open-face bench. It logically followed that such a design would operate on principles similar to those employed in a laminar-flow room. By placing a super-interception filter as close as possible to the work place, it was possible to bathe the work area in super-clean laminar-flow air. A self-contained air-handling system was built around this idea. Air intakes were placed below the working surface, and a blower was installed inside the bench. This blower

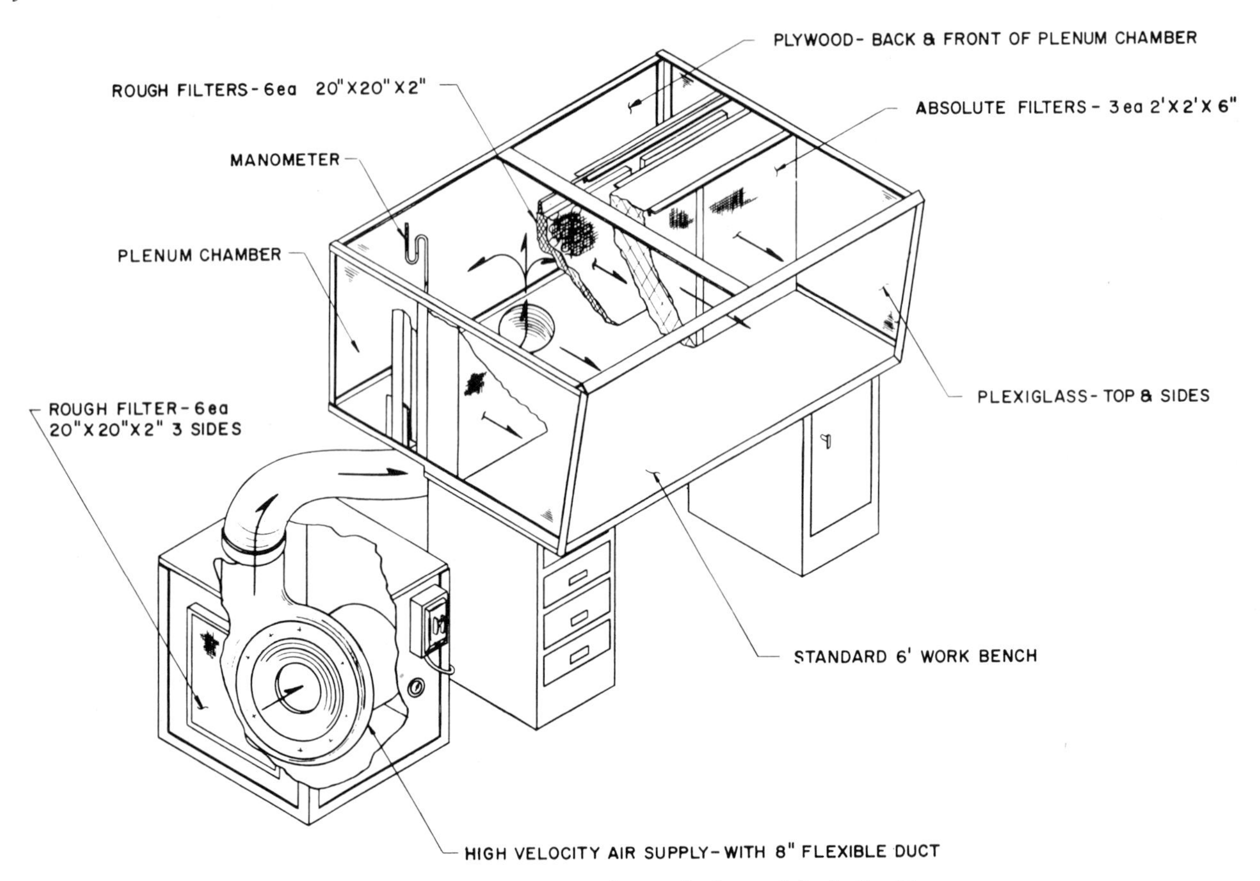

FIGURE 12-6. Isometric view of the original Sandia clean work station. *Courtesy Sandia Corp.*

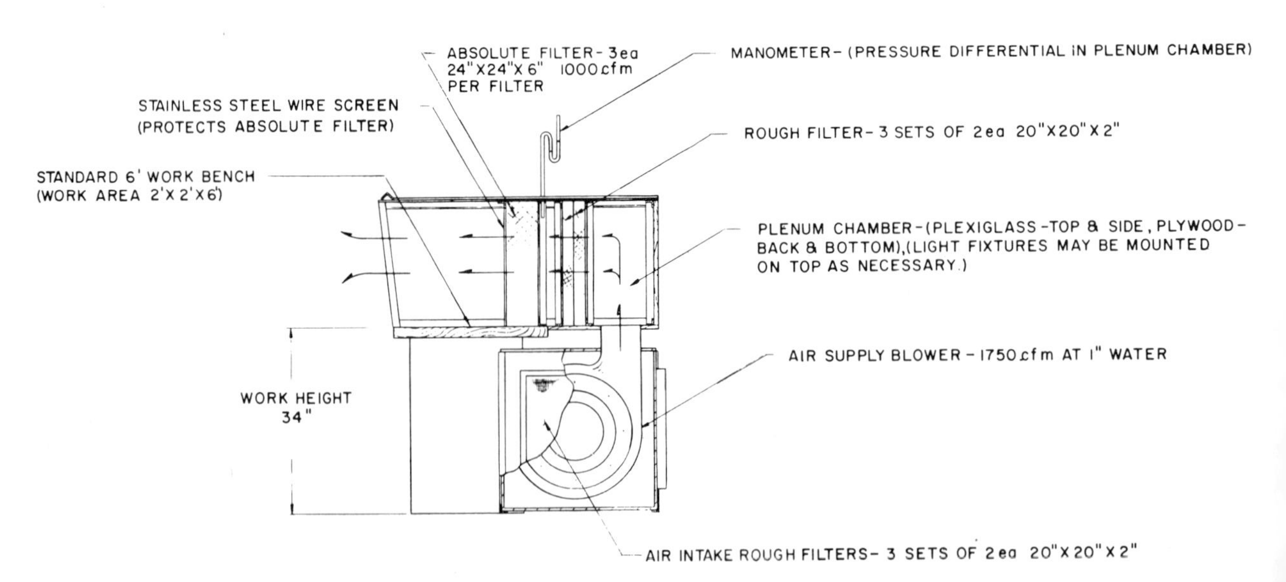

FIGURE 12-7. Cross-sectional view of the original Sandia clean work station. *Courtesy Sandia Corp.*

pressurized a plenum chamber immediately behind the filter, forcing the air through the filter and producing an even pressure of super-clean air at the face of the filter. Since the air flow is confined by the top, sides, and working surface of the bench, and since the air inlet and exit to the space formed each has an area equal to the cross section of the confined space, laminar flow is produced. (See Figure 12-4.) It should be stressed that these design features are essential to producing laminar flow. A cross-sectional flow area at the inlet or at the filter face that is smaller than that of the cross-sectional area at the work surface will produce a "nozzle effect" with subsequent expansion of the air stream at the downstream side of the throat of the nozzle. This expansion will cause bending of the air flow on the outer edges of the "nozzle," which will produce vortex or turbulent flow in that area. Such an effect will disrupt laminar flow. Since the air-flow pattern cannot be predicted, the cleanliness level of such a unit will be unpredictable also. This is primarily due to the mixing of generated contaminants back into the clean air stream.

The clean work station was to have the capability of operating outside a clean room; therefore, prefilters were added to filter the incoming air to

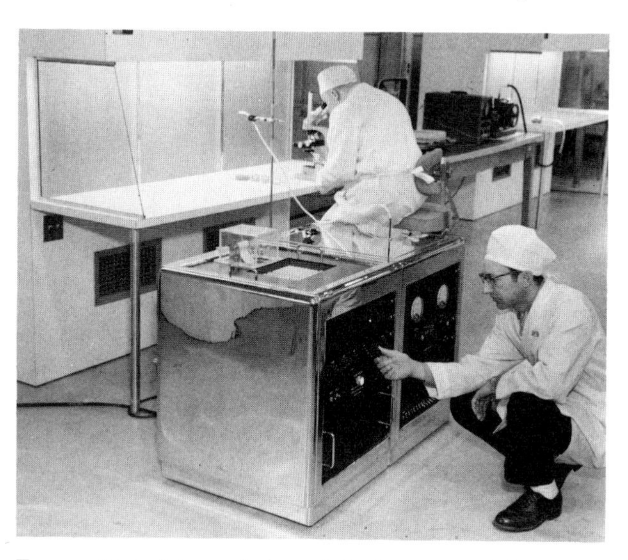

FIGURE 12-8. Two of the original commercially available clean work stations in use at the Olmsted AFB clean room laboratory. Note Royco particle counter in foreground. *Courtesy MAMES, Olmsted AFB, Pa.*

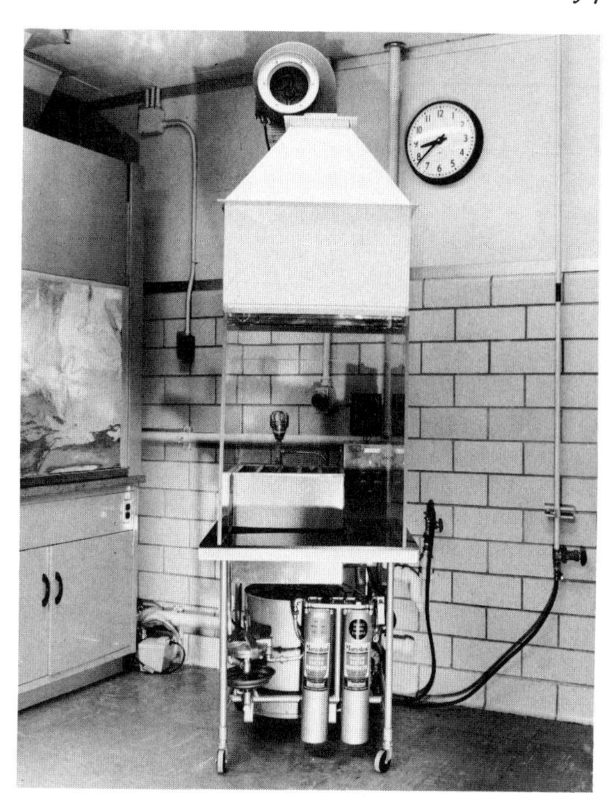

FIGURE 12-9. Experimental vertical-flow clean work station for protecting a high-purity deionized water washing unit. *Courtesy Sandia Corp.*

eliminate large-size particles and prolong the life of the HEPA filter. One of the most successful prefilters is a ½-inch-thick polyurethane expanded foam sheet. This sheet can be vacuumed with ease or washed in a mild detergent and wrung out like a sponge. Good design will allow the prefilters to be cleaned without disturbing the HEPA filter and without requiring access to the rear of the unit. Front removal of the HEPA filter is also desirable.

The atmosphere produced by this bench is potentially as clean as that developed by the Sandia laminar-flow room. (See Figure 12-5.) Care must be exercised, however, when using the bench in an uncontrolled area. Since filters are percentage devices, they will pass a greater number of particles when filtering dirtier atmospheres. It is also necessary to protect the work area with an overhead surface to prevent large particles from falling out onto the bench. This can be done by designing the bench with an overhead surface that is even with, or pro-

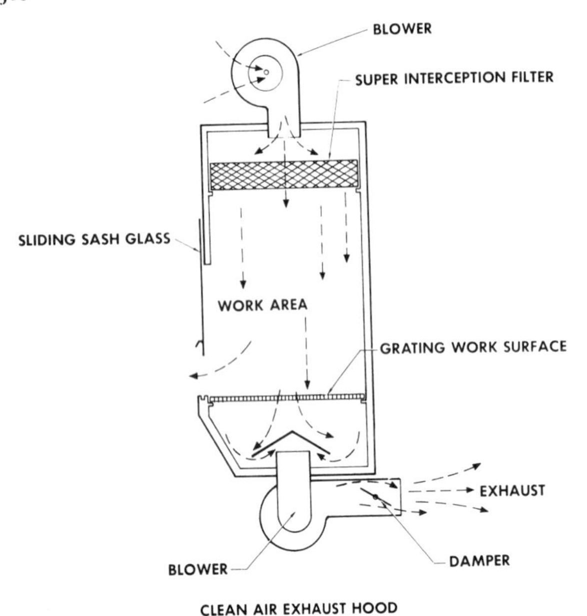

FIGURE 12-10. Cross-sectional view of clean air exhaust hood. *Courtesy Sandia Corp.*

trudes in front of, the working surface. The use of the bench will almost eliminate the problem of a critical-size particle's landing in a critical area. The laminar flow produced will give any particle generated in the bench only one pass at the component. Special work techniques to prevent transfer contamination are still necessary and, in fact, are especially important when the bench is used in an uncontrolled area.

The level of cleanliness acnieved by a clean work station is in the range of 100 particles per cubic foot, 0.5 micron and larger. The level is so low that it is almost impossible to get a particle count on an automatic counter. This presents a problem when checking to determine if the clean work station is performing satisfactorily. Also, since the air flow is laminar, the counter will monitor only the streamline in which the intake is placed. There could be a great deal of contamination in another streamline, and the counter would be unable to pick it up. Two tests are necessary to ascertain if the work station is providing a clean atmosphere. These tests are the leak test and the air-flow test. To perform the leak test, smoke is introduced into the intake of the bench, and the filters are scanned with a smoke photometer to check for leaks. The photometer will react quickly to the presence of smoke, and a leaky seal or ruptured filter passing this smoke can readily be detected. The other test is a velocity check. The velocity across the filter is scanned with a velometer to determine if the velocity of the air flow is adequate. If the bench passes both of these tests, then it can be deduced that it will perform satisfactorily. We have found that the sealing of the filter is quite critical, and therefore it is very important to perform the leak test when receiving a new unit or changing a filter. These topics will be discussed in detail in Chapter 13.

Horizontal-Flow Clean Work Station

The original Sandia "evaluation model" of a clean work station was designed as a bench-mounted unit with a separate air supply unit. (See Figures 12-6 and 12-7.) The first commercially available unit was floor-mounted and was constructed of formica-covered plywood. (See Figure 12-8.) This unit, manufactured by Agnew-Higgins, Inc., utilized two fans which feed air to a single plenum chamber. Access to both the prefilter and the HEPA filter was by removing a panel at the rear

FIGURE 12-11. Vertical-flow clean work station (exhaust hood) manufactured by Comfort Air Service. *Courtesy Sandia Corp.*

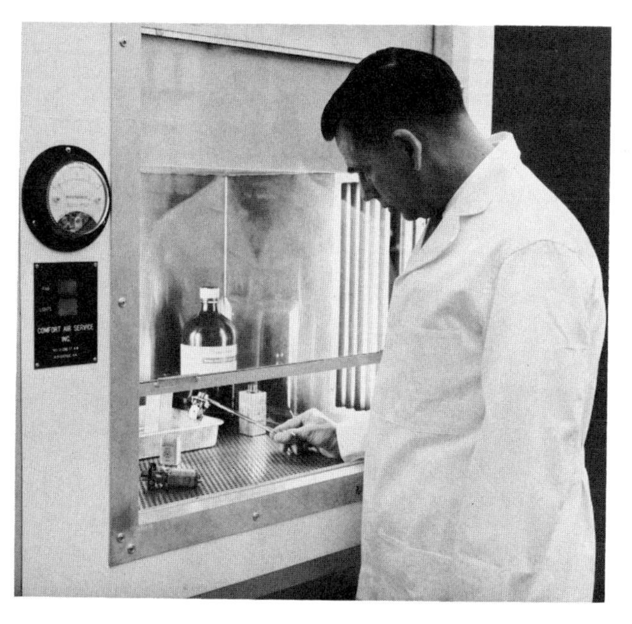

FIGURE 12-12. Vertical-flow clean work station in operation. *Courtesy Sandia Corp.*

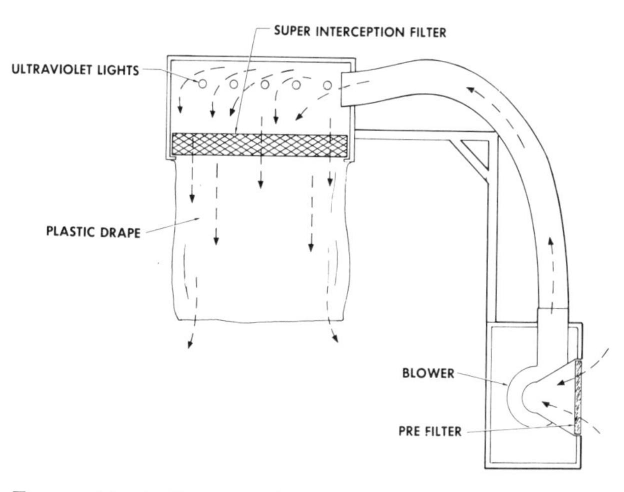

FIGURE 12-13. Cross section of overhead laminar-flow unit. *Courtesy Sandia Corp.*

of the unit. Subsequent commercial models were essentially the same in design but with refinements. Some of the refinements included construction of baked enamel on mild steel, stainless steel, plastic, and epoxy-coated steel. Some models feature removable legs for table-top operation. Some have air intakes at the top. Access to the filters has been improved, as has the air distribution system. The latter has enabled production of smaller units with essentially the same amount of useful working area. Units are available in various sizes, starting with a 2-foot-wide model and progressing in 2-foot intervals. The size is dictated by the filter size, the most popular being 2 feet by 2 feet. Benches larger than 6 feet are a rarity, however.

Essentially all horizontal-flow benches are quite similar; the design limitations preclude any basic difference. Competition has developed by stressing such features as noiseless, vibration-free operation; accessibility of filters for cleaning and changing; savings in floor space; and various other items such as manometers, meters, and alarms. Another popular feature is a variable speed blower to compensate for filter loading and the altitude at which the unit is to be used.

Vertical-Flow Clean Work Station[2]

One of the most frequent uses of vertical-flow clean work stations has been in conjunction with

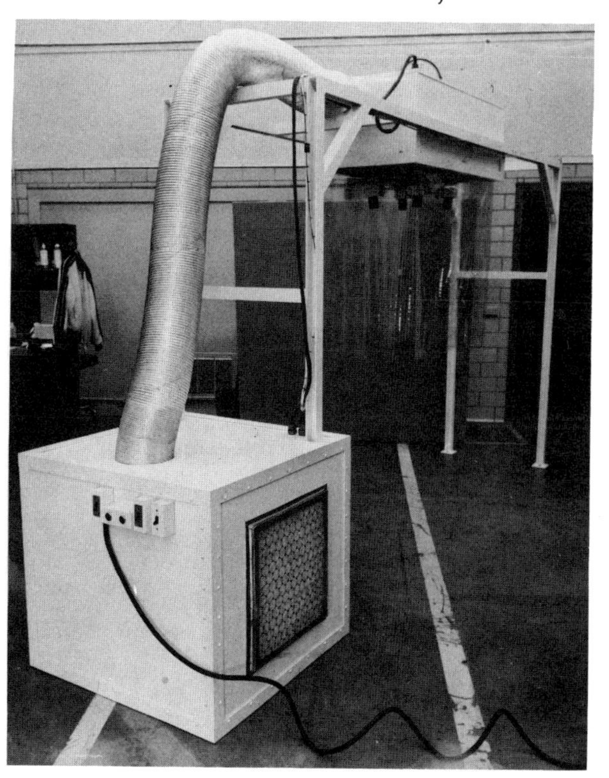

FIGURE 12-14. Down-flow curtain unit under evaluation. Note the throwaway prefilter. *Courtesy Sandia Corp.*

[2] Abstracted from reference 2.

precision cleaning equipment. These cleaning processes are sensitive to airborne contamination for two reasons. First, the high-purity solvents or other cleaning media must be kept clean during handling, pouring, and exposure during the cleaning process. Second, freshly cleaned parts or assemblies must be kept clean until they are dried and protected in some manner.

An example of an experimental device using vertical laminar flow is a deionized water washing unit. (See Figure 12-9.) The unit provides high-purity distilled and deionized water to five wash tanks.

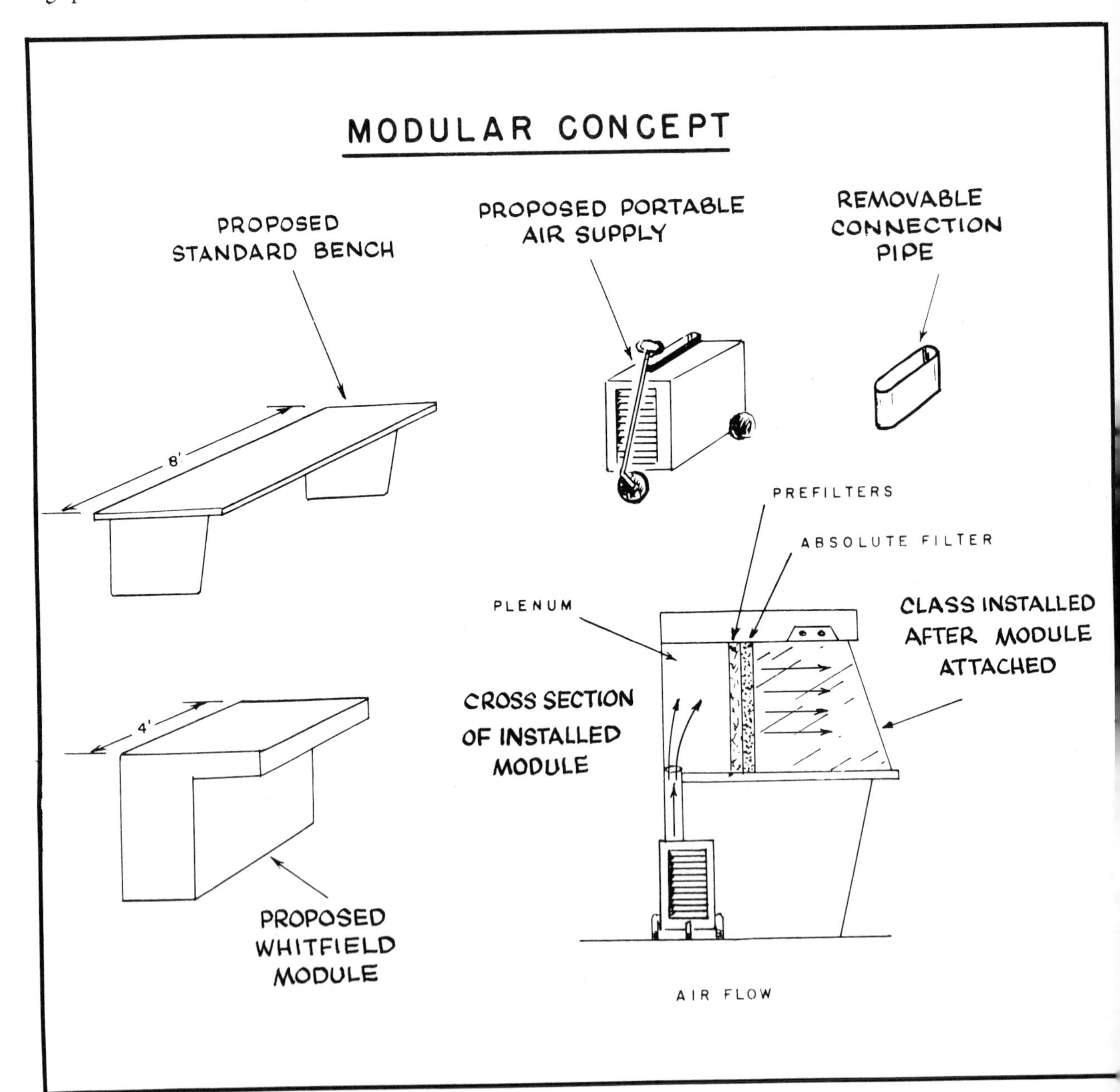

FIGURE 12-15. Modular clean work station concept as developed by MAMES, Olmsted Air Force Base. *Courtesy MAMES, Olmsted AFB, Pa.*

During cleaning operations the tanks cannot be covered, and contamination can fall into the high-purity water. By placing a laminar-flow hood over the tanks, the purity of the water is assured. Since the surrounding air is also clean, parts can be dried without subsequent recontamination from the air. This unit was constructed with Lucite sides, 2-foot

FIGURE 12-16. Six-foot clean work station constructed of plywood covered with formica by Agnew-Higgins. *Courtesy Agnew-Higgins, Inc.*

FIGURE 12-17. Stainless-steel 6-foot bench by Dexon. *Courtesy Dexon, Inc.*

FIGURE 12-18. Six-foot steel clean work station with baked enamel finish by Pure Aire. *Courtesy Pure Aire Corp. of America*

FIGURE 12-19. Six-foot bench constructed of steel with a baked enamel finish by Farr Co. This view shows the intake grille and one prefilter removed. *Courtesy Farr Co.*

by 2-foot HEPA filter, and an integral blower and motor. Similar designs can be used for other operations requiring extreme cleanliness.

Since most cleaning operations use a solvent that gives off vapors, some of which are toxic, it is not

FIGURE 12-20. Agnew-Higgins 4-foot clean work station. The black box on the bench top is a velometer for checking air-flow velocity. *Courtesy Agnew-Higgins, Inc.*

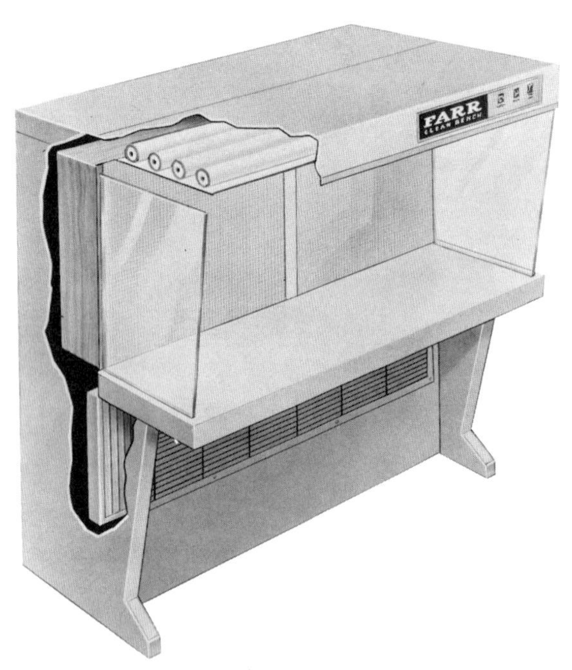

FIGURE 12-21. Four-foot Farr bench showing the location of the HEPA filters and prefilters. *Courtesy Farr Co.*

advisable to allow such vapor into the clean room. Regardless of toxicity, the vapor itself will be a room contaminant. In order to protect the worker and the room, a positive exhaust must be provided for this type of cleaning. This is accomplished by installing an open grating as the working surface and utilizing an additional blower to exhaust air through the grating and out of the room. The same type of filter unit is used overhead, as was previously described for the deionized cleaner. Figure 12-10 illustrates the clean air exhaust hood. The damper on the exhaust allows the system to be balanced so that no air will flow through the front opening or so that air will flow into the hood or out of the hood. Regardless of the setting, the operation in the hood is completely isolated from the outside air. If air is flowing into or out of the hood, only the first 4 inches of streamline are affected; and since these are uncontaminated, the efficiency of the unit is not affected. Laminar-flow super-clean air is continually bathing the work, while vapors and contamination are immediately removed and exhausted. Such a unit is ideal for ultrasonic cleaning operations. A commercially available model of this type of vertical-

FIGURE 12-22. Pure Aire bench 40 inches wide for special application at General Electric. *Courtesy Pure Aire Corp. of America*

flow clean work station is shown in Figures 12-11 and 12-12.

Another vertical-flow unit with varied applications is the down-flow curtain unit. (See Figure 12-13.) This unit can be used for medical and industrial applications where a bath of super-clean air is needed. For medical applications, ultraviolet lamps are added to the plenum behind the filter to sterilize the air and prevent any build-up of viable material on the filters.

The essential parts of this unit are the HEPA filter and the plastic curtain which should extend down to just above the area to be protected. This curtain assures the maintenance of laminar flow.

Figure 12-14 shows an evaluation model of this type of unit. Such a device can be used to protect critical missile components where it would be impractical, because of size, to control the whole area around the missile. A similar device can be used for protecting guidance packages during calibration. In this case it may be necessary to shut off the unit

FIGURE 12-24. Three-foot steel Baker laminar-flow work bench. Notice rounded exterior work surface edge. *Courtesy The Baker Company, Inc.*

FIGURE 12-23. Four-foot Microvoid II laminar-flow work station constructed of pressed wood and melamine laminated on all surfaces. *Courtesy Air Control, Inc.*

FIGURE 12-25. Two Baker 3-foot laminar-flow work benches placed together to form a 6-foot-wide bench. *Courtesy The Baker Company, Inc.*

Figure 12-26. Four-foot table model clean bench by Agnew-Higgins. *Courtesy Agnew-Higgins, Inc.*

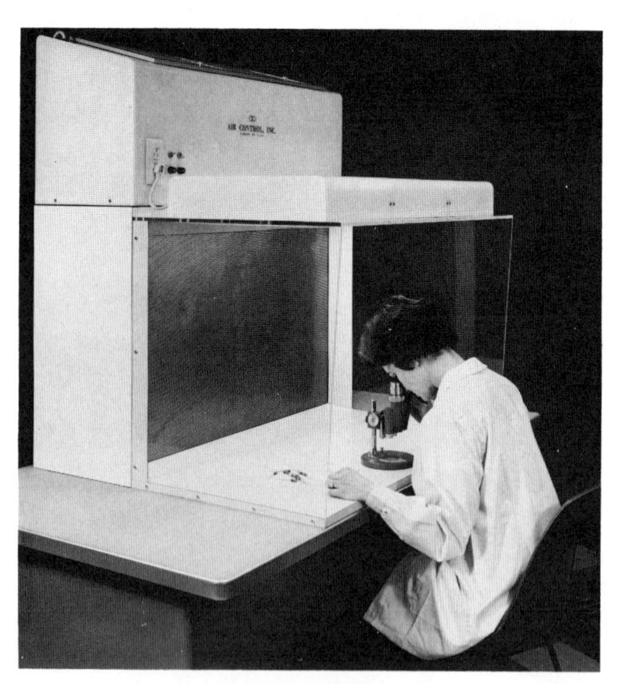

Figure 12-27. Table-mounted unit of mostly plastic construction by Air Control. *Courtesy Air Control, Inc.*

during extremely sensitive adjustments. When this is necessary, the curtain is extended to the floor to protect the instrument from stray air currents during shutdown. Many similar applications can be found. An extremely large down-flow unit is being used by the Rawlings Corporation over an automated color television tube assembly line. This unit is some 500 feet long. Deposition of phosphorus is extremely sensitive to airborne contamination.

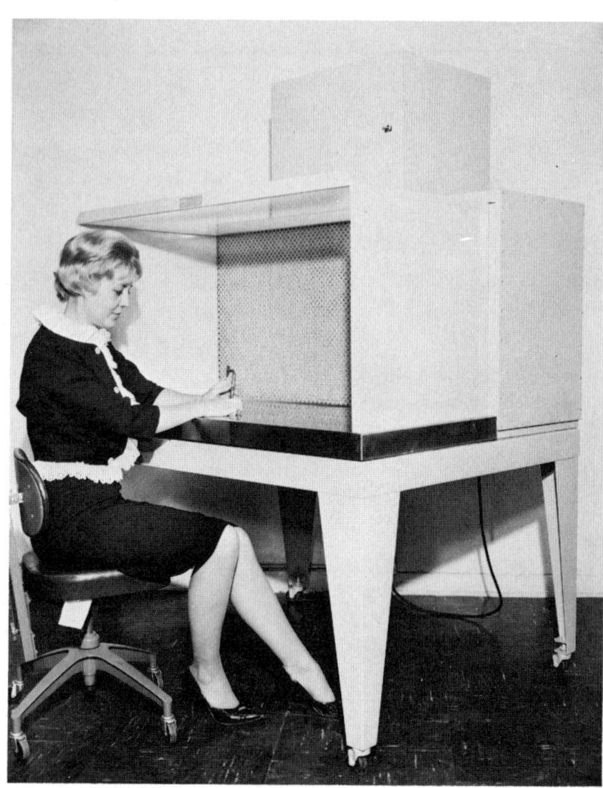

Figure 12-28. Bench-mounted unit by Pure Aire. *Courtesy Pure Aire Corp. of America*

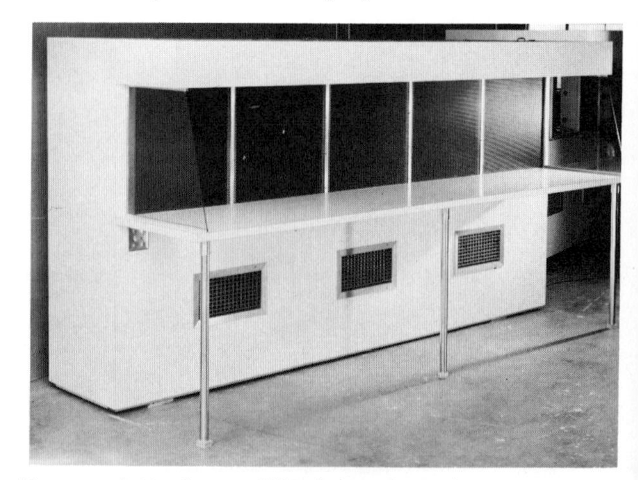

Figure 12-29. Agnew-Higgins 10-foot clean work station. *Courtesy Agnew-Higgins, Inc.*

The Modular Concept

The use of clean work stations was pursued by the Air Force as the answer to a problem that had existed for many years. Most components worked on in clean rooms required varying degrees of cleanliness. In some cases all components could be handled economically in a clean room of the highest degree needed. Most of the time, however, costly super-clean areas were used for all operations when only a small percentage of the work required this control. It is for this reason that the question has been asked, "Why clean up the whole universe when we are only interested in a small area?"*(3)*. The Air Force and industry had been using dust-free hoods for area clean-up, but these hoods had definite disadvantages (previously discussed). It is for this reason that clean work stations were developed to supplement the Air Force standard clean room.

The great majority of Air Force clean room work was bench-type work (well over 90%), readily adaptable to the use of clean work stations. When increased dust control was needed on a particular product in a particular spot in a production line, a clean work station was installed. The Air Force is unique in that it must adapt its clean

FIGURE 12-30. Baker Company 8-foot-wide, 4-foot-high laminar-flow bench. *Courtesy The Baker Company, Inc.*

FIGURE 12-31. Stainless-steel customized work station built by The Baker Company for a special high-temperature oven operation. Entrance to the ovens is provided through the square openings in the side panels of the bench. The working surface is cut out to allow installation of special handling equipment. *Courtesy The Baker Company, Inc.*

room facilities to a great variety of products from a large number of different manufacturers. In addition, the work load and content may change at a moment's notice. The lack of standardization of clean room requirements aggravated this situation. Air Force clean rooms must, necessarily, be as adaptable as possible to changing workloads. Ideally, the work benches, clean work stations, exhaust hoods, service islands, etc., would be completely compatible and interchangeable (the modular concept).

Several designs have been suggested that would provide interchangeability. (See Figure 12-15.) The work benches would be similar to those already used in clean rooms with some additional attaching points and hold-downs added so that a clean work station or a vent hood could be installed. When a clean work station is needed in a certain location, a

FIGURE 12-32. Stainless-steel cleaning bench which provides for three cleaning units to be installed in its working surface. *Courtesy Air Controls, Inc.*

portable air supply would be wheeled into place, a station would be clamped to the bench, and the connection pipe installed. A similar arrangement would be used for a vented hood. In this case, the exhaust from the hood would have to be vented outside. This could be accomplished on an individual basis.

A portable exhaust unit similar to the air supply unit and a custom piping system can be used, or the clean room could be fitted with a universal exhaust collection system with numerous outlets for connecting up with newly installed hoods.

The idea of the modular concept is good; however, competition in the manufacture of clean work stations has produced such a variety of units at competitive prices that it is doubted if a system similar to that just described will ever be implemented. Figures 12-16 through 12-29 show commercially available benches made by different manufacturers.

Customized Clean Work Stations

As is to be expected, clean work stations serve many varied uses. A good percentage of clean operations can be performed on a standard clean work station which offers a flat surface. There are instances, however, when cleanliness must be provided to operations which do not lend themselves to the standard designs. In these cases, it is not only economical but a necessity that customized clean work stations be obtained. Some examples of such customizing are shown in Figures 12-30 to 12-33.

Other Adaptations

Clean work stations have been used for a number of purposes other than for manufacturing. One of the most significant is in the medical profession. Since the HEPA filter will eliminate all bacteria, it can be a very useful tool. There are certain cases where a patient must be protected from bacteria but cannot be completely isolated from airborne contamination. One example would be a burn case. Such a patient can be placed under a down-flow curtain device similar to that shown in Figure 12-13. Plastic enclosures of the recirculating type have also been used for this purpose. These have the advantage of complete isolation, since the patient may be worked on through glove ports or similar

FIGURE 12-33. Special side-return laminar-flow unit built by Air Control. *Courtesy Air Controls, Inc.*

devices. (These recirculating devices can also be made with laminar flow.)

The photographic processing and motion picture industry uses clean work stations for film editing. The presence of dust on a strip of film has long been a problem. Editing often exposes the film to the possible deposition of dust and possible scratching of a valuable master negative. In addition to scratching, a relatively small invisible particle is magnified by projection to a very undesirable spot on the screen. Clean work stations will insure that no dust falls on film in process.

Auxiliary Cleaning Devices

Another benefit derived from the use of clean work stations is their capacity to "clean up" the atmosphere in which they are placed. The recirculation of room air through HEPA filters will dilute the contamination in the room. Each 6-foot bench

FIGURE 12-34. Filter bank module for upgrading existing rooms or installing at the end of a clean room "tunnel." *Courtesy Pure Aire Corp. of America*

FIGURE 12-35. A laminar-flow tunnel for use in overhauling large optical devices. *Courtesy Robins AFB, Ga.*

FIGURE 12-36. The laminar-flow tunnel during construction. Note the two sets of filter frames, one for throw away prefilters and one for HEPA filters. *Courtesy Robins AFB, Ga.*

will circulate approximately 1200 cfm of air. It has been estimated that a clean room utilizing clean work stations over 20% of its floor area will experience over one hundred room air changes per hour.[3] Such recirculation and filtration will cause the room contamination level to approach the cleanliness level of the clean work station. The lowest level reached will depend on the work being done and the amount of activity within the room. The value derived from this "fringe benefit" of using clean work stations should not be overlooked. If a certain clean

[3] MAMES, Olmsted Air Force Base, Pa.

FIGURE 12-37. Tunnel air supply blowers and plenum chamber. The HEPA filters have been installed. The prefilters and plenum chamber door are not mounted. *Courtesy Robins AFB, Ga.*

room fails to meet the contamination levels necessary for a new product, it may be possible to upgrade the room through the use of clean work stations. Several companies have marketed a clean work station type of device, minus the working surface, for just such a purpose. It consists of a stack of filters and a blower system through which the room air is recirculated. (See Figure 12-34.) This device is intended for upgrading rooms in which clean work stations would not be advantageous. If we consider the people and operations as particle producers, and these devices as particle removers, the problem is a matter of balancing out the system so that the desired level of cleanliness is achieved. This type of device has also been used at the end of a "tunnel" made of angle iron supports and plastic covering (or other suitable materials). Such a tunnel will exhibit laminar-flow characteristics. The air at the open end of the tunnel will be dumped and not recirculated. It is important in devices of this type that the full cross-sectional area of the tunnel be composed of filters. If this is not done, nozzle effects will create air currents that will reintroduce floor contaminants into the air stream.

An example of such a tunnel can be seen in Figure 12-35. This unit was constructed at minimum cost and with materials available to the builder. The tunnel frame is made of welded angle iron covered with mild steel walls which have been painted with a good-quality enamel paint. Other construction materials may be substituted with no effect on the cleanliness level. The only precise workmanship required is in establishing a strong flat and smooth surface on the filter mounting frame. The filter mounting frame, plenum, and air supply openings can be seen in Figure 12-36. The front of these openings was later baffled to prevent a high-velocity air stream from hitting the prefilter bank at this point. Throwaway prefilters were installed behind the HEPA filters. Both banks of filters are maintained by entering a door in the side of the plenum chamber. (See Figure 12-37.) The view through the doorway shows the HEPA filters in place and the mount for the prefilters. The blower plenum is fed by twelve blowers which deliver 1000 cfm each. Lighting is provided by fluorescent fixtures in the ceiling. The entire unit may be disassembled and moved to a new location in a few hours.

The velocity in the tunnel is 127 fpm, and the cleanliness level approaches that of the HEPA filter. This level continues out of the end of the tunnel for approximately 8 feet. This particular unit was used for overhaul of large optical equipment which could not be handled in a clean work station. For this use the tunnel was cut off at 11 feet (the filter bank is 8 feet high and 12 feet wide). For other applications however, it can be extended to many times this distance. The use of this unit in an existing controlled area has considerably upgraded the cleanliness level.

REFERENCES

1. Timmerman, S. W. "Clean Bench." *Conference on Clean Room Specifications.* SCR-652. Office of Technical Services, Department of Commerce, Washington, D.C. May, 1963.

2. Marsh, R. C. "Adaptability of Laminar Air Flow for Contamination Control." *Conference on Clean Room Specifications.* SCR-652. Office of Technical Services, Department of Commerce, Washington, D.C. May, 1963.

3. Perkin, I. R. *Minutes of Meeting–To Discuss the Whitfield Principle and Determine Its Adaptability to Clean Room Use.* Olmsted AFB, Pa., September, 1962.

Chapter 13. *Clean Work Station Operation*

Introduction

It has been established in the previous discussion that the clean work station will yield the lowest contamination level attainable. This is the result of working in close proximity to a HEPA filter. A cleaner working area will result only with an improvement in filtration. Having this clean area available does not solve all our contamination problems. It eliminates the problem of airborne contamination, which has been the most difficult to evaluate. (See Chapter 1.) But airborne contamination is only a minor contributor to the total contamination possibilities. Process-generated contamination (for example, particles caused by the seating of the screws holding a dust cover in place) can occur inside a critical component. This particular type of problem must be solved by proper design and the use of proper materials. Transfer and contact contamination are the other possibilities. These must be controlled by proper methods (work techniques). Proper work techniques include initial checkout, operation, and maintenance of the clean work station.

Again, let us stress the fact that eliminating airborne contamination does not solve all the problems, although some of the literature would lead us to believe this.

Preparation of Station for Work

Degradation of a clean work station can take two primary forms: (1) a leak, which will allow improperly filtrated air to enter, and (2) air flow lower than the minimum specified for efficient operation.

To determine if the clean work station is achieving the contamination level for which it was designed is difficult on a quantitative basis. As was stated in Chapter 9, automatic digital counters are slow to react and will not pick up small concentrations of particulate matter. In order to detect pinholes in HEPA filters and leaks around filter seals, it is necessary to introduce contamination to the downstream side of the filter with the bench in operation. A cigarette is an excellent source of smoke. Smoke particles produced by a cigarette are in the size range from 0.01 to 1.0 micron and will find leaks and pinholes very nicely. Several smoke generators can be made that will give excellent results. One consists of an ordinary squeeze bulb and a length of hose. (See Figure 13-1.) This "generator" has the disadvantage of dropping ashes at random wherever it is used. The smoke generator in Figure 13-2 is more sophisticated and will not contaminate the area with ashes. It can be made of aluminum or glass tubing and a short length of aluminum pipe with a screw or press-on cap.

The use of a hand-activated chemical smoke generator used for ventilation studies is not recommended. These devices are constructed of a squeeze bulb and a small glass tube filled with granulated pumice which has been treated with fuming stannic chloride. When air is passed through the tube, a

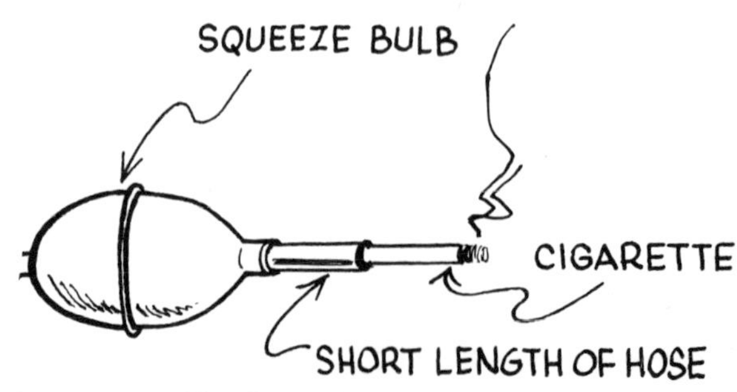

FIGURE 13-1. Simple smoke generator using an ordinary cigarette.

white smoke (fog) of stannic acid and hydrochloric acid is formed, owing to the presence of moisture in the air. This smoke will be highly detrimental to clean room operations.

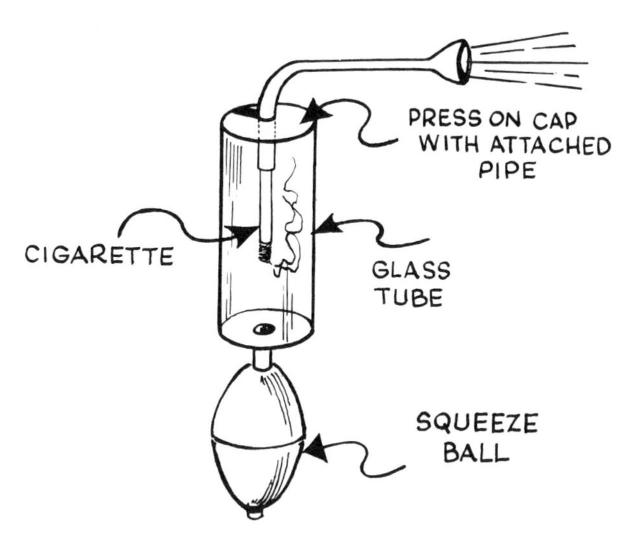

FIGURE 13-2. Directional cigarette smoke generatoı which will prevent ashes from contaminating the room.

When more sophisticated equipment is desired or when greater quantities of smoke are needed, an air-operated aerosol generator may be constructed. Several designs for simple, portable, air-operated aerosol generators have been developed by the U. S.

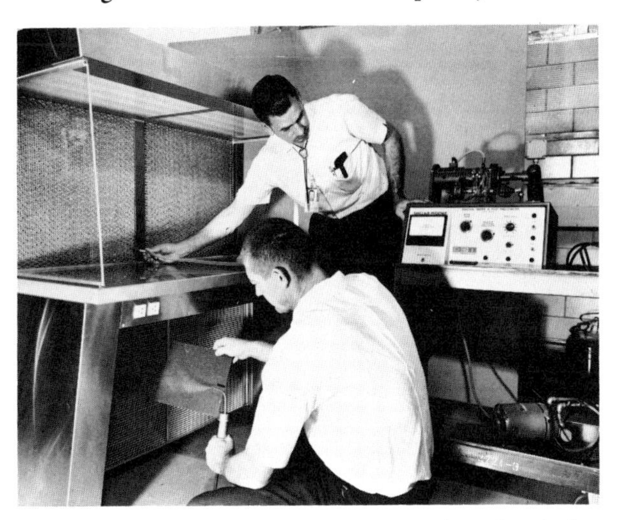

FIGURE 13-4. Checking clean work station for leaks, using a smoke generator and photometer. *Courtesy Sandia Corp.*

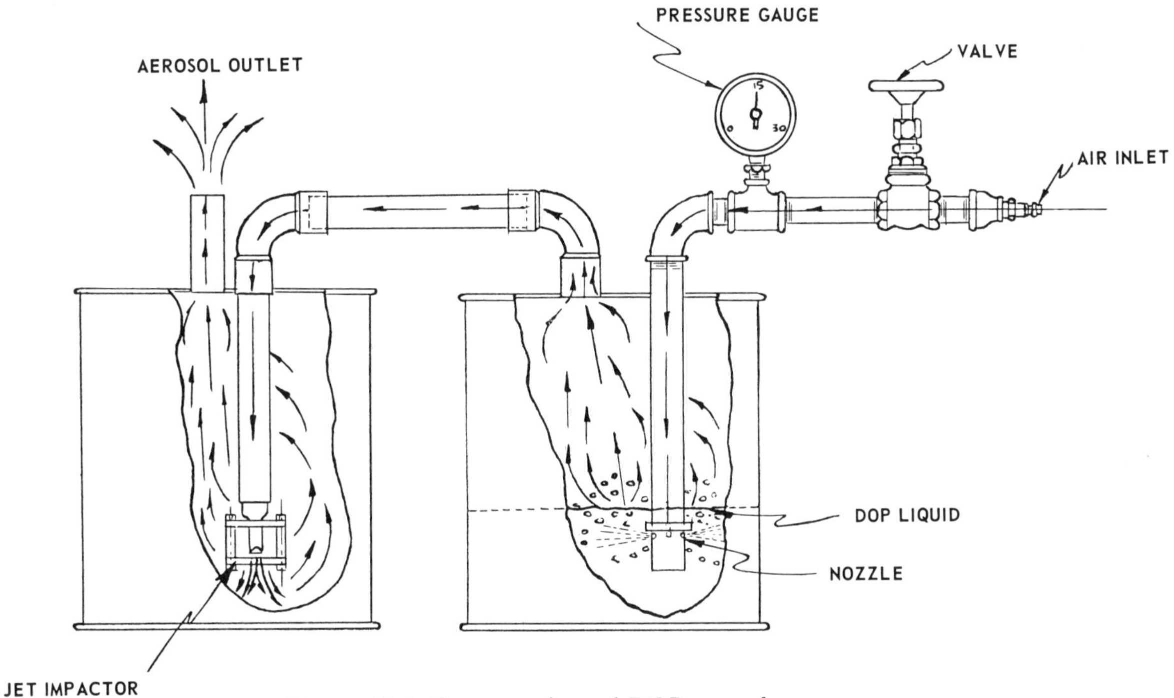

FIGURE 13-3. Cutaway view of DOP aerosol generator ideal for checking filter installations.

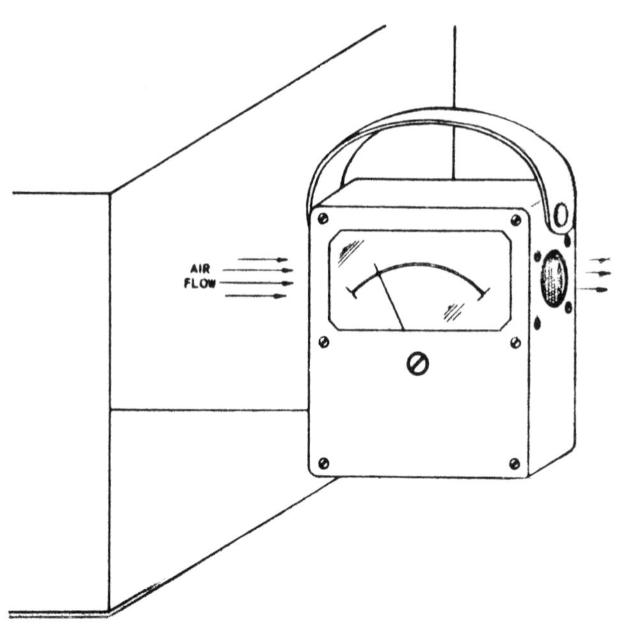

FIGURE 13-5. The Alnor velometer for checking the velocity of air flow.

Naval Research Laboratory (*1*). *These generators* produce a polydisperse liquid aerosol when supplied with filtered, well-regulated, compressed air. At a given pressure the polydispersion produced by these generators is reproducible both in particle size distribution and aerosol concentration.

When it is desired to check or evaluate high-efficiency filter systems, monodispersity and a low mean particle diameter (one that approaches 0.3 micron) are desirable but not entirely necessary. Such generators, when using DOP liquid, will produce a light-scattering geometric mean particle size (approaching 0.5 micron). Since filter gasket bypass, coupled with leakage due to imperfection within the filter units, is almost always greater than filter penetration, this type of generator will prove very effective for checking installed filters.

The Navy generators were developed as the result of research effort and vary somewhat in design; in principle, however, they are all similar. Each has its own reproducible characteristics. The heart of the generator is the atomizer nozzle. Air enters the nozzle under pressure and produces a high-velocity stream in the liquid to be dispersed. The liquid is aspirated through liquid feed holes located at the nozzle outlet. The liquid column, droplets, or film which appears in and near the region of the vena contracta (smallest portion of the jet) is atomized by the shearing action of the high-velocity air stream. (See Figure 13-3.)

A tighter particle size distribution may be obtained by the addition of a jet impactor. Larger particles are removed by means of the inertial mechanism. Efficiency of removal is dependent on the velocity, diameter, and density of the particle and on the jet-to-impacting plate distance. The details for construction of these units may be obtained from the reference document (*1*).

When the smoke is introduced into the clean work station filters, the air coming through the filters must be closely monitored. Digital automatic counters with small flow rate and long sampling time are not responsive enough for this job. Analog devices (photometers) have been found satisfactory for monitoring rapid changes in contamination level. (See Chapters 8 and 9.)

The procedure for detecting leaks is to carefully check the edge of the filter for smoke. This is accomplished by "walking" the probe from the photometer around the edge and noting the response on the meter. (See Figure 13-4.) A leak will be registered as a fast and large needle deflection. How large a meter deflection depends on the size of the hole and the sensitivity setting of the instrument. The filter is checked for holes by scanning the entire face of the filter in a similar manner. Once it has been determined that a leak exists, the exact location of the leak should be established. A leak in

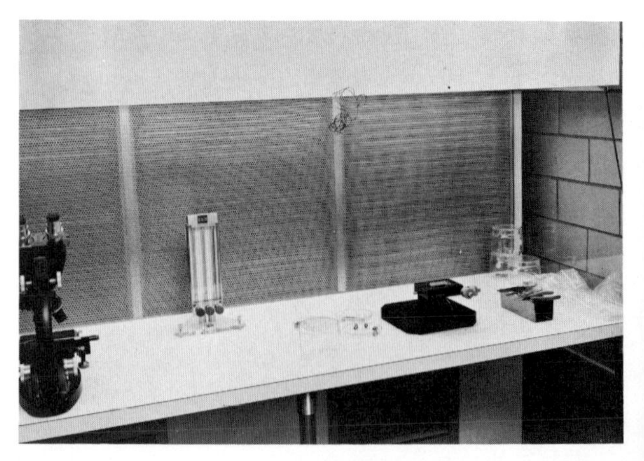

FIGURE 13-6. An uncluttered clean work station. *Courtesy Sandia Corp.*

the filter indicates that a new filter is needed. A leak at the edge indicates a poor seal between the filter and the filter holder. This should be corrected by tightening the pressure on the filter or perhaps by some other mechanical means. Rechecks should be made after tightening. It has been stated that about 90% of HEPA filters leak after installation.[1] Therefore, constant rechecks should be made on new filter installations until there is no doubt of the security of the seal.

The other test that must be performed to ensure quality performance is the air-flow test. The purpose of this test is to determine if the proper air-flow velocity is being maintained across the front opening of the bench. This is accomplished by means of an air-flow velocity meter which will measure a range of flow from approximately 50 to 150 fpm. (See Figure 13-5.) With the air supply to the bench operating, the velocity meter is held approximately 2 feet from the filter face. While the face of the filter is being scanned with the velocity meter, any deviations on the meter should be noted. Scanning is accomplished by moving the meter from one side of the filter to the other and then back on a lower level, etc., until the entire filter has

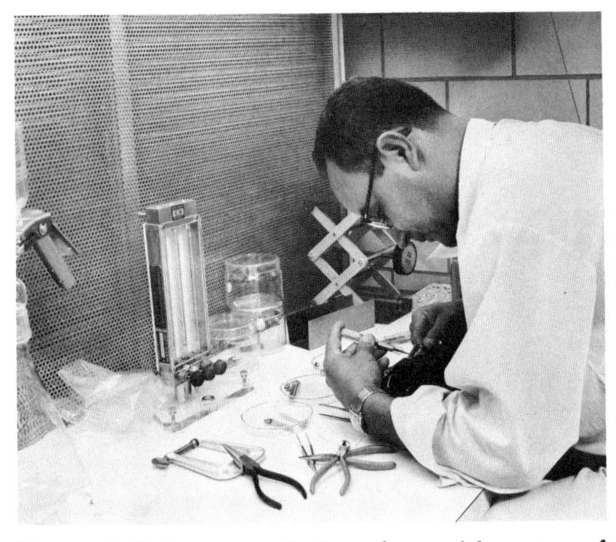

FIGURE 13-7. Improper placing of material on top of clean work station. *Courtesy Sandia Corp.*

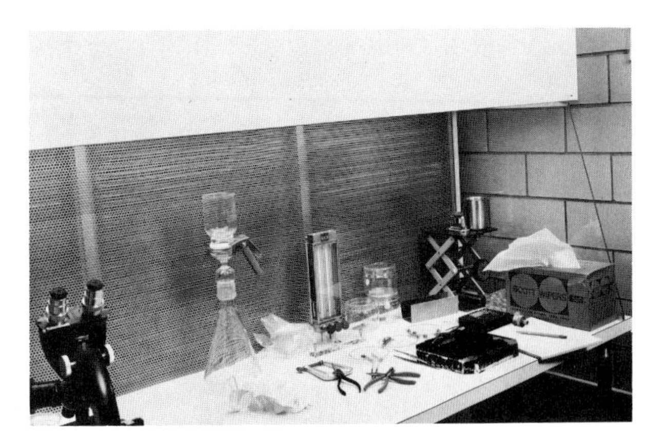

FIGURE 13-8. Improperly used clean work station. *Courtesy Sandia Corp.*

been completely covered in one smooth continuous path.

An air flow of less than 75 fpm should be considered as inadequate. Similarly, a variation of more than 25 fpm is not satisfactory, and either condition is cause for a check of the clean work station to determine the cause. It is felt that a velocity of less than 75 fpm will degrade the effectiveness of a horizontal clean work station.

Manufacturers' operating characteristics and recommended minimum velocities should be consulted.

The leak and air-flow tests should be performed when a new unit is received, when a new filter has been installed, and at least once per month, thereafter, or when trouble is suspected.

Random checks should be made of clean work stations in operation—that is, with personnel performing operations at the bench. The operational contamination level should not exceed 1000 particles per cubic foot 0.5 micron and larger. This value should be met when the bench is operated in a clean room that has a particle count no greater than 100,000 particles 0.5 micron and larger.[2] When benches are operated in uncontrolled areas, the particle count during operation will be higher than for benches operated in clean rooms. Should contamination in a clean work station be out of operational limits, the cause for this condition should be found and corrected. If the operation itself is the

[1] Lieberman, at conference on U. S. Air Force Technical Order 00-25-203, Olmsted Air Force Base, Pa., September 1962. Realization of this problem, to date, has improved filter sealing.

[2] An Air Force standard clean room as per U. S. Air Force Technical Order 00-25-203, or Class 100,000 clean room by Federal Standard 209.

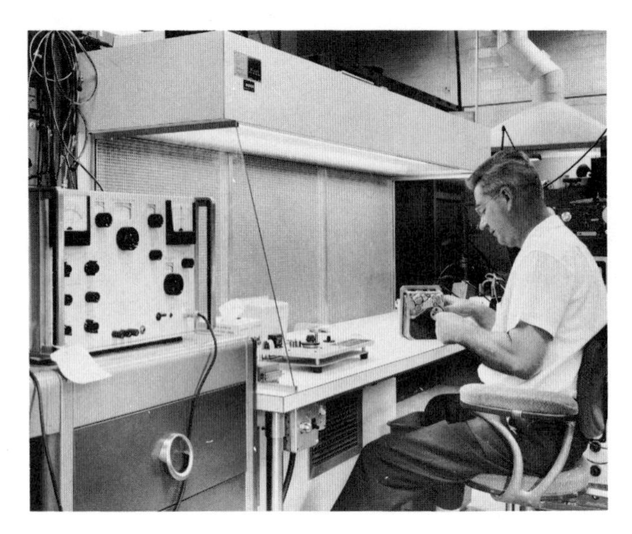

FIGURE 13-9. Miniature airborne recorder unit being tested by a telemetering component control section. *Courtesy Sandia Corp.*

cause, it should be performed in a vertical-flow clean work station where particles generated will be directly removed without the possibility of contaminating other portions of the work station.

Controls during Operation

Introduction

As has been stated several times previously, the clean work station controls airborne contamination only. (This cannot be stressed too highly.) The contamination generated by the worker or clinging to his clothes and body can result in contamination of the work area. Similarly, everything outside the work bench should be considered contaminated, since the dust level in this area is much higher than that inside the bench. This is especially true when the bench is operated in an uncontrolled area. Since all material (containers, tools, parts, etc.) transported to the bench will carry contamination, education of the workers in contamination control is essential. They should be cognizant of the possible sources of contamination and the techniques for their control. The degree to which any user controls clean work station technique is determined by the tolerances of the work piece. The following sections will describe, for the most part, the tightest control possible. Less stringent requirements will allow a relaxation of controls.

Area Evaluation

The first step toward ensuring a clean work space inside the station is an evaluation of the area in which the clean work station will be operating. When a horizontal-flow clean work station is used in an uncontrolled area, the working surface may be contaminated by fallout of heavy particles. Furthermore, ambient uncontrolled area contamination levels may be high enough so that the "at-rest" contamination level of the bench may be greater than 100 particles per cubic foot 0.5 micron and larger. In most designs fallout is prevented by extending the station top to, or beyond, the edge of the working surface. Since filters are percentage devices, they will pass a greater number of particles when used in filtering dirtier atmospheres. If the particle count is critical or if agglomeration is a possibility, this effect cannot be overlooked. Finally, the clean work station should not be operated in an area where high-velocity particles (from drilling, grinding, etc.) might have an opportunity to penetrate the station air stream. It is essential that the area in which a clean work station is to operate be carefully selected.

Station Control

It is recommended that the air supply be turned on at least 10 minutes before work is performed in the station. When the unit is activated, the pro-

FIGURE 13-10. High-vacuum system built to house solid-state research equipment. *Courtesy Sandia Corp.*

tective screen should be vacuumed to remove any particles that may have settled there during shutdown. A vacuum with a plastic nozzle is recommended, since it will leave no particles of its own. During this operation the working surface should be cleared of all materials and tools. Just prior to using the station operationally, and after the station has been vacuumed and run for 10 minutes, the working surface should be wiped clean. The purpose of this is to remove any fallout particles that were the result of the cleaning of the screen or had settled there during shutdown. The cleaning is best accomplished with a synthetic sponge or cloth dampened in filtered (0.5 micron) isopropyl alcohol. This cloth or sponge should possess limited-linting properties. Additional cleaning of the working surface may be necessary if there is opportunity for it to receive contamination during the shift due to "traffic" in and out of the working area. If multiple shifts use the work station, with no interim shutdown or start-up preparation, the station should be cleaned at least once per shift.

Work Area Control

The clean work station derives some of its cleanliness efficiency from the flow of laminar air. It is

FIGURE 13-11. A view of the bench shown in Fig. 13-10 prior to instrumentation. *Courtesy Sandia Corp.*

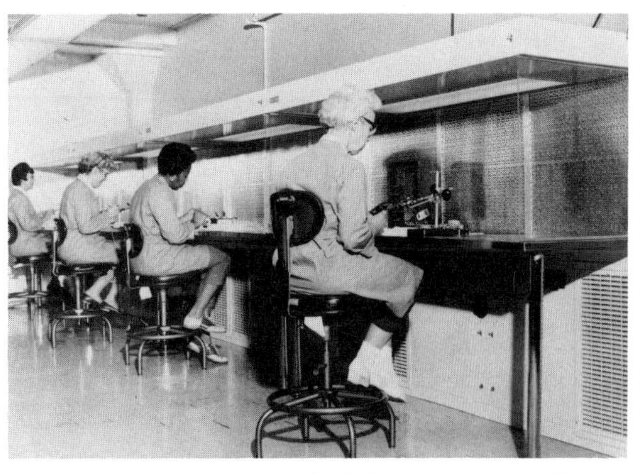

FIGURE 13-12. Assembly of miniature circuits using assembly line procedures at Lockheed Missile and Space Corp. *Courtesy Pure Aire Corp. of America*

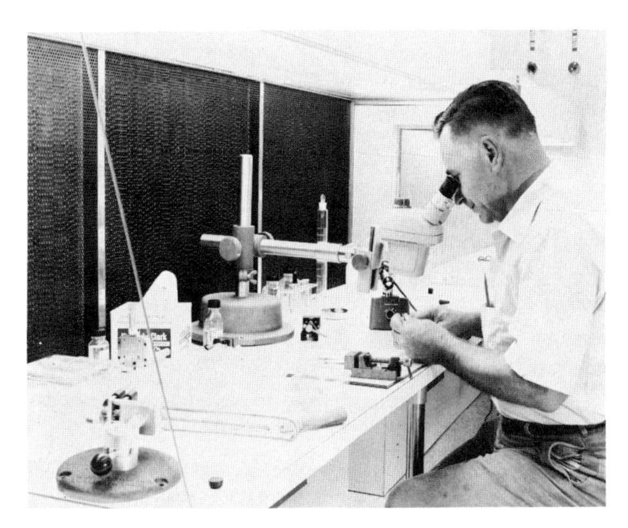

FIGURE 13-13. Inspecting a small firing mechanism part. *Courtesy Sandia Corp.*

important, therefore, not to restrict the air flow. Nothing should be placed between the work piece and the filters. If material must be stored inside the work station, it should be placed along the sides of working area. Tools should be stored in a tray or fixture that will allow them to remain off the working surface and in the air stream. (See Figure 13-6.) It is essential that all objects placed in the work area be free from contamination. Paper work and pencils should not be allowed in the station. Another possible source of trouble is the top or canopy of the station. This is a tempting storage space but must not be used for this purpose. In removing stored

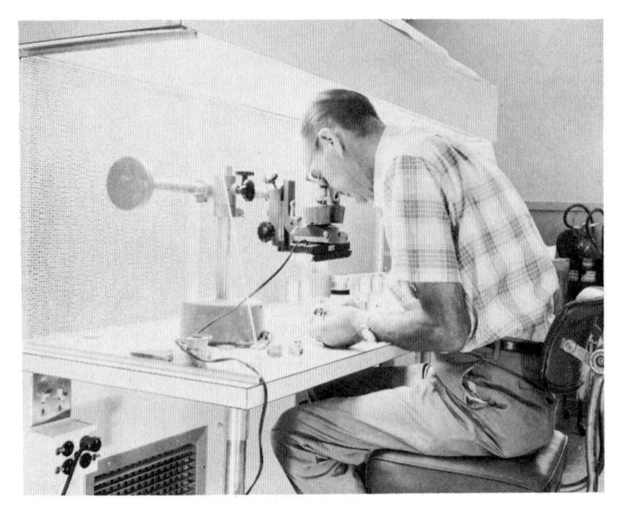

FIGURE 13-14. Assembling a velocity gauge. *Courtesy Sandia Corp.*

objects, there is a possibility of releasing large particles which could enter the air stream and cause trouble. Figure 13-7 is an example of this.

Worker Control

As has been stated many times, contact and transfer contamination are potentially the greatest threat to cleanliness. Since the worker will be placing a portion of his body inside the clean work station, this action must not degrade the effectiveness of the station. The hands, forearms, sleeves, etc., must be free from loose dirt and lint. When it is not necessary to protect the part from contact with bare skin or from skin flakes, smocks with snug fitting wrist bands will suffice. Gauntlet gloves, finger cots, or other hand coverings will be necessary when additional protection is necessary. Hand coverings must be protected from possible contamination. They should not be used outside the work station. The operator must not rub his face or hair while wearing such coverings. Such actions should be watched for by supervisory personnel because they may be involuntary acts and the worker may not be aware of this action. Scratching an ear is a good example. If the worker cannot break the habit, he must be transferred to another job. Work requiring the worker to lean over the bench will expose the part to fallout from the worker's head. In this case, it is essential that a tight-fitting head cover be worn. Figure 13-8 shows a worker leaning over his work without a head cover. He also is blocking the air flow with his hands and equipment.

In order to minimize the possibility of any fallout contamination's reaching the part, the hands should be downstream from the part as much as possible. When moving the hands, arms, and parts into the work station, a shadow of contaminated air is carried in behind them. Tests indicate that the depth of penetration is slight, but it could present a problem if repeated rapid movements are made in and out of the work station(2). A slow arm motion will allow the clean air to dilute the "shadow" and carry it away.

Parts Control

The original application of the clean work stations was by contractors of the Atomic Energy Commission. Extremely miniature timing and firing devices were assembled. This assembly work was so critical that in some cases "operating-room" team work was developed between the parts handler and the assembler. Hospital personnel have, since the time of Louis Pasteur, been extremely conscious of contact and transfer contamination. Since we have almost completely eliminated the problem of airborne contamination, our next big step is to minimize or eliminate contact and transfer contamination. The AEC contractors found the following procedure to be satisfactory. Clean parts were transported in protective containers and removed only

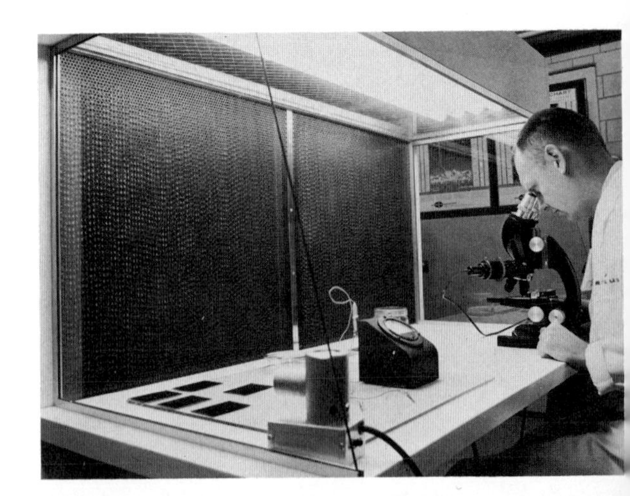

FIGURE 13-15. Laboratory thin-film studies. *Courtesy Sandia Corp.*

inside the clean work station or in the unobstructed air stream immediately adjacent to the working area. The containers were not removed from the air stream until properly closed. The containers were placed to one side and downstream from the work piece, and this spot was maintained just for the containers. The parts container carries some contamination into the work station which can be transferred to the working surface. Therefore, critical parts must not be placed in this spot. In some cases it was possible to store parts containers above the working surface on a platform or shelf. This approach has been mentioned previously for tool storage.

Check List

The following clean work station check list is quoted from U. S. Air Force Technical Order 00-25-203:

a. Affirmatives.
 (1) Do store all containers to the side of and downstream of the work place.
 (2) Do place open dishes containing parts in the unobstructed clean air flow from the filters.
 (3) Do locate the fixture for handling the work piece in the unobstructed air flow.
 (4) Do place tools on fixtures to keep them free of any contamination on horizontal surfaces such as bench surfaces.

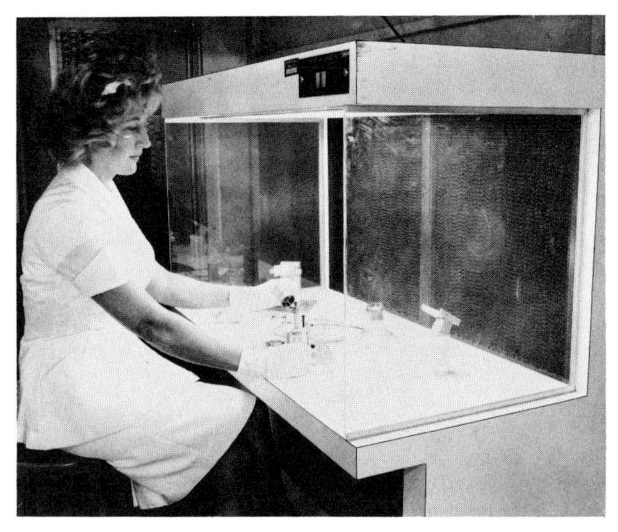

FIGURE 13-16. Photomultiplier tube assembly being potted at Gulton Industries Inc., on Comfort Air Service 4-foot bench. *Courtesy Sandia Corp.*

FIGURE 13-17. Bench being modified for high-vacuum research. *Courtesy Sandia Corp.*

 (5) Do keep the top or canopy of the work stations free of any material.
 (6) Do keep the station clean and orderly.

b. Negatives.
 (1) Do not place clean parts containers and bags with other equipment in front of the filters, blocking the direct air flow to the work piece. Figure 13-8 is an example of this.
 (2) Do not place open dishes containing parts downstream of any obstructions.
 (3) Do not clutter up the working area with extra tools, equipment, paper towels, and linting material.
 (4) Do not use lead pencils or paper in the clean work station.
 (5) Do not keep boxes on the top or canopy of bench type clean work stations.

Station Shutdown

At the end of the work period, all critical parts, components, and tools should be removed from the clean work station (with the proper procedure) and placed in storage. The storage area should be protected from fallout and possible contamination. This storage area should be used for parts in parts containers as well as for tools. It is important to protect the parts container as much as possible, since it contributes contamination also. It should be remembered that all tools and storage containers left on the clean work station will have to be moved for the "start-up" cleanup. After these precautions are taken, the work bench may be turned off.

FIGURE 13-18. Baker Company laminar-flow work benches in operation in advanced products area. *Courtesy Weston Instruments and Electronics Division, Daystrom, Inc.*

Maintenance of Station

The only periodic maintenance required on a clean work station is the checking of the filters. This check takes two forms—checking the prefilter and checking the final filter. The prefilter check assures that the final filter is not being excessively loaded with contaminant. The final filter check assures that clean air is being supplied to the work station.

Prefilter maintenance will vary from manufacturer to manufacturer because of different filters and filter material being used for the prefilter. In all cases the manufacturer's recommendations should be followed. A popular prefilter is Scott foam.[3] This material has the advantage of being washable. A good rule of thumb to follow is to check prefilters every 2 months. Filters made of Scott foam may be vacuumed or washed in mild detergent if excessively dirty. HEPA filters should be checked by using the air-flow and leak tests as described above. These tests are more time-consuming and require a higher degree of skill than prefilter checking. They should be made at least every 6 months and if possible more frequently. HEPA filters should be changed when a filter is ruptured or when it is so loaded with particulate that it will not produce the proper velocity across the working surface. When it is necessary to change a HEPA filter, it should be done with care, remembering the previous statement that 90% of all HEPA filters leak when first installed. The leak and air-flow tests should be performed on all new filter installations.

[3] A product of Scott Paper Company.

Examples of Utilization of Clean Work Stations

Figure 13-9 through 13-17 are examples of clean work stations in operation.

Figure 13-18 shows Baker laminar-flow work benches in operation at Weston Instruments and Electronics, Newark, New Jersey. These benches are used for the manufacture and assembly of advanced miniature precision electro-mechanical units for space applications. The benches in this picture are connected by a series of Baker Sterishields which protect the products after cleaning and before assembly. Notice that a pass-through is positioned on the right face of the foreground bench and leads to the rear of the Sterishield.

It is of interest to note that excellent cleanliness conditions have been obtained in the general work area of the Weston clean room as a result of the recirculation of air through the clean benches. Temperature and humidity are controlled by two window air conditioners.

REFERENCES

1. ECHOLS, W. H., YOUNG, J. A. *Studies of Portable Air-Operated Aerosol Generator.* NRL 5929. U. S. Naval Research Laboratory, Washington, D.C., July, 1963.

2. TIMMERMAN, S. W. "Clean Bench." *Conference on Clean Room Specifications.* SCR-652. Office of Technical Services, Department of Commerce, Washington, D.C., May 1963.

Chapter 14. *Clean Room Standards*

Air Force Technical Order 00-25-203

Soon after the Air Force constructed its first clean rooms, it became apparent that there would be difficulty in resolving the differences between the various manufacturers' environmental requirements. This was complicated by lack of knowledge in the field. The need for a comparison was a problem that was unique with the Air Force. It was required to overhaul many types of sophisticated components from many different manufacturers. In an effort to resolve the problem of supplying all the different environmental conditions specified, the Air Force conducted a survey of industry to determine how it could provide clean rooms compatable with these requirements.

The results of this survey were incorporated in the original Air Force Technical Order 00-25-203, published in March of 1961. This technical order established four classes of clean rooms (see Table 14-1). In the absence of data recently developed on size-distribution relationships (see Chapter 2), these classes were set up on a somewhat arbitrary basis. The difficulty encountered with this classification can be seen by quoting from a talk given by Lt. Philip R. Austin to the Second National Convention of the American Association of Contamination Control in Boston, 1963, prior to the acceptance and publishing of the revised Technical Order 00-25-203.

Let us first discuss requirements for Air Force Clean Room items. Observing Figure 14-1, we note the larger area which is representative of products such as instruments, gyros, electronic components, precision measurement equipment, hydraulic systems, pneumatic systems, and items having 0.005-inch clearances. Notice also that the lower end of this curve defines an area for missiles and LOX systems. Running through the larger area, we see a line marked "Industrial Air Generalized." This line defines the ambient contamination level and slope which we would expect to find in a normal metropolitan city or good factory area. Our studies have shown that the majority of products having clearances from 0.0001 to 0.0010 inch can be overhauled in what we have defined as an Air Force standard clean room. For product requirements one order of magnitude more stringent than those stated by the Air Force standard clean room, we shall use a tool called a clean work station. This clean work station will be employed on products having clearances in the range of 20 to 100 millionths of an inch, such as optics, miniature ball bearings, miniature contacts, and miniature gyros.

Let us see why the current classes of clean room as stated by the Air Force are inadequate by referring to Figure 14-2. Class I Clean Room defines a contamination level which is greater than industrial air. This is really not a clean room but a controlled factory area. A Class II environment is somewhat better, but yet it is still poorer than industrialized air if we consider meeting the larger particle size requirement. If we meet the lower particle size requirement for Class II, then because of the size-distribution relationships for airborne particulate matter, we will have a room much better than industrialized air. The contamination level for a current Class III clean room shows a discontinuous slope. The smaller size particle requirement is not in agreement with the size-distribution relationship for airborne contamination. The specification for the larger size particles is a good value. The current Air Force IV clean room is the best stated with respect to size distribution relationships for air. Having defined our product requirements and the standard clean room and the clean work station, we find that the Class IV clean room in one case is better than what we require and, in the second case, not good enough for the product; thus we feel that this is unnecessary in our system.[1]

The latest revision of Technical Order 00-25-203 is dated July 1, 1963. It establishes one class of clean

[1] Abstracted from reference 2.

room and lists design and operating standards for this room. These sections of the technical order are reproduced below.

Section II, AF Standard Clean Room Standards

2-1. ENVIRONMENTAL DESIGN STANDARDS

a. The following standards are to be met when only the environmental control systems are operating. Temperature, humidity, and airborne particle count readings will be taken at bench height or working level in accordance with the sampling plan outlined in appendix IV, figure 4A-1 (Figure 9-7).

b. The air filtration method for the room is to be determined by the design agency to meet the requirement of not more than 20,000 particles per cubic foot of atmosphere 0.5 micron size and larger, with not more than 4,000 particles per cubic foot of atmosphere 1.0 micron size and larger. These two points will give

Table 14–1 (*1*)

	CLASS I	*CLASS II*	*CLASS III*	*CLASS IV*
Air conditioning	Temperature limits — commercial air conditioning designed for 20°F. Temperature differential humidity limits — relative humidity 40% ± 10%	Temperature limits — 72° ± 5° Humidity limits — relative humidity 40% ± 10%	Temperature limits — 72° ± 3° Humidity limits — relative humidity 40% ± 5%	Temperature limits — 72° ± 1° Humidity limits — relative humidity 40% ± 5%
Pressure differential	Positive pressure differential within the clean room will be maintained in order to eliminate infiltration of dust-laden outside air	Positive pressure differential — clean room to have highest pressure; anteroom or entrance, lowest pressure; air conditioning to operate 24 hours a day every day of the year and reheat capability to maintain temperature	Same as Class II	Same as Class II
Particle-count tolerance	1. Design criteria — 85% efficient 2. Operating criteria — 250,000 countable particles per cubic foot of air; light-field technique	1. Design criteria — 50,000 particles per cubic foot of air 2. Operating criteria *A*. Maximum 85,000 particles per cubic foot of air between 0.3 microns and 10 microns *B*. Maximum 15,000 particles per cubic foot greater than 10 microns; light-field technique	1. Design criteria — 20,000 particles per cubic foot of air 2. Operating criteria — maximum 35,000 particles per cubic foot of air between 0.3 and 10 microns and a maximum 6,000 particles per cubic foot of air greater than 1 micron; dark-field technique	Operating criteria 1. Maximum 10,000 particles per cubic foot of air between 0.3 and 10 microns 2. Maximum 2,000 particles per cubic foot of air between 0.5 and 10 microns; dark-field technique

the slope of the particle size distribution relationship which has been established.[2] The size dimension shall be taken as the maximum dimension of the particle. (See appendix II, figure 2A-1, "Particle Size—Distribution Curve") (Figure 14-3). The design standard is the "at rest" standard.

c. The air conditioning system must be able to provide a temperature range of 67°F to 77°F and be able to control the room rate of change to 2.5°F per hour. A design temperature of 72°F is recommended at working level. This condition will be met regardless of the seasonal variations of temperature and humidity of the ambient air.

d. A humidity level of 40% will be the maximum allowable limit for a room. No minimum allowable limit will be stated; this will be at the discretion of the using activity. This condition will be met regardless of the seasonal variations of temperature and humidity of the ambient air.

e. With the entry door closed, a minimum posi-

[2] *Size Distribution Relationships for Airborne Particulate Matter*," Report 17.0002.04.01, MAMES, Olmsted AFB Pa., April 1963 (Distribution limited).

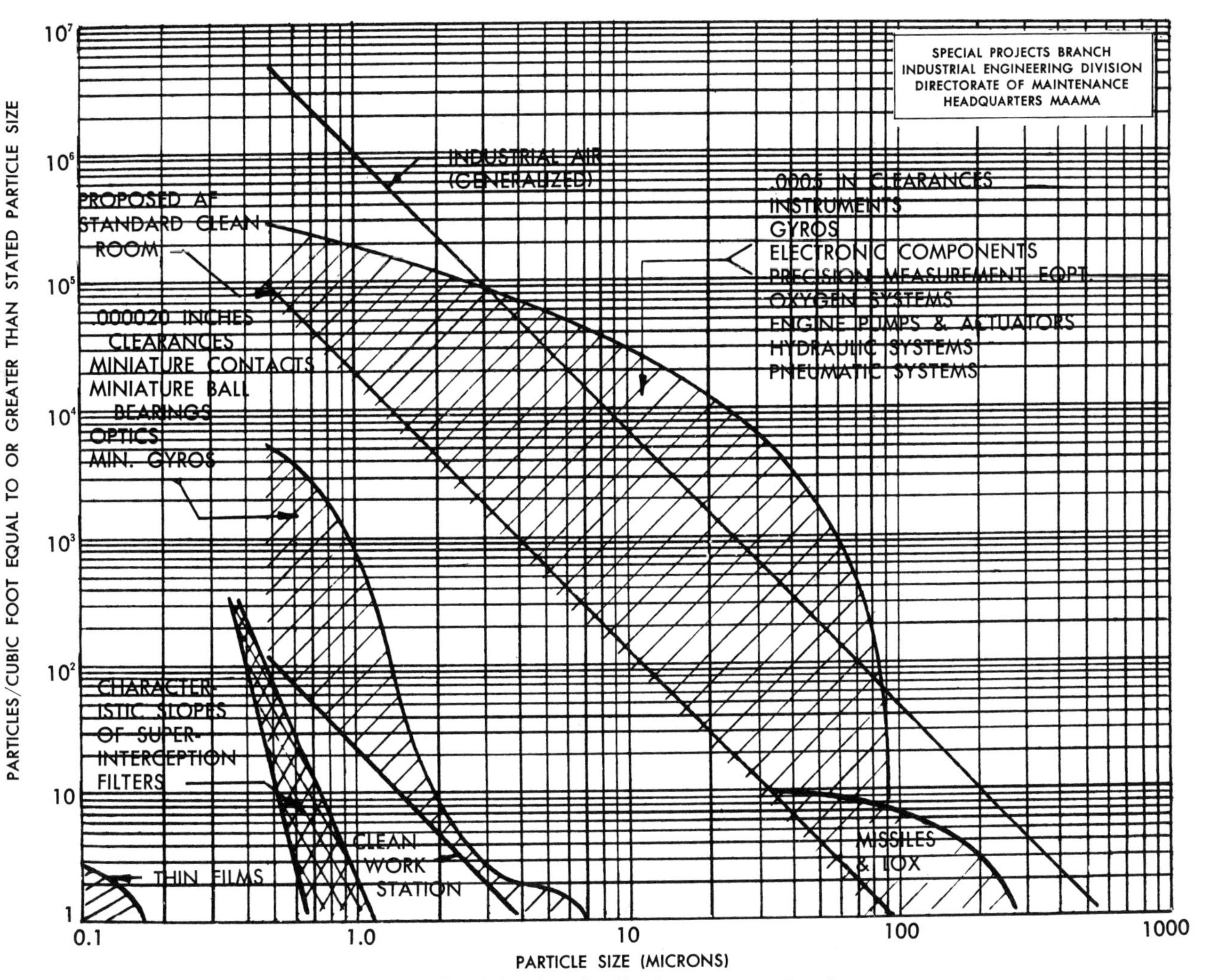

FIGURE 14-1. Particle size-distribution curves showing cleanliness requirements. *Courtesy MAMES, Olmsted AFB, Pa.*

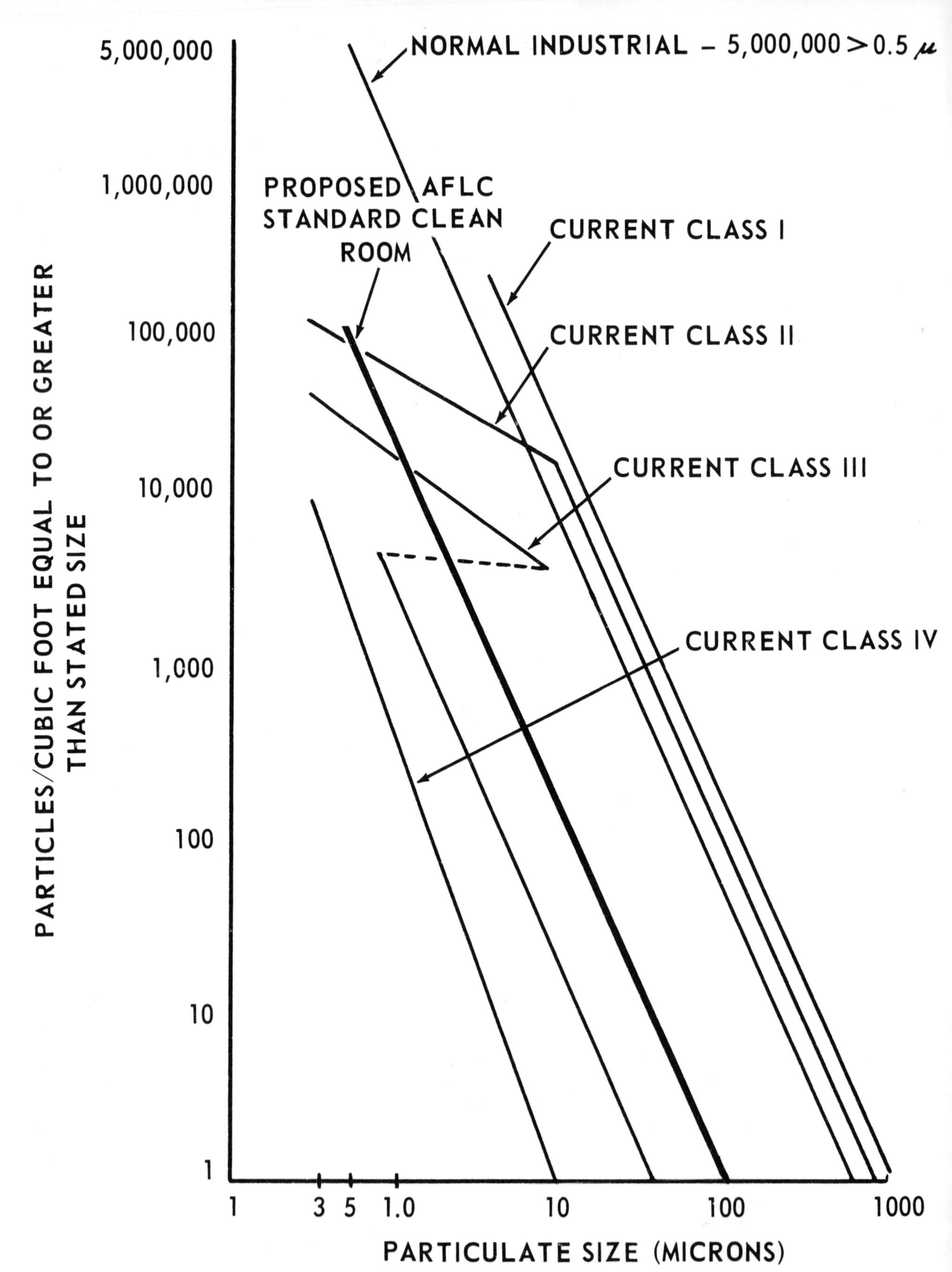

FIGURE 14-2. Particle size-distribution curves showing clean room classes. *Courtesy MAMES, Olmsted AFB, Pa.*

tive pressure differential of 0.10 inch of water will be maintained between the clean room and uncontaminated section. This will insure an outflow velocity of air from the clean room when an entry door is opened. A minimum positive pressure differential of 0.05 inch of water will be maintained between the uncontaminated section and the semi-contaminated section, such that when the door is opened between these sections, there will be an outflow velocity from the uncontaminated section. A minimum positive pressure differential of 0.01 inch of water will be maintained between the semi-contaminated section and the locker area, such that there will be an outflow velocity of air from the semi-contaminated section. (Each pressure differential is measured with the entry door closed.)

f. Shadowless illumination with a minimum intensity of 125 foot candles will be provided at bench or working level.

g. Noxious vapor control will be positive and complete. All such vapors will be drawn out of the work space and handled as required by safety regulations.

h. Room Evaluation Procedure

(1) Newly constructed Standard Clean Rooms will have a minimum five-day cycling test. This will consist of meeting the "at rest" conditions on five successive days for a minimum period of eight hours.

(2) For rooms in operation, the "at rest" condition should be checked periodically to determine if the environmental control system is functioning properly. If the contamination level cannot be met, improper room cleanup, faulty filters, improperly sealed filters, or faulty environmental control system are indicated. A check of the entire wall and ceiling areas for cracks and leaks, especially around any openings; should also be made.

2-2. Environmental Operation Standards

a. The following standards are to be met when the environmental control systems are operating, product overhaul and repair equipments are operating, and personnel are performing assigned tasks within the room. Temperature, humidity and airborne particle count reading will be taken at bench height or working level in accordance with the sampling plan outlined in appendix IV, figure 4A-1.

b. The particle count and size requirement for a room in operation will be not more than 100,000 particles per cubic foot of atmosphere 0.5 micron size and larger, with not more than 20,000 particles per cubic foot of atmosphere 1.0 micron size and larger. This condition is to be met at bench height or working level.

c. The air conditioning system must be able to provide a temperature range of 67°F to 77°F and be able to control the room rate of change to 4.0°F per hour. A mean temperature of 72°F is recommended at working level.

d. A humidity level of 45% will be the maximum allowable limit for a room. The minimum limit will be at the discretion of the using activity. (See paragraph 4-1.d.)

e. With the entry door closed, a minimum positive pressure differential of 0.10 inch of water will be maintained between the clean room and the uncontaminated section. This will insure an outflow velocity of air from the clean room when an entry door is opened. A minimum positive pressure differential of 0.05 inch of water will be maintained between the uncontaminated section and the semi-contaminated section, such that when the door is opened between these sections there will be an outflow velocity from the uncontaminated section. A minimum positive pressure differential of 0.01 inch of water will be maintained between the semi-contaminated section and the locker area, such that there will be an outflow velocity of air from the semi-contaminated section. (Each pressure differential is measured with the entry door closed.)

f. Shadowless illumination with a minimum intensity of 100 foot candles will be provided at bench or working level.

g. Noxious vapor control will be positive and complete. All such vapors will be drawn out of the work space and handled as required by safety regulations.

h. Room Evaluation Procedure—Standard clean rooms will monitor operational standards using the procedure outlined in section IV, paragraphs 4-2 to 4-5 inclusive.

i. Special Requirements–The following paragraphs must be met during the operation of a clean room:

Paragraph	*Title*
4-6.a.(1)	Clothing Requirements
4-7.b, 4-7.c.	Personnel Indoctrination
4-8.	Employee Disciplines (Clean Room)
4-9.	Employee Disciplines (Change Room)
4-12.a.	Personnel Training (3)

Clean work stations are utilized for atmospheres which must be cleaner than the standard clean room. The design and operating standards for this device are as follows:

Section V, AF Clean Work Station Standards

5-1. Environmental Design Standards

(See figure 6-1.)

a. The air filtration method for the clean work station is to be determined by the design agency to meet the requirement of no more than 100 particles per cubic foot of atmosphere 0.5 micron size and larger. This condition is to be met throughout the entire work station upstream of the work piece. The distribution of particles for this requirement is to be no greater than as shown in appendix II. The design standard is the "at rest" standard.

b. A minimum average velocity of 100 feet per minute is to be maintained throughout the work station, with laminar flow being essentially maintained in and at the work station. This condition may be altered if it can be shown that during operation of the work station, the above air filtration design standard is met and that particulate matter will make a maximum of one pass by the work piece.

c. Shadowless illumination with a minimum intensity of 100 foot candles will be provided at the working level of the work station.

5.2. ENVIRONMENTAL OPERATIONAL STANDARDS

a. The particle count for a clean work station in operation will be not more than 1,000 particles per cubic foot of atmosphere 0.5 micron size and larger. The distribution of particles for this requirement is to be no greater than as shown in appendix II.

b. The minimum average velocity throughout the work station will be allowed to decrease to 75 feet per minute before corrective action to increase the average velocity is required.

c. Shadowless illumination with a minimum intensity of 100 foot candles will be provided at the working level of the work station. Increase or auxiliary pinpoint lighting is to be employed as the product demands.

d. Filters used in the design of a clean work station must be inspected according to the manufacturer's instructions to insure continuous contamination control of the work station.

e. Special Requirements—The following paragraphs must be met during the operation of a clean work station:

Paragraph	*Title*
7-3.d.	Station Control
7-5.	Operational Techniques and Disciplines
7-6.	Clean Work Station Check List (4)

The standards for dust counts are further defined by plotting them on a particle size-distribution curve which is also included in the technical order and is shown here as Figure 14-3. This graph establishes the slope of the distribution line and permits identifying the level of a room by the total number of particles equal to or greater than a certain size.

The size chosen for standardization is 0.5 micron. This size was chosen because it was felt that sizes smaller than this are acted upon by additional forces (see Chapter 2 for a more complete discussion of this subject) and are therefore not part of the size-distribution (straight-line) relationship established for sizes 0.5 micron and larger.

Federal Standard 209

While Technical Order 00-25-203 was being revised, a great deal of interest was generated in governmental agencies other than the Air Force. The Atomic Energy Commission had a large investment in clean rooms and, in fact, had the most stringent requirements. The National Aeronautics and Space Administration had realized the necessity for controlling environments around space vehicles and sophisticated components. The result of this interest was the generation of a federal standard which would include all branches of the government.

The development of Federal Standard 209 began with a conference at Sandia Corporation, Albuquerque, New Mexico, in April 1963. Approximately two hundred clean room practitioners were in attendance. Representatives from all interested governmental agencies and selected industrial clean room users were included. Speakers at the conference presented the state of the art at that time, including talks on the new laminar-flow rooms and devices. The result of the conference was the establishment of a working group to write the federal standard. This group consisted of one member from each interested governmental agency and several industry consultants. Before the end of the year, Federal Standard 209 was published, an amazing record considering that coordination was required from all the services and each agency. This was, in part, possible because of the firm foundation and groundwork laid by the Air Force Technical Order group who participated in development of the standard. This standard establishes three classes of clean rooms, named for the acceptable particle count in the room in the size range of 0.5 micron and larger. The three classes are: Class 100,000, Class 10,000 and Class 100. Class 100,000 corresponds to the Air Force standard clean room.

The mandatory portions (Sections 1-5) of Federal Standard 209 are quoted below. Additional nonmandatory recommendations are supplied in the standard to assist the user in achieving the class he wishes to attain. Table 14-2 provides a quick reference to the particle count requirements of the standard. Note the size-distribution relationship in Figure 14-4 which is similar to that used in Technical Order 00-25-203.

1. Scope

1.1 *Scope.* This document establishes standard classes of environmental air control within clean rooms and work stations.

1.2 *Objective.* The objective of this standard is to prescribe air cleanliness classes and other air environmental conditions required for achieving and maintaining the levels of cleanliness specified in the product specifications.

2. Referenced Documents

2.1 *Nongovernmental.* The issues of the following documents in effect on the date of invitation for bids form a part of this standard to the extent specified herein.
American Society for Testing and Materials
ASTM F25-63T
(Tentative method for sizing and counting airborne particulate contamination in clean rooms and other dust controlled areas, designed for electronic and aerospace work.)
(Application for copies should be addressed to the American Society for Testing and Materials, 1916 Race

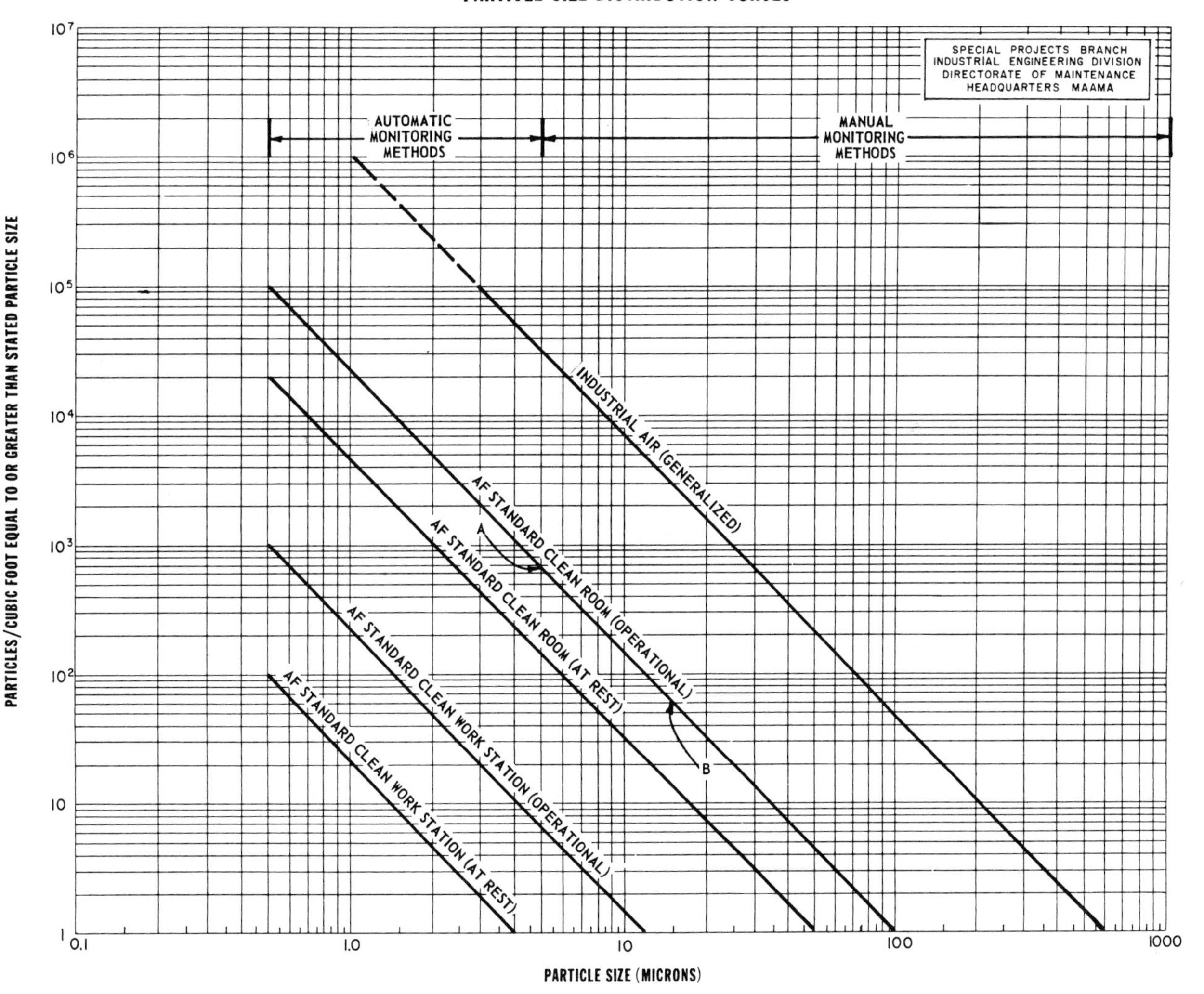

Figure 14-3. Particle size-distribution curves showing Air Force Standards. *U. S. Air Force Technical Order 00-25-203*

Street, Philadelphia 3, Pa.)
Society of Automotive Engineers, Incorporated
SAE-ARP-743
(Procedure for the determination of particulate contamination of air in dust controlled spaces by the particle count method.)
(Application for copies should be addressed to the Society of Automotive Engineers, Incorporated, 485 Lexington Avenue, New York 17, N. Y.)

3. Definitions

3.1 *Clean room.* A clean room is an enclosed area employing control over the particulate matter in air with temperature, humidity and pressure control as required. To meet the requirements of a "clean room" as defined by this standard, all clean rooms must maintain a particulate count as specified in clean room classes, 5.1.

3.2 *Work station.* A work station is a work bench or similar working enclosure characterized by having its own filtered air or gas supply.

3.3 *Operational level.* Operational levels are dust counts taken in a facility during any activity period.

3.4 *Particle size.* Particle size is expressed as the apparent maximum linear dimension or diameter of the particle.

3.5 *Micron.* A unit of measurement equal to one one-millionth of a meter (0.00003937 inch). (e.g., 25 microns is approximately 0.001 inch.)

4. General Requirements

4.1 *General clean room area.* All particle generating operations which will cause out of control conditions

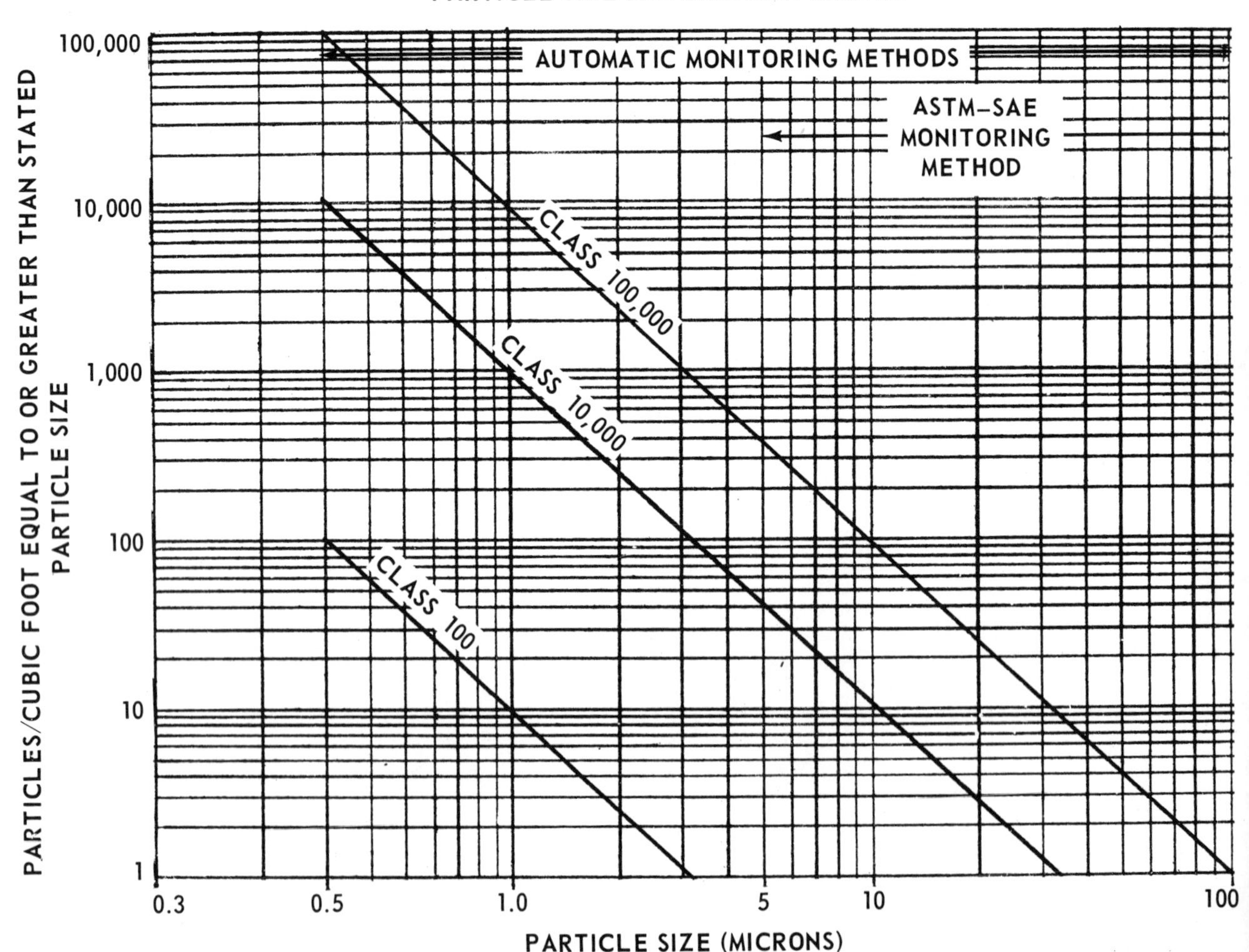

Figure 14-4. Particle size-distribution curves showing Federal Standards. *Federal Standard 209.*

for the clean room or clean work station are prohibited.

4.2 *Equipment calibration.* All equipment used to control, monitor and record clean room and work station conditions shall be calibrated as required.

4.3 *Environmental control.* Environmental conditions such as temperature, humidity, pressure and airborne particle count shall be controlled, recorded and records reviewed as per contractual specification.

5. Detailed Requirements

5.1 *Clean room classes.* The three classes of clean rooms as defined by this standard are shown in Table I. Clean room classifications are based on particle count with a maximum number of particles permissible 0.5 micron or 5.0 microns and larger, and are established as operational levels. All clean rooms and work stations as designated by this standard must be capable of meeting at least one of the following performance classes:

5.1.1 *Class 100.* Particle count not to exceed a total of 100 particles per cubic foot 0.5 micron and larger. (See airborne particle monitoring, 5.5)

5.1.2 *Class 10,000.* Particle count not to exceed a total of 10,000 particles per cubic foot 0.5 micron and larger, or 65 particles per cubic foot 5.0 microns and larger. (See airborne particle monitoring, 5.5)

5.1.3. *Class 100,000.* Particle count not to exceed a total of 100,000 particles per cubic foot 0.5 micron and larger, or 700 particles per cubic foot 5.0 microns and larger. (See airborne particle monitoring, 5.5[3])

5.2 *Clean room air*

5.2.1 *Pressure.* All clean rooms shall maintain a pressure above that of surrounding areas to assure that all leakage shall be outward.

5.3 *Temperature*

5.3.1 *Temperature range.* Temperature controls if applicable, shall be capable of maintaining a specified temperature within a range of 67°F to 77°F within ±5°F in less temperature critical areas, and up to ±0.5°F in temperature sensitive applications.

5.4 *Humidity*

5.4.1 *Humidity range.* The maximum relative humidity shall be 45%. Humidity controls shall be capable of holding a specified relative humidity within ±10% for general applications, and up to ±5% for humidity sensitive applications.

5.5 *Airborne particle monitoring*

5.5.1 *Particle counting methods.* All clean rooms and work stations shall employ one or more of the following particle counting methods.

(a) For particle sizes 0.5 micron and larger, automatic equipment employing light scattering principles shall be used. This applies to particle counting and particle concentration indicating devices which have been calibrated to give particle number information.

(b) For particle sizes 5.0 microns and larger, microscopic counting of particles collected on a membrane filter, through which a sample of air has been drawn, shall be used, as specified in ASTM F25-63T, and SAE-ARP-743.

(c) Other monitoring methods and equipment may be used only if demonstrated to be of accuracy and repeatability equal to those methods listed in paragraphs 5.5.1a and 5.5.1b.

5.5.2 *Monitoring techniques.* Monitoring techniques and routines shall be established to demonstrate the reliability of the system to conform to the class of clean room or work station as required by the contractual document for the product involved.

[3] *Note:* Any required work or storage area permitting higher contamination levels than the limits of this standard, are not considered clean rooms and are outside the scope of this standard.

Notice: Copies of specifications, standards, drawings, and publications required by contractors in connection with specific procurement functions should be obtained from the procuring agency or as directed by the contracting officer.

Copies of this standard for military use may be obtained as indicated in the foreword to, or the general provisions of, the Index of Military Specifications and Standards.

The title and identifying symbol should be stipulated when requesting copies of military standards(5).

Marshall Space Flight Center Standard 246

This document was developed by The Propulsion and Vehicle Engineering Division, George C. Marshall Space Flight Center (MSFC), National Aeronautics and Space Administration (NASA), Huntsville, Alabama, about the same time as the Air Force technical order was revised. In format it is similar to the original Air Force technical order. Four classes of clean rooms are established. These requirements can be seen by quoting Section 1 of

Table 14–2

CLEAN-ROOM CLASSES AS LISTED IN FEDERAL STANDARD 209 (6)

Class	*Maximum Number of Particles per Cubic Foot 0.5 Micron and Larger*	*Maximum Number of Particles per Cubic Foot 5.0 Micron and Larger*
100	100	—
10,000	10,000	65
100,000	100,000	700

this document. Further comparison of contamination levels may be obtained by referring to Table 14-3. It should be pointed out that the size-distribution relationships established by MAMES, Olmsted Air Force Base, Pennsylvania, were not widely publicized at the time of the development of this standard. Therefore, the cleanliness levels established are not compatible with those of the Air Force and federal standards based on these relationships.

1. SCOPE

1.1 *Purpose.* The purpose of this standard is to establish design criteria for use in determining design and functional requirements, for controlled environment work areas. This standard is mandatory for use by all activities of the George C. Marshall Space Flight Center and associated contractors required to meet and maintain cleanliness levels specified for space vehicle systems and associated equipment.

1.2 *Scope.* This standard establishes the design criteria and guide lines for controlling the contamination in and maintaining the cleanliness level of controlled environment work areas.

1.3 *Classification and types.* This standard covers controlled environmental work areas of the following classes and types.

1.3.1 *Classes*

(a) Class I. Class I controlled environment area shall conform to the minimum requirements specified herein and be suitable for cleaning, assembling, inspecting and packaging of less critical space vehicle components, assemblies, sub-systems and systems. These requirements are as follows:

(1) Facility design factors. This type of facility shall be designed and constructed with a view toward high standards of shop cleanliness and the least amount of maintenance and service cost in keeping with the projected workload.

(2) Air conditioning. Unless otherwise specified, air conditioning shall be maintained at a comfortable temperature.

(b) Class II. Class II controlled environment area provides for basic requirements of dust exclusion and atmospheric control required for cleaning, assembling, testing, calibration, and packaging of instruments and electronic or mechanical devices requiring finer tolerances and more precise controlled environment. These requirements are as follows:

(1) Facility design factors. The facility shall be designed to meet the basic requirements specified herein for controlled environment work area. These requirements apply to the overall controlled environment work area, including personnel and material cleaning chambers, air locks, lockers, and pass-throughs.

(2) Air conditioning. Unless otherwise specified, air conditioning shall be maintained at a comfortable temperature. The filter shall be capable of removing 85 percent (0.3 μ) of the contamination from the air.

a. Temperature control. Unless otherwise specified, the temperature shall be maintained at 72 (plus or minus 5) degrees Fahrenheit (F).

b. Humidity control. Unless otherwise specified, the relative humidity shall be 40 (plus or minus 10) percent.

(3) Particle count. The maximum allowable particles per cubic foot shall be as follows:

5 – 25 μ	300
25 – 100 μ	150
Over 100 μ	*
Fibers	30

*Quantity omitted in printing of Standard.

(4) Attire. Personnel working in class II controlled environment work areas shall be required to wear authorized smocks.

(c) Class III. Class III controlled environment work area provides for precision requirements for temperature, humidity, and dust control required in assembling, calibrating, and testing of more advanced instrumentation, electrical and mechanical devices.

(1) Facility design factors. This facility shall be designed and constructed to meet the most advanced requirements of a controlled environment atmosphere.

(2) Air conditioning. Unless otherwise specified, air conditioning shall be maintained at a comfortable temperature. The filter shall be capable of removing 99.9 (0.3 μ) percent of the contamination from the air.

a. Temperature control. Unless otherwise specified, the temperature shall be maintained at 72 (plus or minus 3) degrees F.

b. Humidity control. Unless otherwise specified, the relative humidity shall be 40 (plus or minus 5) percent.

(3) Particle count. The maximum allowable particles per cubic foot shall be as follows:

5 – 25 μ	180
25 – 100 μ	30
Over 100 μ	1
Fibers	1

(4) Attire. Personnel working in class III controlled environment work areas shall be required to wear authorized smocks, caps and boots.

(d) Class IV. Class IV controlled environment work area provides for ultra-precision requirements for temperature, humidity and dust control required in assembling, calibrating, and testing of more advanced instruments, electrical and mechanical devices.

(1) Facility design factor. This facility shall be designed and constructed to meet the most advanced requirements for a controlled environment atmosphere.

(2) Air conditioning. Unless otherwise specified, air conditioning shall be maintained at a comfortable temperature. The filter shall be capable of removing 99.9 (0.3 μ) percent of the contamination from the air.

a. Temperature control. Unless otherwise specified, the temperature shall be maintained at 72 (plus or minus 1) degrees F.

b. Humidity control. Unless otherwise specified, the relative humidity shall be 40 (plus or minus 5) percent.

(3) Particle count. The maximum allowable particles per cubic foot shall be as follows:

5 – 25 μ	20
25 – 100 μ	5
Over 100 μ	1
Fibers	1

(4) Attire. Personnel working in class IV con-

TABLE 14–3

CONTROLLED-ENVIRONMENT AREAS (8)

(Levels of contamination)

	Class I	*Class II*	*Class III*	*Class IV*
Controlled environment	Good housekeeping Air conditioning for comfort	Air-conditioning filter rating 85% (>0.3 micron)* Temperature control Humidity control Personnel control	Air-conditioning filter rating 99.9% (>0.3 micron)† Temperature control Humidity control Personnel control	Air-conditioning filter rating 99.9% (>0.3 micron)* Temperature control Humidity control Personnel control
Maximum allowable particles per cubic foot (ARP 743) (size range)		Sampling frequency‡ once per week	Sampling frequency‡ once per day	Sampling frequency‡ twice per day
5–25 microns		300	180	20
25–100 microns	NA	150	30	5
Over 100 microns		30	1	1
Fibers		30	1	1
Typical operation	Stage assembly Stage check	Panel assembly Engine checkout Engine repairs	LOX, fuel, and pneumatic valve cleaning, inspection, and packaging	Hydraulic component cleaning and assembly
		Closed-loop cleaning-valve functional test Tungsten and metal inert gas welding	Close tolerance measurement LOX, fuel, and pneumatic valve assembly	Gas bearing component cleaning and assembly Critical measurement, particle counting (laboratory)
Dress§	NA	Smocks	Smocks, caps, boots	Suit, cap, boots, gloves

* National Bureau of Standards discoloration test.
† Dioctyl phthalate test.
‡ ARP 743 with black Millipore membrane.
§ The requirements may be less stringent for controlled-environment work stations.

trolled environment work areas shall be required to wear authorized suits, caps, boots, and gloves.

1.3.2 *Types*

(a) Type A. Type A controlled environment area shall specify ambient temperature control, having an allowable variation of plus or minus 2 degrees F.

(b) Type B. Type B controlled environment area shall require a specified ambient temperature control, having an allowable variation of plus or minus 5 degrees F.

(c) Type C. Type C controlled environment area shall require a specified humidity control with no allowable variation greater than the designated maximum, but not less than 30 percent relative humidity, unless a dry box operation is required (7).

Aerospace Industries Association Standard

Although the most used and accepted standards by far, are Technical Order 00-25-203 and Federal Standard 209, various other nongovernmental clean room standards have had limited usage. Some have been similar to the old Air Force technical order; others have been conceived independently and present their own arbitrary values and limits.

One of the nongovernmental standards which resulted from participation by a large number of industry representatives is that of the Aerospace Industries Association. It was conceived by the Aerospace Research and Testing Committee and bears the title "Requirements for Clean Rooms," ARTC-62-131. It is a performance standard and is quoted below.

1. SCOPE

This document describes the requirements for clean rooms and the means of checking conformance thereto, in which, components and systems having various contamination levels prescribed for them for functional reasons can be manufactured, tested and packaged within limits of contamination commensurate with their requirements.

2. DEFINITIONS

2.1 *Clean Room.* A clean room is an enclosed space in which the physical environment is defined and contaminating matter is controlled in size and quantity.

2.2 *Clean Room Class.* Variations in functionally required contamination levels for various parts, components, assemblies and systems suggest that clean rooms may be of various *classes* distinguishable one from another by the requirements of Section 4.

2.3 *Auxiliary Room.* An auxiliary room is a pressurized room with direct access to the clean room.

3. CLEAN ROOM CLASSES

Economics of maintaining a maximum contamination controlled clean room for the tightest functional requirement part, component, assembly or system is not warranted for all manufacturing, testing and packaging operations. Several classes of controlled contamination level clean rooms are economically warranted. Four classes, as described in Section 4, can adequately serve Aerospace Industries' requirements. The class level is defined by conformance to the requirements of Section 4 and does not necessarily limit facility design criteria or materials of construction of the rooms. The class levels are based upon performance only.

4. REQUIREMENTS

Classes of clean rooms are distinguishable from each other by

a. contamination level of room air
b. relative humidity
c. temperature differential tolerance
d. pressure differential tolerance
e. frequency of checking
f. presence of auxiliary rooms

4.1 *Class I*

a. contamination level/one Cu. Ft. of room air allowable number of particulates 50–350 microns—350 allowable number of particulates over 350 microns—1
b. relative humidity 50% maximum
c. temperature tolerance 72° ± 10°F
d. positive pressure differential shall be maintained when room is closed
e. check of items (a)—(d) at least weekly

4.2 *Class II*

a. contamination level/one Cu. Ft. of room air allowable number particulates 50—100 microns—40 allowable number particulates over 100 microns—5
b. relative humidity 50% maximum
c. temperature tolerance 72° ± 10°F
d. pressure tolerance A continuous positive pressure differential shall be maintained
e. check of items (a)—(d) at least semiweekly

4.3 *Class III*

a. contamination level/one Cu. Ft. of room air allowable number particulates 15–25 microns—35 maximum allowable number particulates 25—30 microns—15 maximum allowable number particulates over 50 microns—1 maximum

b. relative humidity
   50% maximum
c. temperature tolerance
   72° ± 5°F
d. pressure differential between clean room and auxiliary room shall be a minimum of 0.1" H_2O
   pressure differential between auxiliary rooms and outside shall be positive
e. checking items (a)—(d)
   at least once per shift

4.4 *Class IV*

a. contamination level/one cu. ft. of room air allowable number particulates 5–15 microns —50 maximum allowable number particulates 16–25 microns—4 maximum allowable number particulates over 26 microns—.3 maximum
b. relative humidity
   50% maximum
c. temperature tolerance
   72° ± 5°F
d. pressure differential between clean room and auxiliary rooms shall be a minimum of 0.1" H_2O.
   pressure differential between auxiliary rooms outside shall be positive
e. checking items (a)–(d)
   at least once per shift

5. Checking Conformance

5.1 Contamination level of room air shall be checked using SAE-ARP-743 procedures with the following exceptions:

a. Size ranges counted shall be those shown in paragraph 4.1 a, 4.2 a, 4.3 a, 4.4 a.
b. Where necessary to reduce value of a blank analysis, filters shall be precleaned and/or samples larger than 10 cu. ft. be drawn. Blank analysis value shall not exceed 10% of the allowable limitations.
c. Stereoptic microscopes may be used for control of class I and II rooms, but shall not be used for class III and IV rooms.
d. Alternate methods that are demonstrated to be equivalent to SAE-ARP-743 may be used for checking room air contamination level.
e. A sufficient number of representative samples shall be taken in areas where contamination sensitive work is being done.

5.2 Normal commercial standards shall be used to determine temperature, pressure differential and relative humidity(*9*).

REFERENCES

1. *U. S. Air Force Technical Order 00-25-203, Standard and Functional Criteria for Design and Operation of Clean Rooms,* Appendix 1. March 1961. (No longer available.)

2. Austin, 1/Lt. P. R. *Revision of Technical Order 00-25-203.* American Association for Contamination Control Convention, Boston, Mass., May 1963.

3. *U. S. Air Force Technical Order 00-25-203, Standards and Guidelines for the Design and Operation of Clean Room and Clean Work Stations,* pp. 2-1, 2-2. Office of Technical Services, Department of Commerce, Washington, D.C., July 1963.

4. *Ibid.,* pp. 5-1, 5-2.

5. *Federal Standard No. 209, Clean Room and Work Station Requirements, Controlled Environment,* Sections 1 through 5. Office of Technical Services, Department of Commerce, Washington, D.C., December 16, 1963.

6. *Ibid.,* Table 1.

7. *Marshall Space Flight Center Standard No. 246, Design and Operating Criteria of Controlled Environment Areas, Standard for,* Section 1. Office of Technical Services, Department of Commerce, Washington, D. C., July 1963.

8. *Ibid.,* Table 1.

9. *Aerospace Industries Association Standard ARTC-62-131, Requirements for Clean Rooms.* Aerospace Industries Association, Washington, D.C., September 1962.

Index

Absolute filters—see Filters, HEPA
Aerosol, 9, 16
Aerosol generator, 401, 402
AIA Standard, 420, 421
Airborne contaminants, 256–266
Air handling
  cross flow room, 205
  down flow room, 203
  ducts, 144
  systems, 138–143
  twin cross flow room, 207
Air locks, 151
Air showers, 151–154
  velocity—time relationship, 152
Analog counting, 292, 294
  also see Counting, automatic
Antistatic finishes, 354
ARF counter, 276–277
Atomic Energy Commission, 81
Austin, P. R., 20, 55–77
Automatic counters—see Counters, automatic

Brownian motion, 80

Cambridge Filter Corp., 84
Cascade impactor, 265, 266
Casella counter, 304
Ceilings, 147
Central vacuum-cleaning system, 158
Certification of clean rooms, 307–314
Change room, 155
  decontamination procedure, 178, 179
  disciplines, 178–180
  exiting procedure, 180
Chemical Warfare Service, 81
Clean-o-meter, 372–375
Clean room
  certification, 307–314
  control of, 2
  conventionally designed—see Conventionally designed clean rooms
  cross flow—see Cross flow room
  definition of, 1
  down-flow—see Down-flow room
  equipment, 156–158
  history of, 2–4
  inflatable, 171
Clean room (*Continued*)
  industry, 4, 5
  pressure, 139
  population, 191, 192
  mathematical model, 136
  military, 5, 7
  support rooms, 154–156, 208
  twin cross-flow—see Twin-cross-flow room
Clean work station
  development of, 384–388
  horizontal flow, 388, 389
  modular concept, 395, 396
  operation of, 400–408
    check list, 407
    controls, 404–407
    maintenance, 408
    population, 400–404
    shut down, 407
    specialized, 396, 397
    tunnel, 398
Cleaning
  construction requirements, 144
  electro-mechanical devices, 360–362
  methods
    acid, 359
    evaluation, 365
    Freon, 364
    solvent, 359
    sonic energy, 357–359, 365–367
    verification, 362–364
  tests
    atomizer, 376–378
    contact angle, 378
    copper dip, 379
    Coulter principle, 381
    electron microscope, 381
    Elm's modification of Mear's test, 379
    ferrocyanide paper, 379
    fluorescent dye, 379
    kerosine viewing of water break, 379
    oil spot, 379
    organic surface contaminants, 372–375
    performance, 368
    probe instrument, 381
    radioactive tracer, 379–382
    ring test, 379
    Rock Island drop, 378

Cleaning (*Continued*)
- solvent, 379
- tissue paper, 376
- visual inspection, 368, 369, 376
- water break, 376
- water spray, 376
- wettability, 370

Comparison of digital and analog counting, 292–294
Construction
- cleaning requirements, 144
- cross-flow room, 205
- down-flow room, 203
- materials of, 143, 144
- twin cross-flow room, 207

Contaminants
- airborne sizing and counting, 256–266
- determination of, 109–111
- affects parameters, 118–120
- gaseous, 12
- properties of, 9–12
  - energy relationships of particles, 12, 13
  - chemical and physical, 13
- sources of, 13–19, 188–191
  - air, 16, 17
  - assembly, 14, 17, 18
  - cleaning, 16
  - manufacture, 13, 14
  - product operation, 18

Contamination
- definition, 2
- electrical contact, 106–111
- garment, 346–350
- index, 78
- level fluctuations, 175, 176

Controls, employee—see Employee disciplines
Conventionally designed clean rooms
- examples of, 158–173
  - Air Force, 172, 173
  - General Electric Co., 170, 171
  - G. E. Space Tech. Center, 160–168
  - Grumman Aircraft Engr. Corp., 169
  - Kearfott, Div. Gen. Prec., 166–168
  - New Departure, Div. G.M., 158–160
  - Norden, Div. United Airc., 169–170
  - Weston Instrument & Electr., 171

Coulter principle, 302–304, 381
Counters, automatic
- fluid, 302–306
  - Casella, 304
  - Coulter, 302–304
  - HIAC, 304
- particle, 274–294
  - Armour Research Foundation, 276–277
  - calibration, 284, 285
  - photometers, 285–294
  - phototape, 294
  - requirements, 274, 275
  - Royco, 278–282

Counters, manual—see Manual counting
Cross-flow clean room, 205–207, 234–236
- advantages, 205, 206
- air handling system, 205
- application, 207
- construction features, 205
- contamination levels, 236–249
- disadvantages, 205, 206
- examples of, 209–218
  - Airesearch, 214–216
  - General Dynamics, 209, 210
  - ITT Federal Labs, 218
  - Lockheed Missiles & Sp., 211–213
  - United Controls, 218
  - Ward-Leonard Electric, 217, 218
- filter arrangement, 203–204
- heat load problems, 206
- operation, 234–236
- specifications for, 219–228

Cryogenic sampling, 371
Cunningham factor, 20
Curtain devices, 209
CWS filters, 81
- see also Filters, HEPA

Decontamination—see Change-room disciplines
Device operation
- constraints, 111, 112
- energy transmission, 113, 114
- mechanical loading, 113
- position and motion, 111, 112

Digital counting, 292–294
- see Monitoring, automatic

Dill dust-spot tester, 83
Dioctyl-phthalate test, 79, 81, 83, 84, 93
Disciplines, employee, 155, 156, 177–179, 181–187
Discoloration test, 83–84
DOP test, 79, 81, 83, 84, 93
Down-flow room, 203, 204, 234
- advantages, 204
- air handling system, 204
- application, 205
- construction, 204
- disadvantages, 204
- filter arrangement, 203
- operation, 234

Dry cleaning, garment, 340–343
Dry slide settling technique, 263–266
- location of slide, 264
- mounting of slide, 264–265
- slide preparation, 263

Duct work, 140
Ducts
- air handling, 144
- intake, 142

Dust free hood, 384

Earles, D. R., 121
Eddins, M. F., 121
Electron microscope, 8, 381
Electrostatic precipitation, 294
Employee controls, 181–187
Employee disciplines, 155, 156, 177, 178
  personnel rules, 178, 179
  training, 176
Energy transmission, 113, 114
Equipment, cleaning, 181
Equipment, clean room, 156–158

Fabric
  anti-static finish, 354
  garment, 323, 339
Failure considerations, 115–118
  gross, 118
  typical mechanisms, 116–118
  typical modes, 116
Failure mechanisms, 114, 115
  cleaning procedure, 125
  description of equipment, 124, 125
  experimental studies, 121–124
  operating procedure, 125
  results, 126
  test aerosols, 125
Federal Standard *209*, 414–417
Fibers
  identification of, 316–318
  man-made texile, 316
Filters
  absolute—see Filters, HEPA
  comparative efficiency of, 84
  cross-flow room, 205
  CWS—see Filters, HEPA
  down-flow room, 203
  HEPA
    application, 139–141, 144, 180, 181, 196
    construction of, 85–87
    design, 86, 87, 93
    development of, 81
    fire extinguishment, 94, 95
    handling, 91
    inspection, 87–91
    installation, 92
    leak check, 292
    life, 234, 235
    packaging, 87
    rating of, 81
    replacement, 93
    shipping, 87
    storage, 91
    tests, 87–91, 400–404
  location, 141
  membrane, 266–270
  sealing of, 142
  selection of, 139, 140
Filters (*Continued*)
  super-interception—see Filters, HEPA
  test
    AFI Code, 82
    ASHRAE Code, 82
    Atmospheric Dust Weight, 82, 83
    Discoloration, 83, 84
    DOP, 79, 81, 83, 84, 93
    Dust Spot, 83
    jet impinger, 84
    special efficiency, 83
    weight, 82
  twin cross-flow room, 207
Filtration
  mechanisms of, 80
  methods of, 79
Floors
  general, 144–146
  particle generation, 145
  scaling of vinyl, 145, 146
Fluid flow device consideration, 120
Fluid sampling procedures, 295–297
  counting, 296, 297
  cryogenic, 371
  filtering, 296
  rigid tube, 370
  surface, 370
Freon—see Cleaning methods
Freudiger, E., 107–110
Frith, C. F., 20, 55–77

Garments
  contamination, 346–350
  dry cleaning, 340–346
  fabrics, 323–339
  laundering, 339–340
  requirements, 318–323
  sampling for cleanliness, 343–346
General Electric Co., Lynn, Mass., 170, 171
General Electric Space Technology Center, 160–166
Glove box, 384
Grumman Aircraft Engineering Corp., 169

Hand cleaner, 158
Heat loading, cross-flow room, 206
Henri, J., 45
HEPA filters—see Filters, HEPA
HIAC counter, 304
High intensity light, 294
Hood devices, 209
Horizontal flow
  see Cross-flow room
  clean work station, 388, 389
Humidity monitoring, 254
Hygiene, personal, 176, 177

Identification of fibers, 316–318
Impaction sampling, 295

Intake ducts, 142
Inflatable clean room, 171

Johnson, C., 39

Kearfott, Div. of General Precision, 166–168
Kelly, K. V., 55
Klein, J. R., 38
Kodel, I. M., 96
Kreeger, E., 40, 50

Laminar flow
 advantages of, 201–203
 clean rooms, 138
  see also Cross-flow rooms, Down-flow rooms, Twin cross-flow rooms
 clean work stations—see Clean work stations
 cost comparison, 233
 cost savings, 202
 curtain devices, 209
 lost time, 232–233
 mobile clean room, 209
 objectives of, 195
 proto type rooms, 197, 198
  air flow tests, 201
  clean up tests, 201
  conditions of tests, 199, 200
  evaluation testing, 199
  knock-down model, 198
  particle concentration test, 200
  rigid all-weather unit, 198, 199
 surgical operating rooms, 249–251
Laundering, garment, 339, 340
Lawrence Radiation Laboratory, 85
Lieberman, A., 10–18, 99, 105, 111–132
Lighting, 147, 148
Linn, K., 41

Maintenance
 clean work station, 408
 room, 180, 181
Man-made textile fibers, 316
Manual counting, 256–271
 apparatus, 256–258
  requirements, 256–258
  preparation of, 258
 calculations, 261
 definitions, 256
 method, outline of, 256
 sampling, 258–271
  procedure, 258
  rate, 270, 271
  time, 262–264
Marsh, R. C., 53
Marshall Space Flight Center Std. *246*, 417–420
Material cleaning, 181
Material handling, 157
Materials of construction, 143, 144
Mechanical loading on devices, 113
Membrane filters, 266–270
Micron, 9
Micro-filtration, 297–299
Microscope, electron, 8, 381
Microscopy, 189, 190
Military Standard *282*, 84
Mobile clean room, 209
Monitoring
 automatic—see Counters, automatic
 cascade impactor, 256, 260
 comparison, manual vs. automatic, 283, 284
 dry slide, 263–266
 garment, 343–346
 high intensity light, 249
 humidity, 254
 particle, 252–254
 phototape, 294
 pressure, 255
 questionnaire, 306
 sampler selection, 255, 256
 temperature, 254
Morphological characteristics, 8, 9

National Bureau of Standards
 certification of standards, 9
 discoloration tests, 83, 84
 static tests, 353
New Departure, Div. of General Motors Corp., 158–160
Newton's second law, 19
Noise problems, 144
Norden, Div. of United Aircraft, 169, 170

Oral emissions, 77
Operating rooms, 2, 249, 251
Operation
 clean work station, 400–408
 cross-flow room, 234–236
 down-flow room, 234

Particle
 counting—see Automatic counting
  see Manual counting
  analog, 8
  digital, 8
  microscope, 8
 generation in flooring, 145
 monitoring, 252–254
Particulate matter, definition of, 8, 9
Parts cleaning, 181
Parts cleaning specifications
 ASTM, 380, 381
 Federal, 380
Pass boxes, 150
Personal hygiene, 176, 177
Personnel selection, 181
Phototape sampler, 294
Pickel, F., 51

Population, room, 191, 192
Portable vacuum, 180, 181
Pre-filters, 94
Precipitation, thermal, 295
Pressure monitoring, 255
Pressure room, 139
Product requirements
  electrical contacts, 104–111
  environmental control, 1
  examples of, 96–100
  hydraulic fluid, 102–104
  miniature ball bearings, 97
  literature survey, 100
  reliability, 6
  servo valve, 102–104
Psychological benefits, 187, 188

Quartermaster Lab static tests, 353–355

Reliability, 6, 191
Reynolds Number, 152
Rillings, K. W., 100
Royco Counter, 278–285

S.A.E. ARP, 598, 102
Sampling—see Fluid sampling
  garment, 343–346
  impaction, 295
  see Monitoring
Sandia Corp., 194–196
Sealing filters—see Filter, sealing
Shoe cleaner, 155, 157, 179
Showers, air, 151, 152
Silting Index, 299–302
Size Distribution Relationships, 19–77
  Cape Kennedy, Fla., 55–77
  Eagle Rock, Cal., 41, 42
  General Dynamics Corp., Cal., 44–49
  Grumman Aircraft Engr. N.Y., 42–44
  Hill, AFB, Utah, 39–41
  Illinois rural air, 42
  Lockheed Corp., Cal., 49–51
  Mass. urban air, 42
  Newark AFS, Ohio, 38, 39
  Norden Div., Conn., 53–55
  Olmsted AFB, Pa., 22–31
  Palo Alto, Cal., 41
  Robins AFB, Ga., 31–38, 42
  Sandia Corp., N. M., 51–53
Smoke generator, 401, 402
Smoke Pentrometer, 84, 93
Sole cleaner, 157, 158
Sonic energy—see Cleaning methods
Stable platforms, 171, 172
Static electricity
  charges on clothing, 352
  electrical ceiling, 352, 353
  National Bureau of Standards, 353
  Quartermaster Laboratory Study, 353–355
  theory, 351, 352
Sticky mat, 182
Stoke's law, 19, 20, 57, 80
  Cunningham factor, 20
Super-interception filters
  see Filters, HEPA
Support rooms, 154–156, 208

Tacky mat, 182
Technical Order 00–25–203, 6, 147, 176, 409–414
Temperature monitoring, 254
Test, filter—see Filter test
Thermal precipitation, 295
Timmerman, S. W., 20, 55–77
Training, employee, 176
Tunnel, clean work station, 398
Twin cross-flow room, 207, 208
  advantages, 207
  air handling system, 207
  application, 208
  construction, 207
  disadvantages, 208
  filter arrangement, 207

Utilities, 148

Vacuum
  portable, 180, 181
  systems, 158
Velocity time curve, air shower, 152
Vertical flow
  clean work station, 388, 389
  see down-flow room
Vibration problems, 144

Walls, 146
Weight analysis, 295
Weston Instrument & Electronics Corp., 171
Williamsen, C. T., 42, 43, 100

Zinky, W. R., 41